DESIGN OF WELDMENTS

by

Omer W. Blodgett

Price:
$5.00 in U.S.A.; $5.50 elsewhere
Postpaid

This Book May Be Ordered Direct from the Publisher

THE JAMES F. LINCOLN ARC WELDING FOUNDATION
CLEVELAND, OHIO

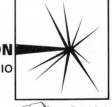

Progress Through Study

Published by

THE JAMES F. LINCOLN ARC WELDING FOUNDATION

First printing 5,000 May 1963
Second printing 5,000 December 1963

Special acknowledgement is herewith made to

Watson N. Nordquist

who has contributed much to the editing
and organization of the material from
which this manual has been prepared

FB-31

Library of Congress Catalog Card Number: 63-16147

Printed in U.S.A.

PREFACE

APPROXIMATELY FORTY YEARS AGO welded steel design was first applied to a mass-produced product, electric motors. The result of this application was a 50% weight and cost reduction. Since that time, welded steel design has gradually and continuously expanded its usefulness into all types of products with comparable results in economy and improvement.

This long and practical experience has created a fund of knowledge which has never been accumulated in one publication and made available to designers and engineers. Much of it has never been published in any form, remaining in the heads and hands of the practitioners of this science and art.

The James F. Lincoln Arc Welding Foundation, created in 1936 by The Lincoln Electric Company to help advance this progress in welded design, has been fortunate in having had access to much of this information through its various award programs and educational activities. The Foundation, believing this knowledge is now of broad general interest, publishes this manual to make this information available to designers and engineers for their use in making the decisions they face in applying welded design. Only by utilizing to the fullest all of our resources in knowledge and materials can our economy, and the companies which comprise it, remain competitive.

This manual is divided into three sections. The first is a general introduction to the subject of weldesign, its mathematics and the general approach to use it efficiently. The second section contains the fundamental theories and formulas needed to apply weldesign with problems to illustrate their application. The third section contains actual designs, worked out using the information in the second section, for all of the major components found in typical machines and products.

It is hoped that the organization of this material will be convenient to use both as a help in studying subjects with which the reader may not be familiar as well as a reference book in solving problems as they arise in designing and fabricating weldments.

The production of this manual has spanned several years over which constant effort was made to eliminate errors. The author will appreciate having called to his attention any errors that have escaped his attention and invites correspondence on subjects about which the reader may have questions. Neither the author nor the publisher, however, can assume responsibility for the results of designers using values and formulas contained in the manual since so many variables affect every design.

_____ Secretary

The James F. Lincoln Arc Welding Foundation

MAY 1963

CREDITS

The author and the publisher gratefully acknowledge the organizations and individuals who have contributed photographs or other illustrative material.

Allis-Chalmers Manufacturing Co.
Aronson Machine Co.
The Arter Grinder Co.
Automation Machines and Equipment Co.
Baldwin-Lima-Hamilton Corp.
Beatty Machine & Mfg. Co.
Bodine Corp.
Brush Instruments, Division of Clevite Corp.
Bryant Chucking Grinder Co.
The Budd Company
Crown Cork & Seal Company, Inc.
Curtis Machine Corporation
Dravo Corp.
Drott Manufacturing Corporation
Ex-Cell-O Corp.
Euclid Division, General Motors Corp.
Falk Corporation
Farrel-Birmingham Co., Inc.
Fox River Tractor Company
General Electric Company
Goss Printing Co.
Halliburton Oil Well Cementing Company

The Heald Machine Company
Hyster Company
International Harvester Co.
The Lees-Bradner Co.
J. M. Lehmann Co.
LeTourneau-Westinghouse Company
Magnaflux Corporation
R. C. Mahon Company
Manitowoc Co., Inc.
New Idea Farm Equipment Co.
Niagara Machine and Tool Works
Oliver Machinery Co.
Pioneer Engineering Works, Inc.
Sanford-Day Corp.
Snyder Corp.
The Springfield Machine Tool Co.
United Shoe Corporation
Verson Allsteel Press Co.
Welding Engineer
Baxter D. Whitney & Sons, Inc.
Worthington Corp.
Zagar, Inc.

In certain subject areas, the author has made adaptations of work done by earlier investigators, to wit:

S. Timoshenko
"Theory of Elasticity"
McGraw-Hill Book Co., New York, N. Y.

S. Timoshenko and S. Woinowsky Krieger
"Theory of Plates and Shells"
McGraw-Hill Book Co., New York, N. Y.

S. Timoshenko and James Gere
"Theory of Elastic Stability"
McGraw-Hill Book Co., New York, N. Y.

Friedrich Bleich
"Buckling Strength of Metal Structures"
McGraw-Hill Book Co., New York, N. Y.

Raymond Roark
"Formulas for Stress and Strain"
McGraw-Hill Book Co., New York, N. Y.

F. R. Shanley
"Strength of Materials"
McGraw-Hill Book Co., New York, N. Y.

The publisher regrets any omissions from this list, and would appreciate being advised about them so that the records can be corrected.

TABLE OF CONTENTS

LIST OF SYMBOLS AND DEFINITIONS

α = angular acceleration (radians/sec/sec); included angle of beam curvature (degrees); form factor

Δ = perpendicular deflection (in.), bending (Δ_b) or shear (Δ_s)

ϵ = unit strain, elongation or contraction (in./in.)

ϵ_s = unit shear strain (in./in.)

ν = Poisson's ratio (steel = 0.3 usually)

ω = leg size of fillet weld (in.); rate of angular motion about an axis (radians/sec)

ϕ = unit angular twist (radians/linear inch)

Σ = sum

σ = normal stress, tensile or compressive (psi); strength (psi)

τ = shear stress (psi); shear strength (psi)

θ = angle of twist (radians; 1 radian = 57.3 degrees); angle of rotation (radians); any specified angle

a = area of section beyond plane where stress is desired or applied (in.^{2}); length of plate (in.); acceleration or deceleration (ft/min, ft/sec)

b = width of section (in.); distance of area's center of gravity to reference axis (in.)

c = distance from neutral axis to extreme fiber (in.)

d = depth of section (in.); moment arm of force (in.); distance (in.)

e = eccentricity of applied load (in.); total axial strain (in.); moment arm of force (in.); effective width (in.)

f = force per linear inch of weld (lbs/in.); horizontal shear force (lbs/in.); (vectorial) resultant force (lbs/in.): allowable strength of weld (lbs/in.)

g = acceleration of gravity (386.4"/ sec^2)

h = height; height of fall

k = any specified constant or amplification factor

m = mass

n = distance of section's neutral axis from reference axis (in.); number of units in series

p = internal pressure (psi)

r = radius (in.); radius of gyration

s = length of curved beam segment (in.)

t = thickness of section (in.); time (min.); time interval (sec)

u = material's tensile modulus of resilience (in.-lb/in.^{3})

u_u = material's ultimate energy resistance (in.-lb/in.^{3})

w = uniformly distributed load (lbs/linear inch)

x = length of moment arm (curved beam)

y = distance of area's center of gravity to neutral axis of entire section (in.)

A = area (in.^{2}); total area of cross-section

E = modulus of elasticity, tension (psi)

E_s = modulus of elasticity in shear (psi)

E_t = tangential modulus of elasticity (psi)

E_k = kinetic energy

E_p = potential energy

F = total force (lbs); radial force (lbs)

I = moment of inertia (in.^{4})

J = polar moment of inertia (in.^{4})

K = ratio of minimum to maximum load (fatigue); any specified constant

L = length of member (in. or ft.); span between supports (in.)

L_e = effective length of column

M = bending moment (in.-lbs)

M_o = applied bending moment (in.-lbs)

N = number of service cycles

P = concentrated load (lbs)

Q = shear center

R = reaction (lbs); torsional resistance of member (in.^{4})

S = section modulus (in.^{3}) = I/c

T = torque or twisting moment (in.-lbs)

U = stored energy

V = vertical shear load (lbs); shear reaction; velocity; volume

W = total load (lbs); weight (lbs); total width (in.)

C.G. = center of gravity

HP = horsepower

N.A. = neutral axis

RPM = revolutions per minute

Progress Through Welded Steel Construction

WELDED STEEL DESIGN has advanced far beyond the weldment shown in Figure 1. Weldments like this left much to be desired in appearance and cost.

Use of modern design and fabricating techniques would transform the dated weldment of Figure 1 into a modern-looking, low-cost weldment. (A comparable, but modern weldment is shown in Fig. 2.) Mechanical flame-cutting equipment now produces smooth-cut edges on heavy plate. Many of the lighter component sections are sheared.

Automatic welding and modern electrodes for manual welding, along with positioning equipment, produce welds of superior appearance and quality at high speeds.

Heavy press brakes and bending rolls are used to form many of the corners and flanges, so that design is not limited to the welding together of flat plates. Combining forming and welding results in low cost, smooth edges, and clean over-all appearance. In fact, the appearance standards for modern weldments have so far influenced design that it is difficult to determine simply from external appearance whether or not a machine is a casting or weldment.

Weldments, however, are different and must be designed differently. Copying a casting or bolted fabrication either in appearance or in shape is a costly mistake. Weldments require different materials, different design ideas, different production techniques. Weldesign is a complete system for creating machinery components, but as with any other system for creating machinery, the design must be made specifically for the system to be used in order to obtain maximum economy, which is the ultimate criterion of acceptance. All systems are acceptable for meeting practically any requirement of rigidity, strength, vibration, fatigue, impact or appearance. The best system for any given piece of machinery is that which produces maximum performance at the least cost.

It is the purpose of this book to aid designers, when considering the use of Weldesign for machinery, to achieve maximum output from this modern system for producing better machines for less cost.

WHAT TO EXPECT WITH STEEL

Steel weldments, efficiently designed to use the excellent physical properties of the base material, offer outstanding opportunities to improve machine performance and reduce manufacturing costs.

Machine Performance

1. Greater rigidity and strength increases speed of operation, output and accuracy.

2. Machine can operate under increased loads.

3. Machine can withstand larger overloads.

4. Machine can withstand shock loads.

5. Machine stays in alignment without depending on foundation because of the inherent rigidity of welded steel.

Fig. 1 Weldments like this, while acceptable when built, have given way to modern styled weldments as shown in Figure 2.

Fig. 2 The clean-line styling of today's machines is an attribute of modern design concepts as to the efficient use of steel and of arc welding.

6. Flexibility in design to solve vibration problems.

7. No breakage through mishandling in shipment and use.

8. Welded steel is not porous and will not leak.

Manufacturing Operations

1. Low capital investment and overhead operating cost.

2. No pattern cost, repair, storage, insurance, maintenance or handling.

3. Small floor space required.

4. Weldments require little or no clean-up. Can be painted right out of the weld shop.

5. Reduction in machining costs because more parts of the machine will be accurately joined into the weldment, rather than separately machined and bolted together.

6. Manufacturing procedure easy to change for special designs.

7. Operation of welding and fabricating shop flexible to meet general product redesign.

8. Small lead time; plant can get into production of new design in less time.

Low Material Cost for Premium Properties

1. Strength

2. Rigidity

3. Uniformity

4. Freedom from gross porosity, shrinkage cracks, etc.

5. Ductility

These five qualities of steel apply equally to well designed and executed welded joints in steel.

Other Qualities of Steel

1. Available in abundant and reliable supply and at low cost.

2. Procurable in all shapes and sizes, measured from thousandths of an inch to hundreds of feet.

3. Low weight for a given rigidity, when member is properly designed.

4. High degree of design flexibility

5. Unlimited processing flexibility; can be worked by every known process.

6. Unlimited combinations of size and shape, when fabricated by arc welding.

7. Can be fabricated by--

Manual shielded-arc welding
Brazing
Automatic submerged-arc welding
Gas welding
Automatic inert-arc welding
Resistance welding
Semi-or full-automatic vapor-shielded arc welding

8. Can be cut by--

Band saw	Flame cutting
Hack saw	Shearing
Friction saw	Punching or die blanking

9. Can be formed by--

Bending	Forming
Stamping	Drawing
Spinning	Forging
Rolling	Roll-bending
Swaging	Roll-forming

10. Well-designed steel weldments eliminate many multiple machining operations, but all metal removal processes are applicable when required.

Systematic Design of Weldments

1. WHAT THE DESIGNER NEEDS

The engineer who is assigned to design a welded steel base or frame faces many questions related to its planning and layout, how to select the most efficient type of section, how to quickly determine the dimensions of this section, whether stiffeners should be used, their size and where they should be placed. These and many other practical questions must be answered if he is to intelligently develop an efficient design, taking full advantage of welded steel construction.

At one time, the practical approach to designing for steel appeared to be that of designing empirically from past experience. This is easy; but unfortunately, the rule-of-thumb selection of configurations and sections almost invariably results in machine members that "look heavy enough," but actually are too heavy. This means higher material costs, higher fabricating costs, and more welding than necessary.

Fortunately, this practice has been largely discarded, and today's machine designs usually are based on mathematical calculations. New methods of determining forces and their effects allow designers to determine sections according to these calculations. This results in more efficient designs and more efficient use of the many excellent properties of steel.

This handbook offers a sound basis for mathematical analysis and solution of machine design problems related to frames, bases, and other welded steel members. The methods presented here will help by simplifying the use of stress analysis and the complicated, time-consuming design formulas that must be used.

This section of the text suggests a logical approach to designing with steel. The relationship of basic design formulas are also reviewed so that they can be used most effectively.

2. SELECT THE DESIGN APPROACH

    (1) A part at a time

    (2) The whole machine

Advantages of Designing a Part at a Time

Changeover to weldments can be gradual for managements who are hesitant about going into immediate full-scale production by welding. Some advantages of gradual conversion are the lower rate of capitalization and facility change.

For companies having their own foundry, gradual conversion to steel weldments allows them to slowly curtail the production of castings. Thus, there needn't be any abrupt obsolescence of present facilities...or people. The indoctrination of designers and production men into welded construction will be self generating, with confidence growing with experience.

Welded steel parts can be used not only in newly built machines, but also as replacement parts for older machines already in the field. This may permit a substantial reduction in pattern inventory for low-activity parts.

Advantages of Designing the Whole Machine as a Completely New Model

With this approach the previous design does not in any way restrict the designer. Since casting limitations can be ignored, it is often possible to reduce the number of pieces making up the machine member, thus cutting down the amount of welding and over-all assembly time.

In many cases, a single weldment can replace several castings, resulting in a better design at lower cost. Less machining is required to facilitate assembly when several pieces are joined together as a single weldment.

The total effect is a better opportunity to improve appearance and performance, and to reduce weight and cost. These structural improvements can be packaged with an updated power drive system and modern control system to make up a more saleable and more profitable product.

3. SELECTING A BASIS FOR DESIGN

    (1) Previous design

    (2) Loading only

Design Based on a Previous Design

Following a previous design has advantages and disadvantages. It is advantageous in that the old design has performed satisfactorily and offers a safe starting point for the new design. Usually, the previous design has been gradually refined through the years until it now represents a good design functionally. It is disadvantageous in that it channels one's thinking in terms of the previous design and blocks any creative thinking toward developing an entirely new concept in solving the basic problem. Also, any faults in the previous design tend to be perpetuated.

The tables of equivalent sections (see Sect. 1.5) or companion nomographs are used for both strength and rigidity when the design is based on the previous design.

Design Based on Loading Only

A design based only on loading allows the designer to use his creative ability to the fullest extent. There are no preconceived notions from a previous design to hinder him. It is true that an extra effort is required to determine the value and type of load in some cases. It is also necessary to decide on some value of stress allowable (in a strength design) or deflection allowable (in a rigidity design).

Design formulas are used for both strength and rigidity when the design is based on loading only.

4. SELECT DESIGN CRITERION

(1) Strength only

(2) In addition, rigidity

(3) No load

This choice should be looked at for the complete machine, and then reviewed as each member is designed. In some cases, the machine is basically designed for strength while portions are designed for rigidity.

Designing for Strength Only

All designs must have sufficient strength so the members will not fail by breaking or yielding when subjected to the normal operating loads or to a reasonable overload. Strength designs are common in road machinery, farm implements, motor brackets, etc.

If the steel weldment's design is based on a prior casting design, the equivalent-strength relationships are used. If a new design is based directly on calculated loading, the design formulas for strength are used.

Designing for Rigidity in Addition to Strength

In some applications, a design developed for only sufficient strength would produce a section which might deflect excessively when loaded. The section must be made still heavier for sufficient rigidity as well as strength. Rigidity designs are common in machine tools.

If the steel weldment's design is based on a prior design, the equivalent-rigidity relationships are used. If a new design is based directly on calculated loading, the design formulas for rigidity are used.

Designing for No Load

Some parts can be classed as "no load". These are members expected to serve with practically no load and have no specific strength or rigidity requirements. Typical no-load designs are gear guards, covers for access holes, splash and dust shields, etc. Such members occasionally present a noise problem, but the solution to this problem is not rigidity, nor does it affect the basic design. Noise will be discussed in Sect. 3.3 on Vibration Control.

5. DESIGN FORMULAS

Three factors are always present in a design formula. These are:

1. Load

2. Member

3. Stress and strain

All three of these have a relationship with each other in any given formula, depending on the type of load. If any two of these three terms are known, the third may be found. Therefore, all problems of design will be essentially one of the following:

1. To find the resulting internal stress or strain caused by an external load on a given member;

2. To find an external load which may be placed on a given member for any allowable stress or strain; or

3. To select or design a certain member to carry a given load within a given allowable stress or strain.

A member is useful only when it carries a load. The load (force) stresses the member, which results in a strain measured as elongation, contraction, deflection, or angular twist.

Therefore, every member must be designed to carry a certain type of load within a certain allowable stress or within a certain allowable strain.

In designing within these allowables, the designer should select the most efficient material and the most efficient section, size and shape. The combined properties of the material and properties of the section determine the ability of the member to carry a given load.

The components of design formulas related to each of these factors are charted in Table 1.

TABLE 1 - FACTORS IN MACHINE DESIGN FORMULAS

GUIDE TO APPLICATION OF
MACHINE DESIGN FORMULAS

I. LOAD

Application	Type	Value
a. steady	a. tension	a. force, pounds
b. impact	b. compression	b. moment, inch-pounds
c. variable	c. bending	c. torque, inch-pounds
	d. torsion	

II. MEMBER

Material	Section
a. tensile strength, σ_t	a. area, A
b. compressive strength, σ_c	b. length, L
c. shear strength, τ	c. moment of inertia, I (stiffness factor in bending)
d. fatigue strength	d. section modulus, S (strength factor in bending)
e. modulus of elasticity (tension), E_t	e. torsional resistance, R (stiffness factor in twisting)
f. modulus of elasticity (shear), E_s	f. radius of gyration, r

III. STRESS   AND   STRAIN

a. tensile stress, σ_t	a. resulting deformation, elongation or contraction, ϵ
b. compressive stress, σ_c	b. vertical deflection Δ
c. shear stress, τ	c. angular twist, θ

6. THE LOAD FACTOR IN DESIGN FORMULAS

The given information about the load is not complete unless the type, method of application, and the value are fully known.

1. Type
   a. Tension
   b. Compression
   c. Bending
   d. Torsion

2. Application
   a. Steady
   b. Impact
   c. Variable

3. Value
   a. Force, in pounds
   b. Moment, in inch-pounds
   c. Torque, in inch-pounds

7. THE MEMBER FACTOR IN DESIGN FORMULAS

The necessary information about the member is incomplete unless both the property of the material and the corresponding property of the member section are known.

1. Property of material.

The material used in a member has certain physical properties. Allowable loads are determined by applying a factor of safety to the ultimate strength (tension, compression, or shear) or, in some cases, to the yield strength of the material. These values are used in all strength problems. The modulus of elasticity is used in all rigidity problems.

σ_t = allowable tensile strength

σ_c = allowable compressive strength

τ = allowable shear strength

E = modulus of elasticity in tension

E_s = modulus of elasticity in shear

2. Property of section.

The shape and size of a member's cross-section affect its performance. This influence is measured by one of several properties of the section. The section's area is the critical property when the load is axial or shear.

A = area of cross-section

L = unsupported length of member

S = section modulus, strength factor when member is used as a beam

I = moment of inertia, rigidity or stiffness factor when member is used as a beam

R = torsional resistance

The performance of a member is predetermined by the product of the appropriate property of the material and the corresponding property of the section. Since the engineer designs for strength only or, in addition, for rigidity, these properties are grouped as follows:

Strength	Rigidity
$\sigma_t \times A$ (tension)	$E \times A$ (tension or compression)
$\sigma_c \times A$ (compression)	
$\tau \times A$ (shear)	$E_s \times A$ (shear)
$\sigma_t \times S$ (bending)	$E \times I$ (bending)
$\sigma_c \times S$ (bending)	$E_s \times R$ (torsion)

Notice that the rigidity of a member (its ability to resist deflection) in bending is measured by the product of its modulus of elasticity (E) and its moment of inertia (I). All steels have the same modulus of elasticity (E); therefore, it is quickly seen that a high-strength alloy steel will not improve the stiffness of a member.

8. STRESS AND STRAIN FACTORS IN DESIGN FORMULAS

Stress and strain are given in the following terms:

1. Stress

σ_t = tensile stress

σ_c = compressive stress

τ = shear stress

2. Strain is a unit movement (inches per linear inch) which is usually expressed as an over-all movement as follows:

e = elongation or contraction, tension or compression

Δ = vertical deflection, bending or shear

θ = angular twist, torsion

Efficient steel weldments contribute much to profitability of modern gear hobber.

Castings were dominant in earlier version of multi-spindle gear hobber.

Problem Definition

1. THE IMPORTANCE OF PROBLEM DEFINITION

Before applying the various formulas for problem solutions, the problem itself must be analyzed carefully and clearly stated. This is not always obvious, and trying to solve the wrong problem can quickly lead to inefficient designs.

For example, the brake of an automobile stops the wheel from rotating and causes the auto to come to rest. However, this analysis of the problem does not indicate what the actual design requirements are; and brakes developed from this analysis might not operate satisfactorily.

The proper approach would be to realize that the brake absorbs the kinetic energy of the moving auto. When the energy absorbed by the brake just equals the kinetic energy of the moving auto, the auto comes to rest (velocity = zero). The engineer will now design a brake to absorb a given amount of energy in a given length of time without overheating, etc. He has something definite on which to base his design, and it will result in an efficient unit.

The identification and evaluation of load conditions is essential to maintaining product performance while achieving maximum manufacturing economies.

2. LOAD ANALYSIS

When a load is placed on a member, stress and strain result. Stress is the internal resistance to the applied force. Strain is the amount of "give" or deformation caused by this stress, such as deflection in bending, elongation in tension, contraction in compression, and angular twist in torsion.

The property of the section which indicates how well the member serves as a beam for strength, is its section modulus (S). The formulas of Table 1 show that the section moduli for two designs of equivalent strength vary inversely as their allowable tensile strengths.

The property of the section which indicates how well the member serves as a beam for rigidity, is its moment of inertia (I). The formulas below show that the moments of inertia for two designs of equivalent rigidity vary inversely as their moduli of elasticity (E).

In comparing two or more designs, if similar sections are used and the outside dimensions including the depth are the same, the values of the section area (A), the moment of inertia (I) and the section modulus for the stress on the bottom surface (S) will vary as the thickness of the section. This relationship does not hold true in the strictest sense, but from a practical standpoint is very close and sufficient for most purposes. Notice this relationship in the two similar sections of Figure 1.

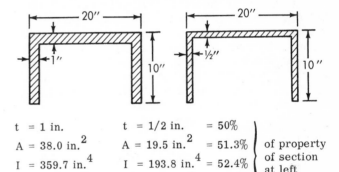

t = 1 in.   t = 1/2 in.   = 50%
A = 38.0 in.^{2} A = 19.5 in.^{2} = 51.3%   of property
I = 359.7 in.^{4} I = 193.8 in.^{4} = 52.4%   of section
S = 50.5 in.^{3} S = 23.9 in.^{3} = 47.3%   at left

Fig. 1 For sections having the same configuration and outside dimensions, the section modulus varies as the thickness of the section.

*   *   *

The following problems serve to illustrate the importance of load analysis.

A fabricating plant sets up an automatic welding head on a boom, Figure 2, with the work moving beneath it on a track. Now, at a later date, it is necessary to extend the length of this boom because of the larger tanks being fabricated.

In defining his problem, the engineer recognizes this as a simple cantilever beam with a concentrated load at the outer end. Knowing the weight of the automatic welding head with its wire reel and flux, he then sets up an allowable vertical deflection of about 1/8" under this load. Even though there is no known horizontal force applied to this beam, he assumes this could possibly reach about 1/4 of the vertical force. He does this to build in some horizontal stability.

1

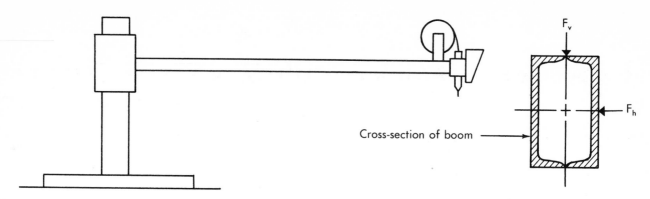

Fig. 2 A long cantilever beam carrying a welding head on the unsupported end is subjected to little horizontal force; yet actual vibration from service conditions may cause more movement in the horizontal direction than the vertical.

The result is a simple box section, deeper than it is wide. Now, how does this perform?

When the welding head is mounted onto the end of the new boom, the boom deflects downward 1/8", and there it will remain for the next 20 years until it is replaced or moved to another location. During the operation of the welding head, the fixture may vibrate slightly, perhaps from being accidentally bumped by the operator, perhaps from a crane passing overhead and shaking the building framework. At any rate, this boom will probably vibrate a greater distance horizontally than vertically, because the moment of inertia about the vertical y-y axis (I_y) is much less than that about the horizontal x-x axis (I_x). If the speed of travel of welding is not too great, the welding head will automatically adjust vertically to maintain constant arc length. There is no such control for horizontal vibrations.

Perhaps the real design problem here is to maintain proper stiffness against possible movement of the boom, which is greatest in the horizontal direction. This might result in a different section of boom than previously designed. It would probably look like the original cross-section (Fig. 2) rotated 90° on its longitudinal centerline.

* * *

TABLE 1 - FORMULAS FOR EQUIVALENT STRENGTH AND RIGIDITY

For Designs of Equivalent Strength in Bending

$$M = K P L, \quad \text{and } M = \sigma S$$

therefore:

$$\boxed{\sigma S = K P L}$$

Comparing two designs to carry the same load (P):

$$\sigma_1 S_1 = K_1 P_1 L_1 \qquad \sigma_1 S_2 = K_2 P_2 L_2$$

or, for equivalent strength —

$$\boxed{\sigma_1 S_1 = \sigma_2 S_2}$$

where:

K = beam constant
M = moment
P = load
L = length of beam
σ = bending stress
S = section modulus ($= I/c$)

For Designs of Equivalent Rigidity in Bending

$$\Delta = \frac{K P L^3}{E I}$$

Comparing two designs to carry the same load (P), with the same deflection (Δ):

$$\Delta_1 = \frac{K_1 P_1 L_1^3}{E_1 I_1} \qquad \Delta_2 = \frac{K_2 P_2 L_2^3}{E_2 I_2}$$

or, for equivalent rigidity —

$$\boxed{E_1 I_1 = E_2 I_2}$$

where:

Δ = deflection
E = modulus of elasticity (tension)
I = moment of inertia

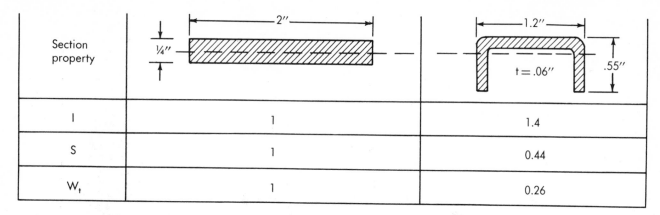

Section property		
I	1	1.4
S	1	0.44
W_t	1	0.26

Fig. 3 When the distance from the neutral axis to the outer fiber increases faster than the resulting moment of inertia, the section modulus (strength) decreases.

Usually the designer is interested in as much strength and stiffness as he can economically obtain. Yet, if the design problem is properly defined, a certain amount of flexibility may have to be designed into the member. For example, some parts of farm implements must have some flexibility to stand up under constant usage.

For example, an engineer has designed a simple beam from a 1/4" × 2" flat bar. Under load, it has a deflection of .0016". He believes this should be made "stronger," so he designs a formed channel section from 16-gage steel. Under the same load, it deflects only .0012". This appears to be a substantial improvement; but when the beam is accidentally overloaded, the engineer is surprised to find that his "stronger" beam actually is the weaker beam. The confusion results from his hazy concept of "strong," instead of a clear understanding of the properties of a section.

The property of a section which indicates its resistance to bending is the moment of inertia (I). The property which indicates its strength in bending is the section modulus (S). Using the original flat bar as a basis, its properties are assigned a factor of 1; see Figure 3. Therefore, the redesign has relative properties as shown.

The first test for vertical deflection, using a gage dial to make the measurement, depended only on the moment of inertia (I). The new channel section has an I value of 1.4 times that of the original, which accounts for the reduction in deflection from .0016" to .0012". A second test, under overload, depended only on the section modulus (S). The new channel section has an S value of 44% that of the flat bar, which accounts for the resulting bending stress far exceeding the yield point of the material. Thus, buckling of the new section occurred. In contrast, the bending stress in the original flat bar was held much below the yield point, and that member is still serving its purpose.

*   *   *

In most cases when a given section is "beefed up" to increase its stiffness (moment of inertia, I), its strength will automatically increase (section modulus, S) so that the engineer seldom checks the resulting section modulus. There are exceptions.

In the example, Figure 4, the addition of stiffeners (B) increases the moment of inertia (stiffness) to 134% of the plate (A); yet the section modulus (strength) is only 67% of the plate. The reason for this is very simple, yet is quite often overlooked. Section modulus (S) is equal to the moment of inertia (I) divided by the distance from the neutral axis to the outer fiber (c).

The distance to the outer fiber (c) for the flat

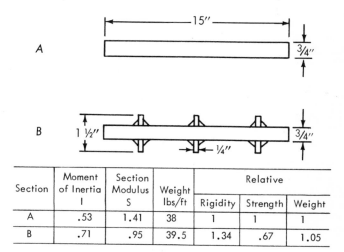

Section	Moment of Inertia I	Section Modulus S	Weight lbs/ft	Relative		
				Rigidity	Strength	Weight
A	.53	1.41	38	1	1	1
B	.71	.95	39.5	1.34	.67	1.05

$$S = \frac{I}{c} = \frac{1.34}{2} = .67$$

Fig. 4 Although not usually the case, the section modulus (strength) may be lowered when a section is redesigned for increased moment of inertia (rigidity).

plate is one-half of the plate thickness, or 3/8". By the addition of 3/8" high stiffeners to each side of the plate, this distance (c) is doubled; yet the moment of inertia has increased to only 134% that of the original plate. The point to remember is this: any time the distance to the outer fiber increases at a faster rate than the resulting moment of inertia, the section modulus (strength) will always be lower.

Someone might argue that although this particular member with stiffener (B) would reach yield stress at the outer fiber of the stiffener sooner, this stiffener would ultimately yield plastically, until the surface of the plate would reach yield, and this condition would then be identical with the plate without stiffeners (A). This is true especially with steel which is ductile.

It would not be true, however, if this member were subjected to fatigue or repeated loading. Since the ultimate fatigue strength would probably be lower than the yield strength, the stiffener would have no opportunity to yield, but would crack when this fatigue strength and stress were reached. This particular member with the stiffeners (B), under these conditions, would be weaker. If some brittle material were used, for example cast iron, this particular member with the stiffeners (B) would be weaker than that with no stiffeners (A) because the material does not have the ability to yield.

3. MATERIAL SELECTION

After load conditions are established and evaluated for a member or the entire machine the next step is selecting the right material and using its properties effectively. To achieve effective use the designer usually establishes the most important design requirement (strength or rigidity) and picks the material which will most economically answer these requirements.

For example; a machine tool company experimented with bases of different steels to learn if higher strength steel might result in a more rigid base. Company engineers were surprised to observe they all had the same deflection under the same load. This was because the property of a material which indicates its rigidity is its modulus of elasticity, and all steels have the same modulus of elasticity and therefore the same rigidity.

$$* \quad * \quad *$$

Another company was experiencing some difficulty with a lever which operated at very high speeds. The engineers reasoned the problem in a very logical manner. The actual load on this lever was very low, the forces being due mainly to inertia forces, the mass of the lever times its acceleration or deceleration.

The engineers decided that if a lighter metal could be used, the mass would be decreased. This

in turn would decrease the inertia forces and reduce the lever's deflection. They carried this to the point of ordering a new lever made of aluminum for testing. At this point, one of the men took his handbook and showed the following:

$$\Delta = \frac{K F L^3}{E I} \quad \text{and } F = m a$$

therefore:

$$\Delta = \frac{K m a L^3}{E I}$$

where:

Δ = deflection

K = beam constant

m = mass

a = acceleration or deceleration

E = modulus of elasticity (tension)

I = moment of inertia

L = length

Since:

density of steel   = 7.9

density of aluminum = 2.8

E of steel   = 30×10^6

E of aluminum   = 10.3×10^6

inserting the ratios of these values (steel to aluminum) into the above deflection formula:

$$\Delta_{Al} = \frac{(1)\left(\frac{2.8}{7.9}\right)(1)(1)^3}{\left(\frac{10.3 \times 10^6}{30 \times 10^6}\right)(1)} \Delta_{st}$$

$$\Delta_{Al} = 1.03 \, \Delta_{st}$$

Thus, the aluminum lever designed for equivalent rigidity would actually have resulted in a deflection of 1.03 times that of the steel lever. (The lower modulus of elasticity of aluminum cancelled out its weight advantage.) The problem was solved by a redesign of the steel lever and not by substituting another material

$$* \quad * \quad *$$

Steel has greater strength than any other commercially available material. If still more section strength is required, a higher-strength alloy steel may be used instead of the usual machine or construction steels.

Steel has greater rigidity or stiffness than any other commercially available material. This property is measured in terms of the material's modulus of elasticity. Figure 5 illustrates the relative stiffness of several commercial metals. All samples have the same section and are loaded so that all deflect the same amount. The relative weights on the samples indicate how the materials differ in their stiffness or modulus of elasticity.

Even though aluminum and magnesium are lighter than steel, their moduli of elasticity are less than that of steel by a greater ratio. Aluminum has a density 35.4% that of steel, yet its modulus of elasticity is only 34.4% of steel's. Magnesium has a density of 22.8% that of steel, but a modulus of elasticity only 21.6% of steel's. A steel section -- for the same stiffness or rigidity -- will weigh less

than a corresponding section of aluminum or magnesium, provided the steel section can have the same depth.

Since aluminum's modulus of elasticity is only 34.4% that of steel, it requires a moment of inertia 2.9 times that of steel or a sectional area approximately 2.9 times that of steel for equivalent rigidity. With a density 35.4% that of steel, the aluminum section would have an over-all weight of 1.03 times that of steel.

Conclusion: weight for weight, mild steel is still the lightest, most economical metal for equivalent rigidity.

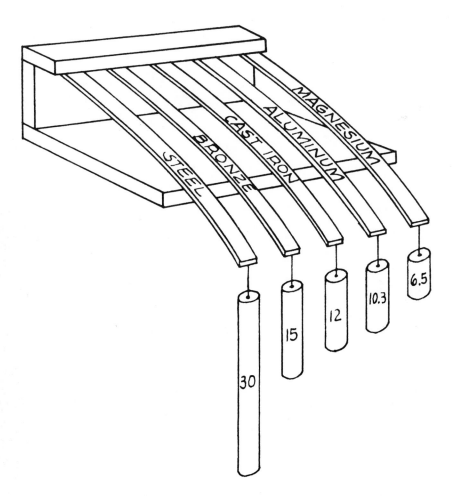

Fig. 5 Comparative stiffness of various materials. Steel supports a greater weight for same deflection as other materials.

The inherent rigidity of all-steel welded presses are essential in maintaining parallelism of bolster faces, resulting in long die life.

Designer's Guide
to Efficient Use of Steel

1. DESIGN FOR EFFICIENT USE OF STEEL

The efficient use of steel in machinery calls for many design decisions -- some major, some minor. Experienced designers who produce successful designs follow a definite sequence in doing so. Many decisions are proposed, accepted or rejected subconsciously. The process is essentially the same as that involved in the creative design of any product or component.

This section presents the major design and fabrication considerations in an easily-followed sequence. The sequence will serve both as an introduction as well as later reference for the young engineer, or the more experienced engineer who hasn't yet had the opportunity to use steel or welds ments extensively in structural members of machinery. The sequence is presented as a series of checklists that constitute a practical systems approach to designing for maximum economy and the best functional designs producible under given manufacturing conditions.

2. DESIGNER'S GUIDE TO EFFICIENT USE OF STEEL

Following is a master check list to help guide designers through the system approach to efficiently using the properties of steel to achieve economy and improve functions in machinery. The list is applicable to either designing one part at a time or designing the entire machine.

(1) Recognition of the problem

(2) Analysis of the present design

(3) Determination of load conditions

(4) Major design considerations

(5) Layout

(6) Plate preparation

(7) Special sections and forming

(8) Welded joint design

(9) Size and amount of welds

(10) Use of subassemblies

(11) Use of jigs, fixtures, and positioners

(12) Assembly

(13) Welding procedure

(14) Control and correction of distortion

(15) Cleaning and inspection

Some of these guideposts refer to manufacturing. These are important to the designer in evaluating the producibility of a proposed design, and in contributing more fully to product planning sessions. Questions to ask in connection with each of these check points are given on following pages.

✔ List No. 1 │ RECOGNITION OF PROBLEM

1. Is this an entirely new machine, or a redesign of a present machine?

2. If a redesign problem, should the conversion to steel be made a part at a time or the entire machine designed as a whole new approach to meeting the basic requirements?

3. What are the primary and secondary functions of the proposed machine?

4. Relate every detail of existing and proposed designs to performance of the machine. Continue to do so as the proposed design develops and takes shape.

✔ List No. 2 │ ANALYSIS OF PRESENT DESIGN

1. Is the machine larger, heavier, more rigid, or capable of longer life than required?

2. What do service records reveal as to the demand for replacement parts? Examine any available history of failures, warranty claims, and owner complaints. Perhaps the machine was overdesigned in some respects, while other members may need to be beefed up.

3. What parts must remain interchangeable so as to meet future need for replacement parts for machines presently in service? Be careful that any such reasoning is sound. In the extreme, it could retard modernization of design for years and permit competition to capture your original equipment market.

4. What do your customers say about the machine? And, what does your sales force think is right or wrong with it?

Fig. 1 Same load stresses simply supported beam almost to yield, while rigidly supported beam resists bending.

5. What features of the present design must be retained?

6. What new features must be added?

7. Have you or other men in your company had any new ideas which they wanted to use on this machine but haven't been able to because the design was frozen? Now would be the time to review these suggestions.

8. Is the appearance dated, non-functional?

9. If the new design is to be based on present cast design, are there any parts now attached to a major casting which might be made integral with the weldment?

10. If the new design is to be based on present cast design, are the present thicknesses of various sections actually required for strength, rigidity or functional reasons? Or, did foundry practice make these necessary?

☑ List No. 3 | DETERMINING LOAD

It is first necessary to define what work the machine must do; then, what conditions of service may cause overloads or vibration. From such information, the load on individual members can be determined.

In seeking a starting point from which or to which loading can be calculated, the designer may find one or more of the following practical methods useful:

1. From the motor horsepower and speed, determine the torque (in inch-pounds) on a shaft or revolving part.

2. Calculate in pounds the force on machine member created by the dead weight of parts.

3. Load on the members of a hoist or lift truck can be figured back from the load required to tilt the machine.

4. On a shovel or ditch digger, for example, the maximum strength of critical cables proven satis-

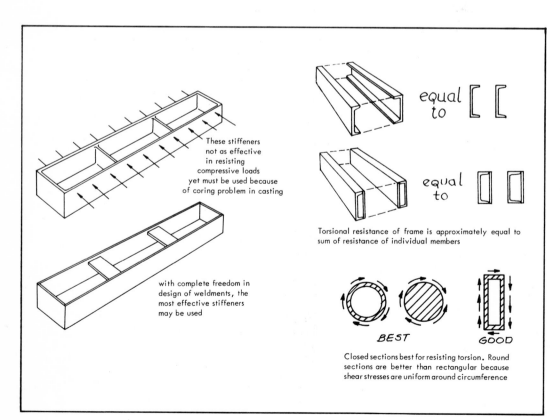

These stiffeners not as effective in resisting compressive loads yet must be used because of coring problem in casting

with complete freedom in design of weldments, the most effective stiffeners may be used

equal to

equal to

Torsional resistance of frame is approximately equal to sum of resistance of individual members

BEST   GOOD

Closed sections best for resisting torsion. Round sections are better than rectangular because shear stresses are uniform around circumference

Fig. 2 Proper use of stiffeners and closed sections increase the rigidity of members and frames.

factory in service can be used to work back to the load on machine parts.

5. The maximum force required to shear a critical pin may be used as a starting point.

6. If a satisfactory starting point cannot be found, design for an assumed load and adjust from experience and test.

✓ List No. 4 | MAJOR DESIGN FACTORS

In developing a design, the designer is seldom able to adhere strictly to a sequence of separate design steps, into which the material here has been grouped. The designer's thoughts must constantly refer both forward and backward as he progresses through the sequence towards the final design. This constant cross-reference frequently generates new ideas relating a machine's function, appearance and cost.

When the designer is at this pure-design stage, he must think ahead to how he will lay out the design for production and how these decisions will affect manufacturing costs. He must be thinking even further ahead to how his decision will be accepted by the user of the machine. The function, the appearance, the cost will eventually be submitted to the judgment of the customer who decides whether to buy or not to buy the machine.

The following design factors determine the performance of the design; hence, the section properties and dimensions of the member. They demand careful consideration to insure maximum design economy.

1. Design should satisfy strength and stiffness requirements. Overdesign costs money in extra material, welding and handling costs.

2. Check safety factor being used. Past experience of performance might indicate that it is set too high.... at unnecessary expense.

3. Specify appearance required. Appearance for its own sake usually increases cost more than necessary. Many welds are completely hidden from view. The weldor is not likely to know which welds are critical appearance-wise and which are not, unless print specifies them.

4. If code work, check restrictions to ascertain that most economical method allowed by code is being used.

5. Use deep sections to resist bending.

6. Symmetrical sections are more efficient for resistance to bending.

7. Weld ends of beams rigid to supports. This increases strength and stiffness (Fig. 1).

8. Proper use of stiffeners will provide rigidity with less weight (Fig. 2).

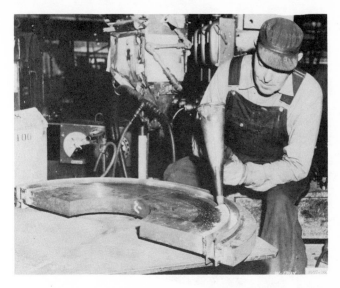

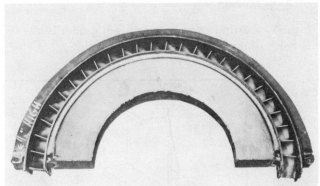

Fig. 3 Shroud bands and nozzle vanes are 405 stainless welded to mild steel web.

9. Use closed sections or diagonal bracing for torsion (twisting). A closed section, for example, may be several times better than an open section (Fig. 2).

10. Specify non-premium grades of steel wherever possible. Remember that higher carbon and alloy steels require preheating, and frequently postheating, which are added cost items.

11. Place higher grades of steel only where required, and use mild steel for rest of structure (Fig. 3).

12. Remember that high-strength steels and other premium materials are not available in as wide a range of standard mill shapes, from stock, as the lower-priced mild steels.

13. If only surface properties (viz. wear-resistance) of a higher-priced or difficult-to-weld material are needed, consider using a mild steel base and hardsurfacing to obtain the desired properties (Fig. 4).

15. Consider first the use of standard rolled sections (Fig. 5). These require less forming and welding.

Fig. 4 Cutting edge on mild steel grader blade is hardsurfaced with wear-resistant alloy.

16. Choose sections according to a planned factory stock list.

17. When delivery time is short or production is low, use plate and bar sizes in stock or easy to get.

18. For maximum economy, use plate and bar sizes standardized for your own or other industries.

19. If bar or plate surface must be machined or ground or hardsurfaced, dimension the section so that initial plate and bar sizes can be readily obtained from plant or vendor inventory (Fig. 6).

20. Provide maintenance accessibility. Do not bury a bearing support or other critical wear point within a closed-box weldment.

21. Sometimes sections can be designed round so that automatic welding can be used more advantageously (Fig. 7).

22. On special machines especially, consider possibility of economies in using commercially-available standard index tables, way units, heads, columns, and chassis.

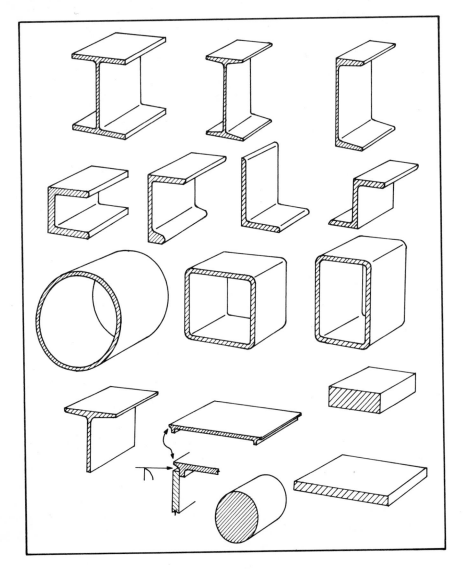

Fig. 5 A great variety of standard rolled shapes are available for economical machine designs.

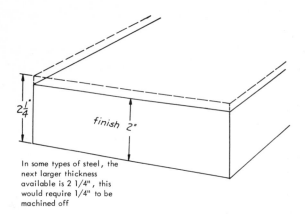

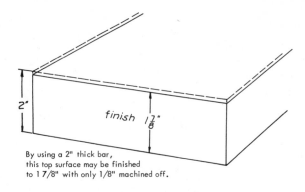

In some types of steel, the next larger thickness available is 2 1/4", this would require 1/4" to be machined off

By using a 2" thick bar, this top surface may be finished to 1 7/8" with only 1/8" machined off.

Fig. 6 Standard rolled bars are economical, when section is dimensioned for minimum finishing.

☑ List No. 5   **LAYOUT**

To the designer familiar only with castings, the problems of laying out a weldment for production may seem complex because of the many possibilties. This variety, however, is one of welded design's advantages. It presents many opportunities for savings.

1. Design for easy handling of materials and for inexpensive tooling.

2. Check with shop for ideas where shop experience can contribute to better methods or cost savings. Do this before firming design.

3. Check tolerances and press fits first specified. Shop may not be able to economically hold them. Close tolerances and fits may not be required.

4. Lay out for fewer number of pieces (Fig. 8). This will reduce assembly time and amount of welding.

5. Lay out parts of various sizes and shapes to be nested when cut or stamped, so as to minimize scrap (Fig. 9).

6. If possible, modify shape and size of scrap cutouts so that material may be used later for other parts: pads, stiffeners, gear blanks, etc. (Fig. 10).

7. If a standard rolled-to-shape section is not available, consider these choices: (a) a large plate flame-cut to developed blank size and then formed up into section; (b) long flat bar stock welded together; or (c) special order rolled-to-shape section, the economy of which will depend upon the footage involved, the number of operations saved, and whether the contour can be developed by standard mill rolls.

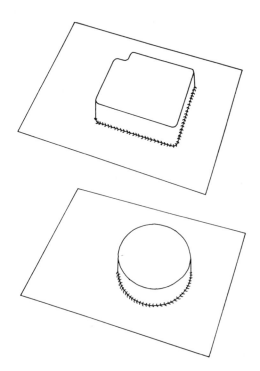

Fig. 7 Design sections for circular or straight seams to permit automatic welding.

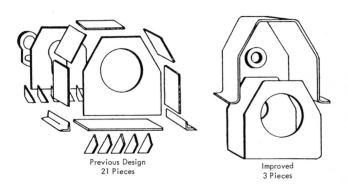

Previous Design
21 Pieces

Improved
3 Pieces

Fig. 8 Design simplicity can save much welding and assembly time.

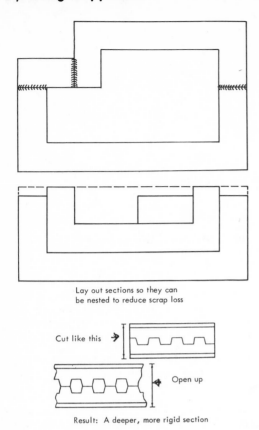

Lay out sections so they can be nested to reduce scrap loss

Cut like this →

Open up

Result: A deeper, more rigid section

Fig. 9 Good design makes it possible for production to make maximum use of stock.

8. For heavy rings, cut segments from plate and nest so that little scrap is produced (Fig. 11).

9. Welding small blanks or pieces of scrap may eliminate extensive cutting from plate, machining, and loss of material (Fig. 12).

V̶ List No. 6 | PLATE PREPARATION

Cutting is the basic step in fabricating a weldment. Many different methods are available, and the most economical will be determined by balancing several factors: material, section, quality required, and equipment available. The decision is generally one of economy.

1. Consider the proper method of producing weldment blanks, as to which is most economical for the quantity and quality required, principally:

    (a)   Flame-cutting

    (b)   Shearing

    (c)   Sawing

    (d)   Punch press blanking

    (e)   Nibbling

    (f)   Lathe cut-off (for bar and tube stock)

2. Factor into the above evaluation, the influence of method on quality of edge for fit-up and whether method can also provide bevel (if required) for groove joints.

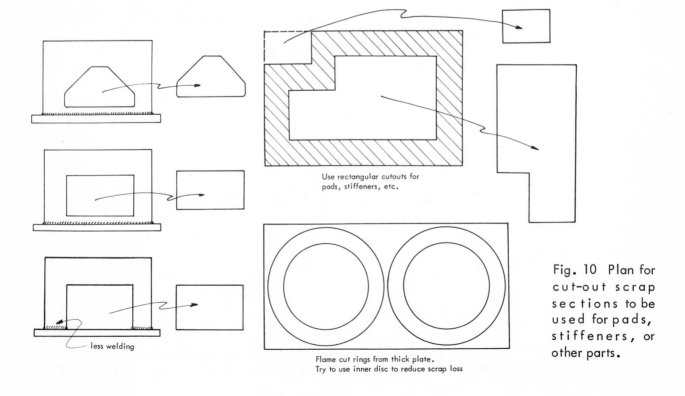

Use rectangular cutouts for pads, stiffeners, etc.

Flame cut rings from thick plate. Try to use inner disc to reduce scrap loss

less welding

Fig. 10 Plan for cut-out sections to be used for pads, stiffeners, or other parts.

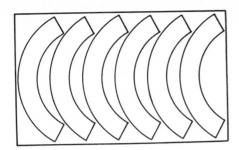

Fig. 11 Cut segments for heavy ring from thick plate and nest to reduce scrap.

3. Consider whether dimensioning of blank requires stock allowance for later preparation of edge and groove.

4. When proposing to combine cutting of blank to size and preparation of edge for welding, remember that not all welds are continuous. A continuously beveled edge that is not continuously welded may be undesirable on exposed joints.

5. For single-bevel or single-V plate preparation, use single-tip flame-cutting torch.

6. For double-bevel or double-V plate preparation, use multiple-tip flame-cutting torch so this can be done in one pass of the cutting machine.

7. If plate planer is available, a thick plate is sometimes prepared with a J or U groove because it requires less weld metal.

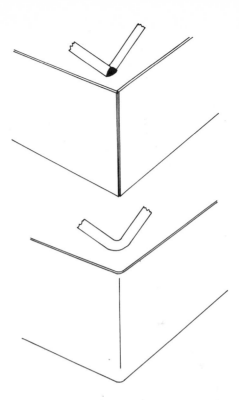

Fig. 13 Forming of corner can often save material, fabricating and welding costs.

8. Consider arc-air gouging, flame gouging, or chipping for back-pass preparation, instead of machining to bevel both edges prior to welding.

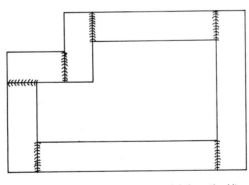

Fig. 12 Efficient welding can save material costs, machining costs, and over-all production costs.

Weld bars together instead of cutting from solid plate, if welding cost is less than scrap saved.

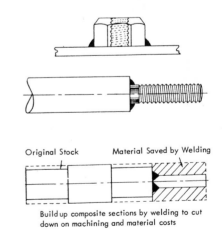

Original Stock   Material Saved by Welding

Build up composite sections by welding to cut down on machining and material costs

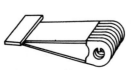

Hub with integral key produced from laminations welded together

Stiffeners can be made of flat plate or bars welded together

⟋ List No. 7 | FORMING AND SPECIAL SECTIONS

The second major step in fabricating a weldment is generally forming. The proper use of forming can greatly reduce the cost of a weldment by eliminating welds and, very often, numerous machining operations. Several factors determine the best method of forming: thickness, over-all dimensions, production volume, and tolerances. Cost again is the final factor.

1. Consider using the following forming methods:

    (a) Press brake

    (b) Bending rolls

    (c) Roll-forming

    (d) Tangent-bending and contour-bending

    (e) Flanging and dishing

    (f) Press-die forming and drawing

2. Consider whether a corner should be bent or formed rather than welded up from two pieces (Fig. 13).

3. Consider possible saving in rolling a ring instead of cutting from plate (Fig. 14).

Fig. 14 Roll rings instead of cutting from heavy plate.

4. Determine whether there would be any saving by forming round or square tubes or rings, instead of buying commercial tubing.

5. Put bend in flat plate sections to increase stiffness (Fig. 15).

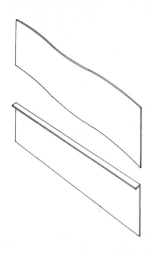

Fig. 15 Flange on flat plate increases stiffness.

6. Press indentations in plate to act as ribs instead of adding needed stiffeners to reduce vibration (Fib. 16)

7. Gain a stiffener by bending up the edge of a sheet before welding it to the next sheet (Fig. 17).

8. Consider using corrugated sheet for extra stiffness.

9. Consider whether incorporating a steel casting or forging in the weldment for a complicated section will simplify the design problem and cost of manufacture.

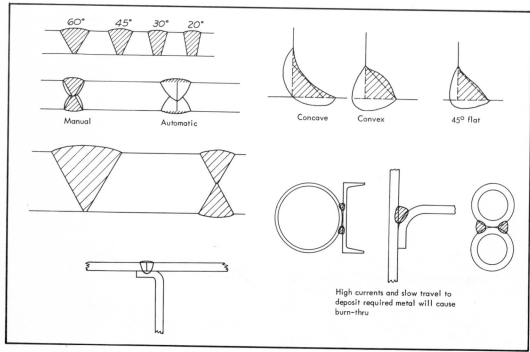

Fig. 18 Use minimum amount of weld metal. Shaded areas indicate amount of added weld metal. Automatic welding eliminates need for much beveling.

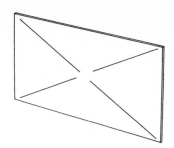

Fig. 16 Press indentation in flat panel increases stiffness.

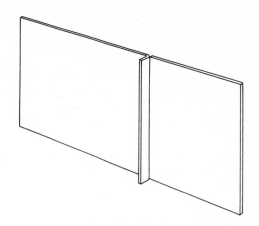

Fig. 17 Bending up edge of sheet before welding to next sheet provides stiffener.

10. A small amount of hardsurfacing alloy can be applied by welding where it will do the most good, instead of using expensive material throughout the section.

11. Wherever flanges, lips, ears or tongues are needed, consider building them up by welding rather than using forgings or considerable machining.

V | List No. 8 | WELDED JOINT DESIGN

The type of joint should be selected primarily on the basis of load requirements. Once, however, the type is selected, variables in design and layout can result in startling cost reductions or cost increases.

1. Select joint requiring a minimum amount of weld filler metal.

2. Eliminate beveling on a large percentage of

joints by using automatic submerged-arc welding which has a deep-penetration arc characteristic (Fig. 18, top left).

3. Use minimum root opening and included angle in order to reduce filler metal required (Fig. 18, top left).

4. On thick plate, use double-V instead of single V to reduce the amount of weld metal (Fig. 18, left).

5. Sometimes a single weld may be used to join three parts (Fig. 18, bottom left).

6. Reduce the convexity of fillet welds. A 45°

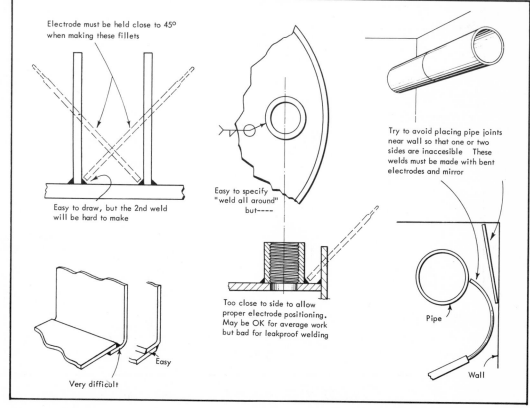

Fig. 19 Design must allow access to joint for welding.

Electrode must be held close to 45° when making these fillets

Easy to draw, but the 2nd weld will be hard to make

Very difficult

Easy

Easy to specify "weld all around" but----

Too close to side to allow proper electrode positioning. May be OK for average work but bad for leakproof welding

Try to avoid placing pipe joints near wall so that one or two sides are inaccesible. These welds must be made with bent electrodes and mirror

Pipe

Wall

flat fillet, very slightly convex, is the most economical and reliable shape (Fig. 18, top right).

7. Avoid joints that create extremely deep grooves. The joint formed by the meeting of a round or tubing with a flat surface of another round or tubing, is one example. This presents two procedure problems; getting proper fusion to the root and not burning through the thin wall while filling the joint with weld metal (Figure 18).

8. Design joint for easy accessibility for welding (Fig. 19). Consider availability of welding positioners.

$\boxed{V \text{ List No. 9}}$ WELD SIZE AND AMOUNT

Overwelding is easy to do and difficult to control. It can be very costly and, unfortunately, it is a common error of both design and production. Control begins with design, but must be carried throughout the assembly and welding operations. The following are basic guides:

1. Be sure to use the proper amount of welding—not too much and not too little. Excessive weld size is costly.

2. Specify by print or Standard Shop Practice that only the needed amount of weld should be fur-nished. The allowables used by the designer have a built-in safety factor. Don't add still another safety factor.

3. The leg size of fillet welds is especially important, since the area or amount of weld fill required increases as the square of the increase in leg size.

4. Always make certain in manual welding that you do not specify a 3/8" horizontal fillet if a 5/16" fillet will do. The 3/8" horizontal fillet requires at least two passes to guarantee size with a 44% increase in cost (Fig. 20, top left).

5. For equivalent strength, longer fillet welds having a smaller leg size are usually less costly than heavy intermittent welds (Fig. 18, top right). Joint length may influence the relationship.

6. Sometimes, especially under light-load or no-load conditions, intermittent fillet welds can be used in place of a continuous weld of the same leg size, thus reducing cost (Fig. 20, center right).

7. Convert several short manual welds into one continuous weld for automatic welding.

8. Place the weld in the section with the least thickness, and base the weld size on the thinner plate.

9. Place the weld on the shortest seam. If there

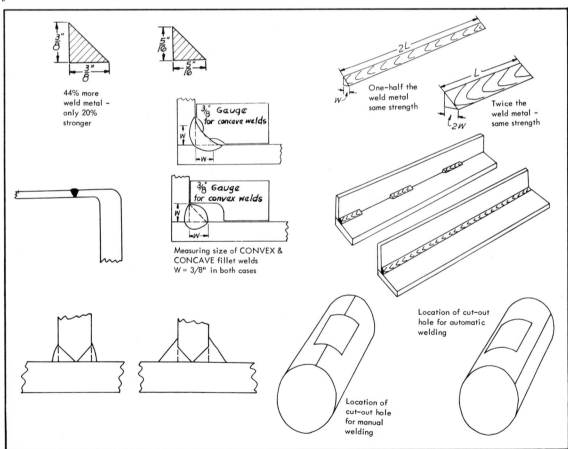

Fig. 20 Overwelding is costly and should be avoided.

is a cut-out section, place the welded seam at the cutout and save on the length of welding. On the other hand, in automatic welding it may be better to place the joint away from the cut-out area to permit making one continuous seam (Fig. 20, lower right).

10. Stiffeners or diaphragms do not need much welding; therefore, they are often overwelded. Reduce the weld leg size or length of weld if possible.

11. Don't overweld the flange to web of beam sections. The weld takes very little load. (Fig. 20, lower left).

12. Keeping the amount of welding to a minimum will minimize distortion, internal stress, hence reduce the need for stress-relieving and straightening.

V List No. 10 USE OF SUBASSEMBLIES

In visualizing assembly procedure, the designer should break the proposed machine down into subassemblies several different ways to determine which, if any, will offer some of the following cost savings:

1. Spreads work out, if machine structure is large or complex. More men can work on whole job. This means shorter delivery time.

2. Usually provides better access for welding.

3. Reduces the possibility of distortion or locked-up stresses which might occur if whole assembly were tacked together and then completely welded.

4. Precision welding possible with modern techniques permits machining to close tolerances before welding into final assembly.

5. Permits stress-relief (if necessary) of certain sections before welding into final assembly.

6. Permits leak testing of compartments or chambers and painting before welding into final assembly.

7. Facilitates in-process inspection before job has progressed too far to rectify errors.

V List No. 11 ASSEMBLY TOOLING

Jigs, fixtures and welding positioners should be used to decrease fabrication time. In planning assemblies and subassemblies, the designer should keep in mind the following points:

1. First decide if jig is simply to aid in assembly and to hold weldment for tacking or whether, in addition, the entire welding operation is to be done while work is in the jig.

2. Determine if jig is to be mounted on welding positioner, pedestal or floor.

3. Jig must provide rigidity necessary to hold dimensions.

4. Tooling must provide easy locating points.

5. Tooling must have means for quick clamping and releasing of work.

6. Tooling must be easy to load and unload.

7. Pre-camber can be built into the tool for control of distortion.

8. Operating factor can be increased by providing two jigs, so that helper can load one while other is being welded.

9. Welding positioners facilitate maximum welding in the flat downhand position, allowing use of larger electrodes and automatic welding for faster welding speeds.

V List No. 12 ASSEMBLY

1. Clean work of oil, rust, dirt before welding to reduce troubles.

2. Determine any need for preheat, interpass, and postheat temperatures; not normally required for welding the mild steels commonly used in machinery construction. Low-hydrogen electrodes will reduce any preheat requirements.

3. The need for preheat may affect numerous decisions relative to tooling, loading, fit-up, etc.

4. Check fit-up. Improve if necessary. Gaps are costly.

5. Clamp into position and hold during welding.

6. Use jigs and fixtures to hold parts with proper fit-up and to maintain alignment during welding.

7. Preset joint to offset expected contraction.

8. Prebend the member to offset any expected distortion.

9. Weld two similar members back-to-back with some prebend.

10. If need for stress-relief, weld two similar members back-to-back without prebend and keep fastened until after stress-relief. Weldment should end up straight.

11. Use strongbacks.

12. Arrange the erection, fitting, and welding sequence so parts have freedom to move in one or more directions for as long as possible during assembly.

13. Use subassemblies and complete the welding in each before final assembly.

14. Where possible, break the weldment into natural sections, so the welding of each can be balanced about its own neutral axis.

15. Weld the more flexible sections together first, so they may be more easily straightened before final assembly of member.

V List No. 13 WELDING PROCEDURE

These checkpoints are primarily for guidance of weld shop personnel. Control of cost and quality, though, is a mutual concern of both Design and Production. The designer must be concerned with what goes on in the shop, and the production man must see that his experience is passed back to the designer. Thus:

1. Use good weldable steel.

2. Try to improve operating factor; use weldor helpers, good fixtures, and handling equipment.

3. Deposit the greatest amount of filler metal in the shortest possible time.

4. Use backup bars to increase speed of welding on the first pass, for groove joints.

5. Eliminate or reduce preheat by using low-hydrogen electrodes.

6. Be sure welding machines and cable are large enough to do the job.

7. Use an electrode holder that allows the use of high welding current.

8. Use manual electrodes down to a 2" stub.

9. Weld in flat downhand position if possible. Overhead and vertical welds are more expensive.

10. If possible, position fillet welds in the flat (trough) position for highest welding speed.

11. Weld sheet metal 45° downhill.

12. Consider welding from one side only (if plates are not too thick) instead of both sides, to eliminate necessity for turning over heavy weldment or using overhead welding.

13. With automatic welding, position fillet welds to obtain greater penetration into the root of the joint: flat plate at an angle of 30° from horizontal and vertical plate 60° from horizontal (Fig. 21).

14. For fillet welds loaded transversely, position the flat plate 30° from horizontal so that the larger leg of the fillet will be in line with the load where it will do the most good. This reduces weld metal being deposited.

15. On T-groove welds, watch reinforcement. Most of it is unnecessary for a full-strength joint (Fig. 14, lower left).

16. One of the best ways to save money is to prevent, before they happen, repairs due to cracking, porosity, etc. which result from poor welding procedures.

17. Weld toward unrestrained portion of the member.

18. Weld first those joints that may have greatest contraction as they cool.

19. Distribute the welding heat as uniformly as possible throughout the member.

20. Use a procedure which eliminates arc blow.

21. Use optimum welding current and speed for best welding performance.

22. Be sure you are using optimum travel speeds. If appearance is not critical and no distortion is being experienced, normal speed frequently can be exceeded.

23. Use the correct current and polarity. Make certain to use the type of electrode that will produce the highest deposition under existing conditions.

24. Consider the use of negative polarity for submerged-arc welding to increase melt-off rate.

25. On small fillets, a smaller diameter electrode may actually deposit the weld faster by not overwelding.

26. Investigate the use of larger electrodes at higher currents.

27. Use semi-automatic or full-automatic welding wherever possible and take advantage of its deeper penetration and uniform deposit.

28. Be especially careful specifying weld size that might increase possibility of burn-through on single-pass welds (Fig. 22).

V List No. 14 DISTORTION CONTROL

The forces of expansion and contraction that tend to cause distortion in steel when heated, can be readily controlled so that distortion is seldom a problem. Here are some measures to be taken:

1. Use high deposition electrode, or automatic welding.

2. Use fewer passes.

3. Use higher welding current.

4. Use minimum weld metal.

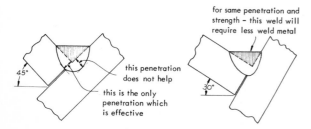

for same penetration and strength — this weld will require less weld metal

this penetration does not help

this is the only penetration which is effective

Fig. 21 Joint can often be positioned for welding so as to minimize weld size without affecting penetration or strength.

5. Take advantage of deeper penetration with automatic welding.

6. Welding should progress toward the unrestrained portion of the member but backstepping may be practical as welding progresses.

7. Balance the welds about the neutral axis of member; that is, position welds opposite each other, preferably equidistant from the neutral axis.

8. On double-V joints, weld alternately on both sides of plate.

9. Flame shrink when advisable.

10. Avoid buckling in section due to improper handling or support.

11. Avoid buckling due to poor choice or performance of flame-cutting, shearing or other plate preparation process.

12. Avoid error in original alignment of members to be joined.

13. Avoid prestressing members being joined together by forcing alignment in order to get better fit-up.

✔ List No. 15 | CLEANING AND INSPECTION

1. Industry now accepts as-welded joints that have uniform appearance; therefore, do not grind the surface of the weld smooth or flush unless required for another reason. This is a very costly operation and usually exceeds the cost of welding.

2. Reduce cleaning time by use of powdered-iron electrodes and automatic welding which minimize spatter and roughness of surface.

3. Spatter films can be applied parallel to the joint, to reduce spatter sticking to the plate. Some electrodes and processes produce little or no spatter.

4. Eliminate as many welding difficulties as possible so as to reduce the amount of inspection needed.

5. Perhaps a slightly reduced welding speed or a lower welding current will minimize weld faults and inspection. Result might be lower repair costs, and lower total cost.

6. Overzealous inspection can run up welding costs very fast. Many plants overinspect.

7. Good welds must always be the goal; however, even a "poor" weld is often stronger than the plates being joined.

8. Inspection should check for overwelding, which can be both costly and a contributing factor in distortion.

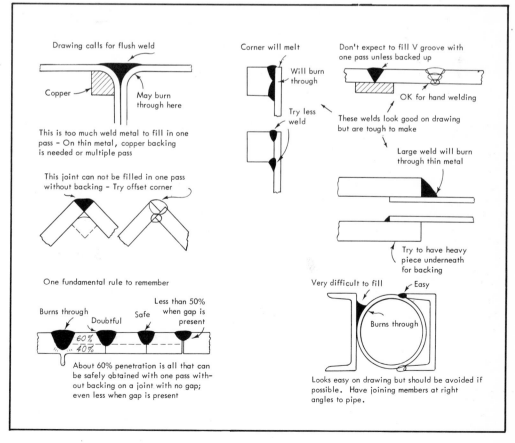

Fig. 22 Single-pass welds requiring large amounts of metal tend to burn through, especially with automatic welding.

Welded headstock for wood turning lathe was manufactured at half the cost of earlier cast iron unit.

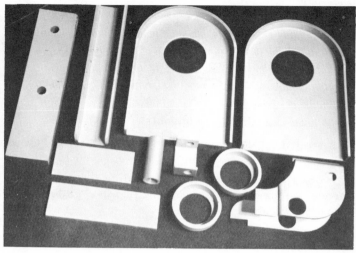

Lathe headstock was welded up from 11 pieces -- low-cost stampings and flat bars.

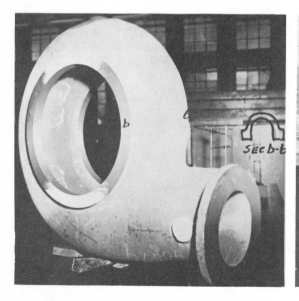

Conventional cast volute for centrifugal pump housing. Section b-b sketched to show contour.

Redesigned pump housing is a lower cost weldment, claimed to be more efficient than the cast design.

Redesigning by Means of Equivalent Sections

1. THE EQUIVALENT-SECTIONS CONCEPT

Although it is preferable in most cases to design a machine on the basis of calculated loading, at times an engineer desires to convert from a casting or a forging to fabricated steel in the simplest way possible.

The Equivalent Sections concept is aimed at this direct conversion from one material to another. Possibly a single member or assembly will be redesigned for steel and must be functional within an over-all machine design still based on cast iron. Or, the decision may be to lean heavily on the plant's casting experience and pretty much duplicate the original machine in steel rather than go into stress analysis. Or, the need may be to convert from one steel design to another in order to take advantage of new manufacturing techniques.

The basic 3-step approach to converting a casting into a steel weldment by means of equivalent sections is this:

STEP 1: Determine the Type of Loading Under Requirements of Strength or Rigidity for Each Member.

STEP 2: Determine the Critical Property of this Cast Member

STEP 3: Determine the Required Property for the Steel Member

Three aids have been developed to simplify an engineer's taking this design approach. They are:

1. Tables of Equivalent Strength and Rigidity Factors

2. Nomographs, for Specific Types of Members

3. The Lincoln I Rule, for Rigidity Problems

The Equivalent Tables were developed from a simplification of traditional engineering formulas. The tables permit the designer to be concerned only with an appropriate property of the section. He doesn't have to work directly with design loads which would be the case when using the traditional formulas.

Nomographs further shorten the design process. In one respect, they are more limited than the Equivalent Tables since each applies to only a specific type of design problem. They eliminate most or all direct mathematical calculations and enable the user to find graphically actual dimensions of the steel member. However, they tend to restrict the designer to the existent casting's configuration.

The Lincoln I Rule supplements the Equivalent Tables in simplifying the solution of rigidity designs. It is especially helpful in finding the moment of inertia (I) of the original casting cross-section. See Sec. 2.3 for a more detailed description on the use of this I rule.

Application of each of these three design aids is discussed in the following paragraphs, using actual design problems for illustration.

2. USE OF EQUIVALENT TABLES

Here again are the basic 3 steps to converting a casting into a steel weldment by means of equivalent sections:

STEP 1: Determine the Type of Loading Under the Requirements of Strength or Rigidity for Each Member

All parts of a structure must have basic jobs to do:

1. Maintain sufficient strength or, in addition, rigidity.

2. Withstand loads applied in tension, compression, bending, or torsion.

STEP 2: Determine the Critical Properties of the Cast Member

The ability of the part to withstand the above loadings is measured by certain properties of its cross-section. These are:

A = Area of the cross-section

I = Moment of inertia, for resistance to bending

S = Section modulus, for flexural strength

J = Polar moment of inertia, for resistance to twisting

$\dfrac{J}{c}$ = Polar section modulus, for strength under torsion

1

TABLE 1 RIGIDITY	**Step 1** Determine the Type of Loading				
	tension	compression short column	compression long column	bending	torsion
Step 2 Determine this property of the cast member. ⇒	Area A	Area A	Moment of Inertia I	Moment of Inertia I	Polar Moment of Inertia J
Step 3 EQUIVALENT FACTORS	Multiply the above property of the cast member by the following factor to **get** the equivalent value for steel. *				
Grey Iron A S T M 20	40 %	40 %	40 %	40 %	40 %
A S T M 30	50	50	50	50	50
A S T M 40	63	63	63	63	63
A S T M 50	67	67	67	67	67
A S T M 60	70	70	70	70	70
Malleable A47-33 35018	83	83	83	83	100
A47-33 32510	83	83	83	83	100
Meehanite Grade GE	40	40	40	40	40
Grade GD	48	48	48	48	48
Grade GC	57	57	57	57	57
Grade GB	60	60	60	60	60
Grade GA	67	67	67	67	67
Cast Steel (.10 - .20%C)	100	100	100	100	100
Magnesium Alloys	22	22	22	22	20
Aluminum Alloys	34	34	34	34	32
	$A_s = \dfrac{E_c}{E_s} A_c$	$A_s = \dfrac{E_c}{E_s} A_c$	$I_s = \dfrac{E_c}{E_s} I_c$	$I_s = \dfrac{E_c}{E_s} I_c$	$J_s = \dfrac{E_c}{E_s} J_c$
subscript "s" is for steel; "c" is for casting					

TABLE 1 - EQUIVALENT

RIGIDITY FACTORS

*The factors above are based on published values of moduli of elasticity.

STEP 3: Determine the Required Properties for the Steel Member

If these properties of a cast part or member are known, Equivalent Tables facilitate determining the corresponding properties of the steel member or part that will have equal rigidity (Table 1) or equal strength (Table 2). It is necessary only to multiply the known properties of the casting by the factor obtained from the appropriate Equivalent Table.

For instance: To determine how much area must be provided in a steel tension member to equal the rigidity of a gray iron casting, refer to Table 1 which shows that the steel member need have only 40% as much area.

To see how the system is applied to an actual problem, consider this gray iron mechanism, Figure 1. The redesign objective is to convert to lower-cost welded steel members of equal rigidity.

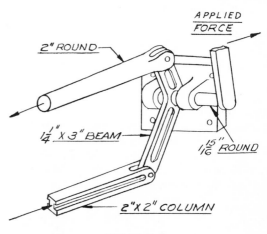

FIGURE 1

STEP 1:

Each member is labeled as to the type of loading to which it is subject, Figure 2.

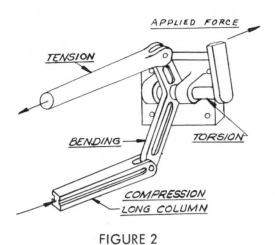

FIGURE 2

STEP 2:

From each cast iron member, a cross-section is chosen which represents the member. Then, by consulting Table 1, the necessary property of each section is determined. The values of these properties, when computed, tell how well each cast member does its job, Figure 3.

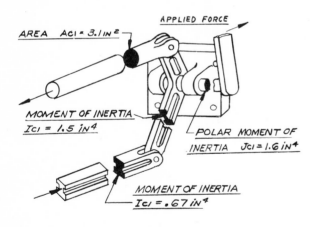

FIGURE 3

STEP 3:

These properties of the gray iron sections are multiplied by the equivalent factors from Table 1. The result of this is a required property value for each steel section, Figure 4. Any steel member having this required property will do the same job as well as the corresponding gray iron member.

Final Design:

From the required properties of the steel sections, several steel designs are considered. Fig-

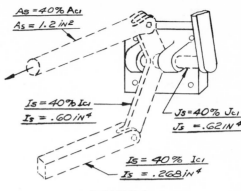

FIGURE 4

ure 5 represents just one solution. This welded steel design of equivalent rigidity resulted in 60% less weight and 45% less cost than the cast iron design it replaced.

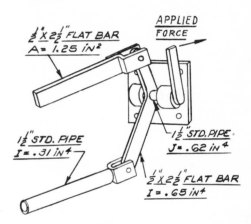

FIGURE 5

3. USE OF NOMOGRAPHS

Bases constitute a type of member common to every class of machinery. Thus, the redesign of a simple base can serve as an example of how nomographs are used in applying the Equivalent Section concept.

The original cast base, Figure 6, is 60" long × 30" wide × 6" deep. It is made of ASTM Class

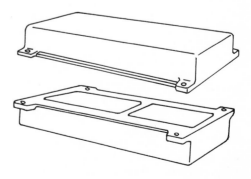

FIGURE 6

20 gray iron. It has one rib underneath and weighs 681 lbs. For purpose of comparison, its cost will be considered equal to 100%.

STEP 1: Determine the Type of Loading

This cast base, on which a motor and pump are mounted, was acceptable in service. Equal or better rigidity is an essential objective in the redesign for welded steel. The design problem is thus one

of rigidity, under a bending load.

STEP 2: Determine the Critical Property of the Cast Member

In a rigidity design, the member must have sufficient moment of inertia (I) to resist a bending load. Where the shape of the cross-section as well as the length and depth of the member are to remain the same, it will be accurate enough (within

TABLE 2 STRENGTH	**Step 1** Determine the Type of Loading			
		compression short		
	tension	column	bending	torsion
Step 2 Determine this property of the cast member. ➤	Area A	Area A	Section Modulus S	Polar Section Modulus $\frac{J}{c}$

TABLE 2 - EQUIVALENT STRENGTH FACTORS

Step 3	Multiply the above property of the cast member by the following factor to get the equivalent value for steel. *			
EQUIVALENT FACTORS				
Gray Iron ASTM 20	21%	94%	21%	28%
ASTM 30	31	123	31	42
ASTM 40	42	136	42	56
ASTM 50	52	156	52	70
ASTM 60	63	167	63	83
Malleable A47-33 35018	68		68	76
A47-33 32510	54		54	70
Meehanite Grade GE	31	125	31	42
Grade GD	36	136	36	49
Grade GC	44	164	44	58
Grade GB	49	174	49	64
Grade GA	57	199	57	73
Cast Steel (.10 - .20%C)	75	75	75	75
Magnesium H-alloy, AZ63, T6, HTA	50	50	50	33
C-alloy, AZ92, T6, HTA	50	50	50	37
Aluminum 195 T4	40.0	40.0	40.0	43.3
Sand T6	45.0	45.0	45.0	50.0
Castings 220 T4	57.5	57.5	57.5	55.0
355 T6	43.7	43.7	43.7	46.6
T7	47.5	47.5	47.5	46.6
356 T6	41.2	41.2	41.2	43.3
T7	42.5	42.5	42.5	40.0
	$A_s = \dfrac{\sigma_c}{\sigma_s} A_c$	$A_s = \dfrac{\sigma_c}{\sigma_s} A_c$	$S_s = \dfrac{\sigma_c}{\sigma_s} S_c$	$\left(\dfrac{J}{c}\right)_s = \dfrac{\sigma_c}{\sigma_s}\left(\dfrac{J}{c}\right)_c$
subscript "s" is for steel; "c" is for casting				

The factors above are based on published values of tensile, compressive and shear strengths using a safety factor of 3 for mild steel and from 4 to 4.8 for the cast materials depending upon ductility.

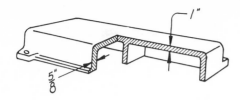

Fig. 7   Cast Iron Base (681 lbs)

5%) to assume that the moment of inertia will vary as the cross-sectional area, or going one step further, as the thickness of the top and sides.

In our cast iron base example, Figure 7, the thickness of the top panel is 1" and that of the side panel is 5/8".

STEP 3: Determine the Required Property for the Steel Member

The minimum thickness of the top and side

FIG. 8 – REQUIRED THICKNESS OF STEEL SECTION
For Rigidity Equal to Cast Section

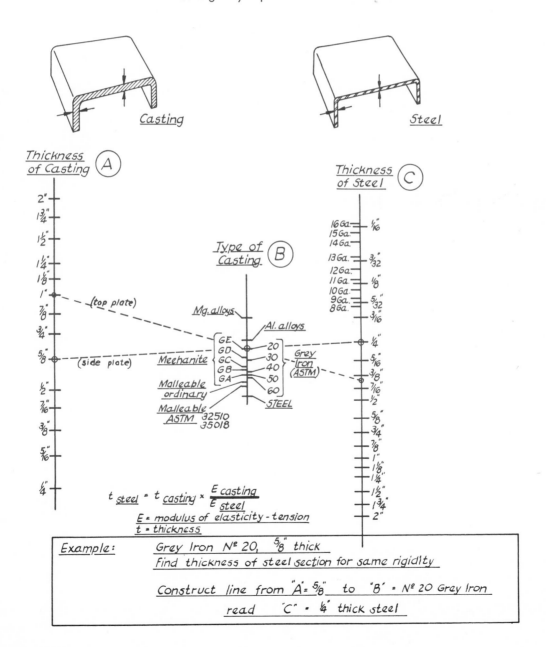

$$t_{steel} = t_{casting} \times \frac{E_{casting}}{E_{steel}}$$

E = modulus of elasticity - tension
t = thickness

Example: Grey Iron № 20, 5/8" thick
find thickness of steel section for same rigidity

Construct line from "A" = 5/8"   to "B" = № 20 Grey Iron
read   "C" = ¼" thick steel

panels of the steel member can be read from the first nomograph, Figure 8. On this nomograph:

Line A = known thickness of casting panel

Line B = known type of cast material

Line C = required thickness of steel panel to have rigidity equivalent to the corresponding cast panel

With a straight edge laid along the point on Line A indicating the 1" thickness of the top panel and the point on Line B indicating the ASTM 20 cast gray iron, Line C will be intersected by the straight edge at approximately 3/8". This is the required thickness of the steel top panel. In similar manner, the required thickness of the steel side panel will be found to be 1/4".

The original cast base has a rib which serves as a stiffener, and thus one or more stiffeners must be provided in the steel member, Figure 9. The important thing here is the stiffener's effect on the unsupported span of top panel relative to the latter's thickness. A thin steel top panel may require more stiffening than the much heavier cast panel.

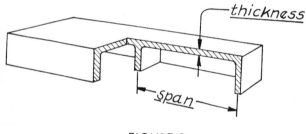

FIGURE 9

The required maximum span of the steel top panel between stiffeners can be read from the second nomograph, Figure 13. On this nomograph:

Line A = thickness of steel top panel (determined from previous nomograph)

Line B = known type of cast material

Line C = reference line

Line D = known thickness of cast top panel

Line E = ratio of length of steel span to length of cast span, or length of panel between stiffeners

With a straight edge laid across the point on Line A indicating the 3/8" required thickness of the steel top panel and the point on Line B representing the ASTM 20 gray cast iron, the point at which Line C is intersected will be a reference point. Now, with the straight edge repositioned across this point on Line C and the point on Line D representing the 1" thickness of the cast top panel, Line E will be intersected at aproximately 52%. This is

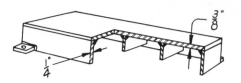

Fig. 10   Welded Steel Base (281 lbs)
3 stiffeners on 15" centers
Total cost relative to that of casting is
34.6% for one, 30.9% for ten

52% of the 30" span in the original casting, meaning that a 15" span is required in the steel member in order for it to have equal rigidity. See Figure 10.

Accepted practice is to make the base ends the same plate thickness as the side panels. The stiffeners do not have to be as deep. The result is a welded steel base which has equivalent rigidity, greater strength, less weight, and lower cost in comparison with the original cast base.

This design has been very simple and quick. Even though it means two different plate thicknesses, 3/8" and 1/4", must be used and welded together, it requires only two operations, shearing and welding. Therefore, the cost is low.

The weight of the base has thus been reduced by 59%, and the cost by 65 to 69% depending on lot size.

Second Redesign:

An even more efficient design can be made by changing the shape of the base cross-section. However, this would require finding the moment of inertia of the proposed section. One procedure for doing this is covered in a later example.

If the moment of inertia of the cast iron can be determined, it can then be multiplied by an equivalent rigidity factor. This factor is the percentage of the rigidity of the cast material to that of steel. This percentage can be found on the first nomograph (Fig. 8) by using the value for steel section that is found when the cast section is 1" thick.

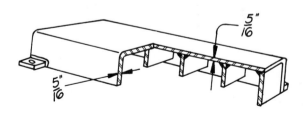

Fig. 11   Second Welded Steel Base (274 lbs)
4 stiffeners on 12" centers
Total cost relative to that of casting is
39.2% for one, 28% for ten

With the redesign based on an equivalent moment of inertia, this steel section can be made of 5/16" plate bent into the form of a channel. See Figure 11. This takes a little thickness from the top and adds it to the sides. The thinner top panel requires an additional stiffener, as determined from the second nomograph (Fig. 13).

By using one thickness throughout, one steel plate does the work of three. Bending down the sides eliminates preparing edges for welding and then welding them back up, a further reduction in cost.

Although this eliminates some flame-cutting or shearing and considerable welding, it introduces an extra operation -- brake forming. This may increase the cost for very small quantities but reduces the cost on larger lots.

Third Redesign:

A slightly better design can be had by flanging

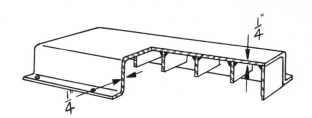

Fig. 12 Third Welded Steel Base (248 lbs)
5 stiffeners on 10" centers
Total cost relative to that of casting is
38.4% for one, 24.7% for ten

the bottom legs of the base, Figure 12. Since this greatly increases the rigidity of the section, a further reduction in plate thickness can be made. This requires additional stiffeners, as determined by the second nomograph (Fig. 13).

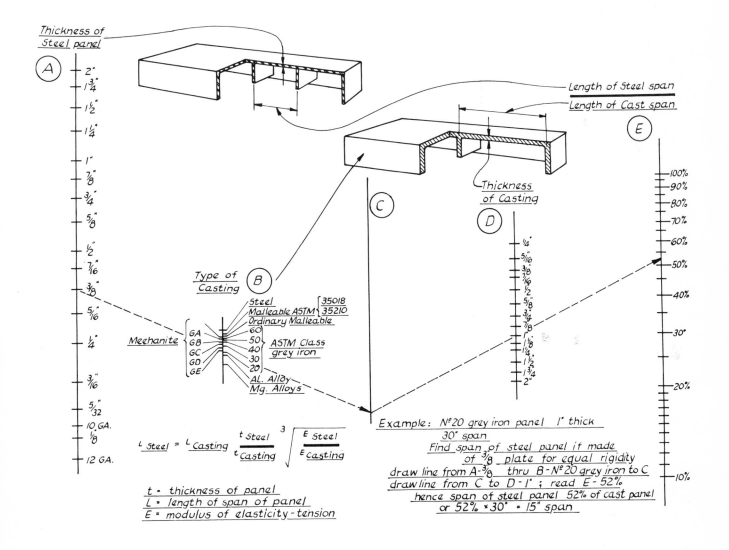

FIG. 13 - REQUIRED RATIO OF STEEL SPAN TO CAST SPAN
For Steel Section to Have Rigidity Equal to Cast Section

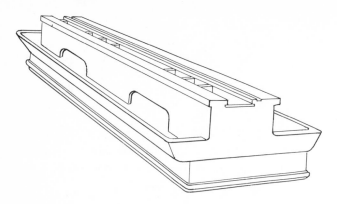

Fig. 14 Cast Iron Base (4900 lbs)

By going to thinner plate, the blank edges may be sheared instead of flame-cut. This is a reduction in cost.

Braces and stiffeners do not require much welding; intermittent fillet welding is sufficient. Diagonal bracing for additional torsional resistance could be used and is discussed in Sect. 3.6 pertaining to Torsion.

This third redesign has now brought the weight of the base down to 36% that of the original casting and the cost (in lots of 10 or more) to 25% of what it was originally.

4. USE OF LINCOLN I RULE

In redesigning machinery members that must have high rigidity under bending loads, the Lincoln I Rule can often be of great help in developing Equivalent Sections. This design aid is especially valuable in finding the moment of inertia of a large unsymmetrical or complex casting.

As an example, a cast machine tool base of ASTM Class 20 gray iron, Figure 14, is redesigned for rolled steel. Each component of the cast base is converted into a steel section by following the 3-step design approach, until the entire base has been redesigned to steel. A good place to start is the cross-section of the base.

STEP 1: Determine the Type of Loading

It is desired that the welded steel base be as rigid or more rigid than the cast iron base. Since the member is subject to bending, its resistance to bending must be evaluated.

STEP 2: Determine the Critical Property of the Cast Member

The property of a section which indicates its resistance to bending as its moment of inertia (I). A complete cross-section view is needed through the cast base, Figure 15, this is usually available as a scale drawing on the pattern print. In the view

shown, the dark areas indicate the sections that run continuously throughout the length of the member, acting as a beam to resist bending. For simplification, this view can be treated as a single section. The Lincoln I Rule is now used to find the moment of inertia about the horizontal axis of this section: See Sect. 2.3 for more detailed description on the use of the I rule.

1. Estimate the neutral axis of the section by imagining where the section would balance if supported on this axis. Draw a horizontal line through this, mark this number 0.

2. Draw a horizontal line across the top extremities of the section and one across the bottom extremities of the section, mark these number 10.

3. Place the Lincoln I Rule on the section, so that the number 10 is on the top line and the number 0 is on the neutral axis. See Figure 16. Mark off the 10 points and draw horizontal lines through them. This will divide the top portion of the section into 10 areas. Then place the rule so that the number 10 is on the bottom line and the number 0 is on the neutral axis, and repeat for the bottom section.

4. With an engineer's scale, measure off the average width of each of the 10 areas in the top portion of the section. (Be sure to consider the scale of the drawing.) Add up the average widths of these 10 areas, and divide by 10. This will give the average width of the top portion of the section.

The I Rule has now transformed the top section (above the neutral axis) into a rectangle, whose width is equal to the average width, whose depth is equal to the depth of the top section, and whose moment of inertia is equal to the moment of inertia of the top section.

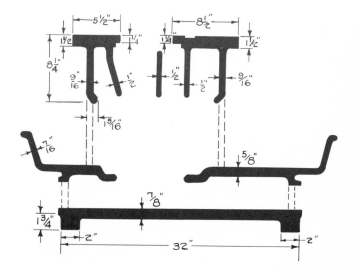

Fig. 15 Cross-section through cast machine base.

This is repeated for the bottom section (below the neutral axis). The following values are obtained:

Area	Top portion	Bottom portion
10	12.0"	4.0"
9	14.0	4.0
8	14.0	4.0
7	9.0	14.1
6	2.3	32.4
5	2.3	10.8
4	2.8	0
3	2.8	0
2	2.8	1.2
1	.6	6.6
Total width	62.6"	77.1"
Average width	6.26"	7.71"
Height	12.4"	12.2"

Since the moment of inertia of a rectangular area about its base is considered to be--

$$I = \frac{\text{width} \times \text{height}^3}{3}$$

the moment of inertia of the cast iron base is--

$$I_{\text{cast iron}} = I_{\text{top portion}} + I_{\text{bottom portion}}$$
$$= 3980 \text{ in.}^4 + 4660 \text{ in.}^4$$
$$= 8640 \text{ in.}^4$$

<u>STEP 3:</u> Determine the Required Property for the Steel Member

Consulting Table 1 (equivalent rigidity), the

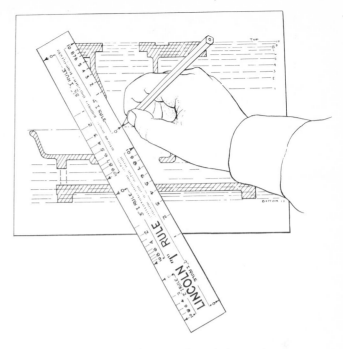

Fig. 16 Using the Lincoln I Rule to determine moment of inertia of a cast member cross-section.

factor for steel to replace ASTM 20 gray cast iron in bending is 40% of the moment of inertia (I) of the casting. Hence:

$$I_{\text{steel}} = 40\% \ I_{\text{cast iron}}$$
$$= 3450 \text{ in.}^4$$

The problem now is to build up a steel section within the outside dimensions of the cast section and having a moment of inertia (I) = 3450 in.[4] Any steel section having at least this value will be more rigid than the cast section. The dimensions and location of the two top flange plates must be retained. The

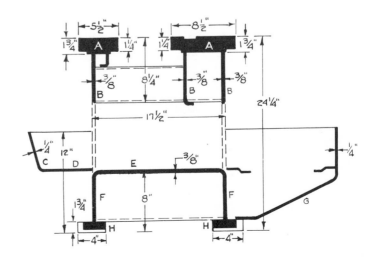

Fig. 17 Cross-section through steel base.

design must lend itself to the most economical methods of fabricating rolled steel.

The steel section shown in Figure 17 is one possible solution. Its moment of inertia (I) is found by the method known as "Adding Areas". This is explained more fully in Sect. 2.3 pertaining to Properties of Sections.

'The "Adding Areas" method was used to develop the following table of properties for each component of the section in order to compute the moment of inertia of the entire section.

The moment of inertia of the steel section is

$$I_{steel} = I - \frac{M^2}{A}$$
$$= 6457 - \frac{106.5^2}{63.78} = 6457 - 178$$
$$= 6280 \text{ in.}^4 \text{ (or 1.8 times as stiff as cast iron)}$$

Since equivalent rigidity would have been achieved with a moment-of-inertia value of only 3450 in.[4], this design is 1.8 times as rigid as the cast

Assume reference axis is 12" up from the bottom.

	Size	Distance y	A	M	Iy	Ig
A	14 × 1 3/4	+12.37	24.50	+303.0	+3745.	......
B	1 1/8 × 6 1/2	+ 7.25	7.31	+ 53.0	384.	25.7
C	1/2 × 4	- 2.0	2.00	- 4.0	8.	......
D	6 × 1/4	- 4.0	1.50	- 6.0	24.	......
E	16.75 × 3/8	- 4.0	6.28	- 25.2	101.	......
F	3/4 × 6 1/4	- 7.13	4.69	- 33.4	238.	15.3
G	14 × 1/4	- 7.13	3.50	- 24.9	178.	......
H	8 × 1 3/4	-11.13	14.00	-156.0	1738.0	......
Total			63.78	+106.5	6457	

where:

y = distance of area's center of gravity from section's reference axis

A = width × height of area

M = $A \times y$

I_y = $M \times y$

I_g = $\dfrac{\text{width} \times \text{height}^3 \text{ of area}}{12}$

base. See Figures 18 and 19 on facing page.

Now that the cross-section of the steel base has been designed, other less important components of the cast base are taken one at a time and converted to steel. Figure 20 shows these various components for the welded steel base, and Figure 21 shows the redesigned base fully assembled.

Although this final steel base is 1.8 times as rigid as the cast base, it weighs 49% less and costs 38% less.

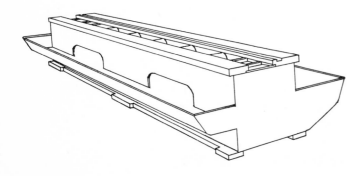

Fig. 21 Welded steel machine base (2500 lbs). Fabrication cost: 62% the cost of the original cast base.

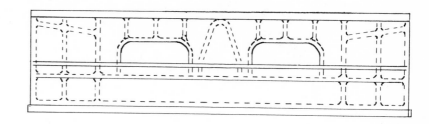

Fig. 18   Front view of cast machine base.

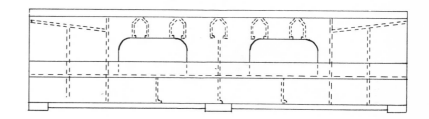

Fig. 19   Front view of welded steel machine base.

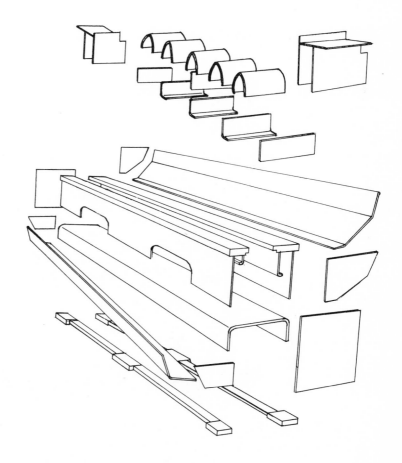

Fig. 20   Exploded view of steel components for welded machine base.

Cast steel cleaning bar forage chopper was redesigned for production as mild steel weldment. Result: 26% cost reduction.

Arc-welded housing of beverage filling machine improved appearance and strength, with 25% less weight and 15% less cost than previous cast design.

Loads and Their Evaluation

1. TYPES OF LOAD

In designing a machine member, it is necessary to recognize the type of load applied to the member. This is true whether the new design is to be based on a previous model, or directly on calculated loading.

The load may be imposed by the dead weight of machine members, or by the work performed by the machine.

Load is the amount of external force applied to an elastic body, tending to deform it. Under load, some dimension or property of the member changes. Stress is the internal molecular resistance to such deformation, tending to restore the body to its original condition once the load has been removed. Strain is the amount of unit deformation that occurs under load.

Usually the change in the property of the section -area, moment of inertia, etc. - caused by loading does not affect the value or nature of the loading. Sometimes it does, and then the member may fail unexpectedly.

There are five basic types of load: tension, compression, shear, bending, and torsion. Figure 1 illustrates these various load conditions. Although later sections of this text will deal more thoroughly with the various types of load, some of the main features of each are described here.

1. Tension is the force that pulls a member from two opposing directions. It results in deformation by elongation. Excessive tensile loading causes failure of the member by pulling it apart. Tension is shown in Figure 1 by two examples: the tension member of the simple bracket "A", and the tension member of the lever system "D".

As a tensile load is increased, the member elongates and its cross-sectional area decreases. Neither change affects the load. However, the decrease in cross-sectional area affects distribution of the load and thereby slightly increases the unit tensile stress. Even this does not affect the proportional relationship of the stress to strain within the elastic limits of the material.

Any eccentricity in applying the load causes a bending moment. This sets up secondary bending stresses which are added to the primary axial tensile stresses. However, this bending moment tends to straighten out the neutral axis of the member so that as the load is increased, the eccentricity decreases.

2. Compression is the force that pushes,

The rugged service requirements of such equipment as this motor scraper demand careful evaluation of the loads and resulting stresses. Steel weldments designed accordingly, meet the requirements.

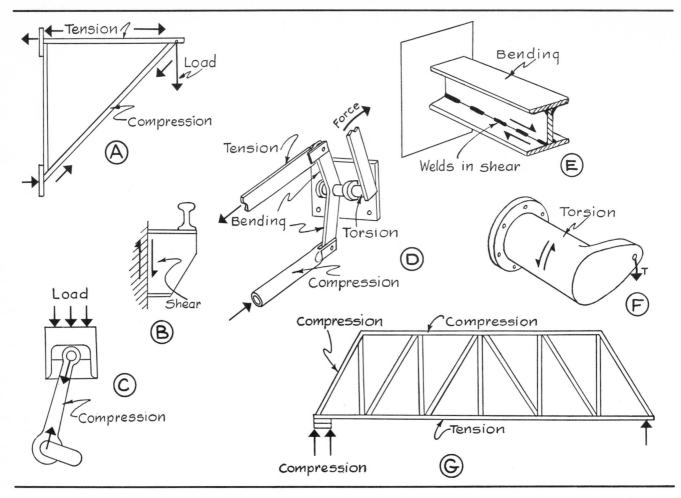

Fig. 1 Typical examples of the various kinds of load to which machine members are subjected.

presses or squeezes a member from opposing directions. It results in deformation by contraction. Excessive loading in compression causes failure by crushing or buckling.

Compression is shown in Figure 1 in the two forms in which it may exist. A long column, which might fail by buckling, often occurs as a compression member in a lever system "D". Similar examples are seen in the compression member of the bracket "A", and in the piston connecting rod "C". A short column, which might fail by crushing, occurs here in the bearing support for a bridge "G".

As compressive loading of a long column is increased, it eventually causes some eccentricity. This in turn sets up a bending moment, causing the column to deflect or buckle slightly. This deflection, no matter how slight, increases the eccentricity and thus the bending moment. This may progress to where the bending moment is increasing at a rate greater than the increase in load. As a result of this vicious cycle, the column soon fails by buckling.

3. Shear loading is the subjection of a member to two equal forces which act in opposite directions

but not along the same line. Failure by shear may follow a direction parallel to the applied forces or along diagonal slip lines in a tensile member.

Shear stresses are often present as a byproduct of the principal stresses or the application of transverse forces. The overhead craneway bracket "B" in Figure 1, is loaded in rather high shear because it is short and carries a large load. The beam "E" is loaded in bending, but the fillet welds joining the flanges to the web are stressed in horizontal shear.

4. Bending loads are forces applied transversely to a member at some distance from the section under consideration. Such a load, as in the beam "E" of Figure 1, produces a bending moment. Application of the load farther out along the beam would increase the bending moment. A bending moment also occurs in the lever system "D".

A bending moment causes a beam to deflect in the direction in which the load is applied.

As the bending load is increased, the deflection increases. However, this deflection of a straight beam has no effect on the position of the load. With large deflection, the cross-section may change in area with a corresponding decrease in its moment of inertia. This would both increase the bending stress and decrease the member's resistance to deflection, so that the possibility of failure increases at an accelerating rate.

Deflection of a straight beam under load takes the form of a curve. Fibers between the neutral axis and the outer surface are under tension, and those along the inside of the bend or deflection are under compression. Failure under a bending load is usually the result of the outer fibers being stressed beyond their tensile limit or buckling of outer fibers in compression.

5. Torsional loading is the subjection of a member to torque forces that cause it to twist about its central axis. Cranks, axles, spindles and other rotating members, such as "F" in Figure 1, are under this type of load.

The principal deflection caused by torsion is measured by the angle of twist. The amount of twist does not affect the torsional moment and therefore has no effect on the value of the moment. Failure under torsional loading is usually a result of shear stresses that develop as the load increases.

At the surface of a round steel shaft, for example, the metal is stressed in shear in a direction perpendicular as well as parallel to the axis of twist. The metal is stressed in tension in a direc-

2. Impact loads are applied suddenly, usually at high velocity. There is, frequently, actual impact (a blow) on the machine member by another machine member or some external body. Impact loads are common to such machines as pile drivers, punch presses, etc.

3. Variable loads are applied in various ways, but in each case the value of force is variable. In some cases the load is constantly varying, as in the connecting rods in an engine. An extreme condition is typified by a rotating shaft which experiences a complete reversal of load on each cycle. If fibers along the top of a shaft are stressed in compression, those along the bottom are stressed in tension. At any point on the shaft, each revolution produces a change from tension to compression.

Over an extended period of time a member can withstand much less stress under severe variable load conditions. As a measure of the maximum unit stress that a material can withstand indefinitely under variable loading, its endurance limit is often established by testing. For this reason, some forms of variable loads are commonly referred to as fatigue loads.

3. VALUE OF LOAD

In order to use many design formulas, it is necessary to determine the amount of load that will be applied to each machine member. The methods of

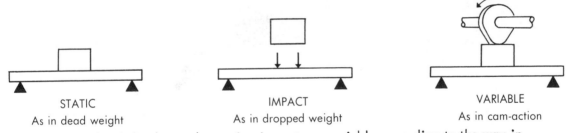

Fig. 2 A load may be static, impact, or variable according to the way in which the load is applied to the machine member.

tion 45° to these shear stresses and in compression at 90° to the tensile stresses. Below the surface these forces decrease as the central axis is approached. Ultimate failure under torsion of a ductile steel shaft is in shear perpendicular to the shaft axis. Ultimate failure under torsion of a brittle shaft is initially in tension at 45° to the shaft axis.

2. APPLICATION OF LOAD

There are three ways in which a load can be applied to a machine member. These are static, impact, and variable (Fig. 2).

1. Static loads are steady, constant or are applied slowly. The load does not change very much in value. Examples include the weight of a fluid in a storage tank, the dead weight of a structure upon its supports, etc.

doing this are many, and are often peculiar to the industry or class of machinery concerned. They have their basis in elementary mechanics and proper analysis of the actual service conditions.

Very often, formulas or nomographs have already been developed to aid in selecting equipment for the power drive system required for the particular class of service. These will also provide the basic load information needed to calculate load on individual machine members.

Here the systems approach can be of use to the frame or chassis designer. Like the drive systems engineer, he starts at the working tool with calculations of required delivered horsepower, for example. Then he works upstream, calculating all secondary forces that effect an increase in the required motor horsepower. This will take into consideration friction, inertia of moving members, rotational forces upon bearings and their housings, flywheel energy, and so on. He now has a graphic picture of the loads emanating from the power train from end to end. From this information he proceeds further to chart the distribution of forces, adding in the dead weight of machine members.

Considering individual members, there are many possibilities. Torque on a shaft or other revolving part is determined from the motor horsepower and speed ($T = 63,030 \times hp/rpm$). Or, tool pressure and work or tool diameter, if known, permit calculating the torque.

Many mechanical and electromechanical transducers are available to help in evaluating loads on existing equipment or on prototypes. Many of these instruments incorporate electrical strain gages in a precision bridge-type sensing element. Such transducers include load cells, pressure gages, torque meters, dynamometers, accelerometers, flow meters, and load beams.

On equipment such as a hoist or lift truck, the maximum load on members can be figured back from the load required to tip the machine over.

When following an existing design on a power shovel or ditch digger for example, the maximum strength of cables that have proven satisfactory in service can be used to work back to the load on machine parts.

If a satisfactory starting point cannot be found, the design can be based upon an assumed load and subsequently adjusted from experience and test.

4. FACTOR OF SAFETY

The anticipated loading, translated into stresses, dictate the proportions of the individual machine member. However, a factor of safety must be included in the calculations in order to ensure the member's withstanding greater forces that may possibly result from:

1. variations in the material;
2. faulty workmanship in fabrication;
3. variations in actual load (Ex: hitting an immovable object with an agricultural implement; interrupted cut in rough machining hard steel on a medium-duty machine tool; overloading a lift hook; etc.); and
4. error in design computations.

There are various ways to determine the factor of safety, and various ways in which to use it. The two decisions are interrelated.

In order for a machine member to have sufficient strength, the maximum unit stress must be limited to some value less than the material's yield strength or ultimate strength with proper consideration for the safety factor. Once the member's proportions are established, this allowable unit stress can then be translated into allowable load.

Ordinarily the allowable stress must be relative to the material's yield strength. In most machine members the permanent deformation that would result from exceeding the yield strength might seriously affect further performance of the member. This is not always the case however; and if a degree of permanent deformation can be tolerated, a design based on ultimate strength can be made at less cost.

In order for a machine member to have sufficient rigidity, the maximum allowable strain or deflection is the determining factor. In the past many designers were under the impression that zero deflection was desirable. This is not at all realistic: if zero deflection is mandatory, zero stress is mandatory. This would mean the member could carry no load at all.

Once the maximum allowable strain is established, the corresponding stress figure can be obtained since stress and strain have a proportional relationship within the elastic range. The safety factor is applied here to determine the maximum allowable stress, which can then be used in proportioning the member.

The relationship of stress to strain is expressed by the material's modulus of elasticity, which is 30,000,000 psi for all steels in tension. Thus, if the maximum allowable strain is 0.001 in./in., the corresponding stress would be 30,000 psi. The modulus of elasticity of a steel in shear is 12,000,000 psi; therefore, it is essential to keep in mind the type of force involved.

Any basic rule-of-thumb safety factor that is sufficient for static loads under ideal conditions must be increased under certain circumstances. It is important to correctly determine the mode of load. Consider not only the condition at time of initial construction, but the possible effects of wear. A cam follower in a barrel cam produces a variable loading. After a relatively short period of service, wear in the cam track often results in an additional severe impact loading.

High speed motion pictures and vibration monitoring equipment frequently reveal variable loading or impact loading conditions where only static loads had been assumed.

A variable load necessitates use of a higher safety factor than a static load does. An impact load also requires use of a higher safety factor.

The presence of local areas of concentrated stresses are usually ignored in assigning a safety factor under static load. However, under impact or variable load, these concentrated stresses have a vital role in reducing the maximum allowable stresses.

High stress calculations are most commonly associated with abrupt section changes. They also are present at points of contact between a member and its support or load. An example of this exists where pressures of high intensity evolve between mechanical fasteners and the members they connect.

Traditional Safety Factor

One procedure for determining the factor of safety, following traditional practices of the machinery builders, is as follows:

1. assign an initial factor of safety of 3; and
2. if a cast material, multiply by $1\frac{1}{3}$; and
3. if a brittle material, multiply by 1.2; and
4. if impact loads, multiply by 2.

For example, the factor of safety of the following materials would be:

1. rolled steel   3.0
2. cast steel $(3 \times 1\frac{1}{3})$ 4.0
3. malleable iron $(3 \times 1\frac{1}{3})$ 4.0
4. gray cast iron $(3 \times 1\frac{1}{3} \times 1.2)$ 4.8
5. extruded aluminum   3.0
6. cast aluminum $(3 \times 1\frac{1}{3})$ 4.0

A malleable iron design subjected to impact loads would thus be assigned a service factor of 8.

These service factor values are based on their being applied to the ultimate strength of a material. In other words, if the bar steel to be used in a tension member has an ultimate tensile strength of 90,000 psi, dividing by the service factor of 3 would give the allowable unit stress of 30,000 psi to be used in design computations.

If working with variable or fatigue loads, the proper endurance value for the material is divided by the factor of safety as found above.

It is sometimes simpler to apply the service factor as a multiplier to the calculated load on the specific member, thereby giving us the allowable load to be used in our computations rather than the allowable unit stress.

In either case, whether the service factor is applied as a divisor to the ultimate strength of the material or as a multiplier to the calculated load in the member, we would end up with a member that would fail only if the applied forces reached 3 times its rated load-bearing capacity.

An error is sometimes made in simply applying the safety factor to the service load on the machine itself. The results are not as reliable, since the influence of dead weight of members, developed horsepower, and other factors involved in the total forces on the individual members are not considered in the resultant safety margin for any individual member.

TABLE 1. - ALLOWABLE STRESSES
Conservative Interpretation of AISC Specifications

Tension	$\sigma = .60\ \sigma_y$
Bending	$\sigma = .60\ \sigma_y$
Shear	$\tau = .40\ \sigma_y$
Compression $\frac{L}{r}$ from zero to C_c	$\sigma = \dfrac{\sigma_y}{1.92} - \dfrac{\sigma_y^2}{7.68\ \pi^2\ E}\left(\dfrac{L}{r}\right)^2$ or $\sigma = \left[1 - \frac{1}{2}\left(\dfrac{L/r}{C_c}\right)^2\right]\dfrac{\sigma_y}{1.92}$
$\frac{L}{r} \geqq C_c$	$\sigma = \dfrac{\pi^2\ E}{1.92\left(\dfrac{L}{r}\right)^2}$ or $\sigma = \left(\dfrac{16,900}{L/r}\right)^2 \dfrac{1}{1.92}$
where: $C_c = \sqrt{\dfrac{2\ \pi^2\ E}{\sigma_y}} = \dfrac{23,900}{\sqrt{\sigma_y}}$	

For further discussion of allowable stresses for Columns, see Sect. 2.5

Structural Safety Factors

The structural field has widely adopted values for the safety factor to be applied to various materials. AISC research and specifications have been interpreted to give corresponding allowable stresses (Table 1).

These AISC (American Institute of Steel Construction) allowable values are realistic in terms of today's superior materials. However, the lower values are based on yield strength of the material and not ultimate strength. In view of the previous arguments in favor of designing to avoid permanent deformation, not just failure, these values appear to be more appropriate to today's need.

Reducing the Safety Factor

The safety factor figured into design calculations is often recognized as being too large and is probably adding unnecessarily to the product cost. Very often safety codes dictate the practice. However, even where no code applies, the designer is loathe to reduce his section dimensions arbitrarily. This is particularly true if his design is based on principal forces and the safety factor has been covering the influence of unknown or unstudied secondary forces.

The safety factor is no longer as critical in de-

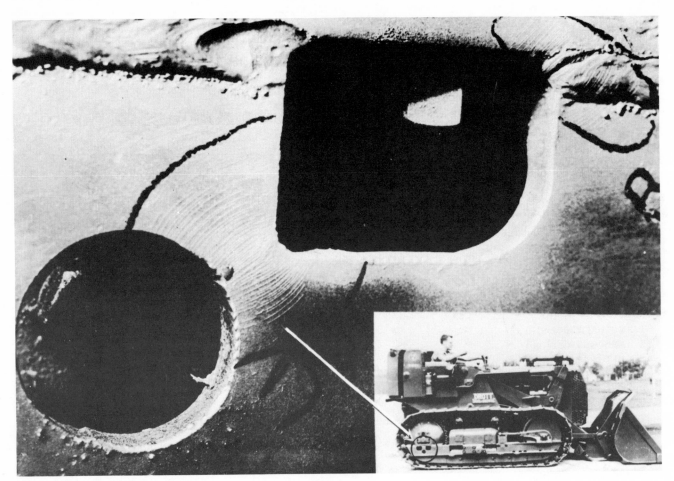

Fig. 3 Brittle coatings are applied to surfaces of actual members for study of surface stress concentrations under various load conditions. Here, Stresscoat patterns are obtained from dynamic loads on tractor track frame.

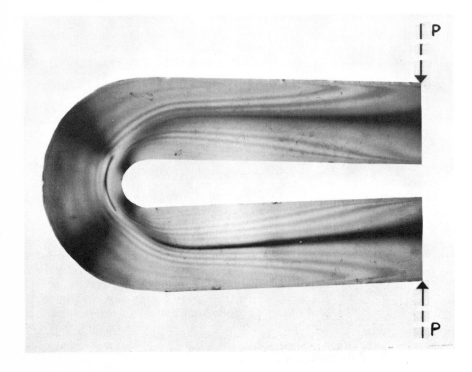

Fig. 4 Stress analysis by photoelasticity is based on study of the stress pattern revealed by passing polarized light through a transparent model of the member subjected to load. Pattern varies as the amount of load varies.

NO LOAD  LOW LOAD 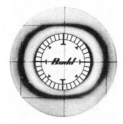 HIGH LOAD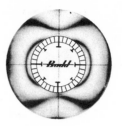

Fig. 5 The principle of stress analysis by photoelasticity has been adapted to direct-readout gages bonded to actual structures and members. Here are PhotoStress rosettes that accurately reveal both orientation and magnitude of principal strains, within areas of limited strain gradient.

sign calculations for many machine members. This is mainly due to the widespread adoption of improved electrical and hydraulic overload controls, slip clutches, overload relief beds in presses for example, more reliable shear pins, qualifying fixtures or stations to prevent oversize castings from entering a machinery station, double-blank detectors on presses, and other such devices. The critical nature of the safety factor is also minimized by generally better reliability of materials, more refined control of manufacturing quality, and other advancements.

Still, overload devices often lead to machine stoppage. The design must balance increasing cost of lost productive time against the further cost reductions in building machinery made possible through lowering the safety factor.

The precise influence of concentrated stresses due to fabricating methods or section changes, for example, can be determined analytically or experimentally.

5. EXPERIMENTAL STRESS ANALYSIS

To aid in reducing the safety factor as well as to improve machine performance, machinery builders are turning more frequently to experimental stress analysis. This provides verification of mathematical analyses, and also more detailed knowledge of complex force fields which discourage mathematical analysis.

The primary measurements are made of strains that develop in the member under load. From these strain values, the stresses can be interpolated.

Four tools of experimental stress analysis are these:

1. Brittle coatings are used to study surface stresses and to locate areas of dangerous stress concentrations (Fig. 3).

2. Photoelasticity is used to study stress distribution through a cross-section (Fig. 4).

3. Mechanical strain gages are used primarily

Fig. 6 The wire-grid and etched-foil strain gages shown here are the most common types. Electromechanical strain gages exhibit a change of electrical resistance with a change in strain. This change is linear and can be measured.

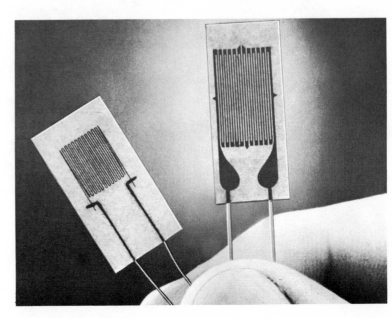

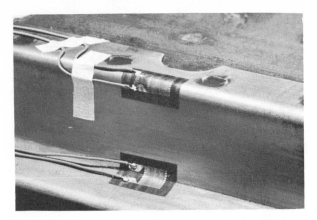

Fig. 7 Here, flexible etched-foil gages are applied to bend lines of a steel member to reveal stress behavior under load.

Instrumentation for use with strain gages provide a continuous reading as strain develops. Thus, they permit a more comprehensive history of elastic behavior under dynamic loading than is possible with either brittle coatings or photoelasticity. However, brittle coatings are inexpensive, simple to use, and frequently provide all of the information needed by revealing distribution of maximum stresses at the surface of the member. Brittle coatings require considerable skill to make an accurate quantitative analysis.

Whereas the other techniques are limited to surface readings, photoelasticity is especially valuable where further knowledge is needed of stress distribution across a section. In general, photoelastic study is more expensive than the other techniques and is fairly slow. It depends on transparent models of the member but is often limited to two-dimensional models. In either case, it may not reflect all of the forces to which the three-dimensional member would be exposed.

These limitations do not apply to (Zandman) photo-elasticity techniques employing PhotoStress gages mounted directly to various surface areas of the machine member (Fig. 5).

Membrane analogy is another useful tool of Experimental Stress Analysis and will be described later in Section 3.6.

to make measurements of large forces, or in the field where other techniques have limitations.

4. Electrical strain gages are very sensitive and flexible in application (Fig. 6). They are very small and often can be used where space does not permit mechanical strain gages. They can detect variations in strain measured in micro-inches.

Fig. 8 Measurements read by electromechanical strain gages are amplified and fed into an oscillograph for permanent continuous record of the member's behavior under load. Here, structural strains on a proposed side-delivery rake design are recorded as equipment is pulled over obstacles.

Properties of Materials

1. IMPORTANCE OF PROPERTIES

All materials have certain properties which must be known in order to promote their proper use. These properties are essential to selection of the best material for a given member.

In the design of machine members, the properties of material which are of primary concern are those that indicate material behavior under certain types of load. Some property of material is called for in each of the basic design formulas.

Properties commonly found in engineering handbooks and suppliers catalogs (Table 1) are these:

1. ultimate tensile strength
2. yield strength in tension
3. elongation
4. modulus of elasticity
5. compressive strength
6. shear strength
7. endurance limit

Other properties such as modulus of resilience and ultimate energy resistance, may also be given.

The various properties are best defined by a description of what happens when a specimen of the material is subjected to load during laboratory tests.

2. TENSILE PROPERTIES

In a tensile test, the machined and ground specimen of the material is marked with a centerpunch at two points 2" apart, as shown in Figure 1. The specimen is placed in a tensile testing machine, and an axial load is applied to it by pulling the jaws holding the ends of the specimen in opposing directions at a slow and constant rate of speed, Figure 2.

As the pulling progresses, the specimen elongates at a uniform rate which is proportionate to the rate at which the load or pulling force increases.

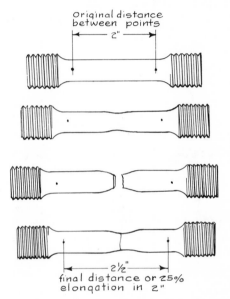

Fig. 1 Tensile test specimen before and after testing to failure, showing maximum elongation.

TABLE 1 - PROPERTIES AND COMPOSITION OF CONSTRUCTIONAL ALLOY STEELS

Producer	Alloy	Yield Point, psi	Ult. Strength, psi	Elong., %	C	Mn	Si	Cu	Mo	Cr	Ni	Other
Great Lakes Steel	N-A-Xtra 80	80,000	95,000	18	0.15	0.80	0.70		0.20	0.65		0.09 Zr
	90	90,000	105,000	18	0.15	0.80	0.70		0.20	0.65		0.09 Zr
	100	100,000	115,000	18	0.15	0.80	0.70		0.20	0.65		0.09 Zr
	110	110,000	125,000	18	0.15	0.80	0.70		0.20	0.65		0.09 Zr
Jones & Laughlin	Jalloy-S-90	90,000	105,000	18	0.15	1.25	0.25		0.25			
	Jalloy-S-100	100,000	115,000	18	0.15	1.25	0.25		0.25			Cb
	Jalloy-S-110	110,000	125,000	18	0.15	1.25	0.25		0.25			Cb
Lukens Steel	T-1	100,000	115,000	18	0.15	0.80	0.25	0.35	0.55	0.60	0.85	V, B
Republic Steel	Republic 65	65,000	85,000	20	0.15	1.00	0.15	1.15	0.25		1.25	
	70	70,000	90,000	18	0.20	1.00	0.15	1.25	0.25		1.50	
US Steel	T-1	100,000	115,000	18	0.15	0.80	0.25	0.35	0.55	0.60	0.85	V, B
Youngstown Sheet & Tube	Yoloy S	65,000	95,000	20	0.12	0.60	0.30	1.00			1.80	

– Table courtesy PRODUCT ENGINEERING Magazine

TABLE 2 – PROPERTIES AND COMPOSITION OF HIGH-STRENGTH LOW ALLOY STEELS

Producer	Alloy	Yield Point, psi	Ult. Strength, psi	Elong., %	C	Mn	Si	Cu	Mo	Cr	Ni	Other
Alan Wood Steel	Dynalloy I	50,000	70,000	22	0.15	0.80	0.30	0.45	0.10		0.55	
	Dynalloy II	45,000	62,000	25	0.15	0.80	0.30	0.45	0.10		0.55	
Armco Steel	High Strength No. 1	50,000	70,000	22	0.15	0.70	0.15	0.60			0.75	
	2	45,000	64,000		0.15	0.70	0.15	0.60			0.75	
	3	40,000	60,000	35	0.10	0.60	0.10	0.20				0.02 V
	4	50,000	70,000	22	0.25	1.35	0.25	0.20				
	5	45,000	60,000	25	0.22	1.25	0.30	0.20				0.02 V
Bethlehem Steel	Mayari R	50,000	70,000	22	0.12	0.75	0.55	0.50		0.70	1.0	0.10 Zr
	Medium Manganese	50,000	75,000	20	0.25	1.35	0.30	0.30				
	Manganese Vanadium	50,000	70,000	22	0.22	1.25	0.30	0.20				0.02 V
Crucible Steel of America	Maxeloy	50,000	70,000	22	0.15	1.20	0.50	0.20			0.50	
Colorado Fuel & Iron	Clay-Loy	50,000	70,000		0.22	1.25	0.35	0.50				0.2 V
Inland Steel	Hi-Steel	50,000	70,000	22	0.12	0.75	0.15	0.95	0.18		0.55	
	Hi-Man	50,000	75,000	20	0.25	1.35	0.30	0.20				
	Hi-Man 440 (A440)	50,000	70,000		0.28	1.35	0.30	0.20				
	Tri-Steel	50,000	70,000	22	0.22	1.25	0.30	0.20				0.02 V
Jones & Laughlin	Jalten No. 1	50,000	70,000	22	0.15	1.30	0.10	0.30				0.05 V
	2	50,000	70,000	22	0.15	1.40	0.10	0.30				
	3	50,000	70,000	22	0.25	1.50	0.25	0.20				
	JLX-45-W	45,000	65,000	22	0.15	0.75	0.10					0.03 Cb
	-50-W	50,000	70,000	22	0.15	0.75	0.10					0.03 Cb
	-55-W	55,000	75,000	22	0.15	0.75	0.10					0.03 Cb
	-60-W	60,000	80,000	22	0.15	0.75	0.10					0.03 Cb
Kaiser Steel	Kaisaloy No. 1	50,000	70,000	23	0.20	1.25	0.60	0.35	0.15	0.25	0.60	V, Ti
	2	45,000	60,000	25	0.12	0.60	0.50	0.30	0.10	0.25	0.60	V, Ti
	3	58,000	83,000	15	0.30	1.50	0.35	0.35	0.10	0.25	0.40	V, Ti
	Structural High Strength	50,000	75,000	18	0.27	1.60	0.30	0.20				
Lukens Steel	Cor-Ten	50,000	70,000	22	0.12	0.35	0.50	0.40		0.80	0.65	
National Steel (Great Lakes Steel and Weirton Steel)	GLX-45-W	45,000	65,000	22	0.15	0.75	0.10					0.03 Cb
	GLX-50-W	50,000	70,000	22	0.15	0.75	0.10					0.03 Cb
	GLX-55-W	55,000	75,000	22	0.15	0.75	0.10					0.03 Cb
	GLX-60-W	60,000	80,000	22	0.15	0.75	0.10					0.03 Cb
	N-A-X High Tensile	50,000	70,000	22	0.15	0.75	0.75	0.25	0.20	0.55		0.10 Zr
	N-A-X High Manganese	50,000	70,000	22	0.25	1.35	0.30	0.20				
Pittsburgh Steel	Pitt-Ten No. 1	50,000	70,000	22	0.12	0.75	0.20	0.85			0.70	
Republic Steel	Republic 50	50,000	70,000	22	0.15	0.75		0.65	0.10	0.30	0.75	
	Republic M	50,000	75,000	20	0.25	1.35	0.30	0.20				
US Steel	Cor-Ten	50,000	70,000	22	0.12	0.35	0.50	0.40		0.80	0.65	
	Ex-Ten-45	45,000			0.20	0.75	0.10					0.01 Cb
	Ex-Ten-50	50,000			0.25	0.75	0.10					0.01 Cb
	Man-Ten	50,000	75,000	20	0.25	1.35	0.30	0.20				
	Man-Ten (A440)	50,000	70,000		0.28	1.35	0.30	0.20				
	Par-Ten	45,000	62,000	28	0.12	0.75	0.10					0.04 V
	Tri-Ten	50,000	70,000	22	0.22	1.25	0.30	0.20				0.02 V
Youngstown Sheet & Tube	Yoloy	50,000	70,000	22	0.15	0.75	0.30	1.00			1.70	
	Yoloy A242	50,000	70,000	22	0.22	1.25	0.30	0.20				0.02 V
	Yoloy E HSX	45,000	80,000	25	0.18	1.00	0.30	0.35		0.40	0.70	
	Yoloy EHS	50,000	70,000	22	0.18	1.00	0.30	0.35	0.40	0.40	0.70	
	Yoloy M-A	50,000	70,000	20	0.25	1.60	0.30	0.35				
	Yoloy M-B	45,000	70,000	22	0.23	1.40	0.25	0.20				
	Yoloy 45W	45,000	65,000	30	0.15	0.65						Cb
	Yoloy 50W	50,000	70,000	28	0.15	0.65						Cb

– Table courtesy PRODUCT ENGINEERING Magazine

Fig. 2 A tensile testing machine applies a pulling force on the test piece. The maximum load applied before failure of the piece, divided by the original cross-section, equals the material's ultimate tensile strength.

The load divided by the cross-sectional area of the specimen within the gage marks represents the unit stress or resistance of the material to the pulling or tensile force. This stress (σ) is expressed in pounds per square inch, psi. The elongation of the specimen represents the strain (ϵ) induced in the material and is expressed in inches per inch of length, in./in. Stress and strain are plotted in a diagram, shown in simplified form in Figure 3.

The proportional relationship of load to elongation, or of stress to strain, continues until a point is reached where the elongation begins to increase at a faster rate. This point, beyond which the elongation of the specimen no longer is proportional to the loading, is the proportional elastic limit of the material. When the load is removed, the specimen returns to its original dimensions.

Beyond the elastic limit, further movement of the

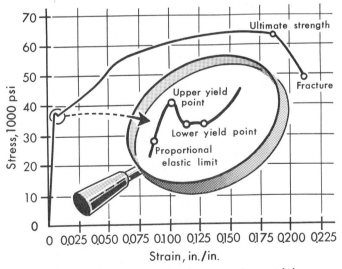

Fig. 3 A stress-strain diagram for mild steel, showing ultimate tensile strength and other properties. Here, the most critical portion of the curve is magnified.

test machine jaws in opposing directions causes a permanent elongation or deformation of the specimen material. In the case of a low- or medium-carbon steel, a point is reached beyond which the metal stretches briefly without an increase in load. This is the yield point.

For low- and medium-carbon steels, the unit stress at the yield point is considered to be the material's tensile yield strength (σ_y).* For other metals, the yield strength is the stress required to strain the specimen by a specified small amount beyond the elastic limit. For ordinary commercial purposes, the elastic limit is assumed to coincide with the yield strength.

Beyond the material's elastic limit, continued pulling causes the specimen to neck down across its diameter or width. This action is accompanied by a further acceleration of the axial elongation, which is now largely confined within the relatively short necked-down section.

The pulling force eventually reaches a maximum value and then falls off rapidly, with little additional elongation of the specimen before failure occurs. In failing, the specimen breaks in two within the necked-down portion. The maximum pulling load, expressed as a stress in psi of the original cross-sectional area of the specimen, is the material's ultimate tensile strength (σ_u).*

Ductility and Elasticity

The two halves of the specimen are then put together, and the distance between the two punch marks is measured (Fig. 1). The increase in length gives the elongation of the specimen in 2", and is usually expressed as a percentage. The cross-section at point of failure is also measured to give the reduction in area, which is usually expressed as a percentage. Both elongation percentage and re-

*The symbols commonly used for yield strength, ultimate strength, and axial strain do not indicate the type of load.

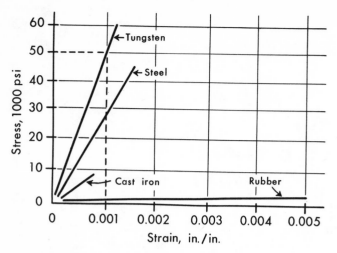

Fig. 4 Stress-strain curves for several materials show their relative elasticity. Only that portion of curve displaying a proportional relationship between stress and strain is diagrammed.

duction of area percentage indicate the material's ductility.

In the design of most design members, it is essential to keep the stresses resulting from loading within the elastic range. If the elastic limit (very close to the material's yield strength) is exceeded, permanent deformation takes place due to plastic flow or slippage along molecular slip planes. When this happens, the material is strain-hardened and thereafter has a higher effective elastic limit and higher yield strength.

Cold working operations during manufacture of a member, to deliberately strain-harden or work-harden the material, are becoming more common practice. Although such operations increase the yield strength and resistance to deformation, they have no effect on the member's ultimate strength and may create a degree of risk on some applications because of the lowered ductility.

Under the same amount of stress, some materials stretch less than others. The modulus of elasticity (E) of a material simplifies the comparison of its stiffness with that of another material. This property is the ratio of the stress to the strain within the elastic range:

$$\frac{\text{Stress } \sigma}{\text{Strain } \epsilon} = \text{Modulus of elasticity E}$$

On a stress-strain diagram, the modulus of elasticity is represented visually by the straight portion of the curve where the stress is directly proportional to the strain. The steeper the curve, the higher the modulus of elasticity and the stiffer the material (Fig. 4).

Any steel has a modulus of elasticity in tension of approximately 30,000,000 psi. Other materials

may vary according to the specific alloy. Cast iron, for example, has a modulus of elasticity in tension between 10,000,000 and 25,000,000 psi, depending on the grade.

3. COMPRESSIVE STRENGTH

The general design practice is to assume that the compressive strength of a steel is equal to its tensile strength. This practice is also adhered to in some rigidity design calculations, where the modulus of elasticity of the material in tension is used even though the loading is compressive.

The actual ultimate compressive strength of steels may be somewhat greater than the ultimate tensile strength. The variation in compressive values is at least partially dependent on the condition of the steel: the compressive strength of an

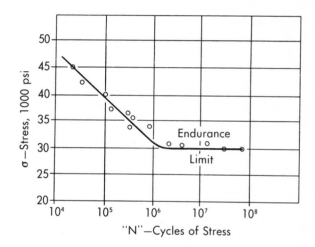

Fig. 5 Fatigue test results are plotted on σ-N diagram; stress vs. number of cycles before failure.

annealed steel is closer to its tensile strength than would be the case with a cold-worked steel. (There is less of a relationship between the compressive strength and the tensile strength of cast iron and non-ferrous metals.)

A compressive test is conducted similar to that for tensile properties, but a short specimen is subjected to a compressive load. That is, force is applied on the specimen from two directions in axial opposition. The ultimate compressive strength is reached when the specimen fails by crushing.

A stress-strain diagram is developed during the test, and values are obtained for compressive yield strength and other properties. However, instead of the Young's modulus of elasticity conventionally used, the tangential modulus of elasticity (E_t) is usually obtained. This will be discussed in Section 2.5 on Compression.

Compression of long columns is more complex, since failure develops under the influence of a bending moment that increases as the deflection increases. Geometry of the member has much to do with its capacity to withstand compressive loads, and this will be discussed more completely under Section 2.5 on Compression.

With long columns, the effect of eccentric loading is more severe in the case of compression than tension.

4. SHEAR STRENGTH

There is no recognized standard method of testing for shear strength of a material. Fortunately, pure shear loads are seldom encountered in machinery design but shear stresses frequently develop as a byproduct of principal stresses or the application of transverse forces.

The ultimate shear strength (τ) is generally assumed to be ¾ the material's ultimate tensile strength.

Some shear values are obtained from torsional loading, but these are not valid for stresses beyond the elastic limit. The ultimate shear strength is often obtained from an actual shearing of the metal, usually in a punch-and-die setup using a ram moving slowly at a constant rate of speed. The maximum load required to punch through the metal is observed, and ultimate shear strength is calculated from this.

5. ENDURANCE LIMIT

When the load on a member is constantly varying in value, is repeated at relatively high frequency, or constitutes a complete reversal of stresses with each operating cycle, the material's endurance limit must be substituted for the ultimate strength where called for by the design formulas.

Under high load values, the variable or fatigue mode of loading reduces the material's effective ultimate strength as the number of cycles increases. At a given high stress value, the material has a definite service or fatigue life, expressed as "N" cycles of operation.

A series of identical specimens are tested, each under a specific load value expressible as a unit stress. The unit stress is plotted for each specimen against the number of cycles before failure. The result is a σ-N diagram (Fig. 5).

The endurance limit (usually σ_r) is the maximum stress to which the material can be subjected for an indefinite service life. Although the standards vary for various types of members and different industries, it is a common practice to accept the assumption that carrying a certain load for several million cycles of stress reversals indicates that load can be carried for an indefinite time.

Theoretically the load on the test specimens should be of the same nature as the load on the proposed machine member, i.e. tensile, torsional, etc. (Fig. 6).

Since the geometry of the member, the presence of local areas of high stress concentration, and the condition of the material have considerable influence on the real endurance limit, prototypes of the member would give the most reliable information as test specimens. This is not always practical however. When building one-of-a-kind, fatigue tests are seldom possible. Lacking any test data or handbook values on endurance limit, see Section 3.2 on Fatigue.

6. IMPACT PROPERTIES

Impact strength is the ability of a metal to absorb the energy of a load delivered onto the member at high velocity. A metal may have good tensile strength and good ductility under static loading, and yet break if subjected to a high-velocity blow.

The two most important properties that indicate the material's resistance to impact loading are obtained from the stress-strain diagram (Fig. 7). The first of these is the modulus of resilience (u) which is a measure of how well the material absorbs

Fig. 6 Typical setup for fatigue testing under pulsating axial stresses.

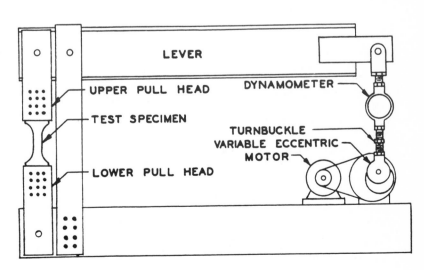

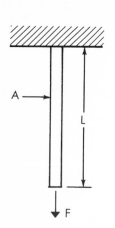

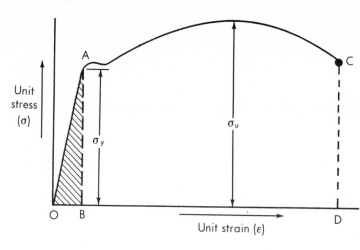

Fig. 7 In the stress-strain diagram for impact, the elongation at moment of ultimate stress is a factor in determining the toughness of the material in terms of ultimate energy resistance.

energy providing it is not stressed above the elastic limit or yield point. It indicates the material's resistance to deformation from impact loading. (See Section 3.1 on Impact.)

The modulus of resilience (u) is the triangular area OAB under the stress-strain curve having its apex at the elastic limit. For practicality let the yield strength (σ_y) be the altitude of the right triangle and the resultant strain (ϵ_y) be the base. Thus,

$$u = \frac{\sigma^2}{2\,E}$$

where E = modulus of elasticity.

Since the absorption of energy is actually a volumetric property, the u in psi = u in in.-lbs/cu. in.

When impact loading exceeds the elastic limit (or yield strength) of the material, it calls for toughness in the material rather than resilience. Toughness, the ability of the metal to resist fracture under impact loading, is indicated by its ultimate energy resistance (u_u). This is a measure of how well the material absorbs energy without fracture.

The ultimate energy resistance (u_u) is the total area OACD under the stress-strain curve. For practicality the following formula can be used:

$$u_u = \frac{\sigma_y + \sigma_u}{2}\epsilon_u$$

where:

σ_y = material's shear strength

σ_u = material's ultimate strength

ϵ_u = strain of the material at point of ultimate stress

Since the absorption of energy is actually a volumetric property, the u_u in psi = u_u in in.-lbs/cu.in.

Tests developed for determining the impact strength of materials are often misleading in their results. Nearly all testing is done with notched specimens, in which case it is more accurately the testing for notch toughness.

The two standard tests are the Izod and Charpy. The two types of specimens used in these tests and the method of applying the load are shown in Figure 8. Both tests can be made in a universal impact testing machine. The minimum amount of energy in a falling pendulum required to fracture the specimen is considered to be a measure of the material's impact strength. In actuality, test conditions are seldom duplicated in the machine member and application of these test data is unrealistic.

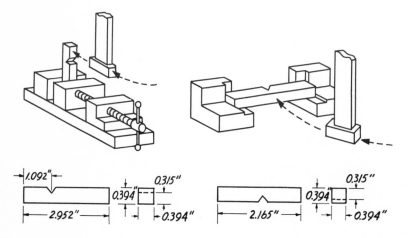

Fig. 8 Typical Izod (left) and Charpy (right) impact test specimens, methods of holding and of applying the test load. The V-notch specimens shown have an included angle of 45° and a bottom radius of 0.010" in the notch.

Properties of Sections

1. IMPORTANCE OF SECTION PROPERTY

The basic formulas used in the design of machine members include as one factor the critical property of the material and as another factor the corresponding critical property of the member's cross-section. The property of the section dictates how efficiently the property of the material will be utilized.

The property of section having the greatest importance is the section's area (A). However, most design problems are not so simple that the area is used directly. Instead there is usually a bending aspect to the problem and, therefore, the rigidity factor normally is the section's moment of inertia (I) and the simple strength factor is the section modulus (S).

Another property of section that is of major importance is the section's torsional resistance (R), a modified value for standard sections.

2. AREA OF THE SECTION (A)

The area (A) of the member's cross-section is used directly in computations for simple tension, compression, and shear. This is true in both rigidity and strength designs. Area (A) of a section is expressed in square inches.

If the section is not uniform throughout the length of the member, it is necessary to determine the section in which the greatest unit stresses will be incurred.

In those computations for bending where the section is a complex configuration, the area of the section is frequently of subordinate influence on the results. In such cases, it is sometimes sufficiently accurate to consider this area as made up of a series of rectangular elements rather than figure the section area precisely.

3. MOMENT OF INERTIA (I)

Whereas a moment is the tendency toward rotation about an axis, the moment of inertia of the cross-section of a machine member is a measure of the resistance to rotation offered by the section's geometry and size. Thus, the moment of inertia is a useful property in solving design problems where a bending moment or torsional moment is involved.

The moment of inertia is needed in solving any rigidity problem in which the member is a beam or long column. It is a measure of the stiffness of a beam. Moment of inertia is also required for figuring the value of the polar moment of inertia (J), unless a formula is available for finding torsional resistance (R).

The moment of inertia (I) is used in finding the section modulus (S) and thus has a role in solving simple strength designs as well as rigidity designs. The moment of inertia of a section is expressed in inches raised to the fourth power (in.^{4}).

Finding the Neutral Axis

In working with the section's moment of inertia, the neutral axis (N.A.) of the section must usually be located. In a member subjected to a bending load for example, the neutral axis extends through the length of the member parallel to the member's structural axis and perpendicular to the line of applied force. The neutral axis represents zero strain and therefore zero stress. Fibers between the neutral axis and the surface to the inside of the arc caused by deflection under load, are under compression. Fibers between the neutral axis and the surface to the outside of the arc caused by deflection under load, are under tension.

For practical purposes this neutral axis is assumed to have a fixed relationship (n) to some reference axis, usually along the top or bottom of the section. In Figure 1, the reference axis is taken through the base line of the section. The total section is next broken into rectangular elements. The moment (M) of each element about the section's reference axis, is determined:

M = area of element multiplied by the distance
(y) of element's center of gravity from reference axis of section

The moments of the various elements are then all added together. This summation of moments is next divided by the total area (A) of the section. This gives the distance (n) of the neutral axis from the reference axis, which in this case is the base line or extreme fiber.

1

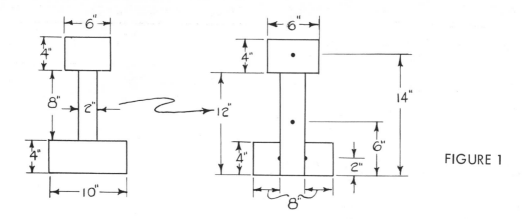

FIGURE 1

Problem 1

The neutral axis of the compound section shown in Figure 1 is located in the following manner:

$$\boxed{n = \frac{\Sigma M}{\Sigma A}} \text{ or } \frac{\text{sum of all moments}}{\text{total area}} \quad \ldots\ldots\ldots\ldots(1)$$

$$= \frac{(4 \cdot 6 \cdot 14) + (2 \cdot 12 \cdot 6) + (4 \cdot 8 \cdot 2)}{(4 \cdot 6) + (2 \cdot 12) + (4 \cdot 8)}$$

$$= \frac{336 + 44 + 64}{24 + 24 + 32} = \frac{544}{80}$$

$$= 6.8"$$

Thus, the neutral axis is located 6.8" above the reference axis or base line and is parallel to it.

Finding the Moment of Inertia

There are various methods to select from to get the value of moment of inertia (I). Six good methods are presented here.

Moment of Inertia for Typical Sections (First Method)

The first method for finding the moment of inertia is to use the simplified formulas given for typical sections. These are shown in Table 1. This method for finding I is the most appropriate for simple sections that cannot be broken down into smaller elements. In using these formulas, be sure to take the moment of inertia about the correct line. Notice that the moment of inertia for a rectangle about its neutral axis is —

$$\boxed{I_n = \frac{b d^3}{12}} \quad \ldots\ldots\ldots\ldots\ldots\ldots\ldots\ldots\ldots\ldots\ldots(2)$$

but the moment of inertia for a rectangle about its base line is —

$$\boxed{I_b = \frac{b d^3}{3}} \quad \ldots\ldots\ldots\ldots\ldots\ldots\ldots\ldots(3)$$

where b = width of rectangle, and
d = depth of rectangle

Moment of Inertia by Elements (Second Method)

In the second method, the whole section is broken into rectangular elements. The neutral axis of the whole section is first found. Each element has a moment of inertia about its own centroid or center of gravity (C.G.) equal to that obtained by the formula shown for rectangular sections. (See Table 1.)

In addition, there is a much greater moment of inertia for each element because of the distance of its center of gravity to the neutral axis of the whole section. This moment of inertia is equal to the area of the element multiplied by the distance of its C.G. to the neutral axis squared.

Thus, the moment of inertia of the entire section about its neutral axis equals the summation of the two moments of inertia of the individual elements.

Problem 2

Having already located the neutral axis of the section in Figure 1, the resulting moment of inertia

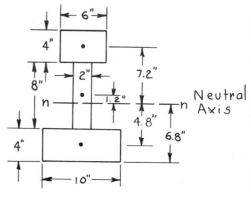

FIGURE 2

of the section (detailed further in Fig. 2) about its neutral axis is found as follows:

$$I_n = \frac{6 \cdot 4^3}{12} + (6 \cdot 4 \cdot 7.2^2) + \frac{2 \cdot 8^3}{12} + (2 \cdot 8 \cdot 1.2^2) +$$

$$\frac{10 \cdot 4^3}{12} + (10 \cdot 4 \cdot 4.8^2)$$

$$= 32 + 1244 + 85.3 + 23 + 53.3 + 921.6$$

$$= \underline{2359 \text{ in.}^4}$$

Moment of Inertia by Adding Areas (Third Method)

With the third method it is possible to figure moment of inertia of built-up sections without first directly making a calculation for the neutral axis.

This method is recommended for use with welments because the designer can stop briefly as a plate is added to quickly find the new moment of inertia. If this value is not high enough, he simply continues to add more plate and again checks this value without losing any of his previous calculations. Likewise if the value is too high, the designer may deduct some of the plates and again check his result. This is done in the same manner as one using an adding machine, whereby you can stop at any time during adding and take a sub-total, and then proceed along without disrupting the previous figures.

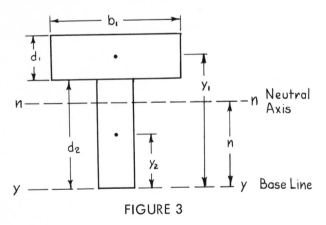

FIGURE 3

Using the parallel axis theorem for shifting the axis for a moment of inertia, the moment of inertia of the whole section about the reference line y-y is –

$$\boxed{I_y = I_n + A\,n^2} \quad \dots\dots\dots\dots\dots\dots\dots\dots \text{(4)}$$

or

$$\boxed{I_n = I_y - A\,n^2} \quad \dots\dots\dots\dots\dots\dots\dots\dots \text{(5)}$$

Since $n = \dfrac{\text{total moments about base}}{\text{total area}} = \dfrac{M}{A}$

and of course $n^2 = \dfrac{M^2}{A^2}$

Substituting this back into equation (5):

$$I_n = I_y - \frac{A\,M^2}{A^2}$$

Note: neutral axis (n) has dropped out

TABLE 1 – PROPERTIES OF STANDARD SECTIONS

	Moment of Inertia I	Section Modulus S	Radius of Gyration r
rectangle (b, d)	$\dfrac{bd^3}{12}$	$\dfrac{bd^2}{6}$	$\dfrac{d}{\sqrt{12}}$
rectangle (b, d) base	$\dfrac{bd^3}{3}$	$\dfrac{bd^2}{3}$	$\dfrac{d}{\sqrt{3}}$
triangle	$\dfrac{bd^3}{36}$	$\dfrac{bd^2}{24}$	$\dfrac{d}{\sqrt{18}}$
triangle base	$\dfrac{bd^3}{12}$	$\dfrac{bd^2}{12}$	$\dfrac{d}{\sqrt{6}}$
circle	$\dfrac{\pi d^4}{64}$	$\dfrac{\pi d^3}{32}$	$\dfrac{d}{4}$
hollow circle	$\dfrac{\pi}{64}(D^4 - d^4)$	$\dfrac{\pi}{32}\dfrac{(D^4 - d^4)}{D}$	$\dfrac{\sqrt{D^2 + d^2}}{4}$
ellipse	$\dfrac{\pi a^3 b}{4}$	$\dfrac{\pi a^2 b}{4}$	$\dfrac{a}{2}$
hollow ellipse	$\dfrac{\pi}{4}\left(a^3 b - c^3 d\right)$	$\dfrac{\pi(a^3 b - c^3 d)}{4a}$	$\dfrac{1}{a}\sqrt{\dfrac{a^3 b - c^3 d}{ab - cd}}$

Thus:

$$\boxed{I_n = I_y - \frac{M^2}{A}} \quad \dots\dots\dots\dots\dots\dots\dots \text{(6)}$$

where:

I_n = moment of inertia of whole section about its neutral axis, n-n

I_y = sum of the moments of inertia of all elements about a common reference axis, y-y

M = sum of the moments of all elements about the same reference axis, y-y

A = total area, or sum of the areas of all elements of section

Although I_y for any individual element is equal to its area (A) multiplied by the distance squared from its center of gravity to the reference axis (y^2), each element has in addition a moment of inertia (I_g) about its own center of gravity. This must be added in if it is large enough, although in most cases it may be neglected:

$$I_n = I_y + I_g - \frac{M^2}{A} \dots\dots\dots\dots\dots\dots(7)$$

The best way to illustrate this method is to work a problem.

Problem 3

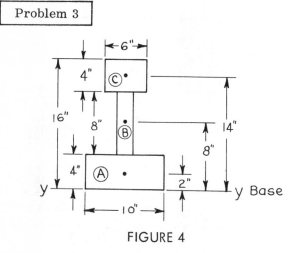

FIGURE 4

The base of this section will be used as a reference axis, y-y. Every time a plate is added, its dimensions are put down in table form, along with its distance (y) from the reference axis. No other information is needed. It is suggested that the plate section size be listed as width times depth (b × d); that is, its width first and depth last.

Plate	Size	Distance y	$A = b \cdot d$ in.²	$M = A \cdot y$ in.³	$I_y = Ay^2 = My$ in.⁴	$I_g = \frac{bd^3}{12}$ in.⁴
A	10"×4"	2"				
B	2"×8"	8"				
C	6"×4"	14"				
Total						

The above table has been filled out with all of the given information from the plates. The rest of the computations are very quickly done on slide rule or calculator and placed into the table. Notice how easy and fast each plate is taken care of.

Starting with plate A, 10" is multiplied by 4" to give an area of 40 sq. in. This value is entered into the table under A. Without resetting the slide rule, this figure for A is multiplied by (distance y) 2" to give 80 inches cubed. This value for the element's moment is placed under M in the table. Without

resetting the slide rule, this figure for M is multiplied by (distance y) 2" again to give 160 inches to the fourth power. This value for the element's moment of inertia about the common reference axis y-y is recorded under (I_y) in the table.

If the moment of inertia (I_g) of the plate about its own center of gravity appears to be significant, this value is figured by multiplying the width of the plate by the cube of its depth and dividing by 12. This value for I_g is then placed in the extreme right-hand column, to be later added in with the sum of I_y. Thus,

$$I_g = \frac{b d^3}{12}$$

$$= \frac{10 \cdot 4^3}{12}$$

$$= 53.3 \text{ in.}^4$$

Usually the value of I_g is small enough that it need not be considered. In our example, this value of 53.3 could be considered, although it will not make much difference in the final value. The greater the depth of any element relative to the maximum width of the section, the more the likelihood of its I_g value being significant.

The table will now be filled out for plates B and C as well:

Plate	Size	Distance y	$A = b \cdot d$ in.²	$M = A \cdot y$ in.³	$I_y = Ay^2 = My$ in.⁴	$I_g = \frac{bd^3}{12}$ in.⁴
A	10"×4"	2"	40.0	80.0	160.0	53.3
B	2"×8"	8"	16.0	128.0	1024.0	85.3
C	6"×4"	14"	24.0	336.0	4704.0	32.0
Total			80.0	544.0	5888.0	170.6
						6058

$$I_n = I_y + I_g - \frac{M^2}{A}$$

$$= 5888 + 170.6 - \frac{(544)^2}{80} = 6059 - 3700$$

$$= 2359 \text{ in.}^4$$

and $n = \dfrac{M}{A} = \dfrac{544}{80}$

$$= 6.8" \text{ (up from bottom)}$$

A recommended method of treating M^2/A on the slide rule, is to divide M by A on the rule. Here we have 544 divided by 80 which gives us 6.8. This happens to be the distance of the neutral axis from the base reference line. Then without resetting the slide rule, multiply this by 544 again by just sliding the indicator of the rule down to 544 and read the answer as 3700. Many times it is necessary to know the neutral axis, and it can easily be found without any extra work.

Problem 4

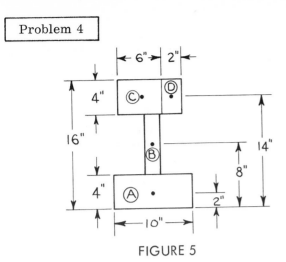

FIGURE 5

To show a further advantage of this system, assume that this resulting moment of inertia (2359 in.[4]) is not large enough and the section must be made larger. Increasing the plate size at the top from 6" × 4" to 8" × 4" is the same as adding a 2" × 4" area to the already existing section. See Figure 5. The previous column totals are carried forward, and properties of only the added area need to be entered. I_n is then solved, using the corrected totals.

Plate	Size	Distance y	$A = b \cdot d$ in.[2]	$M = A \cdot y$ in.[3]	$I_y = Ay^2 = My$ in.[4]	$I_g = \dfrac{bd^3}{12}$ in.[4]
Previous Section		—	80.0	544.0	5888.0	170.6
New D	2"×4"	14"	8.0	112.0	1568.0	10.6
Total			88.0	656.0	7456.0	181.2
						7637

$$I_n = I_y + I_g - \frac{M^2}{A}$$

$$= 7637 - \frac{(656)^2}{88}$$

$$= 2747 \text{ in.}^4$$

$$\text{and } n = \frac{M}{A} = \frac{656}{88}$$

$$= 7.45'' \text{ (up from bottom)}$$

Moment of Inertia of Rolled Sections (Fourth Method)

The fourth method is the use of steel tables found in the A.I.S.C. handbook and other steel handbooks. These values are for any steel section which is rolled, and should be used whenever standard steel sections are used.

Moment of Inertia by Lincoln "I" Rule (Fifth Method)

The fifth method was developed by the Lincoln Electric Company, and the Lincoln Moment of Inertia Rule, Figure 6, must be used. An actual scale drawing of the member's cross-section is needed. This method is especially valuable for finding the moment of inertia for complex cast sections.

The reader can easily make his own "I" Rule by following instructions on the next right page, which has the necessary scale for cut-out purposes.

Basically the Lincoln "I" Rule functions by converting an irregular cross-section to two simple

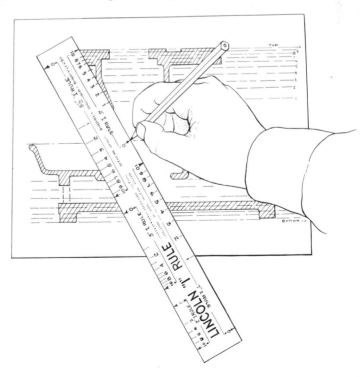

Fig. 6 The "I" Rule permits an irregular section's moment of inertia to be quickly estimated from the sectional view of the member.

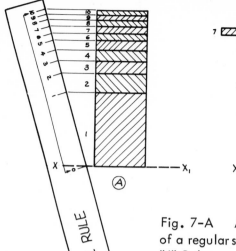

Fig. 7-B   An irregular section divided into 10 areas by
the "I" Rule. Contribution of
each area to total moment of
inertia is proportional to
width of area.

Fig. 7-A   A rectangle representing the top half
of a regular section, divided into 10 areas by the
"I" Rule.

rectangles so that standard formulas can be used. Fundamental principles involved include:

(1) The moment of inertia of a section about its neutral axis equals the sum of moments of inertia of its top and bottom portions about the neutral axis.

(2) The moment of inertia of a rectangle about its base equals the sum of the moments of all of its parts about the same base line.

The Lincoln "I" Rule divides the top and bottom portions into 10 parts. The scale of the rule is such that the contribution of each of the 10 parts to the total moment of inertia of the section is proportional to the width of the individual part. Thus, in Figure 7-A below, all 10 areas have the same width and the same moment of inertia about axis x-x_1. In Figure 7-B, area No. 2 is twice as wide as a majority of the other areas and, consequently, has twice the moment of inertia. Area No. 7 is three times as wide and has three times the moment of inertia.

Knowing that the moment of inertia (I) of a rectangular section about its base is --

$$I = \frac{b\,d^3}{3}$$

it is very easy to solve for the moment of inertia of Figure 7-A.

To find the moment of inertia of Figure 7-B, it is first necessary to convert the irregular shape to an equivalent rectangle. This is done by simply totaling the widths of the 10 areas, then dividing by 10. The resultant figure is the width of a rectangle which has the same moment of inertia about x-x_1 as the irregular section and can be used in the same formula.

The following steps are used in obtaining the moment of inertia of an irregular part, using an

actual scale drawing of the cross-section:

1. Estimate the center of gravity of the section by imagining where the section would balance if supported at this point. Draw a horizontal line through this. This is called the neutral axis; label this "0".

2. Draw lines parallel to the neutral axis at the top and bottom of the section, and label these "10".

3. Place the "I" rule on upper portion of section so that the rule's number 10 is on the top line and its 0 is on the neutral axis. Mark off all 10 points and draw horizontal lines through them. This divides the top portion of the section into 10 areas.

4. With an engineer's scale (the same scale as the drawing), measure off the average width of occupancy in each of the 10 areas in the top portion of the section. Add these up and divide by 10. This will give an average width of the entire top section.

The rule has now transformed the top portion of the section into a rectangle, whose width is equal to the average width of the 10 sections and whose depth is equal to the depth of the section above the neutral axis. Its moment of inertia equals the moment of inertia of the original irregular top portion of the section.

5. Using the formula for finding I of a rectangular area about its base line, find the moment of inertia of the top portion of the section.

6. This same procedure is then repeated for the bottom portion of the section. Remember that the zero mark of the "I" Rule is always placed on the neutral axis and the 10 mark on the outside of the area.

7. Add the moments of inertia of the top and bottom portions to obtain the moment of inertia of the entire section.

MAKE YOUR OWN "I" RULE

You can make your own "I" Rule simply by cutting out the paper rules to the right on this page, then adhesive-mounting them (one on each side) to a strip of plastic, metal, or card stock also cut to size. Cut so as to remove the outer guide lines.

If the rule base is of suitable thickness, cut right around both paper rules and wrap over the edge of the plastic or other base.

The printed rule bears the most common scales used by machinery designers.

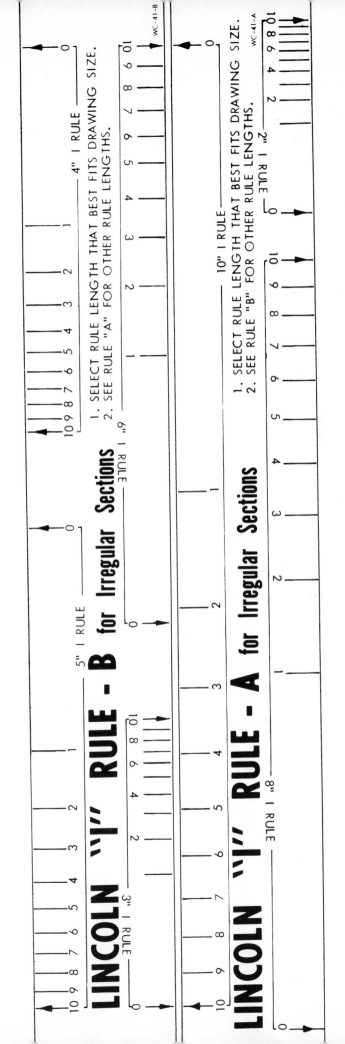

The Lincoln "I" Rule is very accurate. At the top and bottom of any section, where material contributes most to the moment of inertia of the section, there are more lines and individual areas, hence the average width can be determined quite accurately. Near the neutral axis, where the individual areas are deeper and determination of average width less accurate, material contributes less to the moment of inertia and accuracy is relatively unimportant. In other words, the "I" Rule is accurate where it needs to be, and where it is less accurate, it does not matter.

The only consequential source of error is introduced when locating the neutral axis. Even then, if the neutral axis is placed anywhere within 20% of the true neutral axis, the maximum error possible is only about 5%. See Figure 8.

When the axis is incorrectly located, it causes the moment of inertia of one half of the section to be high while the moment of inertia of the other half will be low. Thus their sum, which makes up the total moment of inertia of the entire section, will remain fairly constant.

With a little experience, it is possible to estimate the neutral axis very closely. The resulting moment of inertia should be accurate to 1 or 2%.

However, if the section modulus also is required, it is necessary to more accurately determine the neutral axis since the section modulus equals the

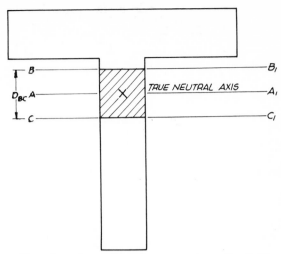

Fig. 8   Assuming the neutral axis is at B-B₁ or C-C₁ results in a 5% maximum error, even though distance Dbc is a full 20% of the total depth.

moment of inertia divided by the distance from N.A. to the outer fiber.

Problem 5

To find the moment of inertia of the cross-section shown in Figure 9, the following steps are involved:

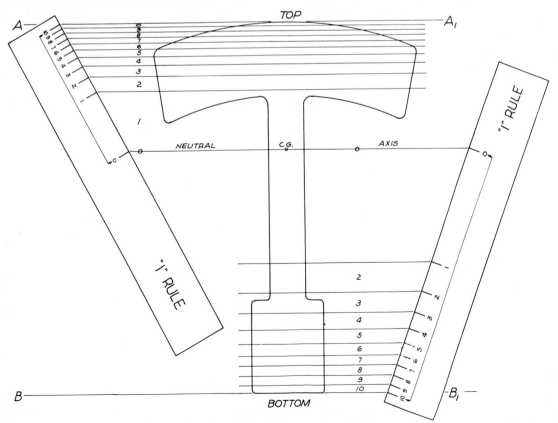

Fig. 9   Top and bottom portions of irregular section are divided into 10 areas each by the "I" Rule.

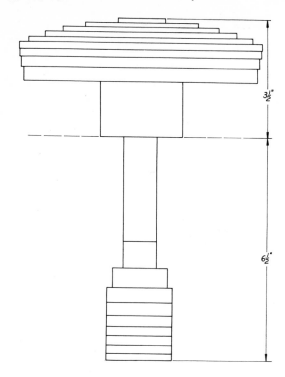

Fig. 10 Irregular section converted to series of rectangles.

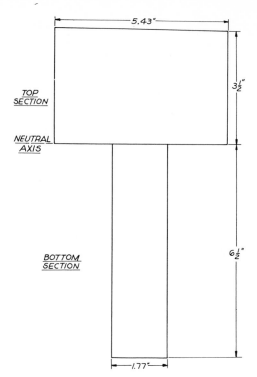

Fig. 11 Irregular section converted to two simple rectangles.

1. Estimate the section's center of gravity (CG).
2. Draw neutral axis.
3. Draw lines A-A₁ and B-B₁.
4. Select the scale on the "I" Rule that fits the section.
5. Scale the average width of each individual area (Fig. 10).

6. Total the average widths and divide by 10. The result is average width (b), (Fig. 11).
7. Scale the distance from the neutral axis to the line A-A₁. This is depth (d).
8. Compute the moment of inertia of the top section above the neutral axis. Computations are given below.
9. Repeat this procedure for the bottom section. Computations are given below.
10. Add the moments for the top and bottom sections together to obtain the moment of inertia for the entire section.

Moment of Inertia by Unit Properties (Sixth Method)

This sixth method, called the Unit Properties Method, is very easy to use and will save a lot of time. The four sets of Tables (2, 3, 4, and 5) give unit values for section modulus (S) above and moment of inertia (I) below, for several sections which may be fabricated by welding or forming.

Values given in each table are for a section unit 1" deep, all other dimensions being based on the depth. In each table, values are given for various ratios of section width to depth, ranging from a width of 1/2 the depth to a width of 3 times the depth. The thickness of the plate is expressed as a percentage of the depth and varies from 2% to 30% of the depth.

To obtain the moment of inertia for a large section, first determine the ratio of its width to its depth and also what percentage its plate thickness is

TOP PORTION		BOTTOM PORTION	
Section	Width	Section	Width
10	1.45	1	1.00
9	3.45	2	1.00
8	4.78	3	1.67
7	5.87	4	2.00
6	6.85	5	2.00
5	7.45	6	2.00
4	7.43	7	2.00
3	7.32	8	2.00
2	7.20	9	2.00
1	2.48	10	2.00

Total Width = 54.28" Average Width (b) = 5.43" Depth (d) = 3.5"	Total Width = 17.67" Average Width (b) = 1.77" Depth (d) = 6.50"
$I_{top} = \dfrac{bd^3}{3} = 78$ in.⁴	$I_{bottom} = \dfrac{bd^3}{3} = 162.0$ in.⁴

$I_{total} = I_{top} + I_{bottom}$

$I_{total} = 240$ in.⁴

SECTION UNIT PROPERTIES

TABLE 2:

TABLE 3:

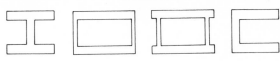

RATIO OF WIDTH TO DEPTH

	½	¾	1	2	3
2.	.0047	.0051	.0053	.0057	.0061
3.	.0070	.0075	.0079	.0086	.0091
4.	.0094	.0101	.0106	.0116	.0120
5.	.01184	.01266	.01321	.01431	.01492
10.	.02252	.02415	.02525	.02735	.02833
15.	.0320	.0345	.0364	.0393	.0409
20.	.0410	.04415	.04635	.05065	.0531
25.	.0490	.0530	.0558	.0616	.0651
30.	.05660	.0616	.0648	.07220	.07662

% Thickness of Depth

(A) Unit Strength Factor

RATIO OF WIDTH TO DEPTH

	½	¾	1	2	3
2.	.0134	.0182	.0240	.0410	.060
3.	.0226	.0258	.0334	.0610	.0880
4.	.024	.0330	.0424	.080	.1140
5.	.02850	.03970	.05124	.0964	.14160
10.	.04914	.069470	.08986	.1712	.24972
15.	.0630	.0914	.1166	.2230	.3290
20.	.07254	.1052	.1353	.2634	.3914
25.	.078	.1136	.1478	.2910	.436
30.	.0814	.1203	.1592	.3152	.4710

% Thickness of Depth

The above strength factor values are for unit sections 1" deep. To use these values, multiply them by the cubed depth of the desired section: $S_{unit} \cdot d^3 = S$

RATIO OF WIDTH TO DEPTH

	½	¾	1	2	3
2.	.0031	.0035	.0039	.0048	.0056
3.	.0047	.0054	.0060	.00071	.0083
4.	.0063	.0071	.0077	.0095	.0108
5.	.00767	.00881	.00967	.01164	.01323
10.	.01416	.01637	.01800	.02175	.02363
15.	.0197	.0228	.0250	.0304	.0332
20.	.02427	.02839	.0314	.03845	.04212
25.	.0280	.0332	.0369	.04535	.0501
30.	.03158	.03742	.04171	.051964	.05789

% Thickness of Depth

(B) Unit Stiffness Factor

RATIO OF WIDTH TO DEPTH

	½	¾	1	2	3
2.	.0067	.0091	.0120	.0205	.030
3.	.0095	.0129	.0167	.0305	.0440
4.	.012	.0165	.0212	.040	.0570
5.	.01425	.01985	.02562	.0482	.07080
10.	.02457	.034735	.04493	.0856	.12486
15.	.0315	.0457	.0583	.1115	.1645
20.	.03627	.0526	.06763	.1317	.1957
25.	.0390	.0568	.0739	.1455	.2180
30.	.0407	.06013	.0796	.1576	.2355

% Thickness of Depth

The above stiffness factor values are for unit sections 1" deep. To use these values, multiply them by the depth of the desired section raised to the fourth power: $I_{unit} \cdot d^4 = I$

to its depth. On the appropriate Unit Properties table for sections of similar configuration, find the unit moment of inertia (I_u) for a section having these proportions. Since the I_u value is for a comparable section of 1" depth, it is only necessary to multiply this value by the actual section's depth raised to the fourth power:

$$I = I_u \, d^4 \quad \dots\dots\dots\dots\dots\dots\dots\dots\dots \text{(8)}$$

Similarly, to obtain the section modulus for a particular section, on the appropriate table find the unit section modulus (S_u) and multiply this value by

the actual section's depth cubed:

$$S = S_u \, d^3 \quad \dots\dots\dots\dots\dots\dots\dots\dots\dots \text{(9)}$$

Problem 6

Find the moment of a "T" section having a depth of 10", a width of 5" and a plate thickness of ½". The width is ½ the depth, and the thickness is 5% of the depth.

From lower part of Table 2, $I_u = 0.00767$; hence,
$I = I_u \cdot d^4 = 0.00767 \cdot 10^4 = 76.7$ in.⁴

SECTION UNIT PROPERTIES

TABLE 4:    TABLE 5:

RATIO OF WIDTH TO DEPTH

	½	¾	1	2	3
2.	.0085	.0092	.0099	.0108	.0114
3.	.0128	.0138	.0150	.0159	.0170
4.	.0168	.0182	.0198	.0211	.0275
5.	.02087	.02247	.02445	.02643	.02783
10.	.03930	.04260	.04510	.05050	.05315
15.	.0558	.0608	.0648	.0728	.0770
20.	.07025	.07705	.08190	.09273	.09817
25.	. . . . . .	.092	.0980	.1118	.1185
30.	. . . . . .	.1057	.1132	.1295	.1382

% Thickness of Depth (left axis)

(A) Unit Strength Factor

RATIO OF WIDTH TO DEPTH

	½	¾	1	2	3
2.	.0150	.0210	.0250	.0450	.0620
3.	.0240	.0300	.0360	.0660	.0910
4.	.0280	.0380	.0470	.0850	.1200
5.	.03456	.045772	.057302	.10246	.14746
10.	.05766	.077990	.098374	.17970	.26104
15.	.0710	.100	.1250	.2350	.3490
20.	.07974	.1124	.1425	.2759	.3986
25.	. . . . . .	.120	.1550	.300	.4390
30.	. . . . . .	.1235	.1624	.3184	.4744

% Thickness of Depth (left axis)

The above strength factor values are for unit sections 1″ deep. To use these values, multiply them by the cubed depth of the desired section: $S_{unit} \cdot d^3 = S$

RATIO OF WIDTH TO DEPTH

	½	¾	1	2	3
2.	.0050	.0060	.0062	.0080	.0087
3.	.0075	.0087	.0093	.0117	.0130
4.	.0098	.0114	.0124	.0155	.0173
5.	.0121	.01385	.01536	.01933	.02172
10.	.02197	.02545	.02831	.0360	.04052
15.	.0302	.0347	.0389	.0503	.0560
20.	.03645	.04311	.04852	.06287	.07125
25.	. . . . . .	.050	.0570	.0740	.0845
30.	. . . . . .	.05543	.06315	.08342	.0955

% Thickness of Depth (left axis)

(B) Unit Stiffness Factor

RATIO OF WIDTH TO DEPTH

	½	¾	1	2	3
2.	.0075	.0105	.0125	.0225	.0310
3.	.0120	.0150	.0180	.0330	.0455
4.	.0140	.0190	.0235	.0425	.0600
5.	.01728	.022886	.028651	.05123	.07373
10.	.02883	.038995	.049187	.08985	.13052
15.	.0355	.050	.0625	.1175	.1745
20.	.03987	.0562	.07123	.1378	.1993
25.	. . . . . .	.060	.0775	.150	.2195
30.	. . . . . .	.06173	.08120	.1592	.2372

% Thickness of Depth (left axis)

The above stiffness factor values are for unit sections 1″ deep. To use these values, multiply them by the depth of the desired section raised to the fourth power: $I_{unit} \cdot d^4 = I$

Problem 7

A designer requires a welded section having a certain moment of inertia. He is thinking of a "T" section so proportioned that the width is about ½ of the depth, and the thickness of both flange and web is about 10% of the depth. He would like to know what dimensions should be given this section so that it will have the required moment of inertia $I = 700$ in.[4]

Unless he uses this new Unit Properties method, the designer will probably guess the size of his section, then solve for its neutral axis, and then solve for its moment of inertia. This is time consuming. After about 3 or 4 tries, each taking about 7 minutes, or a total time of about half an hour, a section is finally found which will satisfy the conditions, but which of course will be heavier than required. This trial and error method is costly.

The Unit Properties method not only is fast, with just one solution, but it gives an exact solution in less than 2 minutes.

Given: a "T" section
b = ½ of depth
t = 10% of depth

By referring to Table 2 and using the above information, the unit moment of inertia is found to be

$$I_u = 0.01416 \text{ in.}^4$$

Since $I = I_u d^4$

$$d^4 = \frac{I}{I_u} = \frac{700.0}{.01416} = 49,500$$

and d = 14.9" or 15"; therefore
   b = ½d = 7.5"
   t = 10%d = 1.5"

This would be fabricated by welding a 1½" × 7½" flange plate to a 1½" x 13½" web plate.

> **Problem 8**

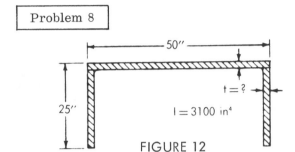

FIGURE 12

A governor base must be designed to give proper support to pumps and control panels and also to house some tanks within the base. Because of the equipment involved, it must have a width of 50" and a height of 25". It is decided to make this base as a channel section out of a top plate and two side plates

having the same thickness (Fig. 12). For proper rigidity, this section must have a moment of inertia (I) of 3100 in.⁴ The problem is to determine the proper thickness of plate to use in fabricating the base.

$$I = I_u d^4$$

$$I_u = \frac{I}{d^4} = \frac{3100}{(25)^4} = .0079 \text{ in.}^4$$

Using the lower part of Table 4 for a simple channel section, since b = 2d and

$$I_u = .0079$$

the required thickness (t) is found to be 2% of the depth, or 2% × 25" = ½" thick.

Therefore, this base would be fabricated out of ½" thick plate. As a check, this final section -- 25" deep, 50" wide, and ½" thick -- may be re-figured in the conventional manner, and its moment of inertia found to be I = 3154 in.⁴ This is just a little higher than the value needed for I.

Moment of Inertia by Torsion Pendulum
(Seventh Method)

For irregular sections made up of a single, rather compact area, the principle of the torsion pendulum may be used to calculate the moment of inertia about any given axis. See Figure 13. The given cross-section is cut out of some material (cardboard, thin wood, sheet metal, etc.) along with a standard rectangular area of the same material

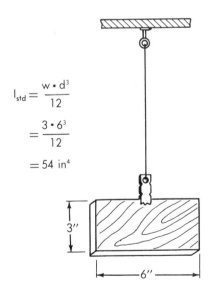

$$I_{std} = \frac{w \cdot d^3}{12}$$

$$= \frac{3 \cdot 6^3}{12}$$

$$= 54 \text{ in}^4$$

3"

6"

16 seconds for 10 oscillations
$T_{std} = 1.6$ sec.

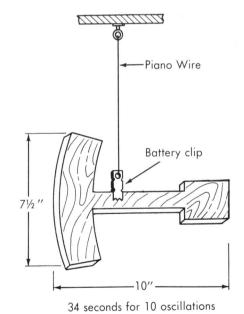

Piano Wire

Battery clip

7½"

10"

34 seconds for 10 oscillations
$T_x = 3.4$ sec.

$$I_x = I_{std} \left(\frac{T_x}{T_{std}} \right)^2 = 54 \left(\frac{3.4}{1.6} \right)^2 = 244 \text{ in}^4$$

Fig. 13   Torsional pendulum method of finding moment of inertia of irregular section.

and thickness. The moment of inertia of the standard rectangle is computed from the following:

$$I_{std} = \frac{b \ d^3}{12}$$

The standard rectangle is then fastened by a small clip to the end of a thin piano wire at the same line as the neutral axis. It is given a slight twist and then released. The time for 10 complete oscillations is measured and this divided by 10 to get the average period of vibration.

The given cross-section is then hung on the wire in place of the standard rectangle and fastened on the axis about which the moment of inertia is desired (usually the neutral axis about the x-x axis). The average period of vibration is found. Using the following equation, the moment of inertia of the given cross-section is calculated.

$$I_{given} = I_{std} \left(\frac{\text{period of given section}}{\text{period of standard section}} \right)^2 \quad \ldots \ldots (10)$$

Air has no effect on the period of vibration. It simply dampens the vibration.

Special Problems

A number of properties can be utilized in meeting special problems associated with the moment of inertia in members subjected to compressive loading. These properties, to be discussed in the later Section 2.5 on Compression, include the minimum moment of inertia, product of inertia, and moment of inertia about any axis.

4. SECTION MODULUS (S)

The section modulus (S) is found by dividing the moment of inertia (I) by the distance (c) from the neutral axis to the outermost fiber of the section:

$$S = \frac{I}{c} \quad \ldots \ldots \ldots \ldots \ldots \ldots \ldots \ldots \ldots (11)$$

Since this distance (c) can be measured in two directions, there are actually two values for this property, although only the smaller value is usually available in tables of rolled sections because it results in the greater stress. If the section is symmetrical, these two values are equal. Section modulus is a measurement of the strength of the beam in bending. In an unsymmetrical section, the outer face having the greater value of (c) will have the lower value of section modulus (S) and of course the greater stress. Since it has the greater stress, this is the value needed.

With some typical sections of symmetrical shape, it is not necessary to solve first for moment of inertia (I). The section modulus can be computed directly from the simplified formulas of Table 1, or from the Unit Properties Tables 2, 3, 4 and 5.

In many cases, however, the moment of inertia (I) must be found before solving for section modulus (S). Any of the previously described methods may be applicable for determining the moment of inertia.

> Problem 9

Using the previously welded "T" section of Problem 7 as a problem in finding the section modulus, its neutral axis is first located, Figure 14.

Using the standard formula (#1) for determining the distance (n) of the neutral axis from any reference axis, in this case the top horizontal face of the flange:

$$n = \frac{M}{A} = \frac{\text{Sum of moments}}{\text{Total area of section}}$$

$$= \frac{(6 \cdot 1.5 \cdot 0.75) + (15 \cdot 1.5 \cdot 7.5)}{(6 \cdot 1.5) \ + \ (15 \cdot 1.5)}$$

$$= \frac{6.75 + 168.75}{9.0 + 22.5}$$

$$= 5.56"$$

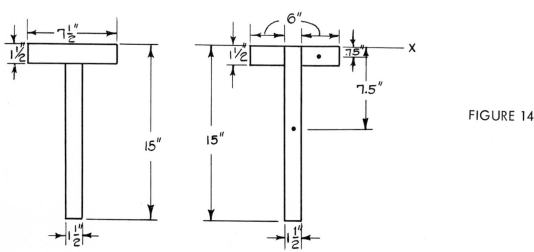

FIGURE 14

Next, the section's moment of inertia is determined, using the elements method (Figure 15):

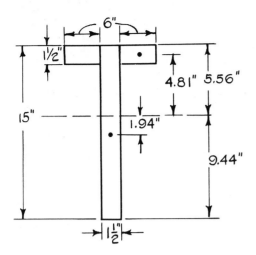

FIGURE 15

$$I_n = \frac{6 \cdot 1.5^3}{12} + (6 \cdot 1.5 \cdot 4.81^2) + \frac{1.5 \cdot 15^3}{12} + (1.5 \cdot 15 \cdot 1.94^2)$$

$$= 1.69 + 208.22 + 421.87 + 84.68$$

$$= 716.5 \text{ in.}^4$$

This value is slightly higher than the required $I = 700$ in.^{4} because depth of section was made $d = 15"$ instead of $14.9"$.

Finally, the section modulus (S) is determined:

$$S = \frac{I}{c} = \frac{716.5}{9.44}$$

$$= 75.8 \text{ in.}^3$$

5. RADIUS OF GYRATION (r)

The radius of gyration (r) is the distance from the neutral axis of a section to an imaginary point at which the whole area of the section could be concentrated and still have the same moment of inertia. This property is used primarily in solving column problems. It is found by taking the square root of the moment of inertia divided by the area of the section and is expressed in inches.

$$r\sqrt{= \frac{I}{A}} \quad \dots \dots \dots \dots \dots \dots \dots \dots (12)$$

6. POLAR MOMENT OF INERTIA (J)

The polar moment of inertia (J) equals the sum of any two moments of inertia about axes at right angles to each other. The polar moment of inertia is taken about an axis which is perpendicular to the plane of the other two axes.

$$J = I_x + I_y \quad \dots \dots \dots \dots \dots \dots \dots (13)$$

Polar moment of inertia is used in determining the polar section modulus (J/c) which is a measure of strength under torsional loading of round solid bars and closed tubular shafts.

7. TORSIONAL RESISTANCE (R)

Torsional resistance (R) has largely replaced the less accurate polar moment of inertia in standard design formula for angular twist of open sections. It should be employed where formulas have been developed for the type of section. These are given in the later Section 3.6 on Torsion.

8. PROPERTIES OF THIN SECTIONS

Because of welding, increasingly greater use is being found for structural shapes having thin cross-sections. Thin sections may be custom roll-formed, rolled by small specialty steel producers, brake-formed, or fabricated by welding. Properties of these sections are needed by the designer, but they are not ordinarily listed among the standard rolled sections of a steel handbook. Properties of thin sections customarily are found by the standard formulas for sections.

With a thin section, the inside dimension is almost as large as the outside dimension; and, in most cases, the property of the section varies as the cubes of these two dimensions. This means dealing with the difference between two very large numbers. In order to get any accuracy, it would be necessary to calculate this out by longhand or by using logarithms rather than use the usual slide rule.

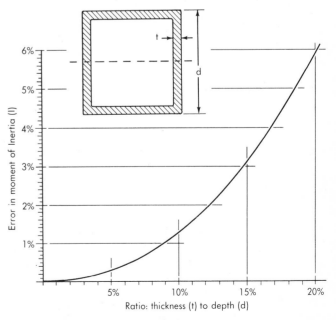

Fig. 16 Possible error in using Line Method is minimal with low ratio of section thickness to depth.

TABLE 6 - PROPERTIES OF THIN SECTIONS
Where thickness (t) is small, b = mean width, and d = mean depth of section

Section	T	I	O	⊓	Γ	○
I_x	$\dfrac{t d^3 (4b+d)}{12(b+d)}$	$\dfrac{t d^2}{12}(6b+d)$	$\dfrac{t d^2}{6}(3b+d)$	$\dfrac{t d^3(2b+d)}{3(b+2d)}$	$\dfrac{t d^3(4b+3d)}{4(b+d)}$	$t\pi r^3$
S_x	$\dfrac{t d^2(4b+d)}{6(2b+d)}$ bottom $\dfrac{t d}{6}(4b+d)$ top *	$\dfrac{t d}{6}(6b+d)$ *	$\dfrac{t d}{3}(3b+d)$ *	$\dfrac{t d}{3}(2b+d)$ top $\dfrac{t d^2(2b+d)}{3(b+d)}$ bottom *	$\dfrac{t d}{2}(4b+3d)$ top $\dfrac{t d^2(4b+3d)}{2(2b+d)}$ bottom *	$t\pi r^2$
I_y	$\dfrac{t b^3}{12}$	$\dfrac{t b^3}{6}$	$\dfrac{t b^2}{6}(b+3d)$	$\dfrac{t b^2}{12}(b+6d)$	$\dfrac{t b^3(3b+4d)}{4(b+d)}$	———
S_y	$\dfrac{t b^2}{6}$	$\dfrac{t b^2}{3}$	$\dfrac{t b}{3}(b+3d)$	$\dfrac{t b}{6}(b+6d)$	$\dfrac{t b^2(3b+4d)}{2(b+2d)}$ right side $\dfrac{t b}{2}(3b+4d)$ left side *	———
I_{xy}	0	0	0	0	$\dfrac{t b^2 d^2}{4(b+d)}$	0
R	$\dfrac{t^3}{3}(b+d)$	$\dfrac{t^3}{3}(2b+d)$	$\dfrac{2 t b^2 d^2}{b+d}$	$\dfrac{t^3}{3}(b+2d)$	$\dfrac{t^3}{3}(b+d)$	$2t\pi r^3$
r_x max. or min.	$\sqrt{\dfrac{\dfrac{d^3(4b+d)}{12}}{b+d}}$	$\sqrt{\dfrac{d^2(6b+d)}{12(2b+d)}}$	$\sqrt{\dfrac{d^2(3b+d)}{12(b+d)}}$	$\sqrt{\dfrac{\dfrac{d^3}{3}(2b+d)}{(b+2d)}}$		0.7071 r
NA	$\dfrac{d^2}{2(b+d)}$ down from top			$\dfrac{d^2}{b+2d}$ down from top	$\dfrac{d^2}{2(b+d)}$ down from top $\dfrac{b^2}{2(b+d)}$	———
r_y min. or max.	$\sqrt{\dfrac{b^3}{12(b+d)}}$	$\sqrt{\dfrac{b^3}{6(2b+d)}}$	$\sqrt{\dfrac{b^2(b+3d)}{12(b+d)}}$	$\sqrt{\dfrac{b^2(b+d)}{12(b+2d)}}$		———

(* = add t/2 to c for S)

To simplify the problem, the section may be "treated as a line", having no thickness. The property of the "line", is then multiplied by the thickness of the section to give the approximate value of the section property within a very narrow tolerance. Table 6 gives simplified formulas for nine properties of six different cross-sections. In this table: d = mean depth, b = mean width of the section, and t = thickness.

The error in calculating the moment of inertia by this Line Method versus the conventional formula is represented by the curve in Figure 16, using a square tubular section as an example. As indicated, the error increases with the ratio of section thickness (t) to depth (d).

Problem 10, which follows, illustrates the use of Table 6. Other excellent examples of the savings in

TABLE 7 – PROPERTIES OF TYPICAL IRREGULAR THIN SECTIONS
Where thickness (t) is small, b = mean width, and d = mean depth of section

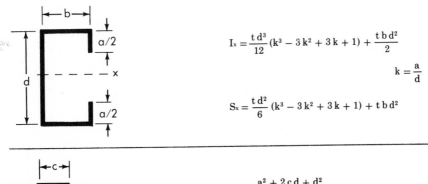

$$I_x = \frac{t\,d^2\left[k\,b^2 + (k+1)^2\,\dfrac{b\,d}{3} + \dfrac{d^2}{3}\right]}{b\,(k+1) + 2\,d} \qquad k = \frac{a}{b}$$

$$c_b = \frac{d\,(b+d)}{b\,(k+1) + 2\,d} \qquad c_t = \frac{d\,(k\,b + d)}{b\,(k+1) + 2\,d}$$

$$S_b = \frac{t\,d\left[k\,b^2 + (k+1)\,\dfrac{2\,b\,d}{3} + \dfrac{d^2}{3}\right]}{b + d}$$

$$S_t = \frac{t\,d\left[k\,b^2 + (k+1)\,\dfrac{2\,b\,d}{3} + \dfrac{d^2}{3}\right]}{k\,b + d}$$

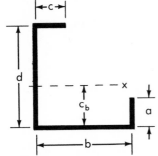

$$I_x = \frac{t\,d^3}{12}(k^3 - 3k^2 + 3k + 1) + \frac{t\,b\,d^2}{2}$$

$$k = \frac{a}{d}$$

$$S_x = \frac{t\,d^2}{6}(k^3 - 3k^2 + 3k + 1) + t\,b\,d^2$$

$$c_b = \frac{a^2 + 2\,c\,d + d^2}{2\,(a + b + c + d)}$$

$$I_x = \frac{t\,(a^3 + 3\,c\,d^2 + d^3)}{3} - \frac{t\,(a^2 + 2\,c\,d + d^2)^2}{4\,(a + b + c + d)}$$

design time offered by use of the Line Method exist as (column) Problem 4 in Sect. 2.5 and as (torsional) Problem 3 in Sect. 3.6.

Table 7 gives the most important properties of additional thin sections of irregular but common configurations.

Reference Sections 7.5, 7.6, and 7.7 at the back of this book provide formulas for quickly finding bending moments (and other forces) on Thin Curved Bars, Thin Circular Rings, and Thin Rings Under Internal Pressure, respectively.

Problem 10

A small machine is supported at the end of a cantilever beam 6 ft. long. During its operation, it exerts a force (F) on this support and must be held within an allowable deflection (Δ), Figure 17.

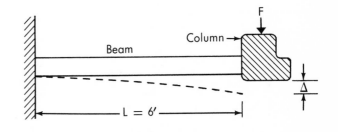

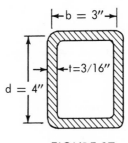

FIGURE 17

Then, using Properties of Thin Sections (Table 6), find the moment of inertia of the section shown in Figure 17:

$$I_x = \frac{t\,d^2}{6}(3b+d)$$

$$= 6.5 \text{ in.}^4$$

A new model of this machine must extend out to a distance of 18.5 ft. and must operate under the same conditions and allowables. It is decided the new beam will have a width equal to half its depth and a wall thickness equal to 5% of its depth.

The increased length will require an increase in moment of inertia (I). For a cantilever beam with concentrated load at its end--

$$\Delta = \frac{F\,L^3}{3\,E\,I}$$

or $I = \dfrac{F\,L^3}{3\,E\,\Delta}$ and $\left(\dfrac{I_2}{I_1}\right) = \dfrac{\left(\dfrac{F_1}{F_2}\right)\left(\dfrac{L_1}{L_2}\right)^3}{\left(\dfrac{E_1}{E_2}\right)\left(\dfrac{\Delta_1}{\Delta_2}\right)}$

$$\therefore \frac{I_2}{I_1} = \left(\frac{L_2}{L_1}\right)^3$$

or $I_2 = I_1\left(\dfrac{L_2}{L_1}\right)^3$

$$= 6.5\left(\frac{18.5}{6}\right)^3$$

$$= \underline{190.5 \text{ in.}^4}$$

the required moment of inertia of the lengthened beam.

Since it is desirable to have:

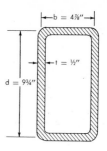

FIGURE 18

$$b = .5\,d \text{ and } t = .05\,d$$

$$\therefore \quad I_2 = \frac{t\,d^2}{6}(3b+d)$$

$$= \frac{(.05\,d)\,(d^2)}{6}\left(3\,\frac{d}{2}+d\right)$$

$$= .02083\,d^4$$

Thus:

$$.02083\,d^4 = 190.5 \text{ in.}^4$$

$$d^4 = \frac{190.5}{.02083} = 9140$$

and:

$$d_2 = 95.60$$

Therefore (Figure 18):

d = 9.78" or <u>use 9 3/4"</u>

b = 4.89" or <u>use 4 7/8"</u>

t = .489" or <u>use 1/2"</u>

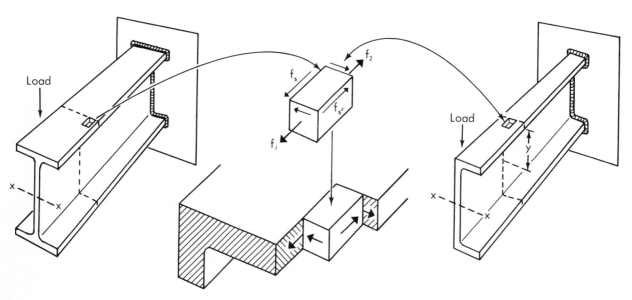

FIGURE 19

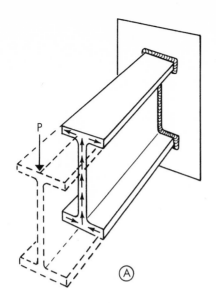

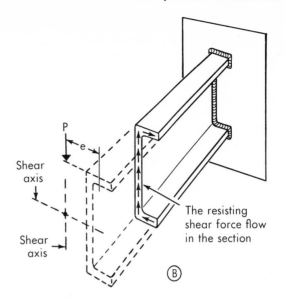

Ⓐ   Ⓑ

The resisting shear force flow in the section

Shear axis

Shear axis

FIGURE 20

9. SHEAR AXIS AND SHEAR CENTER

Since the bending moment decreases as the distance of the load from the support increases, bending force f_1 is slightly less than force f_2, and this difference ($f_2 - f_1$) is transferred inward toward the web by the longitudinal shear force (f_s). See Figure 19.

$$\boxed{f_s = f_s' + \frac{P\,a\,y}{I_x}} \quad\dots\dots\dots\dots\dots\dots\dots(14)$$

This force also has an equal component in the transverse direction. A transverse force applied to a beam sets up transverse (and horizontal) shear forces within the section. See Figure 20.

In the case of a symmetrical section, A, a force

(P) applied in line with the principal axis (y-y) does not result in any twisting action on the member. This is because the torsional moment of the internal transverse shear forces ($\rightarrow$) is equal to zero.

On the other hand, in the case of an unsymmetrical section, B, the internal transverse shear forces ($\rightarrow$) form a twisting moment. Therefore, the force (P) must be applied eccentrically at a proper distance (e) along the shear axis, so that it forms an external torsional moment which is equal and opposite to the internal torsional moment of the transverse shear forces. If this precaution is not taken, there will be a twisting action applied to the member which will twist under load, in addition to bending. See Figure 21.

Any axis of symmetry will also be a shear axis.

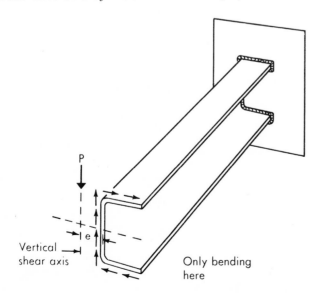

Vertical shear axis

Only bending here

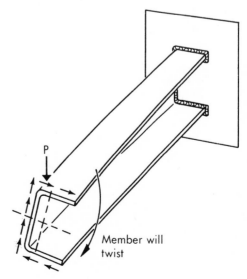

Member will twist

FIGURE 21

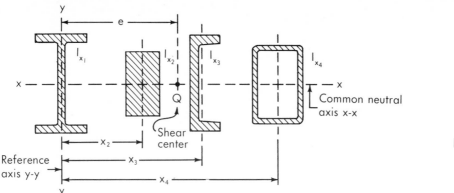

FIGURE 22

There will be two shear axes and their intersection forms the shear center (Q).

A force, if applied at the shear center, may be at any angle in the plane of the cross-section and there will be no twisting moment on the member, just transverse shear and bending.

As stated previously, unless forces which are applied transverse to a member also pass through the shear axis, the member will be subjected to a twisting moment as well as bending. As a result, this beam should be considered as follows:

1. The applied force P should be resolved into a force P′ of the same value passing through the shear center (Q) and parallel to the original applied force P. P′ is then resolved into the two components at right angles to each other and parallel to the principal axes of the section.

2. A twisting moment (T) is produced by the applied force (P) about the shear center (Q).

The stress from the twisting moment (T) is computed separately and then superimposed upon the stresses of the two rectangular components of force P′.

This means that the shear center must be located. Any axis of symmetry will be one of the shear axes.

For open sections lying on one common neutral axis (x-x), the location of the other shear axis is as follows:

$$e = \frac{\Sigma I_x X}{\Sigma I_x}$$

Notice the similarity between this and the following:

$$d = \frac{\Sigma M}{\Sigma A} \text{ or}$$

$$= \frac{\Sigma A d}{\Sigma A}$$

which is used to find the neutral axis of a built-up section.

Just as the areas of individual parts are used to find the neutral axis, now the moments of inertia of individual areas are used to find the shear axis of a composite section, Figure 22. The procedure is the same; select a reference axis (y-y), determine I_x for each member section (about its own neutral axis x-x) and the distance X this member section lies from the reference axis (y-y). The resultant (e) from the formula will then be the distance from the chosen reference axis (y-y) to the parallel shear axis of the built-up section.

Here:

$$e = \frac{I_{x1} X_1 + I_{x2} X_2 + I_{x3} X_3 + I_{x4} X_4}{I_{x1} + I_{x2} + I_{x3} + I_{x4}}$$

or:

$$\boxed{e = \frac{\Sigma I_x X}{\Sigma I_x}} \quad \dots\dots\dots\dots\dots\dots\dots\dots\dots (15)$$

Locating Other Shear Centers

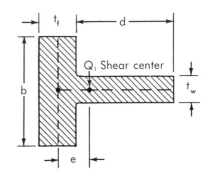

FIGURE 23

Here:

$$e = \frac{\Sigma I_x X}{\Sigma I_x} = \frac{\dfrac{t_f b^3}{12} \times 0 + \dfrac{d t_w^3}{12} \times \dfrac{(t_f + d)}{2}}{I_x}$$

$$= \frac{d t_w^3 (t_f + d)}{24 I_x}$$

Normally Q might be assumed to be at the intersection of the centerlines of the web and the flange.

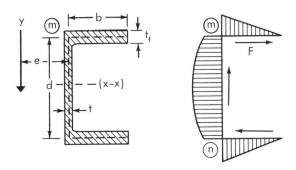

FIGURE 24

Here, at point M:

$$f_s = \frac{V\,a\,y}{I_x} = \frac{V\,(b\,t_f)\,(d/2)}{I_x}$$

$$F = \tfrac{1}{2}\,f_s\,b = \frac{V\,b^2\,d\,t_f}{4\,I_x}$$

$$\Sigma M_n = 0 = + F\,d - V\,e = 0$$

$$e = \frac{F\,d}{V} = \frac{V\,b^2\,d^2\,t_f}{V\,4\,I_x}$$

$$= \frac{b^2\,d^2\,t_f}{4\,I_x}$$

or, since areas have a common (x-x) neutral axis:

$$e = \frac{\Sigma I_x\,X}{\Sigma I_x} = \frac{\dfrac{t\,d^3}{12} \times 0 + 2 \times (b\,t_f)(d/2)^2\,\dfrac{b}{2}}{I_x}$$

$$= \frac{b^2\,d^2\,t_f}{4\,I_x}$$

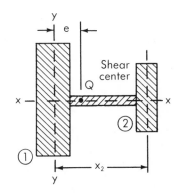

FIGURE 25

Here:

$$e = \frac{\Sigma I_x\,X}{\Sigma I_x} = \frac{I_{x1}\,0 + I_{x2}\,X_2}{I_{x1} + I_{x2}}$$

$$= \frac{X_2\,I_{x2}}{I_x}$$

Figure 26 suggests an approach to locating shear axes of some other typical sections.

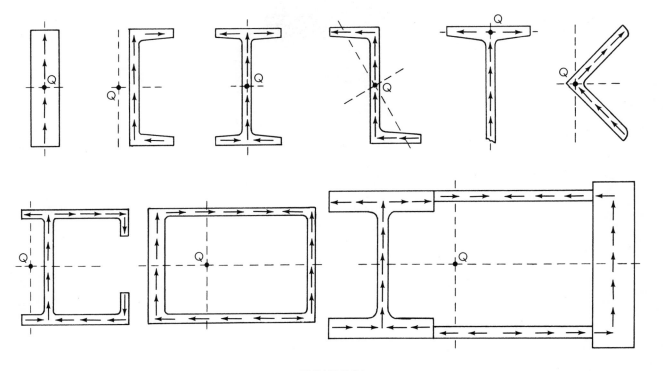

FIGURE 26

Modern high-speed, high-capacity scrapers feature weldments designed on basis of stress analysis to ensure long service life without costly breakdowns.

Diagonal bracing of side walls on welded locomotive shell lowers panel thickness and saves weight, material cost and welding cost.

Analysis of Tension

1. TENSILE STRESS

The simplest type of loading on a member is tension. A tensile load applied (axially) in line with the center of gravity of the section will result in tensile stresses distributed uniformly across the plane of the cross-section lying at right angles to the line of loading. The formula for the stress is --

$$\sigma_t = \frac{P}{A} \quad \dots\dots\dots\dots\dots\dots\dots\dots\dots\dots\dots(1)$$

where P = the tensile force applied to the member

A = area of cross-section at right angles to line of force

σ_t = unit tensile stress

A tensile load that is not applied in line with the center of gravity of the section, but with some eccentricity, will introduce some bending stresses.

These must be combined with the original tensile stresses. An example of this condition would be a curved beam such as a large "C" clamp.

2. TENSILE STRAIN

The unit elongation or strain of the member under tension is found by the following relationship:

$$\epsilon = \frac{\sigma_t}{E} \quad \dots\dots\dots\dots\dots\dots\dots\dots\dots\dots(2)$$

where:

ϵ = unit elongation (tensile strain)

σ_t = unit tensile stress

E = modulus of elasticity (tension)

The total elongation or displacement is equal to this unit strain (ϵ) multiplied by the length (L) of the member.

Elongation = $\epsilon \cdot$ L

Problem 1

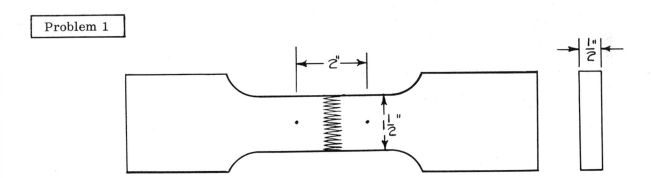

A welded tensile coupon (test specimen) measures ½ " × 1½ " at the reduced section, and has two punch marks 2" apart with which to later measure elongation. Just after the test is started, a load of 10,000 lb is reached.

Find (1) the unit tensile stress on the reduced section, and (2) the total elongation as measured within the two marks.

(1) $\sigma_t = \dfrac{P}{A} = \dfrac{10,000}{½ \cdot 1½}$

   = 13,333 psi

(2) $\epsilon = \dfrac{\sigma_t}{E} = \dfrac{13,330}{30,000,000}$

   = 0.000444 in./in.

and elon.= $\epsilon \cdot$ L = 0.000444 · 2"

   = 0.00089" in 2"

In any calculation for strain or elongation it is understood that the stresses are held below the yield point. Beyond the yield point, the relationship of stress to strain is no longer proportional and the formula does not apply.

This economical weldment combines steel
plate and castings into one integral unit.

Analysis of Compression

1. COMPRESSIVE STRESS

Compressive loading of a member when applied (axially) concentric with the center of gravity of the member's cross-section, results in compressive stresses distributed uniformly across the section. This compressive unit stress is --

$$\sigma_c = \frac{P}{A} \quad \text{.................................(1)}$$

A short column (slenderness ratio L/r equal to about unity or less) that is overloaded in compression may fail by crushing. From a design standpoint, short compression members present little problem. It is important to hold the compressive unit stress within the material's compressive strength.

For steel, the yield and ultimate strengths are considered to be the same in compression as in tension. Many pads, feet, and bearing supports are short compression members and must not be stressed beyond their elastic limit. Permanent deformation of such members may cause misalignment of critical working members of the machine.

Any holes or openings in the section in the path of force translation will weaken the member, unless such openings are completely filled by another member that will carry its share of the load.

Excessive compression of long columns may cause failure by buckling. As compressive loading of a long column is increased, it eventually causes some eccentricity. This in turn sets up a bending moment, causing the column to deflect or buckle slightly. This deflection increases the eccentricity and thus the bending moment. This may progress to where the bending moment is increasing at a rate greater than the increase in load, and the column soon fails by buckling.

2. SLENDERNESS RATIO

As the member becomes longer or more slender, there is more of a tendency for ultimate failure to be caused by buckling. The most common way to indicate this tendency is the slenderness ratio which is equal to --

$$\frac{L}{r}$$

where L = unsupported length of member

r = the least radius of gyration of the section

and --

$$r = \sqrt{\frac{I}{A}} \quad \text{................................. (2)}$$

If the member is made longer, using the same cross-section and the same compressive load, the resulting compressive stress will remain the same, although the tendency for buckling will increase. The slenderness ratio increases as the radius of gyration of the section is reduced or as the length of the member is increased. The allowable compressive load which may be applied to the member decreases as the slenderness ratio increases.

The various column formulas (Tables 3 and 4) give the allowable average compressive stress (σ) for the column. They do not give the actual unit stress developed in the column by the load. The unit stress resulting from these formulas may be multiplied by the cross-sectional area of the column to give the allowable load which may be supported.

3. RADIUS OF GYRATION

The radius of gyration (r) is the distance from the neutral axis of a section to an imaginary point at which the whole area of the section could be concentrated and still have the same amount of inertia. It is found by the expression: $r = \sqrt{I/A}$.

In the design of unsymmetrical sections to be used as columns, the least radius of gyration(r_{min}) of the section must be known in order to make use of the slenderness ratio (L/r) in the column formulas.

If the section in question is not a standard rolled section the properties of which are listed in steel handbooks, it will be necessary to compute this least radius of gyration. Since the least radius of gyration is --

$$r_{min} = \sqrt{\frac{I_{min}}{A}} \quad \dots\dots\dots\dots\dots\dots\dots(3)$$

the minimum moment of inertia of the section must be determined.

Minimum Moment of Inertia

The maximum moment of inertia (I_{max}) and the minimum moment of inertia (I_{min}) of a cross-section are found on principal axes, 90° to each other.

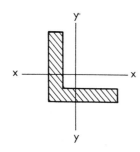

FIGURE 1

$$I_{max \atop min} = \frac{I_x + I_y}{2} \pm \sqrt{\left(\frac{I_x - I_y}{2}\right)^2 + I_{xy}^2} \quad \dots\dots\dots\dots(4)$$

Knowing I_x, I_y, and I_{xy} it will be possible to find I_{min}.

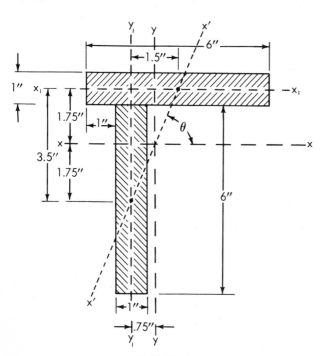

FIGURE 2

Problem 1

Locate the (neutral) x-x and y-y axes of the offset T section shown in Figure 2:

To locate neutral axis x-x:

	A	d	M
6" × 1"	6.0	0	0
1" × 6"	6.0	-3.5	-21.0
Total ➡	12.0		-21.0

where d = distance from center of gravity of element area to parallel axis (here: x_1-x_1)

and, applying formula #1 from Section 2.3, the distance of neutral axis x-x from its parallel axis x_1-x_1 is--

$$NA_{x\text{-}x} = \frac{\Sigma M}{\Sigma A} = \frac{-21.0}{12.0} = -1.75"$$

To locate neutral axis y-y:

	A	d	M
1" × 6"	6.0	+1.5	+9.0
6" × 1"	6.0	0	0
Total ➡	12.0		+9.0

$$NA_{y\text{-}y} = \frac{\Sigma M}{\Sigma A} = \frac{+9.0}{12.0} = +.75"$$

Product of Inertia

It will be necessary to find the product of inertia (I_{xy}) of the section. This is the area (A) times the product of distances d_x and d_y as shown in Figure 3.

In finding the moment of inertia of an area about a given axis (I_x or I_y), it is not necessary to consider the signs of d_x or d_y. However, in finding the product of inertia, it is necessary to know the signs of d_x and d_y because the product of these two could be either positive or negative and this will determine the sign of the resulting product of inertia. The total product of inertia of the whole section, which is the sum of the values of the individual areas, will depend upon these signs. Areas in diagonally opposite quadrants will have products of inertia having the same sign.

The product of inertia of an individual rectangular area, the sides of which are parallel to the x-x and y-y axes of the entire larger section is --

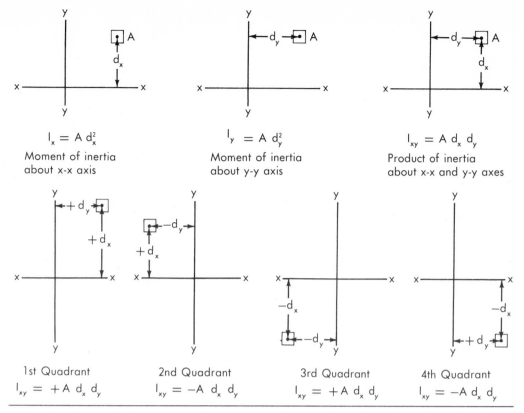

$$I_x = A d_x^2$$

Moment of inertia
about x-x axis

$$I_y = A d_y^2$$

Moment of inertia
about y-y axis

$$I_{xy} = A d_x d_y$$

Product of inertia
about x-x and y-y axes

1st Quadrant	2nd Quadrant	3rd Quadrant	4th Quadrant
$I_{xy} = +A d_x d_y$	$I_{xy} = -A d_x d_y$	$I_{xy} = +A d_x d_y$	$I_{xy} = -A d_x d_y$

FIGURE 3

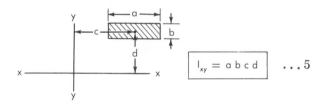

$$\boxed{I_{xy} = a b c d} \quad \ldots 5$$

FIGURE 4

where a and b = dimensions of rectangle (= A)
   d and c = distance of area's center of gravity
      to the x-x and y-y axes (= d_x and d_y)

The product of inertia of a T or angle section
is --

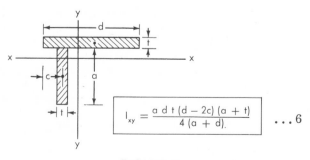

$$\boxed{I_{xy} = \frac{a d t (d - 2c) (a + t)}{4 (a + d)}} \quad \ldots 6$$

FIGURE 5

Here, determine sign by inspection.

Problem 2

Determine the product of inertia of this offset
T section about the x-x and y-y axes:

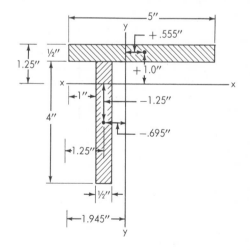

FIGURE 6

$$I_{xy} = \Sigma A (d_x)(d_y)$$

$$= 2.5 (+ 1) (+ .555) + 2 (-1.25) (-.695)$$

$$= + 1.388 + 1.737$$

$$= + 3.125 \text{ in.}^4$$

Now use formula given previously for product of inertia of such a section:

$$I_{xy} = \frac{a\,d\,t\,(d-2c)\,(a+t)}{4\,(a+d)}$$

$$= \frac{(4)\,(5)\,(\frac{1}{2})\,(5-2.5)\,(4+\frac{1}{2})}{4\,(4+5)}$$

$$= +\,3.125 \text{ in.}^4$$

Problem 3

Determine the minimum radius of gyration of the offset T section shown previously (Fig. 2) and repeated here:

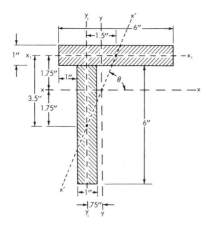

FIGURE 7

Moment of inertia about axis x-x:

	A	d	M	I	I_g
6" × 1"	6.0	0	0	0	.50
1" × 6"	6.0	-3.5	-21.0	+ 73.5	18.00
Total ➤	12.0		-21.0	+ 92.00

$$NA_{x\text{-}x} = \frac{\Sigma M}{\Sigma A} = \frac{-21.0}{12.0} = -1.75\text{''}$$

and —

$$I_x = I - \frac{M^2}{A} = 92.00 - 36.75 = 55.25 \text{ in.}^4$$

Moment of inertia about axis y-y:

	A	d	M	I	I_g
1" × 6"	6.0	+1.5	+9.0	13.5	18.00
6" × 1"	6.0	0	0	0	.50
Total ➤	12.0		+9.0	+ 32.00

$$NA_{y\text{-}y} = \frac{\Sigma M}{\Sigma A} = \frac{+9.0}{12.0} = +.75\text{''}$$

and —

$$I_y = I - \frac{M^2}{A} = 32.00 - 6.75 = 25.25 \text{ in.}^4$$

Product of inertia:

$$I_{xy} = \Sigma A\,(d_x)\,(d_y)$$
$$= (1\times6)\,(+1.75)\,(+.75) + (1\times6)\,(-1.75)\,(-.75)$$
$$= +15.75 \text{ in.}^4$$

Minimum moment of inertia:

$$I_{min} = \frac{I_x + I_y}{2} - \sqrt{\left(\frac{I_x + I_y}{2}\right)^2 + I_{xy}^2}$$

$$= \frac{55.25 + 25.25}{2} - \sqrt{\left(\frac{55.25 - 25.25}{2}\right)^2 + (15.75)^2}$$

$$= 40.25 - 21.75$$

$$= 18.50 \text{ in.}^4$$

Minimum radius of gyration:

$$r_{min} = \sqrt{\frac{I_{min}}{A}}$$

$$= \sqrt{\frac{18.50}{12.0}} = \sqrt{1.542}$$

$$= \underline{1.24}\text{''}$$

As a matter of interest, this r_{min} is about axis x'-x', the angle (θ) of which is —

$$\tan 2\theta = -\frac{2\,I_{xy}}{I_x - I_y}$$

$$= -\frac{2(15.75)}{55.25 - 25.25} = -1.05$$

$$2\theta = -46.4° \text{ or } +133.6°$$

and $\qquad \theta = +66.8°$

Any ultimate buckling could be expected to occur about this axis (x' − x').

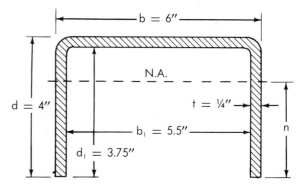

FIGURE 8

Problem 4

The channel section, Figure 8, is to be used as a column. Determine its radius of gyration about its x-x axis.

Using the conventional formulas for the properties of the section --

Area of the section:

$$A = b\,d - b_1\,d_1 = (6)\,(4) - (5.5)\,(3.75) = 3.375 \text{ in.}^2$$

Distance of neutral axis:

$$n = d - \frac{2\,d^2 t + b_1\,t^2}{2\,d\,b - 2\,b_1\,d_1}$$

$$= 4 - \frac{2\,(4)^2\,(.25) + (5.5)\,(.25)^2}{2\,(4)\,(6) - 2\,(5.5)(3.75)}$$

$$= 2.764''$$

Moment of inertia:

$$I = \frac{2\,d^3\,t + b_1\,t^3}{3} - A\,(d - n)^2$$

$$= \frac{2\,(4)^3\,(.25) + (5.5)\,(.25)^3}{3} - 3.375\,(4 - 2.764)^2$$

$$= 5.539 \text{ in.}^4$$

Radius of gyration:

$$r = \sqrt{\frac{I}{A}}$$

$$= \sqrt{\frac{5.539}{3.375}}$$

$$= 1.281''$$

If a slide rule had been used, assuming a possible error of $\pm$ one part in 1000 for every operation, this answer could be as high as 1.336" and as low as 1.197". This represents an error of + 4.3% and -6.6%. For this reason it is necessary, when using these conventional formulas, to make use of logarithms or else do the work longhand. To do this requires about 30 minutes.

The radius of gyration will now be found directly,

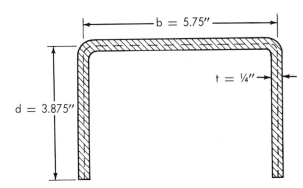

FIGURE 9

using the properties of thin sections, treating them as a line. See Table 6, Section 2.3.

Mean dimensions b and d are used, Figure 9.

$$r_x = \sqrt{\frac{d^3/3\,(2b + d)}{b + 2d}}$$

$$= \sqrt{\frac{3.875^3/3\,(2 \times 5.75 + 3.875)}{5.75 + 2\,(3.875)}}$$

$$= \underline{1.279''}$$

The exact value obtained from this formula for r is 1.279". The value obtained by using the conventional formula is 1.281".

Assuming a possible error of $\pm$ one part in 1000 for every operation of the slide rule, it would be possible to get an answer as high as 1.283" and as low as 1.275". This represents an error of about ¼ of the error using the conventional formulas with slide rule. The time for this last calculation was 2 minutes.

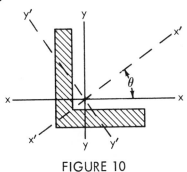

FIGURE 10

Moment of Inertia About Any Axis

Sometimes (as in Problem 3) the moment of inertia of a section is needed about an axis lying at an angle (θ) with the conventional x-x axis. This may be found by using the product of inertia (I_{xy}) of the section about the conventional axes (x-x and y-y) with the moments of inertia (I_x) and (I_y) about these same axes in the following formula:

$$\boxed{I_x = I_x \cos^2\theta + I_y \sin^2\theta - I_{xy} \sin^2\theta} \quad \dots \dots \dots \dots (7)$$

$$\boxed{I_y = I_x \sin^2\theta + I_y \cos^2\theta + I_{xy} \sin^2\theta} \quad \dots \dots \dots \dots (8)$$

4. CRITICAL COMPRESSIVE STRESS

The critical load on a column as given by the Euler formula is --

$$\boxed{P_{cr} = \frac{\pi^2\,E\,I}{L_e^2}} \quad \dots \dots \dots \dots \dots \dots (9)$$

where L_e = effective length of column (See next page).

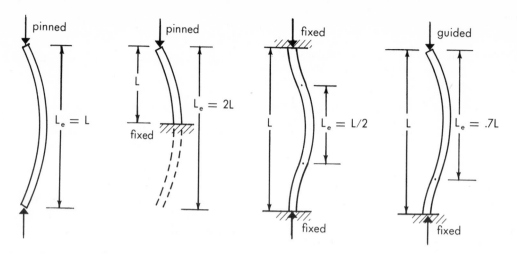

FIGURE 11

This can be changed into terms of average critical stress by dividing by the cross-sectional area of the column. Since $A = I/r^2$, this becomes —

$$\sigma_{cr} = \frac{\pi^2 E}{(L_e/r)^2}$$ ....(10)

Because this formula gives excessively high values for short columns, Engesser modified it by substituting the tangent modulus (E_t) in place of the usual Young's modulus of elasticity (E).

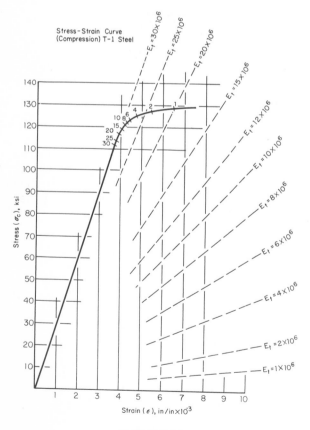

FIGURE 12

The modified formula then becomes —

$$\sigma_{cr} = \frac{\pi^2 E_t}{(L_e/r)^2}$$ ....(11)

where E_t = tangent modulus of elasticity, corresponding to the modulus of elasticity when stressed to σ_{cr}.

    r = least radius of gyration of the cross-section

    L_e = effective length of the column, corresponding to the length of a pinned column that would have the same critical load. See Figure 11.

The Engesser formula is also called the Tangent Modulus formula and checks well with experimental values.

5. TANGENT MODULUS

Use of the Tangent Modulus formula necessitates a stress-strain curve (preferably in compression) of the material. See Figure 12, stress-strain curve for T-1 steel in compression. Whereas the usual Young's modulus of elasticity represents a fixed value for steel (30×10^6) according to the ratio of stress to strain below the proportional limit, the tangent modulus of elasticity takes into consideration the changing effect of plastic strain beyond this point corresponding to the actual stress involved.

Notice, in Figure 12, the broken lines representing the slope for various values of tangent modulus of elasticity (E_t), in this case from 1×10^6 psi up to 30×10^6. The compressive stress level (σ_c) at which a given E_t value applies is determined by moving out parallel from that reference modulus line (dotted), by means of parallel rule or other suitable device, until the stress-strain curve is intersected at one point only. The line is tangent at this point.

The compressive stress-strain curve for any

SLENDERNESS RATIOS: T-1 STEEL

σ_c	E_t	L_e/r
110,000	30.2×10^6	52.1
112,000	30.0	51.4
114,000	26.5	47.9
116,000	22.0	43.4
118,000	17.5	38.3
120,000	13.0	32.7
122,000	9.0	27.0
124,000	5.5	20.9
126,000	3.3	16.1
128,000	1.5	10.8

TABLE 1

Engesser portion of curve

L_e/r	E_t	σ_c
50	30.2×10^6	119,500
60	30.2	82,900
70	30.2	60,900
75	30.2	53,000
80	30.2	46,600
90	30.2	36,800
100	30.2	29,850
110	30.2	27,700
125	30.2	19,100
140	30.2	15,200

TABLE 2

Euler portion of curve

material can be superimposed on this graph and the values of E_t at a given stress level (σ_c) read by the same technique.

The values of tangent modulus (E_t) for T-1 steel, as read from Figure 12, are now plotted against the corresponding compressive stress (σ_c). This is shown in Figure 13.

The Engesser or tangent modulus formula for critical stress (σ_{cr}) is then put into the following form —

$$\boxed{\frac{L_e}{r} = \pi \sqrt{\frac{E_t}{\sigma_{cr}}}} \quad \ldots\ldots\ldots\ldots\ldots\ldots\ldots\ldots\ldots\ldots\ldots (12)$$

and the critical slenderness ratio (L_e/r) is determined for various values of stress (σ_c), resulting in Tables 1 and 2 for T-1 only.

Table 1 gives corresponding values of slenderness ratio (L_e/r) for given values of stress (σ_c) above the proportional limit of T-1.

Below the material's proportional limit, the use of Young's modulus (E) or tangent modulus (E_t) provide the same value. Table 2 for T-1 gives the slenderness ratio (L_e/r) for stress levels (σ_c) within the proportional portion of the stress-strain curve. Since the original Euler formula for σ_{cr} applies here, this portion of the curve is often called the Euler curve.

6. PLOTTING ALLOWABLE STRESS CURVE

These values from Tables 1 and 2 are now plotted to form the curve in Figure 14. The Euler portion of the curve is extended upward by a broken line to indicate the variance that would be obtained by continuing to use the Euler formula beyond the

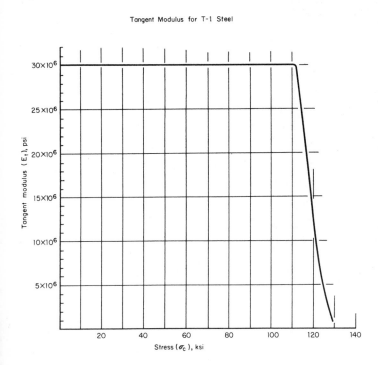

Tangent Modulus for T-1 Steel

FIGURE 13

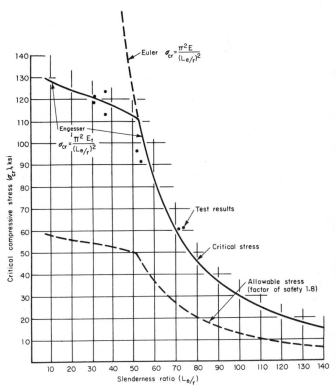

Resulting Critical Compressive Stress for T-1 Steel
(A suitable factor of safety
must be applied to these values)

FIGURE 14

TABLE 3 – ALLOWABLE COMPRESSIVE STRESS
for Various Steels

Yield Strength psi	PINNED ENDS		FIXED ENDS	
	Range of L/r Values	Average Allowable Unit Stress $\sigma = P/A$	Range of L/r Values	Average Allowable Unit Stress $\sigma = P/A$
33,000	0–140	$\dfrac{P}{A} = 15{,}000 - .325\left(\dfrac{L}{r}\right)^2$	0–155	$\dfrac{P}{A} = 15{,}000 - .253\left(\dfrac{L}{r}\right)^2$
	140–200	$\dfrac{P}{A} = \dfrac{15{,}000}{0.5 + \dfrac{1}{15{,}860}\left(\dfrac{L}{r}\right)^2}$	155–200	$\dfrac{P}{A} = \dfrac{15{,}000}{0.5 + \dfrac{1}{20{,}370}\left(\dfrac{L}{r}\right)^2}$
40,000	0–126	$\dfrac{P}{A} = 17{,}800 - .47\left(\dfrac{L}{r}\right)^2$	0–143	$\dfrac{P}{A} = 17{,}800 - .37\left(\dfrac{L}{r}\right)^2$
	126–200	$\dfrac{P}{A} = \dfrac{17{,}800}{0.5 + \dfrac{1}{13{,}000}\left(\dfrac{L}{r}\right)^2}$	143–200	$\dfrac{P}{A} = \dfrac{17{,}000}{0.5 + \dfrac{1}{16{,}900}\left(\dfrac{L}{r}\right)^2}$
45,000	0–120	$\dfrac{P}{A} = 20{,}500 - .605\left(\dfrac{L}{r}\right)^2$	0–135	$\dfrac{P}{A} = 20{,}500 - .47\left(\dfrac{L}{r}\right)^2$
	120–200	$\dfrac{P}{A} = \dfrac{20{,}500}{0.5 + \dfrac{1}{11{,}630}\left(\dfrac{L}{r}\right)^2}$	135–200	$\dfrac{P}{A} = \dfrac{20{,}500}{0.5 + \dfrac{1}{14{,}930}\left(\dfrac{L}{r}\right)^2}$
50,000	0–110	$\dfrac{P}{A} = 22{,}500 - .738\left(\dfrac{L}{r}\right)^2$	0–125	$\dfrac{P}{A} = 22{,}500 - .574\left(\dfrac{L}{r}\right)^2$
	110–200	$\dfrac{P}{A} = \dfrac{22{,}500}{0.5 + \dfrac{1}{10{,}460}\left(\dfrac{L}{r}\right)^2}$	125–200	$\dfrac{P}{A} = \dfrac{22{,}500}{0.5 + \dfrac{1}{13{,}440}\left(\dfrac{L}{r}\right)^2}$
55,000	0–105	$\dfrac{P}{A} = 25{,}000 - .902\left(\dfrac{L}{r}\right)^2$	0–120	$\dfrac{P}{A} = 25{,}000 - .702\left(\dfrac{L}{r}\right)^2$
	105–200	$\dfrac{P}{A} = \dfrac{25{,}000}{0.5 + \dfrac{1}{9{,}510}\left(\dfrac{L}{r}\right)^2}$	120–200	$\dfrac{P}{A} = \dfrac{25{,}000}{0.5 + \dfrac{1}{12{,}220}\left(\dfrac{L}{r}\right)^2}$
60,000	0–102	$\dfrac{P}{A} = 26{,}500 - 1.05\left(\dfrac{L}{r}\right)^2$	0–116	$\dfrac{P}{A} = 26{,}500 - .82\left(\dfrac{L}{r}\right)^2$
	102–200	$\dfrac{P}{A} = \dfrac{26{,}500}{0.5 + \dfrac{1}{8{,}720}\left(\dfrac{L}{r}\right)^2}$	116–200	$\dfrac{P}{A} = \dfrac{26{,}500}{0.5 + \dfrac{1}{11{,}200}\left(\dfrac{L}{r}\right)^2}$

Adapted from "Design Manual for High Strength Steels" (p.24) by Priest and Gilligan, United States Steel Corporation; based on suggestions of ASCE Special Committee on Column Research. Factor of Safety = 1.8 approx.

proportional limit. This must be kept in mind in designing compression members having a low slenderness ratio (L_e/r)).

A few test results are also shown to indicate the close relationship between the Tangent Modulus formula and actual values.

Note that a corresponding curve has been plotted below the main curve, representing the allowable stress (σ) after applying a factor of safety of 1.8.

7. SECANT FORMULA

For the structural field, the American Society of Civil Engineers (ASCE), as a result of extensive research on full scale columns, has recommended the Secant Formula. In its original form, it can only be used by a series of successive approximations, and as a result it is usually put into a more workable form.

The column formulas in Table 3 have been adapted from "Design Manual for High Strength Steels" (1954, 1961) by H. Malcom Priest and John A. Gilligan, United States Steel Corp. The table covers steels having a yield strength of 33,000 to 60,000 psi. A factor of safety of 1.8 has been used.

In order to visualize relative savings in metal by the use of higher-strength steels, Figure 15 indicates the allowable compressive stress (σ) from the above formulas for four different yield strengths. Notice that the advantage of the higher strengths drops off as the column becomes more slender.

If the allowable stress curve of T-1 (Fig. 14) were now superimposed on this graph, the even greater strength advantage of T-1 at lower slenderness ratios would be readily apparent.

TABLE 4 - ALLOWABLE COMPRESSIVE STRESS (AISC)

Range of $\frac{L}{r}$ Values	Average Allowable Compressive Unit Stress (σ)
0 to C_c	$\sigma = \left[1 - \dfrac{\left(\dfrac{L}{r}\right)^2}{2\,C_c^2} \right] \dfrac{\sigma_y}{F.S.}$
C_c to 200	$\sigma = \dfrac{149,000,000}{\left(\dfrac{L}{r}\right)^2}$

where:

$$C_c = \sqrt{\frac{2\pi^2\,E}{\sigma_y}}$$

$$F.S. = \frac{5}{3} + \frac{3\left(\dfrac{L}{r}\right)}{8\,C_c} - \frac{\left(\dfrac{L}{r}\right)^3}{8\,C_c^{\,3}}$$

1. For very short columns this provides a factor of safety of 1.67; for longer columns this gradually increases)by 15% max.) up to 1.92. (The earlier-developed formulas of Table 3 are based on a uniform 1.8 factor of safety.)

2. When the "effective length" is known, the value of L_e should be substituted for L in the above formulas:

Practical examples of long columns built for maximum resistance to compressive loading are included in the later Section 4.5, and short columns (feet and legs) are illustrated in the same section.

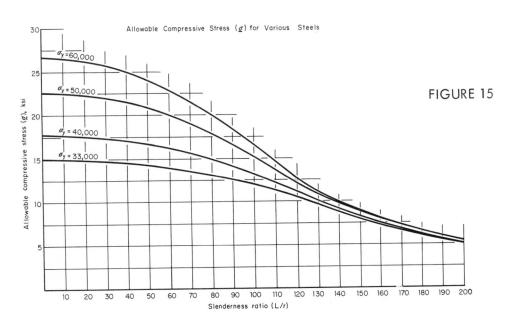

Allowable Compressive Stress (σ) for Various Steels

FIGURE 15

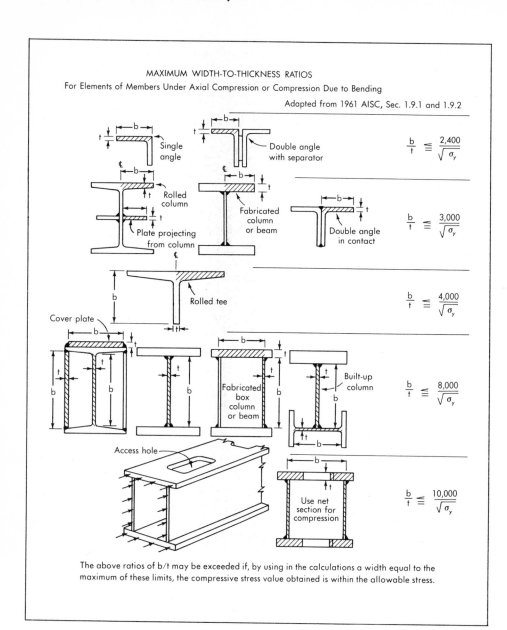

MAXIMUM WIDTH-TO-THICKNESS RATIOS

For Elements of Members Under Axial Compression or Compression Due to Bending

Adapted from 1961 AISC, Sec. 1.9.1 and 1.9.2

Single angle

Double angle with separator

$$\frac{b}{t} \leqq \frac{2,400}{\sqrt{\sigma_y}}$$

Rolled column

Fabricated column or beam

Plate projecting from column

Double angle in contact

$$\frac{b}{t} \leqq \frac{3,000}{\sqrt{\sigma_y}}$$

Rolled tee

$$\frac{b}{t} \leqq \frac{4,000}{\sqrt{\sigma_y}}$$

Cover plate

Fabricated box column or beam

Built-up column

$$\frac{b}{t} \leqq \frac{8,000}{\sqrt{\sigma_y}}$$

Access hole

Use net section for compression

$$\frac{b}{t} \leqq \frac{10,000}{\sqrt{\sigma_y}}$$

FIGURE 16

The above ratios of b/t may be exceeded if, by using in the calculations a width equal to the maximum of these limits, the compressive stress value obtained is within the allowable stress.

8. AISC COLUMN FORMULAS

The 1961 AISC (American Institute of Steel Construction) specifications for structural buildings contain new column formulas based on the (then) recent Column Research Council Report. A great amount of new information on the behavior of structural columns was developed, including the use of the new high-strength steels.

The column formulas, Table 4, resulting from this research may be of value in designing certain classes of machinery where the most precise values are required: for safety on long slender columns, or for maximum economy on columns of low slenderness ratio.

Where the specially prepared tables (Tables 6-10) are not applicable, the basic formulas -- while giving more accurate results -- are more cumbersome to work with than those of Table 3 which were developed from the earlier ASCE investigation. For most machine columns, the Table 3 formulas or Figure 15 curves will be sufficiently accurate to justify the simplicity of their use.

For various conditions of column cross-section, Figure 16, there is a limiting ratio of element width to thickness (b/t). This ratio is expressed as being equal to or less than ($\leqq$) a certain value divided by the square root of the material's yield strength. The related Table 5 permits direct reading of a compression element's b/t ratio for various yield strengths of steel.

At times it may be desirable to exceed the limiting b/t ratio of an element. This can be done if, in the calculations, substituting the shorter maximum width allowed (by the Fig. 16 limits) would give a compressive unit stress value within the allowable stress.

To help in visualizing the variance in using these newer formulas, Figure 17 indicates the allowable compressive stress (σ) obtained from the above formulas for five different yield strengths. When compared to corresponding curves of Figure 15, it will be seen that the new formulas offer considerable possible economy of material when the slenderness ratio is low, and a somewhat more conservative value when the slenderness ratio is high.

The allowable compressive unit stress (σ) for a given slenderness ratio (L/r), from unity through 200, is quickly read from Tables 6 through 10 for steels of various yield strengths.

Above L/r of 130, the higher-strength steels offer no advantage as to allowable compressive stress (σ). Above this point, use Table 7 for the more economical steel of 36,000 psi yield strength.

TABLE 5 - LIMITING b/t RATIOS OF SECTION ELEMENTS UNDER COMPRESSION

Limits of ratio of width to thickness of compression elements for different yield strengths of steel

Figure 16 Ratio σ_y	$\dfrac{2,400}{\sqrt{\sigma_y}}$	$\dfrac{3,000}{\sqrt{\sigma_y}}$	$\dfrac{4,000}{\sqrt{\sigma_y}}$	$\dfrac{8,000}{\sqrt{\sigma_y}}$	$\dfrac{10,000}{\sqrt{\sigma_y}}$
33,000	13	16	22	44	55
36,000	13	16	21	42	53
42,000	12	15	20	39	49
46,000	11	14	19	37	45
50,000	11	13	18	36	45

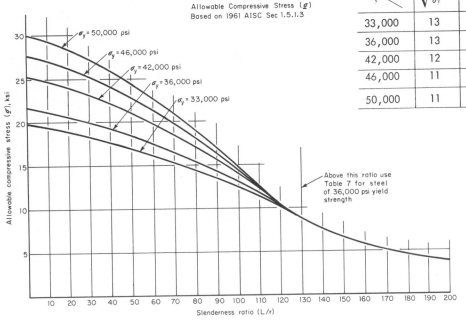

Allowable Compressive Stress (σ)
Based on 1961 AISC Sec 1.5.1.3

σ_y = 50,000 psi
σ_y = 46,000 psi
σ_y = 42,000 psi
σ_y = 36,000 psi
σ_y = 33,000 psi

Above this ratio use Table 7 for steel of 36,000 psi yield strength

FIGURE 17

TABLES 6, 7, 8, 9, 10 – ALLOWABLE COMPRESSIVE (σ) VALUES (1961 AISC)

TABLE 6 – 33,000 psi yield steel

L/r ratio		1	2	3	4	5	6	7	8	9
10	19,410	19,770	19,730	19,690	19,660	19,620	19,580	19,540	19,500	19,460
20	18,930	19,370	19,320	19,280	19,230	19,180	19,130	19,080	19,030	18,980
30	18,360	18,880	18,820	18,770	18,710	18,660	18,600	18,540	18,480	18,420
40	17,710	18,300	18,240	18,180	18,110	18,050	17,980	17,920	17,850	17,780
50	16,990	17,640	17,570	17,500	17,430	17,360	17,290	17,220	17,140	17,070
60	16,200	16,920	16,840	16,760	16,680	16,600	16,520	16,440	16,360	16,280
70	15,340	16,120	16,030	15,950	15,860	15,780	15,690	15,610	15,520	15,430
80	14,420	15,250	15,160	15,070	14,980	14,890	14,800	14,700	14,610	14,510
90	13,430	14,320	14,230	14,130	14,030	13,930	13,840	13,740	13,640	13,530
100	12,380	13,330	13,230	13,130	13,020	12,920	12,810	12,710	12,600	12,490
110	11,270	12,280	12,170	12,060	11,950	11,830	11,720	11,610	11,500	11,380
120	10,090	11,150	11,040	10,920	10,800	10,690	10,570	10,450	10,330	10,210
130	8,830	9,960	9,840	9,720	9,590	9,470	9,340	9,220	9,090	8,960
140	7,620	8,700	8,570	8,440	8,320	8,190	8,070	7,960	7,840	7,730
150	6,640	7,510	7,410	7,300	7,200	7,100	7,010	6,910	6,820	6,730
160	5,830	6,550	6,460	6,380	6,300	6,220	6,140	6,060	5,980	5,910
170	5,170	5,760	5,690	5,620	5,550	5,490	5,420	5,350	5,290	5,230
180	4,610	5,110	5,050	4,990	4,930	4,880	4,820	4,770	4,710	4,660
190	4,140	4,560	4,510	4,460	4,410	4,360	4,320	4,270	4,230	4,180
200	3,730	4,090	4,050	4,010	3,970	3,930	3,890	3,850	3,810	3,770

TABLE 7 – 36,000 psi yield steel

L/r ratio		1	2	3	4	5	6	7	8	9
10	21,160	21,560	21,520	21,480	21,440	21,390	21,350	21,300	21,250	21,210
20	20,600	21,100	21,050	21,000	20,950	20,890	20,830	20,780	20,720	20,660
30	19,940	20,540	20,480	20,410	20,350	20,280	20,220	20,150	20,080	20,010
40	19,190	19,870	19,800	19,730	19,650	19,580	19,500	19,420	19,350	19,270
50	18,350	19,110	19,030	18,950	18,860	18,780	18,700	18,610	18,530	18,440
60	17,430	18,260	18,170	18,080	17,990	17,900	17,810	17,710	17,620	17,530
70	16,430	17,330	17,240	17,140	17,040	16,940	16,840	16,740	16,640	16,530
80	15,360	16,330	16,220	16,120	16,020	15,900	15,790	15,690	15,580	15,470
90	14,200	15,240	15,130	15,020	14,900	14,790	14,670	14,560	14,440	14,320
100	12,980	14,090	13,970	13,840	13,720	13,600	13,480	13,350	13,230	13,100
110	11,670	12,850	12,720	12,590	12,470	12,330	12,200	12,070	11,940	11,810
120	10,280	11,540	11,400	11,260	11,130	10,990	10,850	10,710	10,570	10,430
130	8,840	10,140	9,990	9,850	9,700	9,550	9,410	9,260	9,110	8,970
140	7,620	8,700	8,570	8,440	8,320	8,190	8,070	7,960	7,840	7,730
150	6,640	7,510	7,410	7,300	7,200	7,100	7,010	6,910	6,820	6,730
160	5,830	6,550	6,460	6,380	6,300	6,220	6,140	6,060	5,980	5,910
170	5,170	5,760	5,690	5,620	5,550	5,490	5,420	5,350	5,290	5,230
180	4,610	5,110	5,050	4,990	4,930	4,880	4,820	4,770	4,710	4,660
190	4,140	4,560	4,510	4,460	4,410	4,360	4,320	4,270	4,230	4,180
200	3,730	4,090	4,050	4,010	3,970	3,930	3,890	3,850	3,810	3,770

TABLE 8 – 42,000 psi yield steel

L/r ratio		1	2	3	4	5	6	7	8	9
10	24,630	25,150	25,100	25,050	24,990	24,940	24,880	24,820	24,760	24,700
20	23,920	24,570	24,500	24,430	24,360	24,290	24,220	24,150	24,070	24,000
30	23,060	23,840	23,760	23,680	23,590	23,510	23,420	23,330	23,240	23,150
40	22,080	22,970	22,880	22,780	22,690	22,590	22,490	22,390	22,290	22,190
50	20,990	21,980	21,870	21,770	21,660	21,550	21,440	21,330	21,220	21,100
60	19,790	20,870	20,760	20,640	20,530	20,400	20,280	20,160	20,030	19,910
70	18,480	19,660	19,530	19,400	19,270	19,140	19,010	18,880	18,750	18,610
80	17,060	18,340	18,200	18,060	17,920	17,780	17,640	17,500	17,350	17,210
90	15,550	16,920	16,770	16,620	16,470	16,320	16,170	16,010	15,860	15,710
100	13,930	15,390	15,230	15,070	14,910	14,750	14,590	14,430	14,260	14,090
110	12,190	13,760	13,590	13,420	13,250	13,080	12,900	12,730	12,550	12,370
120	10,370	12,010	11,830	11,650	11,470	11,280	11,100	10,910	10,720	10,550
130	8,840	10,200	10,030	9,870	9,710	9,560	9,410	9,260	9,110	8,970

TABLE 9 – 46,000 psi yield steel

L/r ratio		1	2	3	4	5	6	7	8	9
10	26,950	27,540	27,480	27,420	27,360	27,300	27,230	27,160	27,090	27,020
20	26,110	26,870	26,790	26,720	26,630	26,550	26,470	26,380	26,290	26,210
30	25,120	26,020	25,930	25,830	25,730	25,640	25,540	25,430	25,330	25,230
40	23,970	25,010	24,900	24,790	24,680	24,560	24,450	24,330	24,210	24,100
50	22,690	23,850	23,730	23,600	23,480	23,350	23,220	23,090	22,960	22,830
60	21,280	22,560	22,420	22,280	22,140	22,000	21,860	21,720	21,570	21,430
70	19,740	21,130	20,980	20,830	20,680	20,530	20,370	20,220	20,060	19,900
80	18,080	19,580	19,420	19,260	19,100	18,930	18,760	18,600	18,430	18,260
90	16,300	17,910	17,740	17,560	17,390	17,210	17,030	16,850	16,670	16,480
100	14,390	16,120	15,930	15,740	15,550	15,360	15,170	14,970	14,780	14,580
110	12,330	14,190	13,990	13,790	13,580	13,380	13,170	12,960	12,750	12,540
120	10,370	12,120	11,900	11,690	11,490	11,290	11,100	10,910	10,720	10,550
130	8,840	10,200	10,030	9,870	9,710	9,560	9,410	9,260	9,110	8,970

TABLE 10 – 50,000 psi yield steel

L/r ratio		1	2	3	4	5	6	7	8	9
10	29,260	29,940	29,870	29,800	29,730	29,660	29,580	29,500	29,420	29,340
20	28,300	29,170	29,080	28,990	28,900	28,800	28,710	28,610	28,510	28,400
30	27,150	28,190	28,080	27,970	27,860	27,750	27,630	27,520	27,400	27,280
40	25,830	27,030	26,900	26,770	26,640	26,510	26,380	26,250	26,110	25,970
50	24,350	25,690	25,550	25,400	25,260	25,110	24,960	24,810	24,660	24,510
60	22,720	24,190	24,040	23,880	23,720	23,550	23,390	23,220	23,060	22,890
70	20,940	22,550	22,370	22,200	22,020	21,850	21,670	21,490	21,310	21,120
80	19,010	20,750	20,560	20,380	20,190	19,990	19,800	19,610	19,410	19,210
90	16,940	18,810	18,610	18,410	18,200	17,990	17,790	17,580	17,370	17,150
100	14,710	16,720	16,500	16,290	16,060	15,840	15,620	15,390	15,170	14,940
110	12,340	14,470	14,240	14,000	13,770	13,530	13,290	13,040	12,800	12,570
120	10,370	12,120	11,900	11,690	11,490	11,290	11,100	10,910	10,720	10,550
130	8,840	10,200	10,030	9,870	9,710	9,560	9,410	9,260	9,110	8,970

Above L/r of 130, the higher-strength steels offer no advantage as to allowable compressive stress (σ). Above this point, use Table 7 for the more economical steel of 36,000 psi yield strength.

Analysis of Bending

1. BENDING STRESS

Any force applied transversely to the structural axis of a partially supported member sets up bending moments (M) along the length of the member. These in turn stress the cross-sections in bending.

As shown in Figure 1, the bending stresses are zero at the neutral axis, and are assumed to increase lineally to a maximum at the outer fiber of the section. The fibers stressed in tension elongate; the fibers stressed in compression contract. This causes each section so stressed to rotate. The cumulative effect of this movement is an over-all deflection (or bending) of the member.

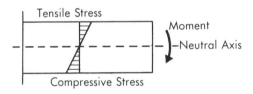

FIGURE 1

The cantilever beam shown in Figure 1 is in tension along the top and in compression along the bottom. In contrast, the relationship of the applied force and the points of support on the member shown in Figure 2 is such that the curve of deflection is inverted, and the member is in tension along the bottom and in compression along the top.

Within the elastic range (i.e. below the proportional elastic limit or the yield point), the bending stress (σ_b) at any point in the cross-section of a beam is--

$$\sigma_b = \frac{Mc}{I} \quad \dots\dots\dots\dots\dots\dots\dots\dots\dots\dots (1)$$

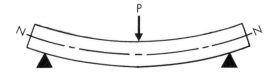

FIGURE 2

where:

M = bending moment at the section in question, in.-lbs

I = moment of inertia of the section, in.^{4}

c = distance from neutral axis to the point at which stress is desired, in.

σ_b = bending stress, may be tension or compression, psi

TABLE 1 - BEAM DIAGRAMS

Type of Beam	Maximum moment	Maximum deflection	Maximum shear
	$M = PL$ Fixed end	$\Delta = \dfrac{PL^3}{3EI}$ Free end	$V = P$
	$M = \dfrac{PL}{4}$ center	$\Delta = \dfrac{PL^3}{48EI}$ center	$V = \dfrac{P}{2}$
	$M = \dfrac{3PL}{16}$ Fixed end	$\Delta = \dfrac{PL^3}{48EI\sqrt{5}}$	$V = \dfrac{11}{16}P$
	$M = \dfrac{PL}{2}$ both ends	$\Delta = \dfrac{PL^3}{12EI}$ guided end	$V = P$
	$M = \dfrac{PL}{8}$ center & ends	$\Delta = \dfrac{PL^3}{192EI}$ center	$V = \dfrac{P}{2}$
	$M = \dfrac{PL}{2}$ Fixed end	$\Delta = \dfrac{PL^3}{8EI}$ Free end	$V = P$
	$M = \dfrac{PL}{8}$ center	$\Delta = \dfrac{5PL^3}{384EI}$ center	$V = \dfrac{P}{2}$
	$M = \dfrac{PL}{8}$ Fixed end	$\Delta = \dfrac{PL^3}{185EI}$	$V = \dfrac{5}{8}P$
	$M = \dfrac{PL}{3}$ Fixed end	$\Delta = \dfrac{PL^3}{24EI}$ guided end	$V = P$
	$M = \dfrac{PL}{12}$ both ends	$\Delta = \dfrac{PL^3}{384EI}$ center	$V = \dfrac{P}{2}$
	$M = Pe$ whole beam	$\Delta = \dfrac{PeL^2}{2EI}$ right angles to force	$V = 0$

1

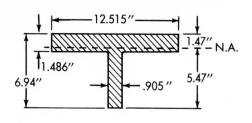

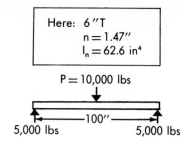

Here: $6''T$
$n = 1.47''$
$I_n = 62.6$ in⁴

FIGURE 3

The bending moment (M) may be determined from standard beam diagrams. Table 1 lists several of these, along with the formulas for bending moment, shear, and deflection. A more complete presentation is included in the Reference Section on Beam Diagrams.

Normally there is no interest in knowing what the bending stresses are somewhere inside a beam. Usually the bending stress at the outer fiber is needed because it is of maximum value. In an unsymmetrical section, the distance c must be taken in the correct direction across that portion of the section which is in tension or that portion which is in compression, as desired. Ordinarily only the maximum stress is needed and this is the stress at the outer fiber under tension, which rests at the greater distance c from the neutral axis.

Problem 1

A standard rolled "T" section (ST-6" wide flange, 80.5 lbs) is used as a beam, 100" long, supported on each end and bearing a concentrated load of 10,000 lbs at the middle. Find the maximum tensile and maximum compressive bending stresses.

Figure 3 shows the cross-section of this beam, together with its load diagram.

Referring to Table 1, the formula for the bending moment of this type of beam is found to be--

$$M = \frac{PL}{4} \quad \text{and therefore}$$

$$= \frac{(10,000)(100)}{4}$$

$$= 250,000 \text{ in.-lbs}$$

Since the bottom portion of the beam is stressed in tension, substituting appropriate known values into the formula:

$$\sigma_t = \frac{Mc}{I}$$

$$= \frac{(250,000)(5.47)}{(62.6)}$$

$$= 21,845 \text{ psi (tension)}$$

The top portion of the beam being in compression,

$$\sigma_c = \frac{Mc}{I}$$

$$= \frac{(250,000)(1.47)}{62.6}$$

$$= 5,870 \text{ psi (compression)}$$

Problem 2

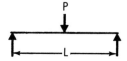

FIGURE 4

Find the maximum deflection of the previous beam under the same loading. From the beam diagrams, Table 1, the appropriate formula is found to be--

$$\Delta_{max} = \frac{PL^3}{48EI} \quad \text{and therefore}$$

$$= \frac{(10,000)(100)^3}{48(30 \times 10^6)(62.6)}$$

$$= .111''$$

2. HORIZONTAL SHEAR STRESS

In addition to pure bending stresses, horizontal shear stress is often present in beams, Figure 5. It depends on vertical shear and only occurs if the bending moment varies along the beam. (Any beam, or portion of the beam's length, that has uniform bending moment has no vertical shear and therefore no horizontal shear).

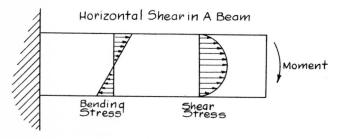

FIGURE 5

Unlike bending stress, the horizontal shear stress is zero at the outer fibers of the beam and is maximum at the neutral axis of the beam. It tends to cause one part of the beam to slide past the other.

The horizontal shear stress at any point in the cross-section of a beam, Figure 6, is--

$$\boxed{\tau = \frac{V a y}{I t}} \quad\dots\dots\dots\dots\dots\dots\dots\dots\dots (2)$$

where:

V = external vertical shear on beam, lbs

I = moment of inertia of whole section, in.[4]

t = thickness of section at plane where stress is desired, in.

a = area of section beyond plane where stress is desired, in.[2]

y = distance of center of gravity of area to neutral axis of entire section, in.

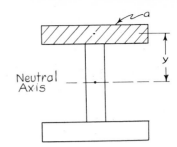

FIGURE 6

(a) substituting the above values into the formula, the horizontal shear stress (τ) is found:

$$\tau = \frac{V a y}{I t}$$

$$= \frac{(5000)(18.6)(0.727)}{(62.6)(0.903)}$$

$$= \underline{1196 \text{ psi}}$$

(b) Since the shear force is borne entirely by the web of the "T", the horizontal shear force (f) depends on the thickness of the web in the plane of interest:

f = τ t and thus

= 1196 × 0.903

= 1080 lbs/in.

There are two fillet welds, one on each side of the "T" joining the flange to the web. Each will have to support half of the shear force or 540 lbs/in. and its leg size would be:

$$\omega = \frac{540}{9600}$$

$$= .056''$$

This would be an extremely small continuous fillet weld. Based upon the AWS, the minimum size fillet weld for the thicker 1.47" plate would be 5/16".

If manual intermittent fillet welds are to be used, the percentage of the length of the joint to be welded would be:

$$\% = \frac{\text{calculated leg size of continuous fillet weld}}{\text{actual leg size of intermittent fillet weld used}} \times 100$$

$$= \frac{.056}{5/16} = 18\%$$

A $\overline{\quad 5/16 \quad}$ ◸ 3-12 ◿ fillet weld would satisfy this requirement because it results in 25% of the length of the joint being welded.

3. HOW TO USE STEEL EFFICIENTLY FOR BENDING LOADS

Every structural member must have

1. Sufficient strength to carry given loads.

2. Necessary rigidity to hold deflection within certain allowable limits.

Problem 3

Assume that the "T" beam in our previous example (Problem 1) is fabricated by welding. Under the same load conditions,

(a) Find the horizontal shear stress in the plane where the web joins the flange.

(b) Then find the size of continuous fillet welds on both sides, joining the web to the flange.

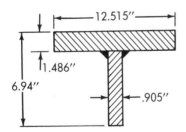

FIGURE 7

From the beam diagrams, Table 1, the appropriate formula for vertical shear (V) is found to be

$$V = \frac{P}{2} \text{ and thus}$$

$$= \frac{10,000}{2}$$

$$= 5,000 \text{ lbs}$$

The following values also are known or determined to be--

I = 62.6 in.[4]

a = 1.486 × 12.515 = 18.6 in.[2]

y = 0.727"

t = 0.903"

THE FOLLOWING 4 RULES WILL RESULT IN THE MOST EFFECTIVE USE OF STEEL FOR BENDING LOADS

1. Place flange material as far as possible from the neutral axis. Connect flanges with web section.

2. Avoid reductions in sectional area below requirements for horizontal stiffness.

3. Weld ends of beams rigidly to supporting members for maximum strength and stiffness.

4. Place joints in low stress areas.

For efficient designs, material must be placed where it does the most work per pound of metal. The section of a member, therefore, must be selected within practical limits to provide the required strength and rigidity. For example, a beam section obviously should not be so deep to withstand vertical loads with minimum sectional area, yet be too weak and flexible for horizontal transverse forces. Secondly, a structural section must not be so thin as to be impractical to fabricate.

It is important, therefore, to know the limits to which a designer can go in theory and where to stop for practical reasons.

RULE 1. Place Flanges as Far as Possible from the Neutral Axis. Connect Flanges with Web Section

The moment of inertia (I) of a section determines its resistance to bending. To get the most from each pound of steel it is important to know what sections of the area are most effective structurally to resist bending.

For example, a rectangular section, Figure 8, is divided into 10 areas. Each area as shown has the same resistance to bending since it has the same moment of inertia about the neutral axis. Actually, the extreme areas at the top and bottom account for 10% of the bending resistance of the entire section. On the other hand, the center area, which has 14 times the area of the top and bottom outer areas, does not offer any more bending resistance.

The net effect of placing material as far as possible from the neutral axis is shown in Figure 9. Its similarity to increasingly deeper "I" sections is evident.

Each of the areas has equal bending resistance, if the web is disregarded. Flange area becomes less as the section depth is increased. At first this indicates that a deep, thin section is best for maximum resistance to bending per pound of metal.

However, the practical limitation is given in Rule 2, which says:

RULE 2. Avoid Reductions in Sectional Area Below Requirements for Horizontal Stiffness

Each of the sections shown in Figure 10 has the same resistance to bending about the x-x axis. As the depth of the section increases, the area (A) decreases. As a result, the strength of the section is decreasing also, since $S = I/c$ and c is increasing as depth increases, but I remains constant.

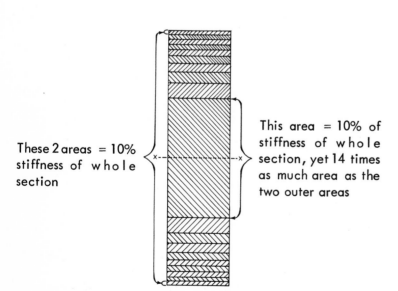

These 2 areas = 10% stiffness of whole section

This area = 10% of stiffness of whole section, yet 14 times as much area as the two outer areas

Each area has same I about x-x

FIGURE 8

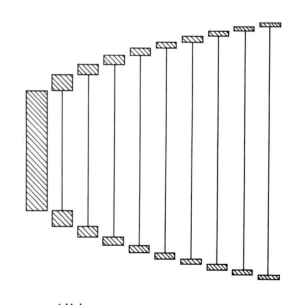

All have same moment of inertia

FIGURE 9

These Sections Are Equal in Stiffness in the Vertical Direction

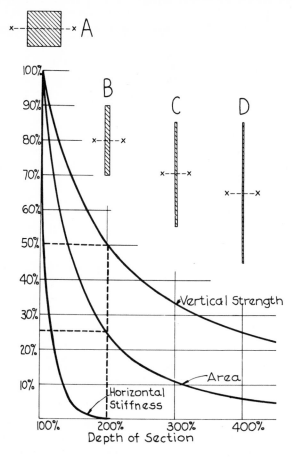

FIGURE 10

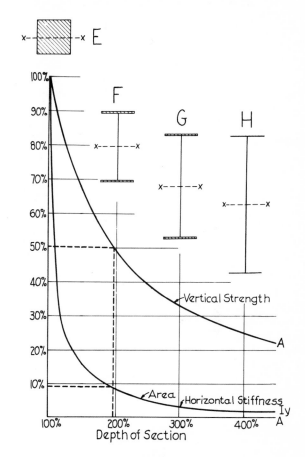

FIGURE 11

Since a member designed for rigidity (to withstand deflection) is generally 5 to 10 times stronger than necessary to prevent failure, the area of a section can generally be reduced without exceeding allowable stresses as illustrated in the graphs, Figures 10 and 11.

In Figure 10, if the depth of the section is made twice the depth of the initial square section (A), the resulting area (B) is only 25% of the initial square area (A) but is still 50% as strong...which is more than adequate.

The objection to a modified section such as the area (B) is that bending resistance or stiffness in the horizontal direction is nearly zero as indicated on the graph. To avoid this, good design practice assumes a horizontal force along with a given vertical load...which leads to the use of flanged sections.

The flanged sections shown in Figure 11 have equal bending resistance. As the depth of the section increases, the flange area drops off and the strength decreases. The essential difference, however, between the sections in Figure 12 and those in Figure 10 is the fact that the area drops off at a faster rate with the use of flanges.

For a 50% reduction in strength, the depth of section F is twice the depth of section E. In these respects, section F and section B are the same. However, the resulting area of section F is only 9% of the original section area compared to the 25% in the case of section B. Horizontal bending resistance of F is 9% of the original compared to near zero in the case of B.

Thus, choosing a flanged section instead of a simple vertical web member achieves the same principal bending resistance and strength with less material but with the added benefit of greater resistance to horizontal bending.

RULE 3. Weld Ends of Beams Rigidly to Supporting Members for Maximum Strength and Stiffness

The deflection of a beam with concentrated load at midspan can be reduced to 1/4 its value when the ends are rigidly fixed. This is easily seen in any beam table, see Figure 12. Deflection of a uniformly loaded beam can be reduced to 1/5. Strength of the beam is greatly increased.

In the demonstration setup, Figure 13, beam A is simply supported at the ends. The background

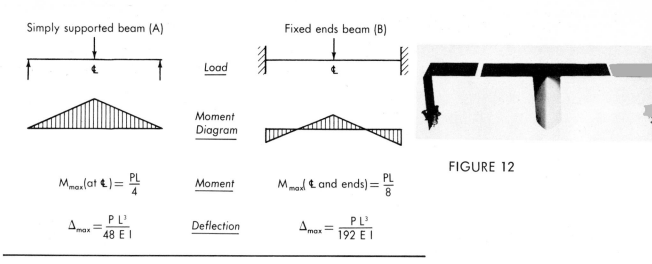

Simply supported beam (A)

Load

Moment Diagram

$$M_{max}(at\ \text{℄}) = \frac{PL}{4}$$

Moment

$$\Delta_{max} = \frac{P\,L^3}{48\,E\,I}$$

Deflection

Fixed ends beam (B)

$$M_{max}(\text{℄ and ends}) = \frac{PL}{8}$$

$$\Delta_{max} = \frac{P\,L^3}{192\,E\,I}$$

FIGURE 12

sketch shows the bending moment when loaded at midspan. There is no bending moment at the end. Maximum bending moment is at midspan.

Beam B is a rigid frame since the ends of the beam are rigidly connected to the supporting columns. As a result, some of the moment is carried through the end connection into the supporting column. Although some bending moment is introduced in the column, the rigid connection reduces the maximum bending moment in the central portion of the beam, reducing in turn the bending stress and deflection in the beam.

Graphic illustration of what happens when both beams are loaded is shown in Figure 14.

The simply supported beam (A) is stressed beyond its yield point and fails by buckling. If it had not failed the beam would have been stressed to 49,150 psi.

The rigidly supported beam (B) is stressed to only 28,000 psi and is far from failing.

RULE 4. Place Joints in Low Stress Area

In a rigid beam, the bending moment passes through zero twice along the length of the beam. These two points are called points of inflection. Because bending stresses at these points are almost zero, a joint at this position does not require much welding, usually just enough to take the shear load. It frequently is practical to fabricate beams of this type in three sections so that the amount of welding for the joint can be drastically reduced.

In the background of Figure 15 is just such a

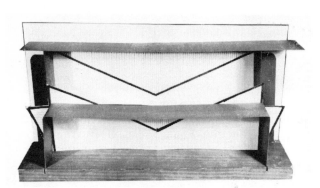

FIGURE 13

FIGURE 14

FIGURE 15

beam, made of three sections with the joint at the points of inflection. The greatest moment occurs at midspan of the beam and at the ends where it connects to the columns. This beam when loaded identically with a rigid beam having no joint, as illustrated in the foreground of Figure 15, exhibits the same strength and stiffness. The mechanical joints at the inflection points, even though not welded for purposes of this demonstration, have no effect on the properties of the beam. Its deflection curve is identical with that of the solid beam.

Figure 16 illustrates the application of these principles in machine design. This cross supporting beam must be removable for functional reasons, yet when in place must be very rigid. By fixing the ends of the beam into the side members, the beam will be 4 to 5 times as rigid as it would be if simply supported; yet this means a very rigid end connection. A mechanical joint at this point of high bending moment would be very cumbersome.

By welding the ends directly to the sides of the frame, as in Figure 17, and making a service joint at each point of inflection, only a single bolt at each point is required to hold this section in place. The main shear load is taken by the small clip welded to the bottom of the cantilever section of the beam. This type of construction gives the same results as a continuous beam welded directly to the sides of the base without any removable feature.

Another practical application of this principle is in the design of a rectangular steam chest, Figure 18. Instead of using four flat plates joined at the corners by welding, it was decided to form the corners on the two end plates in a press brake and thereby eliminate welding at the corners. This places the welds farther back from the corner and they become groove butt welds. Perhaps the simplest design would have been to make the entire frame from just two plates, each with two bends. This would have necessitated just two groove butt welds.

The rectangular section with uniform pressure applied inside becomes a frame, uniformly loaded. The moment diagram of this frame is shown. Notice in this case that the maximum bending moment is at the corners. This means any corner weld would be subjected to the maximum bending stress which would vary from zero to maximum every time the unit was operated and pressure applied. Corner welds would be flexed (tending to open up) as the pressure varied.

The final location of the welds is at the point of inflection, i.e. where the bending moment is zero (see the moment diagram) and at which point there is no flexing; even though the pressure fluctuates, the weld remains perfectly straight. This would be the ideal point to locate the weld in this type of structure, especially since it is a type of fatigue loading because the pressure varies as the unit is operated.

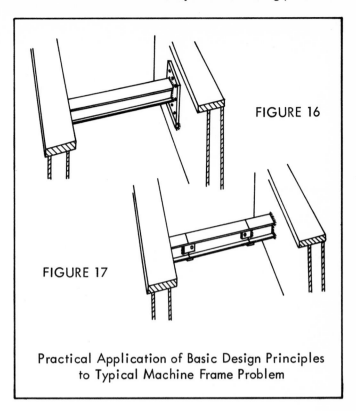

FIGURE 16

FIGURE 17

Practical Application of Basic Design Principles to Typical Machine Frame Problem

Welding This Steam Chest at Points of Inflection And Not at Corners Eliminates Flexing Problem

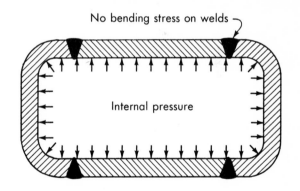

No bending stress on welds

Internal pressure

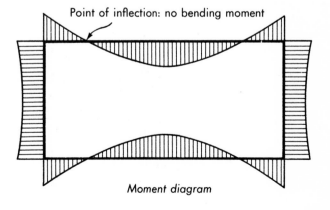

Point of inflection: no bending moment

Moment diagram

FIGURE 18

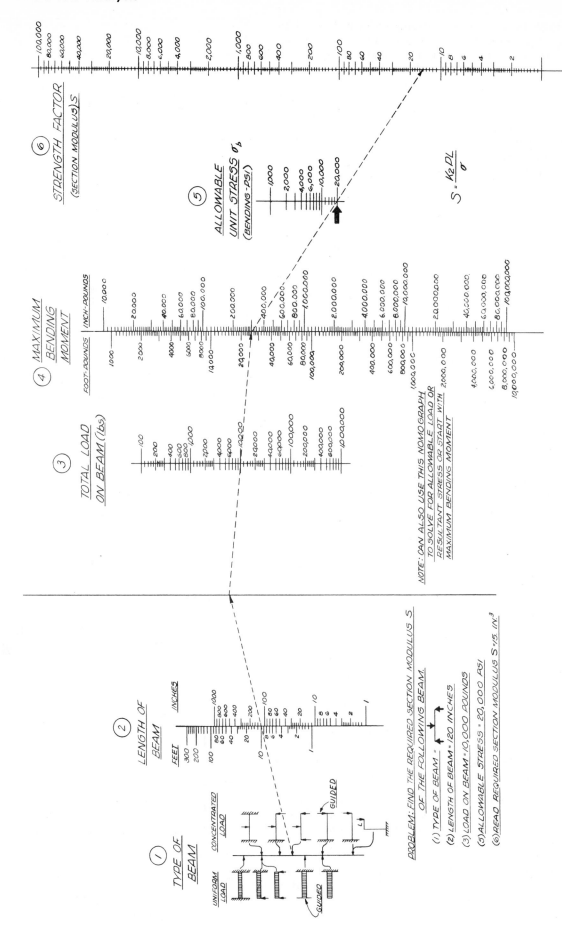

FIGURE 19 – REQUIRED SECTION MODULUS OF BEAM UNDER BENDING LOAD
(Strength Nomograph)

4. QUICK METHOD FOR FINDING REQUIRED SECTION MODULUS (STRENGTH) OR MOMENT OF INERTIA (STIFFNESS)

To aid in designing members for bending loads, the following two nomographs have been constructed. The first nomograph determines the required strength of a straight beam. The second nomograph determines the required stiffness of the beam.

In both nomographs several types of beams are included for concentrated loads as well as uniform loads. The length of the beam is shown both in inches and in feet, the load in pounds. In the first nomograph (Fig. 19) an allowable bending stress (σ_b) is shown and the strength property of the beam is read as section modulus (S). In the second nomograph (Fig. 20) an allowable unit deflection (Δ/L) is shown. This is the resulting deflection of the beam divided by the length of the beam. The stiffness property of the beam is read as moment of inertia (I).

By using these nomographs the designer can quickly find the required section modulus (strength) or moment of inertia (stiffness) of the beam. He can then refer to a steel handbook to choose a steel section that will meet these requirements.

If he wishes to fabricate the section from welded steel, he may use any of the methods for building up a steel section having the required values of section modulus or moment of inertia discussed in Properties of Sections.

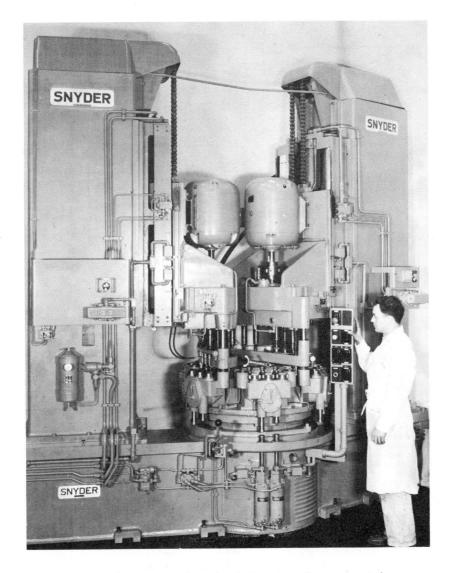

Steel Weldments speed up the delivery cycle on special-purpose machines, while ensuring maximum rigidity and dimensional stability.

FIGURE 20 – REQUIRED MOMENT OF INERTIA OF BEAM UNDER BENDING LOAD
(Stiffness Nomograph)

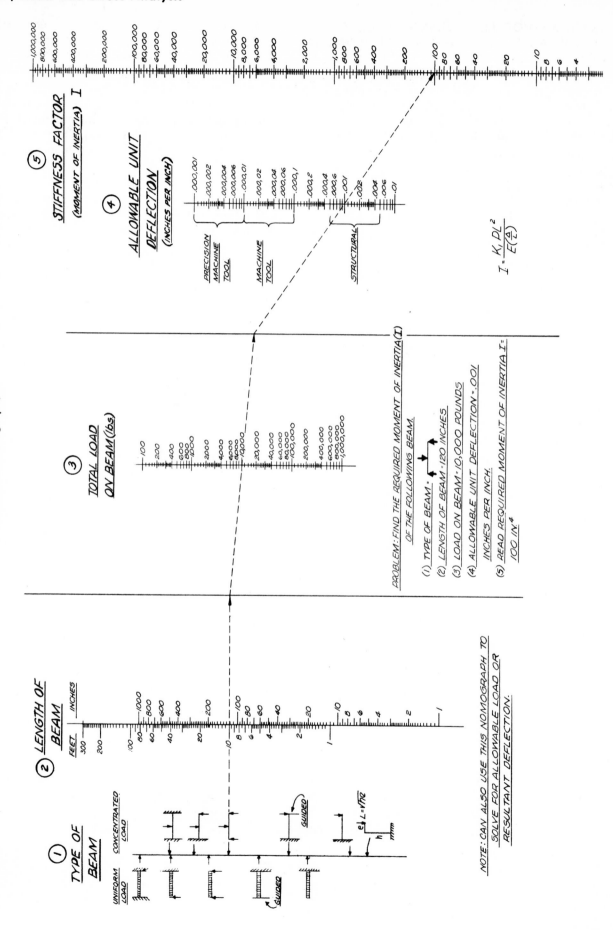

Analysis of Combined Stresses

1. CONCEPT OF CUBICAL UNIT

Machine members are often subjected to combined loading, such as axial tension and transverse bending. These external forces induce internal stresses as forces of resistance. Even without combined loading, there may be combined stress at points within the member.

The analysis of combined stresses is based on the concept of a cubic unit taken at any point of intersection of three planes perpendicular to each other. The total forces in play against these planes result in proportionate forces of the same nature acting against faces of the cube, tending to hold it in equilibrium. Since any member is made up of a multitude of such cubes, the analysis of stresses at a critical point is the key to analysis of the member's resistance to combined external forces.

2. COMBINING STRESSES

Biaxial and triaxial stresses are tensile and compressive stresses combined together.

Combined stresses are tensile and compressive stresses combined with shear stresses.

Principal planes are planes of no shear stress.

Principal stresses are normal stresses (tensile or compressive) acting on these principal planes. These are the greatest and smallest of all the normal stresses in the element.

Normal stresses, either tensile or compressive, act normal or at right angles to their reference planes. Shear stresses act parallel to their reference planes.

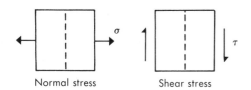

Normal stress   Shear stress

FIGURE 1

These stresses may be represented graphically on Mohr's circle of stress. By locating the points

(σ_3, τ_1) and (σ_2, τ_1) on a graph, Figure 2, and drawing a circle through these two points, the other stresses at various planes may be determined.

By observation of Mohr's circle of stress, it is found that--

$$\tau_{max} = \frac{\sigma_3 - \sigma_2}{2} \qquad \ldots \ldots \ldots \ldots \ldots \ldots \ldots (1)$$

In this case, σ_3 and σ_2 are principal stresses σ_{3p} and σ_{2p} since they act on planes of zero shear stress.

Stress in Member   Mohr's Circle of Stress

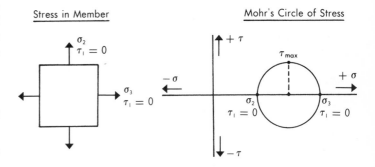

FIGURE 2

For any angle of rotation on Mohr's circle of stress, the corresponding planes on which these stresses act in the member rotate through just half this angle and in the same direction.

Notice in Figure 3, σ_2 lies at $+180°$ from σ_3 in Mohr's circle of stress, and the plane (b) on which σ_2 acts in the member lies at $+90°$ from the plane (a) on which σ_3 acts.

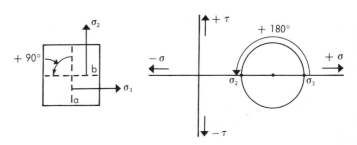

FIGURE 3

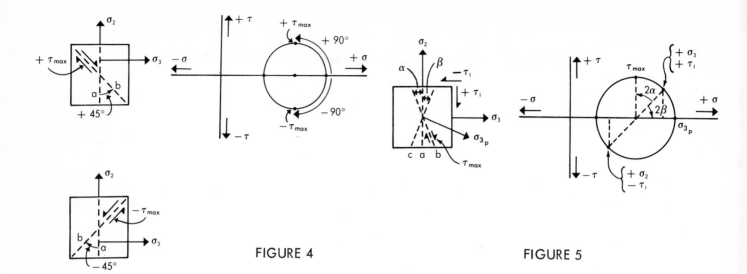

FIGURE 4

FIGURE 5

Notice in Figure 4, τ_{max} lies at $+90°$ from σ_3 and the plane (b) on which τ_{max} acts in the member lies at $+45°$ from the plane (a) on which σ_3 acts. In this case σ_2 and σ_3 are principal stresses because there is no applied shear on these planes.

This is a simple method to graphically show how stresses within a member combine; see Figure 5. On the graph, right, locate the two stress points $(+\sigma_3, +\tau_1)$ and $(+\sigma_2, -\tau_1)$ and draw a circle through these points. Now determine maximum normal and shear stresses.

By observation of Mohr's circle of stress, it is found that--

$$\sigma_{3p} \text{ (max)} = \frac{\sigma_3 + \sigma_2}{2} + \sqrt{\left(\frac{\sigma_3 - \sigma_2}{2}\right)^2 + \tau_1^2} \quad \ldots\ldots\ldots(2)$$

$$\tau_{max} = \sqrt{\left(\frac{\sigma_3 - \sigma_2}{2}\right)^2 + \tau_1^2} \quad \ldots\ldots\ldots\ldots\ldots\ldots(3)$$

The above formula for the maximum shear

stress (τ_{max}) is true for the flat plane considered; however, there are really two other planes not yet considered and their maximum shear stress could possibly be greater than this value.

This is a very common mistake among engineers. To be absolutely sure, when dealing with biaxial stresses, always let the third normal stress be zero instead of ignoring it, and treat the problem as a triaxial stress problem.

The example in Figure 2 will now be reworked, Figure 6, and the third normal stress (σ_1) will be set equal to zero.

On graph, right: Locate stress points (σ_1), (σ_2), (σ_3) and draw three circles through these points. Now determine the three maximum shear stresses.

There are three values for the maximum shear stress, each equal to half of the difference between two principal (normal) stresses. The plane of maximum shear stress (shaded in the following sketches) is always at $45°$ to the planes of principal stress.

Here, left:

$\sigma_3 = +12,000 \text{ psi} \qquad \tau_3 = 0$

$\sigma_2 = + 8,000 \text{ psi} \qquad \tau_2 = 0$

$\sigma_1 = 0 \qquad\qquad\qquad \tau_1 = 0$

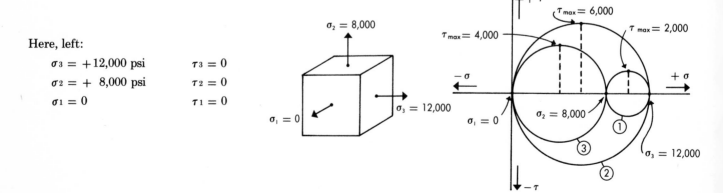

FIGURE 6

Circle 1

$$\tau_{max} = \frac{\sigma_3 - \sigma_2}{2}$$

$$= \frac{12,000-8,000}{2}$$

$$= 2,000 \text{ psi}$$

Circle 2

$$\tau_{max} = \frac{\sigma_3 - \sigma_1}{2}$$

$$= \frac{12,000-0}{2}$$

$$= 6,000 \text{ psi}$$

Circle 3

$$\tau_{max} = \frac{\sigma_2 - \sigma_1}{2}$$

$$= \frac{8,000-0}{2}$$

$$= 4,000 \text{ psi}$$

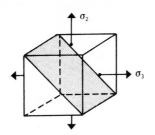

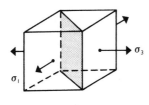

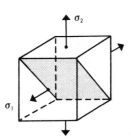

It is seen that, in this example, the maximum shear stress is 6,000 psi, and not the 2,000 psi value that would usually be found from the conventional formulas for biaxial stress.

3. TRIAXIAL STRESS COMBINED WITH SHEAR STRESS

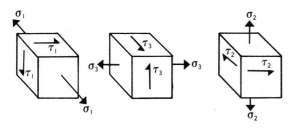

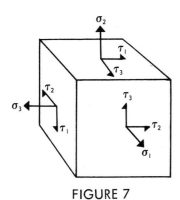

FIGURE 7

The three principal stresses (σ_{1p}, σ_{2p}, σ_{3p}) are given by the three roots (σ_p) of this cubic equation:

$$\sigma_p{}^3 - (\sigma_1 + \sigma_2 + \sigma_3)\sigma_p{}^2$$
$$+ (\sigma_1\sigma_2 + \sigma_2\sigma_3 + \sigma_1\sigma_3 - \tau_1{}^2 - \tau_2{}^2 - \tau_3{}^2)\sigma_p$$
$$- (\sigma_1\sigma_2\sigma_3 + 2\tau_1\tau_2\tau_3 - \sigma_1\tau_1{}^2 - \sigma_2\tau_2{}^2 - \sigma_3\tau_3{}^2) = 0 \quad (4)$$

For maximum shear stress, use the two principal stresses (σ_p) whose algebraic difference is the greatest. The maximum shear stress (τ_{max}) is equal to half of this difference.

*Since a, b, and c are coefficients of this equation:

$$a = -(\sigma_1 + \sigma_2 + \sigma_3)$$
$$b = \sigma_1\sigma_2 + \sigma_2\sigma_3 + \sigma_1\sigma_3 - \tau_1{}^2 - \tau_2{}^2 - \tau_3{}^2$$
$$c = \sigma_1\tau_1{}^2 + \sigma_2\tau_2{}^2 + \sigma_3\tau_3{}^2 - \sigma_1\sigma_2\sigma_3 - 2\tau_1\tau_2\tau_3$$

Let $N = \dfrac{b}{3} - \left(\dfrac{a}{3}\right)^2$

and $Q = \dfrac{c}{2} - \dfrac{ab}{6} + \left(\dfrac{a}{3}\right)^3$

Then calculate —

$$K = \frac{N^3}{Q^2} \text{ as a test ratio.}$$

Case 1

When $(1 + K)$ is positive (one real root) or when $(1 + K)$ is zero (three real roots, two of which are equal)
calculate —

$$S = \sqrt[3]{Q[1 + (1 + K)^{1/2}]}$$

and compute the root —

$$\sigma_{1p} = \frac{N}{S} - S - \frac{a}{3}$$

Case 2

When $(1 + K)$ is negative (three real and unequal roots)
calculate--

$$T = \sqrt{-K}$$

and compute the root--

$$\sigma_{1p} = \mp\sqrt{-3N}\left(\frac{T + 0.386}{T + 0.2}\right) - \frac{a}{3}$$

The ambiguous sign is opposite to the sign of Q (approximate, but very accurate).

For either Case 1 or Case 2

The additional two roots (σ_{2p}, σ_{3p}) of the general cubic equation are calculated by solving for σ_p using the

*Solution of Cubic Equation from "Practical Solution of Cubic Equations", G. L. Sullivan, MACHINE DESIGN, Feb. 21, 1957.

exact quadratic:

$$\sigma_p^2 + (a + \sigma_{1p})\sigma_p - \frac{c}{\sigma_{1p}} = 0$$

$$\text{or } \sigma_p = \frac{-(a + \sigma_{1p}) \pm \sqrt{(a + \sigma_{1p})^2 + \dfrac{4c}{\sigma_{1p}}}}{2}$$

Problem 1

Determine the maximum normal and shear stress in this web section, Figure 8:

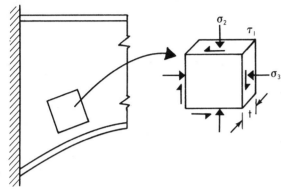

FIGURE 8

where:

$\sigma_1 = 0$	$\tau_1 = 11,000$ psi
$\sigma_2 = -13,650$ psi	$\tau_2 = 0$
$\sigma_3 = -14,500$ psi	$\tau_3 = 0$

Substituting these values into the general cubic equation:

$$\sigma_p^3 - (-13,650 - 14,500)\sigma_p^2 +$$
$$[(-13,650)(-14,500) - (11,000)^2]\sigma_p = 0$$
$$\sigma_p^2 + 28,150\,\sigma_p + 76,925,000 = 0$$

the three principal normal stresses are —

$$\sigma_{1p} = 0$$
$$\sigma_{2p} = -25,075 \text{ psi}$$
$$\sigma_{3p} = -3,075 \text{ psi}$$

and taking one-half of the greatest difference of two principal stresses:

$$\tau_{max} = \frac{25,075 - 0}{2} = \underline{12,535 \text{ psi}}$$

These various values are shown diagramed on Mohr's Circle of Stress, Figure 9.

4. STRENGTH UNDER COMBINED LOADING

A very convenient method of treating combined loadings is the interaction method. Here each type of load is expressed as a ratio of the actual load (P, M, T) to the ultimate load (P_u, M_u, T_u) which would cause failure if acting alone.

Axial load

$$R_a = \frac{P}{P_u}$$

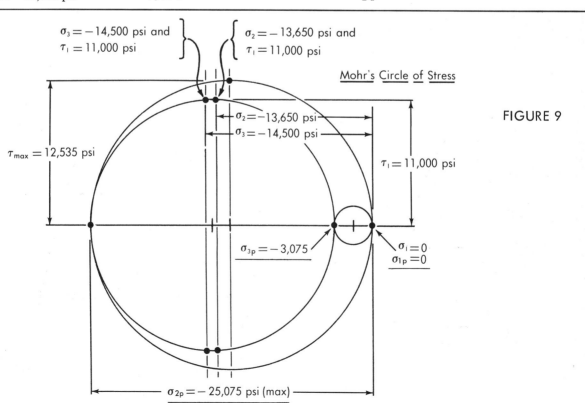

Mohr's Circle of Stress

$\sigma_3 = -14,500$ psi and $\tau_1 = 11,000$ psi

$\sigma_2 = -13,650$ psi and $\tau_1 = 11,000$ psi

$\sigma_2 = -13,650$ psi

$\sigma_3 = -14,500$ psi

$\tau_1 = 11,000$ psi

$\tau_{max} = 12,535$ psi

$\sigma_{3p} = -3,075$

$\sigma_1 = 0$
$\sigma_{1p} = 0$

$\sigma_{2p} = -25,075$ psi (max)

FIGURE 9

Bending load

$$R_b = \frac{M}{M_u}$$

Torsional load

$$R_t = \frac{T}{T_u}$$

In the general example shown in Figure 10, the effect of two types of loads (x) and (y) upon each other is illustrated.

The value of $R_y = 1$ at the upper end of the vertical axis is the ultimate value for this type of load on the member. The value $R_x = 1$ at the extreme right end of the horizontal axis is the ultimate value for this type of load on the member. These values are determined by experiment; or when this data is not available, suitable calculations may be made to estimate them.

The interaction curve is usually determined by actual testing of members under various combined-load conditions, and from this a simple formula is derived to express this relationship.

If points $\underline{a}$ and $\underline{b}$ are the ratios produced by the actual loads, point $\underline{c}$ represents the combination of these conditions, and the margin of safety is indicated by how close point $\underline{c}$ lies to the inter-action curve. A suitable factor of safety is then applied to these values.

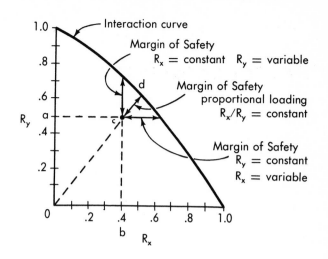

FIGURE 10

Combined axial compression and bending

In this case, the axial compression will cause additional deflection, which in turn increases the moment of the bending load. This increase can easily be taken care of by an amplification factor (k). See Figures 13 and 14.

Combined bending and torsion

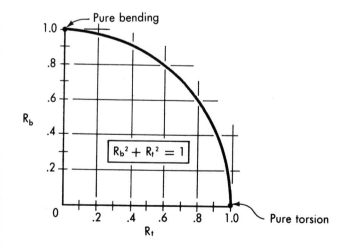

FIGURE 11

Combined axial loading and torsion

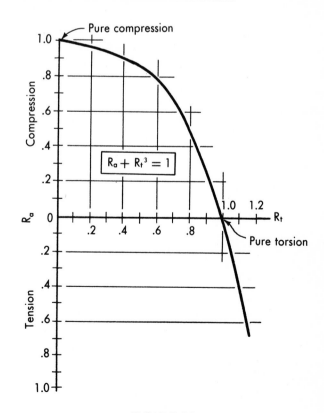

FIGURE 12

For sinusoidal initial bending moment curve

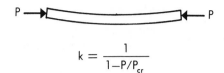

$$k = \frac{1}{1 - P/P_{cr}}$$

FIGURE 13

For constant bending moment

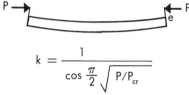

$$k = \frac{1}{\cos \frac{\pi}{2} \sqrt{P/P_{cr}}}$$

FIGURE 14

Here:

$$P_{cr} = \frac{\pi^2 E I}{L^2}$$

The bending moment applied to the member (chosen at the cross-section where it is maximum)

is then multiplied by this amplification factor (k), and this value is then used as the applied moment (M) in the ratio:

$$R_b = \frac{M}{M_u}$$

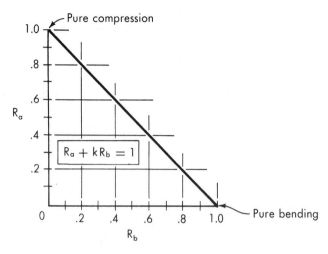

FIGURE 15

The chart in Figure 16 is used to determine the amplification factor (k) for the bending moment applied to a beam when it is also subject to axial

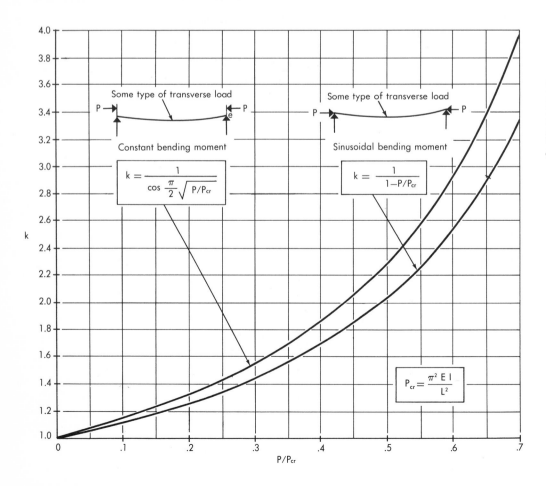

Fig. 16 Amplification factor (k) for bending moment on beam also subject to axial compression.

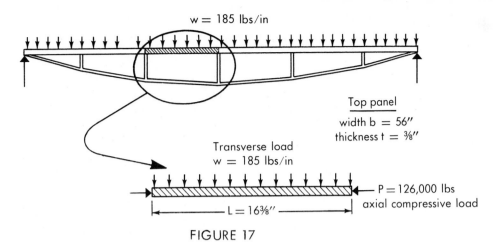

FIGURE 17

compression.

The resulting combined stress is found from the following formula:

$$\sigma = \frac{P}{A} \pm \frac{k\,M\,c}{I}$$

Problem 2

A loading platform is made of a 3/8" top plate and a 10-gage bottom sheet. The whole structure is in the form of a truss, Figure 17.

Determination of combined stress (axial compression and bending) in top compression panel:

With L = 16⅜"

A = 21 in.²

I = .247 in.⁴

First the critical load —

$$P_{cr} = \frac{\pi^2 E\,I}{L^2}$$

$$= \frac{\pi^2\,(30 \times 10^6)\,(.247)}{(16\frac{3}{8})^2}$$

$$= 272{,}000 \text{ lbs}$$

Then the ratio —

$$P/P_{cr} = \frac{126{,}000}{272{,}000}$$

$$= .464$$

The bending moment —

$$M = \frac{w\,L^2}{8}$$

$$= \frac{(185)\,(16\frac{3}{8})^2}{8}$$

$$= 6200 \text{ in.-lbs}$$

Obtaining the amplification factor (k) for the sinusoidal bending moment from the curve, Figure 16—

k = 1.87

The actual applied moment due to extra deflection is found to be—

k M = (1.87)(6200)

= 11,600 in.-lbs

The resulting combined stress formula being—

$$\sigma = \frac{P}{A} \pm \frac{k\,M\,c}{I}$$

of which there are two components:

(a) the compressive stress above the neutral axis of the top panel being—

$$\sigma_c = \frac{126{,}000}{21} + \frac{11{,}600\,(\frac{3}{16})}{.247}$$

$$= \underline{14{,}800 \text{ psi}}$$

(b) and the tensile stress below the neutral axis of the top panel being—

$$\sigma_t = \frac{126{,}000}{21} - \frac{11{,}600\,(\frac{3}{16})}{.247}$$

$$= \underline{2{,}800 \text{ psi}}$$

Determination of factor of safety:

The ultimate load values for this member in compression alone and in bending alone are unknown, so the following are used.

For compression alone—

*Since $\frac{L}{r} = 150$ (where r = radius of gyration)

assume $P_u = P_{cr} = 272{,}000$ lbs

*This L/r ratio of 150 is high enough so we can assume the ultimate load carrying capacity of the column (P_{cr}) is about equal to the critical value (P_{cr}). If this had been an ex-   tremely short column (very low L/r ratio), the critical value (P_{cr}) could be quite a bit higher than the actual ultimate value (P_u).

For <u>bending</u> alone--

The plastic or ultimate bending moment is--

$$M_u = \left(b\sigma_y \frac{t}{2}\right)\frac{t}{2} = \frac{b\,t^2\sigma_y}{4}$$

$$= \frac{(56)\,(\%)^2\,(33,000)}{4}$$

$$= 64,900 \text{ in.-lbs}$$

These ultimate values are represented on the following interaction curve, Figure 19. Plotting the present load values at a against the curve, indicates there is about a <u>2:1 factor of safety</u> before the top compression panel will buckle.

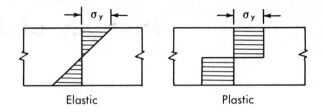

Elastic   Plastic

FIGURE 18

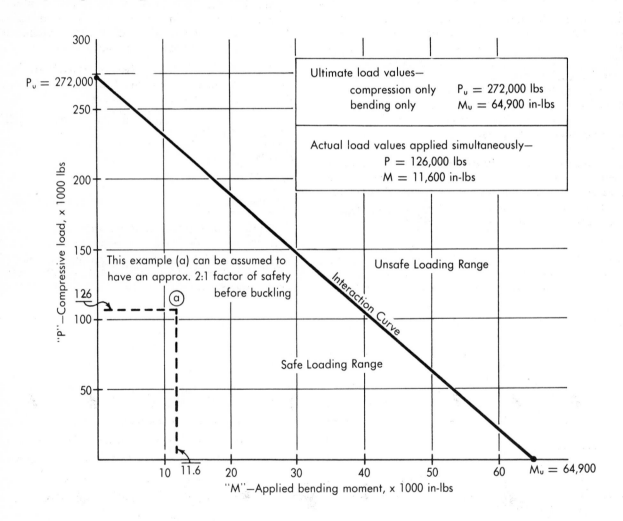

Ultimate load values—
compression only P_u = 272,000 lbs
bending only M_u = 64,900 in-lbs

Actual load values applied simultaneously—
P = 126,000 lbs
M = 11,600 in-lbs

This example (a) can be assumed to have an approx. 2:1 factor of safety before buckling

Unsafe Loading Range

Interaction Curve

Safe Loading Range

"P"—Compressive load, x 1000 lbs

"M"—Applied bending moment, x 1000 in-lbs

P_u = 272,000

126

M_u = 64,900

Fig. 19   Interaction curve for Problem 2.

Strength of Curved Beams

1. BEHAVIOR OF NEUTRAL AXIS

As a beam becomes curved, the neutral axis shifts in toward the inner face of the beam. See Figure 1. This shift of the axis greatly increases the stress on the inner face. The smaller the radius of curvature, the greater is the error in the straight beam formulas. If the radius of curvature is more than 10 times the depth of the beam, this error is not serious; but below this ratio, curved beam formulas must be used.

The major step in determining the strength of a curved beam is determining the shift (e) of the neutral axis away from the center of gravity. After this value has been found, the bending stress can be easily determined.

The simplest method is to divide the cross-section of the curved beam into individual rectangular areas and treat each area or element separately. All measurements of radius are taken from the center of curvature of the beam. See Figure 2. For each of these elements it is necessary to know the following: cross-sectional area (A), width (b), radius of inner face (r_i), mean radius (r_m), and radius to the outer face (r_o).

The radius of the center of gravity (r_g) equals the sum of all the moments taken about the center of gravity divided by the total area. The moment of each area about the center of gravity equals the product of cross-sectional area (A) and the mean radius (r_m). Thus, the radius of the center of gravity:

$$r_g = \frac{\Sigma(A\, r_m)}{\Sigma A} \quad \dots\dots\dots\dots\dots\dots\dots\dots(1)$$

The radius of the neutral axis (r_n) equals the total area divided by the sum of the individual products, width of area (b) times the log to the base e ($\log_e$) of the ratio of the outer radius (r_o) to the inner radius (r_i).

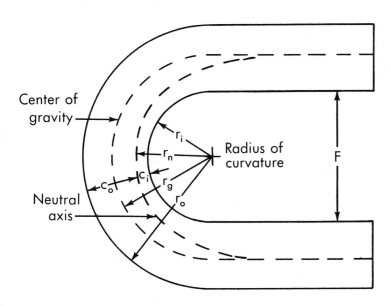

where:

A = area of cross-section

e = shift of neutral axis from C.G. = $r_g - r_n$

r_n = radius neutral axis from center of curvature

c_o = distance outer fiber to neutral axis = $r_o - r_n$

c_i = distance inner fiber to neutral axis = $r_n - r_i$

r_g = radius center of gravity from center of curvature

d = distance line of force to neutral axis of section

Fig. 1   Shift of neutral axis increases stress on inner face.

Thus, the radius of the neutral axis:

$$r_n = \frac{\Sigma A}{\Sigma\left(b \log_e \dfrac{r_o}{r_i}\right)} \quad \dotfill (2)$$

or:

$$r_n = \frac{\Sigma A}{\Sigma\left(2.3026\, b \log_{10} \dfrac{r_o}{r_i}\right)}$$

Log$_e$ of Formula 2 is not the familiar log to the base 10 but is the Natural or Naperian Log. If a table of the Natural or Naperian Log is not available, use $\log_e x = 2.3026 \log_{10} x$.

2. CURVED BEAM FORMULAS

The formulas shown below are for curved beams. They give the internal stress on both the inner face of the beam (σ_i) and the outer face of the beam (σ_o) due to bending. The stress at either face is tension or compression according to the sign of the bending moment. There is still a uniform tensile stress, or compressive stress, (σ_a) acting across the same section of the beam due only to the external load. If this is tensile, it must be added to the tensile stress due to bending and subtracted from the compressive stress due to bending.

Bending stress on inside face

$$\sigma_i = \frac{M\,(r_n - r_i)}{A\,(r_g - r_n)\,r_i} = \frac{M\,c_i}{A\,e\,r_i} \quad \dotfill (3)$$

Bending stress on outside face

$$\sigma_o = \frac{M\,(r_o - r_n)}{A\,(r_g - r_n)\,r_o} = \frac{M\,c_o}{A\,e\,r_o} \quad \dotfill (4)$$

Axial stress on section

$$\sigma_a = \frac{F}{A} \quad \dotfill (5)$$

In order to get the moment applied to this cross-section, the force (F) is multiplied by the moment arm (d). The moment arm is measured from the shifted neutral axis, and not the center of gravity, of the section to the application of the force (F).

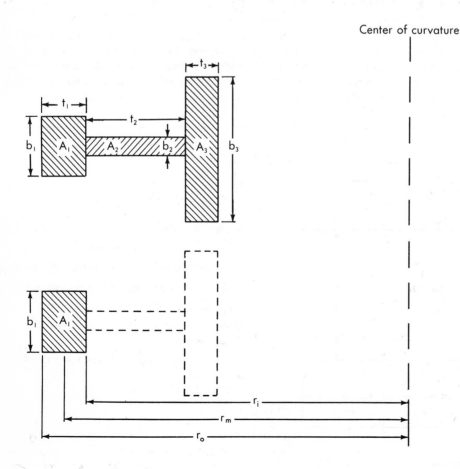

Center of curvature

Fig. 2 In solving curved beam problems, the beam cross-section commonly is divided into approximate rectangular areas.

Problem 1

Figure 3 shows the outer fiber stress on the outside and inside faces of five types of sections used for curved beams. All have the same cross-sectional area (1 sq in.); the same bending moment (200 in.-lbs acting 10" from the neutral axis of the section); and the same radius of curvature (3" from the center of gravity). The center of curvature can be assumed as located somewhere to the right of the section view. Also, the bending moment applied is tending to enlarge this radius of curvature.

The round section has the highest stress; this is for two reasons. First, it is not as deep as the other sections. Secondly, the inner face (right) and the outer face (left) have very little surface to take this maximum fiber stress.

The next section in the form of a rectangle is better because it is deeper (relative to the center of curvature) and therefore stronger. Even though this is an improvement over the round section, it does not proportion its stress equally between the high tensile stress on the inner face and the lower compressive stress on the outer face.

In the third section a flange is added on the inner face to lower this high tensile stress by spreading it out along more surface. Of course in doing this, since the area is held constant in these examples, the depth of the section is less and this will increase the stresses somewhat. However, the compressive stress and the tensile stress are almost equal, giving a good distribution of stress. Further, this section is very efficient as far as weight is concerned.

By adding a small flange on the outer compression side, in the fourth section the efficient distribution of stress is upset. The tensile stress on the inner face is much greater than the compressive stress on the outer face. This design should be discouraged.

The fifth section in the form of a trapezoid could be just as efficient as the third section using only a flange on the inner face. However, the trapezoid would be difficult to fabricate.

The ideal section for fabrication would be the third section using a web with a flange welded on the inner face. In many cases, two webs and a single flange on the inner face are used. If there is some concern about buckling under the compressive stresses at the outer face, a thin flange may be added across the open ends of the webs.

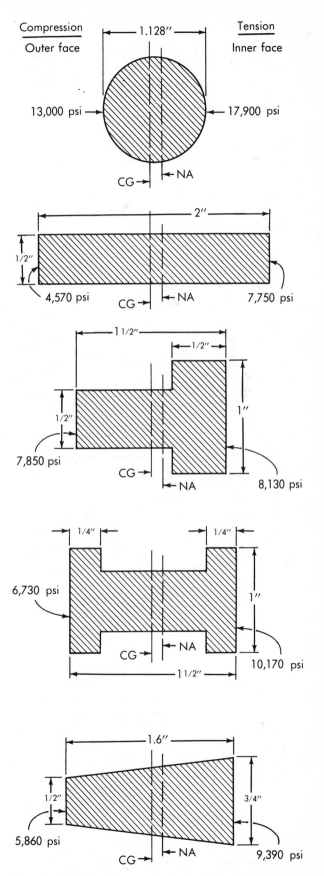

Fig. 3 Typical beam sections, all of same area.

Problem 2

A curved hook Figure 4, is to be designed for picking up 20-ton coils of steel strip. It is to be made of 1020 mild steel and designed within an allowable stress of 20,000 psi.

The main portion of the curved hook is flame-cut from 2½" thick plate. It is reinforced with two 1½" thick sections, welded together. The resultant section, as shown in Figure 5, is similar to the third section of Figure 3 and can be expected to similarly result in a good distribution of stresses about the neutral axis.

The design can be easily verified. From Figure 5:

$$r_i = 10''$$
$$r_o = 24'' \text{ (and for reinforcement 16'')}$$
$$\Sigma A = 2 (6 \times 1.5) + (14 \times 2.5)$$
$$= 53 \text{ in.}^2$$

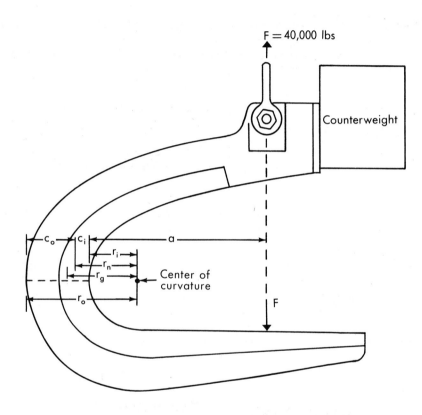

Fig. 4 Crane hook to be designed for lifting 20-ton steel coils.

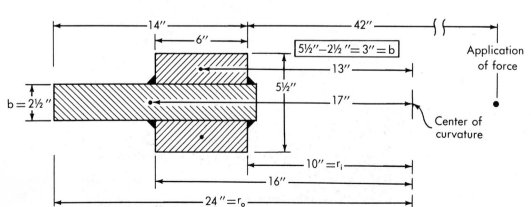

Fig. 5 Proposed hook section to be built up from flame-cut plates welded together.

The radius of the shifted neutral axis from center of curvature is--

$$r_n = \frac{\Sigma A}{\Sigma \left[b \, \log_e \left(\frac{r_o}{r_i} \right) \right]}$$

$$= \frac{(2.5 \times 14) + (3 \times 6)}{2.5 \log_e \frac{24}{10} + 3 \log_e \frac{16}{10}}$$

$$= \frac{35 + 18}{2.188 + 1.410} = \frac{53}{3.598}$$

$$= 14.72''$$

The radius of section's center of gravity from center of curvature is--

$$r_g = \frac{\Sigma(A \, r_m)}{\Sigma A}$$

$$= \frac{(35 \times 17) + (18 \times 13)}{35 + 18} = \frac{829}{53}$$

$$= 15.64''$$

Then:

$$e = r_g - r_n$$
$$= 15.64 - 14.72$$
$$= .92''$$

$$c_o = r_o - r_n$$
$$= 24 - 14.72$$
$$= 9.28''$$

$$c_i = r_n - r_i$$
$$= 14.72 - 10$$
$$= 4.72''$$

The uniform axial stress is--

$$\sigma_a = \frac{P}{A}$$

$$= \frac{40,000}{53}$$

$$= + 755 \text{ psi tension}$$

The bending stress at the inner face is--

$$\sigma_i = \frac{M \, c_i}{A \, e \, r_i}$$

$$= \frac{(40,000 \times 46.72) \, (4.72)}{(53) \quad (.92) \quad (10)}$$

$$= 18,100 \text{ psi tension}$$

The combined bending and axial stress at the inner face is--

$$\sigma_i + \sigma_a = 18,100 + 755$$

$$= + \underline{18,855} \text{ psi total tension}$$

The bending stress at the outer face is--

$$\sigma_o = \frac{M \, c_o}{A \, e \, r_o} = \frac{(40,000 \times 46.72) \, (9.28)}{(53) \, (.92) \, (24)} =$$

$$= 14,820 \text{ psi compression}$$

The combined bending and axial stress at the outer face is--

$$\sigma_o + \sigma_a = (-14,820) + 755$$

$$= - \underline{14,065} \text{ psi total compression}$$

Thus, the stress at neither the inner nor the outer face under a working load exceeds the allowable stress of 20,000 psi. Further, the stresses at the two faces are in fairly good balance. The finished crane hook is shown in Figure 6.

Fig. 6 Finished welded steel crane hook ready for the rugged job of moving 20-ton coils of strip steel.

Assembly floor of plant manufacturing C-frame presses of modern welded plate design. Analysis of stresses permits design for minimum total deflection, essential to smooth ram action and long die **life.**

Deflection by Bending

1. RIGIDITY DESIGN

Machinery members must frequently be very rigid. This is especially true in machine tools and other equipment where the usual amount of deflection would affect the quality of the end products, or would lower the life of a cutting tool.

In the past many machine designers were under the impression that zero deflection was both desirable and attainable. This goal is unrealistic since there must be strain where there is stress.

Where rigidity is important, the engineer should design for a certain allowable deflection. Such values are usually established on the basis of empirical data obtained from performance of similar previous designs.

Under a transverse bending load, the normally straight neutral axis of a beam becomes a curved line. The deflection of interest is the linear displacement of some point on the neutral axis along a path parallel to the line of applied force. Usually it is the maximum deflection that is of value on our computations, although occasionally the deflection at a specific point is needed.

Rigidity design formulas for use when bending loads are experienced, are based on the maximum deflection being--

$$\boxed{\Delta_{max} = k \frac{P L^3}{E I}} \dots\dots\dots\dots\dots\dots\dots(1)$$

Two of the components in this formula have been discussed previously in detail. The critical property of the material is its modulus of elasticity (E). In the case of all steels, this has the very high value of 30,000,000 psi. The related property of the sec-

tion is its moment of inertia (I), which is dependent on dimensions of the beam cross-section.

If the values for E and I are held constant, and the load (P) is a specified value, the length of the beam span (L) is one variable which will influence the deflection. The constant (k) is a function of the type of loading and also the manner in which the load is supported, and thus is subject to the designer's will. In practice "I" also is subject to the designer's will.

The several components of the basic formula are best handled by constructing a bending moment diagram from the actual beam, and then applying the appropriate standard simplified beam formula. These formulas are available in the Reference Section on Beam Diagrams included at the end of this book.

There are several methods for finding the deflection of a beam. Four of these will be shown:

1. Successive integration method

2. Virtual work method

3. Area moment method

4. Conjugate beam method

2. FUNDAMENTALS OF BEAM DEFLECTION

A transverse load placed on a beam causes bending moments along the length of the beam. These bending moments set up bending stresses (σ) across all sections of the beam. See Figure 1a, where at any given section:

$$\sigma_x = \frac{M_x c}{I_x}$$

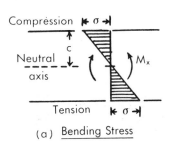

(a) Bending Stress

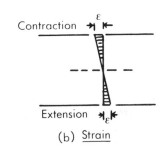

(b) Strain

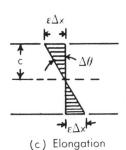

(c) Elongation

FIGURE 1

It is usually assumed that the bending stress (σ) is zero at the neutral axis and then increases linearly to a maximum at the outer fibers. One surface is under compression, while the other surface is under tension. Within the elastic limit, assuming a straight-line relationship between stress and strain, the distribution of bending stress can be converted over into a distribution of strain. Correspondingly, there would be no strain (ε) along the neutral axis and the strain would increase linearly to a maximum at the outer fiber. See Figure 1b where at any given section:

$$\varepsilon_x = \frac{\sigma_x}{E} = \frac{M_x c}{E I_x}$$

Considering a segment of the beam having only a very small increment in length (Δx), Figure 1c, the elongation within this small increment would be $\varepsilon(\Delta x)$. Also, here it can be seen that the small angular rotation ($\Delta\theta$) would be the elongation at the outer fiber divided by the distance (c) to the outer fiber from the neutral axis.

This can be expressed as--

$$\varepsilon(\Delta x) = c(\Delta\theta)$$

$$\therefore \quad \Delta\theta = \frac{\varepsilon(\Delta x)}{c} = \frac{M c(\Delta x)}{E I c}$$

$$\text{or: } (\Delta\theta)_x = \frac{M_x(\Delta x)}{E I_x}$$

In other words, the infinitesimal angle change in any section of the beam is equal to the area under the moment diagram ($M_x \Delta x$) divided by the ($E I_x$) of the section.

The angular rotation relative to stress and strain is further illustrated by Figure 2.

Figure 2a represents a straight beam under zero bending moment. Here any two given sections (a and b) would parallel each other and, in a stress-free condition, would then have a radius of curvature (R_x) equal to infinity (∞). These two sections (a and b) can be set close together to define the segment of very small increment in length (Δx).

At Figure 2b, the beam is subjected to a bending moment and this small segment (Δx) will compress on one side and will elongate on the other side where the outer fiber is in tension. This can be related to a small angular movement within this increment. It can be seen that sections a and b are no longer parallel but would converge at some point (0) in space, forming a radius of curvature (R_x).

In the sketch to the right of Figure 2b, dotted lines (a and b) represent the initial incremental segment (Δx) with zero moment, while the solid lines reflect the effect of applied load: $\Delta x(1 - \varepsilon)$ at the surface under compression.

The total angular change (θ) between any two points (a and b) of the beam equals the sum of the incremental changes, or:

$$\theta = \int_{x=a}^{x=b} (\Delta\theta)_x = \int_{x=a}^{x=b} \frac{M_x(\Delta x)}{E I_x} \quad \dots\dots\dots\dots\dots(2)$$

It is also observed from Figure 2b that--

$$(\Delta\theta)_x = \frac{\Delta x}{R_x} = \frac{M_x(\Delta x)}{E I_x}$$

and since —

$$(\Delta\theta)_x = \frac{M_x(\Delta x)}{E I_x}$$

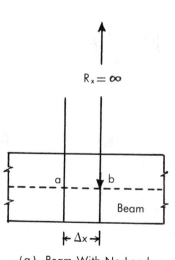

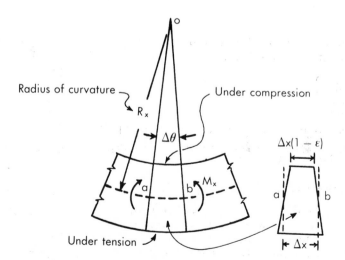

(a) Beam With No Load
(no moment)

(b) Beam Under Load
(with moment)

FIGURE 2

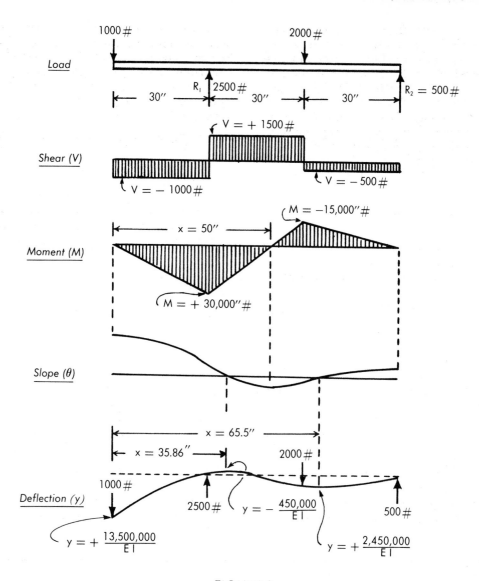

FIGURE 3

the reciprocal of the radius of curvature (1/R) at any given point (x) of the beam is--

$$\boxed{\frac{1}{R_x} = \frac{M_x}{E\,I_x}} \quad \dots\dots\dots\dots\dots\dots\dots\dots(3)$$

The next logical step would seem to be application of the Successive Integration Method to determine the beam deflection.

3. SUCCESSIVE INTEGRATION METHOD

For any given beam with any given load, if the load (w_x) at any point (x) can be expressed mathematically as a function of (x) and if such load condition is known for the entire beam, then:

load

$$\boxed{w_x = f_1(x)} \quad \dots\dots\dots\dots\dots\dots\dots(4)$$

and by successive integrations —

shear

$$\boxed{V_x = \int_{x_1}^{x_2} w_x\,(dx)} \quad \dots\dots\dots\dots\dots\dots(5)$$

moment

$$\boxed{M_x = \int_{x_1}^{x_2} V_x\,(dx)} \quad \dots\dots\dots\dots\dots\dots(6)$$

slope

$$\boxed{\theta_x = \int_{x_1}^{x_2} \frac{M_x\,(dx)}{E\,I_x}} \quad \dots\dots\dots\dots\dots(7)$$

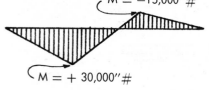

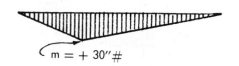

FIGURE 4

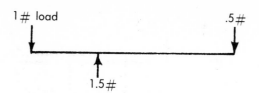

(a) Real Bending Moment (M)

(b) Virtual Bending Moment (m)

deflection

$$y_x = \int_{x_1}^{x_2} \frac{\theta_x (dx)}{E\,I_x} = \int\int_{x_1}^{x_2} \frac{M_x (dx)}{E\,I_x} \quad \dots\dots\dots\dots (8)$$

Unfortunately, it is usually difficult to get a mathematical expression for the load in terns of x for the entire length of the beam for any but the simplest of beam loadings. The method is cumbersome, especially if various loads are applied, if there are various types of support, or if there are various changes in section.

For every integration, there is a constant of integration (C) which must be solved. This is done by setting up known conditions of the beam; for example, the deflection of a beam over a support is zero, the slope of a beam at a fixed end is zero, etc.

This method means several equations must be used and integrated within certain limits of x, with considerable time expended and with the possibility of compounded error.

If possible, integrate graphically rather than mathematically, this process takes on greater importance. Most of the methods in actual use for computing deflection are based on a graphical solution of the problem.

Problem 1

The example in Figure 3 will be worked through

in several ways. In this case, the problem was previously worked out by longhand so it is known exactly what it looks like. Then several methods will be used in finding the deflection (y or Δ) under the conditions illustrated, to show that in each case the answer comes out the same:

$$y = \frac{13,500,000}{E\,I} \text{ inches}$$

4. VIRTUAL WORK METHOD

This is used frequently for finding the deflection of a point on a beam in any direction, caused by the beam load. A virtual load of one pound (or one kip) is placed on the beam at the point where the amount of deflection is desired and in the same direction.

Virtual bending moments (m) caused by the 1-lb load are determined along the entire length of the beam. The internal energy of the beam after deflecting is determined by integration. This is then set equal to the external energy of the 1-lb virtual load moving a distance (y) equal to the deflection.

$$1\# \cdot y = \int \frac{M_x\, m_x\, dx}{E\,I_x} \quad \dots\dots\dots\dots\dots\dots\dots (9)$$

where:

m = virtual bending moment at any point caused by the 1-1b load

M = real bending moment at the same point

I = moment of inertia at this same point

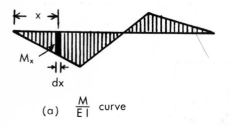

(a) $\frac{M}{EI}$ curve

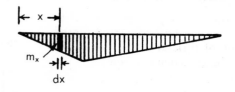

(b) m curve

FIGURE 5

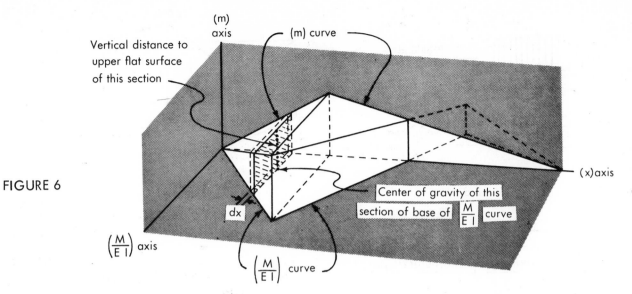

FIGURE 6

dx = length of small increment of the beam

E = modulus of elasticity in tension of the material

This equation can be worked out by calculus; however, its real value is that it lends itself to a graphical approach.

The first step is to apply all of the forces (Problem 1, Fig. 3) to the member, Figure 4a, and to compute the bending diagram—the real bending moment (M) on the beam. The next step is to remove the real load and replace it with a 1-lb load at the point where the deflection is desired and also in the same direction, Figure 4b. The bending moment of this particular load is then computed; this is known as the virtual bending moment (m).

The real moment diagram can be broken down into standard geometric areas; for example, triangles and rectangles for concentrated loads, and parabolas for uniformly distributed loads. The virtual moment diagram by the very nature of the single 1-lb concentrated force is always triangular in shape.

This means that the integration of these moment diagrams to obtain the internal energy may be replaced by working directly with these areas, since their properties are known. This will greatly simplify the work.

Figure 5 separates the two moment diagrams that must be combined in the basic equation #9.

It is seen from the equation that $M_x m_x dx$ is a segment of a volume.

In the triaxial representation, Figure 6, diagrams for both the real moment (M) divided by EI and the virtual moment (m) have a common base line (the x axis). The M/EI curve for the real bend-

ing moment lies flat in the horizontal plane. The m curve for the virtual bending moment is shown in the vertical plane established by the m axis and the x axis. The solid thus defined is a series of smaller volumes with simple geometric faces.

The volume of any element of this solid equals the area of the element's base surface multiplied by the vertical distance from the center of gravity of the base surface to the upper flat surface. This vertical distance is shown by a dotted line.

Thus, in Figure 7, with the M/EI and m diagrams lined up one above the other, it is necessary to know only the height of the virtual moment diagram at the same distance (x) as on the real moment diagram. The M/EI diagram is then divided into simple geometric shapes (in this case, right triangles), and the area of each is found and multiplied by the height of the m diagram along a line through the particular M/EI area's center of gravity.

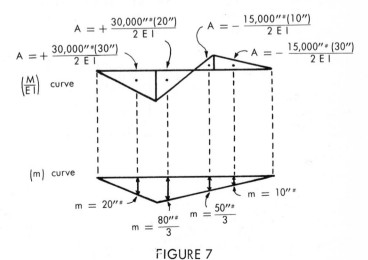

FIGURE 7

from which the volume is obtained:

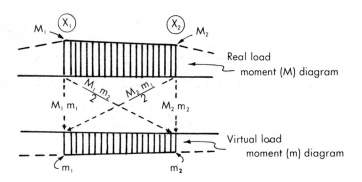

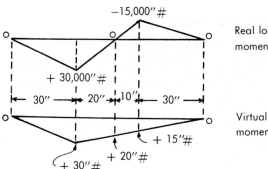

FIGURE 8

FIGURE 9

$$\text{Volume} = \frac{(30,000)(30)(20)}{2\,E\,I} + \frac{(30,000)(20)}{2\,E\,I}\left(\frac{80}{3}\right) -$$

$$\frac{(15,000)(10)}{2\,E\,I}\frac{50}{3} - \frac{(15,000)(30)(10)}{2\,E\,I}$$

$$= +\frac{13,500,000}{E\,I}$$

and since:

$$\text{Volume} = 1'' \cdot y$$

the deflection in inches is--

$$y = \frac{13,500,000}{E\,I}$$

The value of I can now be inserted in this to give the deflection (y) in inches. However, if the beam has a variable section, several values of I would have to be inserted earlier in the computation -- for the section taken through the center of gravity of each geometrical area of the M/EI diagram.

To simplify this further, a method of cross-multiplying has been found to give the same results. The general approach is illustrated by Figure 8, where some segment of the real moment (M) dia-

gram between points x_1 and x_2 is at the top and a corresponding segment of the virtual moment (m) diagram is below.

The required volume can be found directly by multiplying M_1 by m_1 and M_2 by m_2 and then by cross-multiplying M_1 by m_2 and M_2 by m_1 using only ½ of the products of cross-multiplication. This is more fully related to the basic integration equation by the following:

$$\int_{x=1}^{x=2} \frac{M\,m\,dx}{E\,I} = \frac{L}{3\,E\,I}\left(M_1 m_1 + M_2 m_2 + \frac{M_1 m_2}{2} + \frac{M_2 m_1}{2}\right)$$

where L = the distance between points x_1 and x_2.

Figure 9 shows application of this method to the original Problem 1.

From Figure 9:

$$y = \left(\frac{30}{3}\right)\left(\frac{30 \times 30,000}{E\,I}\right) + \left(\frac{20}{3}\right)\left(\frac{30 \times 30,000}{E\,I}\right) + \left(\frac{20}{3}\right)\left(\frac{20 \times 30,000}{2\,E\,I}\right) -$$

$$\left(\frac{10}{3}\right)\left(\frac{15 \times 15,000}{E\,I}\right) - \left(\frac{10}{3}\right)\left(\frac{20 \times 15,000}{2\,E\,I}\right) - \left(\frac{30}{3}\right)\left(\frac{15 \times 15,000}{E\,I}\right)$$

$$= \frac{13,500,000}{E\,I}$$

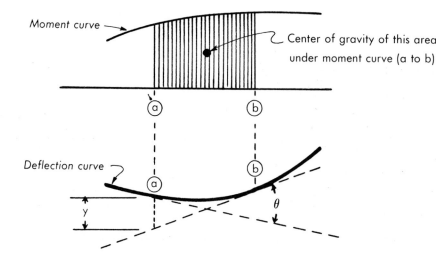

FIGURE 10

5. AREA MOMENT METHOD

This a very useful tool for engineers and is illustrated in Figure 10 by a general moment diagram and the corresponding deflection curve. Here points <u>a</u> and <u>b</u> represent any two points defining a simple geometric area of an actual moment diagram.

The two fundamental rules for use of this method are:

> The change in slope (radians) between two points (a and b) of a loaded beam equals the area under the moment curve, divided by E I, between these two points (a and b).

> The distance of point <u>a</u> of the beam to the tangent at point <u>b</u> of the beam equals the moment of the area under the moment diagram taken about point <u>a</u>, divided by E I.

For symmetrically loaded, simply supported beams this is a convenient method with which to find the maximum deflection of the beam, because in this case the slope of the beam is zero at the mid-span (b) and the distance from <u>a</u> to the tangent at <u>b</u> equals the maximum deflection we are seeking. See Figure 11.

From Figure 11:

$$y = \frac{1}{2}\left(\frac{M}{E\,I}\right)\left(\frac{L}{2}\right)\left(\frac{2}{3}\times\frac{L}{2}\right) = \frac{1}{2}\left(\frac{F\,L}{4\,E\,I}\right)\left(\frac{L}{2}\right)\left(\frac{L}{3}\right)$$

$$= \frac{F\,L^3}{48\,E\,I}$$

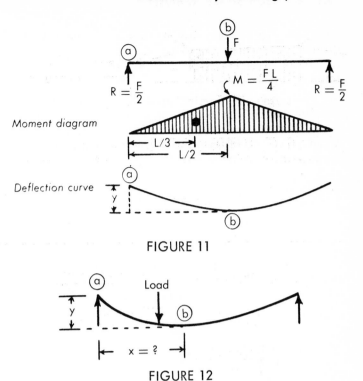

Moment diagram

Deflection curve

FIGURE 11

FIGURE 12

However, for an unsymmetrically loaded beam, the point of the beam having zero slope, or maximum deflection, is unknown (Fig. 12). There are ways of getting around this.

The conditions of Problem 1 are here illustrated by Figure 13. The moments of the area under the moment curve (from point zero to point 30) is taken about point zero to give the vertical distance between point zero and the tangent to the deflection curve at

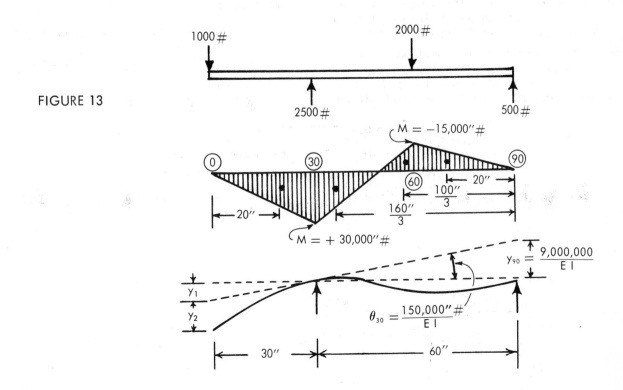

FIGURE 13

point 30. This becomes y_2. This is not the actual deflection, because the slope of the deflection curve at point 30 is not level. This slope is yet to be found.

First find the vertical distance between point 90 and the tangent to the deflection curve at point 30. To find this distance (y_{90}), take the moments, about point 90, of the area of the moment diagram from point 30 to point 90.

$$y_{90} = \frac{(30,000)(20)}{2\,E\,I}\left(\frac{160}{3}\right) - \frac{(15,000)(10)}{2\,E\,I}\left(\frac{100}{3}\right) - \frac{(15,000)(30)(20)}{2\,E\,I}$$

$$= \frac{9,000,000}{E\,I}$$

The angle of this tangent line to the horizon (θ_{30}) is then found by dividing this vertical distance (y_{90}) by the horizontal distance between point 30 and point 90.

$$\theta_{30} = \frac{y_{90}}{60''}$$

$$= \frac{9,000,000}{60\,E\,I}$$

$$= \frac{150,000}{E\,I}$$

This angle (θ_{30}) is the same to the left of point 30, Figure 14, and defines the vertical deflection (y_1) at point zero. This angle then, multiplied by the horizontal distance from point zero to point 30, gives the vertical displacement (y_1).

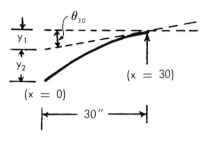

FIGURE 14

$$y_1 = \theta_{30}\,30 = \frac{150,000}{E\,I}\,30 = \frac{4,500,000}{E\,I}$$

Adding this to the initial displacement--

$$y_2 = \frac{(30,000)(30)(20)}{2\,E\,I} = \frac{9,000,000}{E\,I}$$

gives the total deflection at point zero of--

$$y = \frac{13,500,000}{E\,I}$$

6. CONJUGATE BEAM METHOD

In using this method, the bending moment diagram of the real beam is constructed. A substitutional beam or conjugate beam is then set up; the load on this is the moment of the real beam divided by the E I of the real beam; in other words it is loaded with the M/EI of the real beam.

TABLE 1 – COMPARATIVE CONDITIONS OF REAL AND CONJUGATE BEAMS

REAL BEAM	CONJUGATE BEAM
1. Simple supported ends a) zero deflection b) maximum slopes	1. Simply supported ends because – a) zero moment b) maximum shear
2. Fixed ends a) zero deflection b) zero slope	2. Free ends because – a) zero moment b) zero shear hence no support
3. Free ends a) a maximum deflection b) a maximum slope	3. Fixed ends because – a) a maximum moment b) a maximum shear hence a support
4. Interior supports of a continuous beam a) no deflection b) gradual change in slope	4. A hinge without support because – a) no moment b) gradual change in shear hence no support
5. Point of maximum deflection	5. Located at point of zero shear because this is a point of maximum moment
6. Either statically determinate or statically indeterminate	6. Always statically determinate

TABLE 2 – TYPICAL REAL BEAMS AND CORRESPONDING CONJUGATE BEAMS

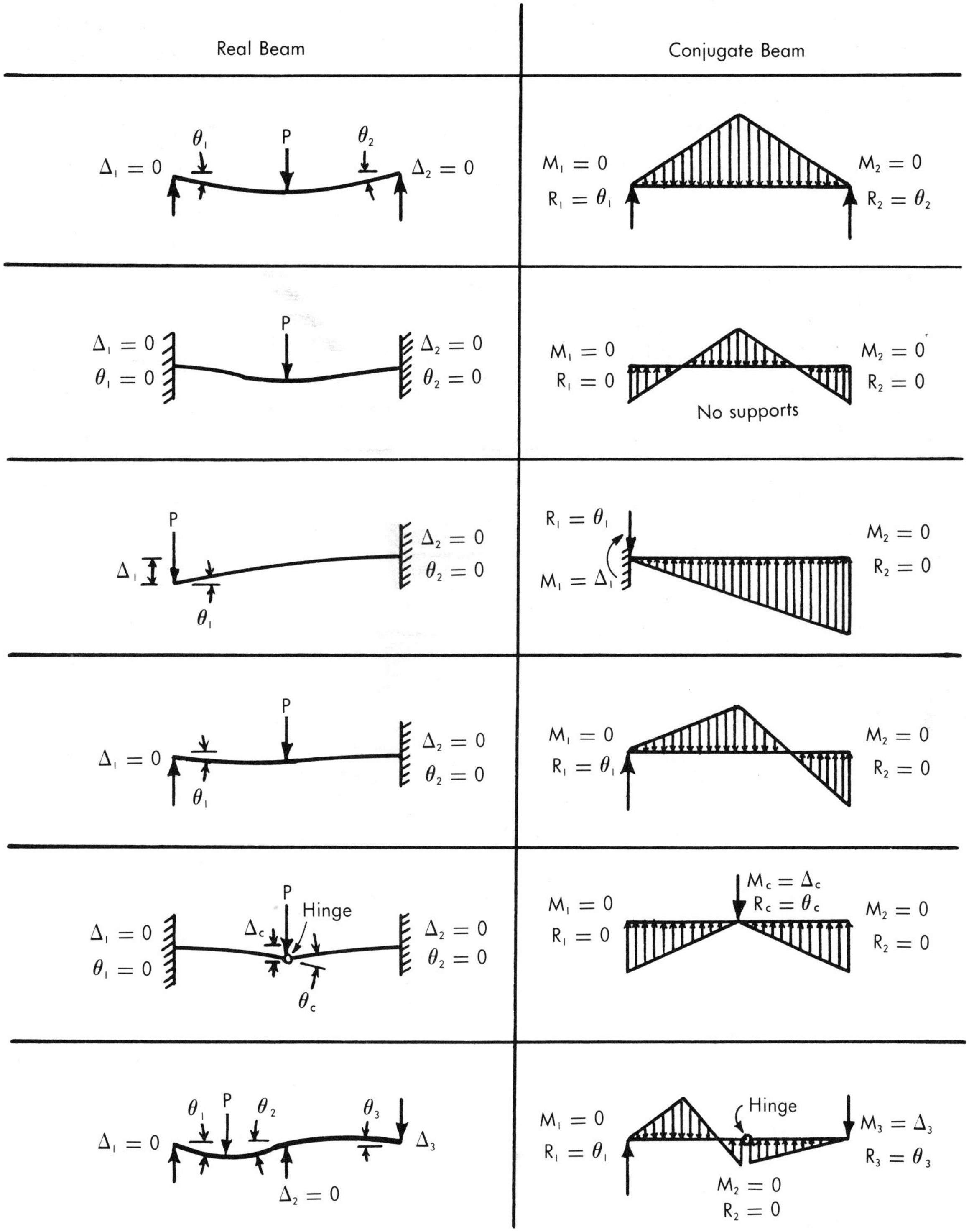

Real Beam	Conjugate Beam

Row 1:

$\Delta_1 = 0$ θ_1 P θ_2 $\Delta_2 = 0$

$M_1 = 0$ $M_2 = 0$

$R_1 = \theta_1$ $R_2 = \theta_2$

Row 2:

$\Delta_1 = 0$ P $\Delta_2 = 0$

$\theta_1 = 0$ $\theta_2 = 0$

$M_1 = 0$ $M_2 = 0$

$R_1 = 0$ $R_2 = 0$

No supports

Row 3:

P $\Delta_2 = 0$

Δ_1 $\theta_2 = 0$

θ_1

$R_1 = \theta_1$ $M_2 = 0$

$M_1 = \Delta_1$ $R_2 = 0$

Row 4:

P $\Delta_2 = 0$

$\Delta_1 = 0$ $\theta_2 = 0$

θ_1

$M_1 = 0$ $M_2 = 0$

$R_1 = \theta_1$ $R_2 = 0$

Row 5:

P   Hinge

$\Delta_1 = 0$ Δ_c $\Delta_2 = 0$

$\theta_1 = 0$ $\theta_2 = 0$

θ_c

$M_c = \Delta_c$

$R_c = \theta_c$

$M_1 = 0$ $M_2 = 0$

$R_1 = 0$ $R_2 = 0$

Row 6:

θ_1 P θ_2 θ_3

$\Delta_1 = 0$ Δ_3

$\Delta_2 = 0$

Hinge

$M_1 = 0$ $M_3 = \Delta_3$

$R_1 = \theta_1$ $R_3 = \theta_3$

$M_2 = 0$

$R_2 = 0$

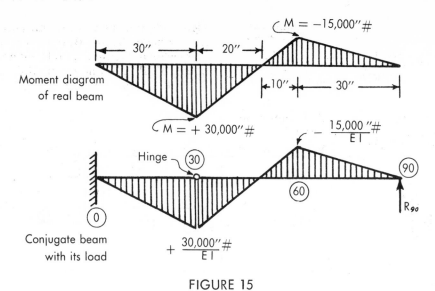

Moment diagram of real beam

$M = -15,000''\#$

$M = +30,000''\#$

Hinge

Conjugate beam with its load

$-\dfrac{15,000''\#}{E\,I}$

$+\dfrac{30,000''\#}{E\,I}$

FIGURE 15

Five conditions must be met:

1. The length of the conjugate beam equals the length of the real beam.

2. There are two equations of equilibrium--

*   The sum of forces acting in any one direction on the conjugate beam equals zero.

*   The sum of moments about any point of the conjugate beam equals zero.

3. The load at any point of the conjugate beam equals the moment of the real beam divided by the E I of the real beam at the same point. The real beam could have variable I.

4. The vertical shear at any point of the conjugate beam equals the slope of the real beam at the same point.

5. The bending moment at any point of the conjugate beam equals the deflection of the real beam at the same point.

The conjugate beam must be so supported that conditions 4 and 5 are satisfied. The above statements of condition may be reversed.

By knowing some of the conditions of the real

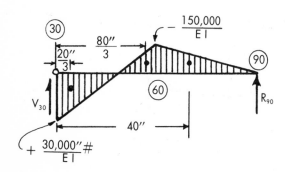

FIGURE 16

beam, it will be possible to reason the nature of the support of the conjugate beam. The comparative statements of Table 1 will help in setting up the conjugate beam.

Some examples of real beams and their corresponding conjugate beams are presented in Table 2. Notice that the support of the conjugate beam can be very unlike the support of the real beam.

The last example in Table 2 is similar to the Problem 1 beam to which several methods of solving deflection have already been applied. Here the conjugate beam is hinged at the point of second support of the real beam, and without this hinge the Conjugate Beam Method would not be workable.

The same Problem 1 is illustrated in Figure 15, where the real beam moment is first diagrammed. This is then divided by E I of the real beam for the load on the conjugate beam shown next.

To find the right hand reaction (R_{90}) take moments, about point 30, on the conjugate beam between points 30 and 90. See Figure 16.

Since:

$$\Sigma\,M_{30} = 0$$

$$\frac{1}{2}\left(\frac{+30,000}{E\,I}\right)(20)\left(\frac{20}{3}\right) + \frac{1}{2}\left(\frac{-15,000}{E\,I}\right)(10)\left(\frac{80}{3}\right) +$$

$$\frac{1}{2}\left(\frac{-15,000}{E\,I}\right)(30)(40) - R_{90}(60) = 0$$

$$\therefore R_{90} = -\frac{150,000 \text{ in.}^2 - \text{lbs}}{E\,I}$$

This negative sign means the reaction is directed opposite to our original assumption; hence it is directed downward.

Since the sum of vertical forces equals zero, V_{30} may be found:

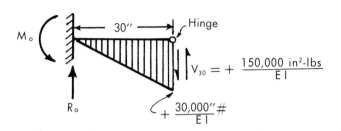

$$-V_{30} + \frac{1}{2}\left(\frac{+30,000}{EI}\right)(20) + \frac{1}{2}\left(\frac{-15,000}{EI}\right)(40) + \frac{\overbrace{150,000}^{\text{downward}}}{EI} = 0$$

assume upward⤹

$$\therefore V_{30} = + \frac{150,000 \text{ in.}^2\text{-lbs}}{EI}$$

This positive sign means original assumption was correct and shear is directed upward.

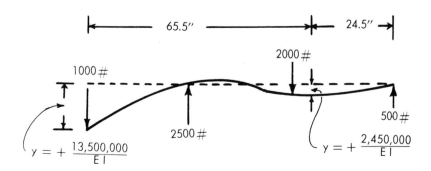

FIGURE 17

The left hand moment (M_o) of the conjugate beam may be found by taking moments of the isolated element, between points zero and 30. See Figure 17.

$$M_o = \frac{1}{2}\left(\frac{+30,000}{EI}\right)(30)(20) + \overbrace{\left(\frac{150,000}{EI}\right)}^{\substack{\text{directed downward} \\ V_{30}}}(30)$$

$$= + \frac{13,500,000 \text{ in.}^3\text{-lbs}}{EI}$$

The deflection of the real beam at point zero (y_o or Δ_{max}) equals the moment of the conjugate beam at this point (M_o); hence:

$$y_o = \frac{13,500,000}{EI} \text{ inches}$$

This would be the solution of this problem; however, to get the deflection at other points it would be necessary to continue this work and find the moment of the conjugate beam throughout its length.

The maximum deflection of the real beam on the

right side occurs at the same point as zero shear of the conjugate beam. By observation this would occur somewhere between points 60 and 90, and the distance of this point of maximum deflection from point 90 is set as x_1. See Figure 18.

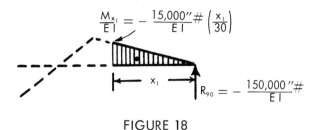

$$\frac{M_{x_1}}{EI} = -\frac{15,000''\#}{EI}\left(\frac{x_1}{30}\right)$$

$$R_{90} = -\frac{150,000''\#}{EI}$$

FIGURE 18

Since:

$$\Sigma V = 0$$

$$\frac{1}{2}\left(\frac{-15,000}{EI}\right)\left(\frac{x_1}{30}\right)x_1 + \frac{150,000}{EI} = 0$$

$$250 x_1^2 = 150,000$$

$$x_1^2 = 600$$

and:

$$x_1 = 24.5''$$

The moment of the conjugate beam at this point is —

$$M_x = \frac{1}{2}\left(\frac{-15,000}{EI}\right)\left(\frac{x_1}{30}\right)(x_1)\left(\frac{x_1}{3}\right) + \frac{150,000}{EI}x_1$$

$$= \frac{2,450,000}{EI}$$

and therefore the maximum deflection (y_{max} or Δ_{max}) of the real beam, Figure 19 —

$$y_{max} = \frac{2,450,000 \text{ in.}^3\text{-lbs}}{EI} \text{ inches}$$

7. DEFLECTION OF BEAMS WITH MULTIPLE SECTIONS

Sometimes the beam under consideration for deflection does not have a uniform cross-section. The area moment method for deflection is used as before,

FIGURE 19

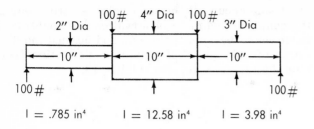

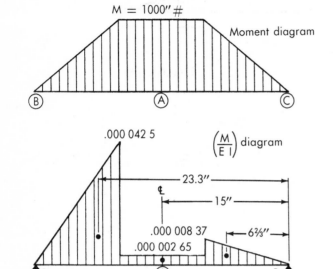

$I = .785 \, in^4$ $I = 12.58 \, in^4$ $I = 3.98 \, in^4$

$M = 1000'' \#$

Moment diagram

$\left(\dfrac{M}{E\,I}\right)$ diagram

Deflection curve

FIGURE 20

but the proper moment of inertia (I) for each section is used.

The weight of the shaft should be considered, although it is omitted in the following example:

Problem 2

The M/EI for the part of the shaft having a 2" dia has a maximum value of—

$$\frac{M}{E\,I} \text{ (max)} = \frac{1000}{(30,000,000)(.785)}$$
$$= .0000425$$

The M/EI across the part of the shaft having a 4" dia between the two concentrated loads, has a uniform value of—

$$\frac{M}{E\,I} = \frac{1000}{(30,000,000)(12.58)}$$
$$= .00000265$$

The M/EI across the part of the shaft having a 3" dia has a maximum value of—

$$\frac{M}{E\,I} \text{ (max)} = \frac{1000}{(30,000,000)(3.98)}$$
$$= .00000837$$

In constructing the conjugate beam, the bending moment on the real beam at each of several points is divided by the corresponding EI of the shaft. (See third diagram, Fig. 20.)

The point of maximum deflection (X) will not be at midspan, but must be found. This point is always where the slope of the real beam (θ) is zero, and is the same point where vertical shear (V) of the conjugate beam (M/EI diagram) is zero. See Table 1.

First find end reactions of the conjugate beam. To do this, take moments about C: This sum must equal zero:

$$\Sigma \, M_C = 0$$
$$= + R_B (30'') - \tfrac{1}{2}(10'')(.0000425)\,23.3''$$
$$- 10(.00000265)\,15''$$
$$- \tfrac{1}{2}(10'')(.00000837)\,6\tfrac{2}{3}'' = 0$$

$$R_B = \frac{.005636}{30}$$
$$= .000188$$

In similar manner, R_c is found to be .000055 although it is not needed in this case. These reaction values are then entered on the conjugate beam (first diagram, Fig. 21).

Now find the point on the conjugate beam where vertical shear is zero. At point D, the vertical shear is—

$$V_D = R_B - \text{the area of conjugate beam section between B and D}$$
$$= .000188 - \tfrac{1}{2} \cdot 10 \,(.0000425)$$
$$= -.0000245 \text{ (negative)}$$

We have passed the point of zero shear; therefore it occurs somewhere between B and D. Let X = distance to point of zero shear from point B. (See second diagram, Fig. 21).

Then:

$$V_X = .000188 - \tfrac{1}{2} X \frac{X\,(.0000425)}{10} = 0$$
$$= .000188 - .000002125 \, X^2 = 0$$

and

$$X^2 = \frac{.000188}{.000002125}$$
$$= 88.5$$

Thus:

$$X = 9.41''$$

So, at point X:

Shear	$V = 0$
Slope	$\theta = 0$
Deflection	$\Delta = $ maximum

The value of shear at other points on the conjugate beam can be found similarly. These are shown in the third view of Figure 21, where the shear diagram of the conjugate beam also equals the slope diagram of the real beam.

The deflection of the real beam at point X equals the vertical distance (h) of B from tangent of X, and also equals the moment about B of the area between B and X on the conjugate (M/EI) diagram.

Thus, where X = 9.41"

$$M_B = \frac{1}{2} \cdot 9.41 \left(\frac{9.41}{10}\right).0000425 \cdot \frac{2}{3} \cdot 9.41$$

$$= .001178''$$

$$\Delta_{max} = \underline{.001178''}$$

8. DEFLECTION OF BEAM WITH VARIABLE SECTION

The area moment method may be used very nicely to find the deflection of beams in which no portion of the beam has a constant moment of inertia.

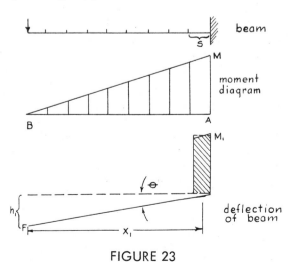

FIGURE 22

The angle between the tangents at A and B = θ = the area of the moment diagram between A and B, divided by EI.

Subdividing this beam into 10 or more segments of equal length (s):

FIGURE 23

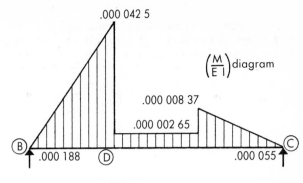

$\left(\frac{M}{EI}\right)$ diagram

.000 042 5

.000 008 37

.000 002 65

.000 188 (D) .000 055 (C)

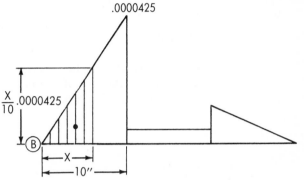

.0000425

$\frac{X}{10}$ .0000425

(B)

X

10"

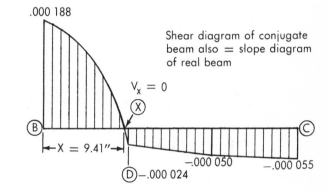

.000 188

Shear diagram of conjugate beam also = slope diagram of real beam

$V_x = 0$

(X)

(B)   X = 9.41"   (C)

−.000 050   −.000 055

(D)−.000 024

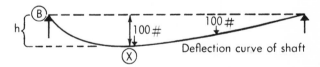

h   100#   100#

Deflection curve of shaft

(X)

FIGURE 21

Each segment of bending moment causes the beam in this segment to bend or rotate. The angle of bend θ = area of moment diagram of this segment divided by EI, or--

$$\theta_n = \frac{M_n s}{E I_n} \quad \dots\dots\dots\dots\dots\dots\dots\dots\dots(10)$$

The resultant vertical movement (h_n) of the load, at the left end of the beam, is —

$$h_n = \theta_n X_n = \frac{M_n s X_n}{E I_n} \quad \dots\dots\dots\dots\dots(11)$$

Each segment of the beam bends under its individual bending moment and its angle change causes the end of the beam to deflect.

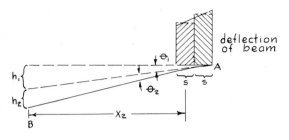

FIGURE 24

The total deflection at the end of the beam equals the sum of the deflections at the end of the beam caused by the angle change of each segment of the beam.

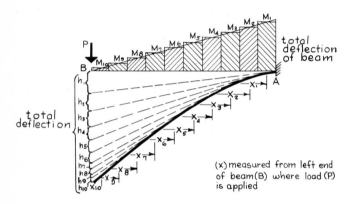

(x) measured from left end of beam (B) where load (P) is applied

FIGURE 25

Restating the preceding, the vertical deflection of B is--

$$\Delta = \Sigma \frac{M_n X_n s}{E I_n} \quad \dots \dots \dots \dots \dots \dots \dots (12)$$

or:

$$\Delta = \frac{s}{E} \Sigma \frac{M_n X_n}{I_n} \quad \dots \dots \dots \dots \dots \dots \dots (13)$$

Note: $\frac{M_n X_n}{I_n}$ is found for each segment. These values are added together, and this sum is multiplied by $\frac{s}{E}$ to give the total deflection.

Problem 3

Now assume the beam to be a solid bar, having a constant width of 1" and a variable depth of 2" at the outer ends and increasing uniformly to 6" at midspan. Find the maximum deflection, using the same loading as in previous problem.

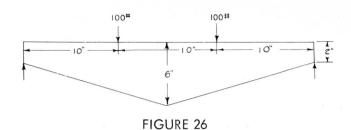

FIGURE 26

Divide the length of the beam into 12 equal segments. The greater the number of segments or divisions, the more accurate will be the answer. Normally 10 divisions would give a fairly accurate result.

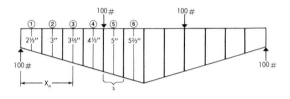

FIGURE 27

Here: $s = 2\frac{1}{2}"$

and $\Delta_{total} = \frac{s}{E} \Sigma \frac{M_n X_n}{I_n}$

The moment of inertia of each segment (I_n) is taken at the sectional centroid of the segment. Since the beam has a uniform width (b) of 1" and the depth (d_n) of each section is obtained by simple geometry, by substitution:

$$I_n = \frac{b\,d_n^3}{12}$$

Thus: $I_2 = \frac{1"\,(3)^3}{12} = 2.25$ in.^{4}

and similarly for other segments.

The formula components M_n, X_n, and I_n are easier to handle in table form:

Segment	I_n	X_n	Moment, M_n		$\dfrac{M_n X_n}{I_n}$
1	1.16	1¼"	100# × 1¼" =	125	134
2	2.25	3¾"	100# × 3¾" =	375	624
3	4.11	6¼"	100# × 6¼" =	625	950
4	6.78	8¾"	100# × 8¾" =	875	1130
5	10.40	11¼"	100# × 11¼" − 100# × 1¼" =	1000	1080
6	15.16	13¾"	100# × 13¾" − 100# × 3¾" =	1000	882
			Total = $\Sigma \dfrac{M_n X_n}{I_n}$ =		4800

Total vertical deflection —

$$\Delta_{total} = \frac{s}{E} \Sigma \frac{M_n X_n}{I_n}$$

$$= \frac{(2\frac{1}{2})\,4800}{30,000,000}$$

$$= \underline{.00040"}$$

9. DESIGNING A BASE TO RESIST BENDING

Normally, the calculation of the maximum deflection of members subjected to bending loads is very complex. The point of maximum deflection must first be found; then, from this, the maximum deflection is found. Unless there are no more than two loads of equal value and equal distance from the ends of the base (Fig. 28), existing beam tables in handbooks do not cover this problem.

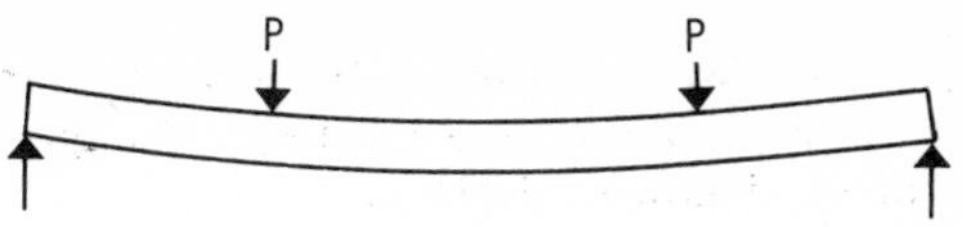

Most bases have more than two loads (Fig. 29). The maximum deflection usually does not occur at the middle or centerline of the base (Fig. 30). Two things can be done to simplify this problem.

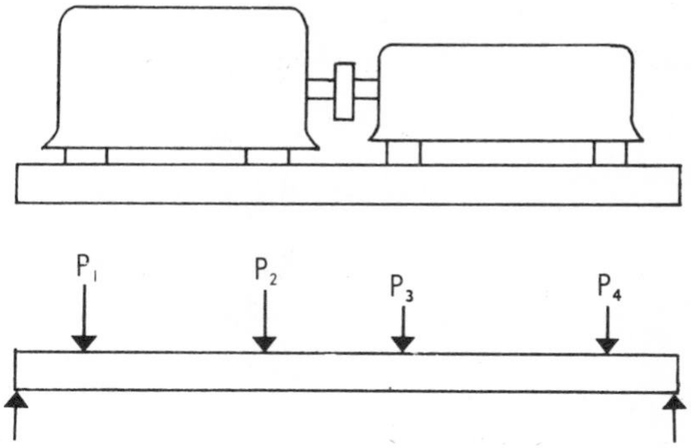

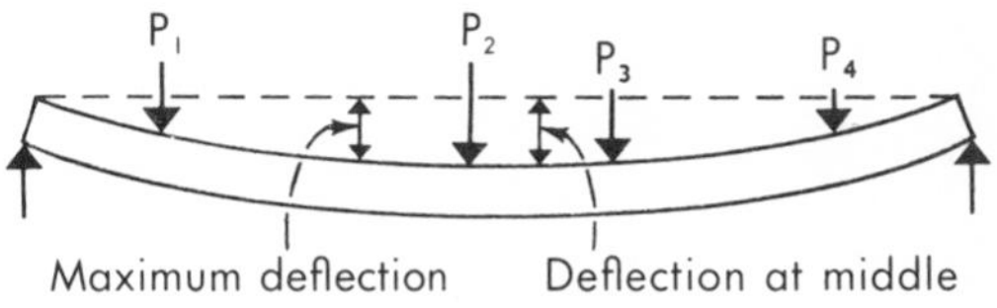

First, consider only the deflection at the middle or centerline of the member, rather than the maximum deflection at some point which is difficult to determine. This is justified, since the deflection at mid-point or centerline is almost as great as the maximum deflection, the greatest deviation coming within 1 or 2% of this value. For example, a simply supported beam with a single concentrated load at the one-quarter point has a deflection at centerline = 98.5% of the maximum deflection.

Secondly, a simple method of adding the required moments of inertia required for each individual load can be used.

For a given size member, Figure 31, it is found that each load, taken one at a time, will cause a certain amount of deflection at the middle or centerline. The total deflection at the centerline will equal the sum of these individual deflections caused by each load.

This principle of adding deflections may be used in a reverse manner to find the required section of the member (I), Figure 32. For a given allowable deflection (Δ) at the centerline, each individual load, taken one at a time, will require the member to have a certain section $(I_1, I_2, \text{etc.})$.

The moment of inertia (I) of the beam section re-

FIGURE 28

FIGURE 29

Maximum deflection   Deflection at middle

FIGURE 30

quired to support all of the vertical loads within this allowable vertical deflection (Δ) will equal the sum of the individual moments of inertia (I_n) required for the several loads.

Any torque or couple applied horizontal to the base will cause it to deflect vertically. This can be handled in the same manner. The required moment of inertia of the member (I_n) for each torque acting separately is found and added into the total requirement for the property of the section (I).

The following two formulas may be used to find

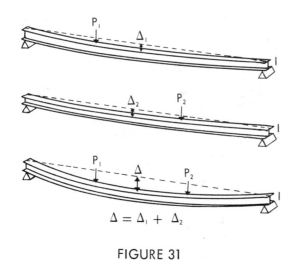

$$\Delta = \Delta_1 + \Delta_2$$

FIGURE 31

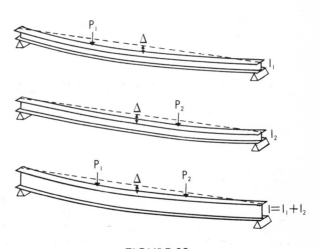

$$I = I_1 + I_2$$

FIGURE 32

FIG. 33 – REQUIRED MOMENT OF INERTIA OF BASE TO RESIST BENDING

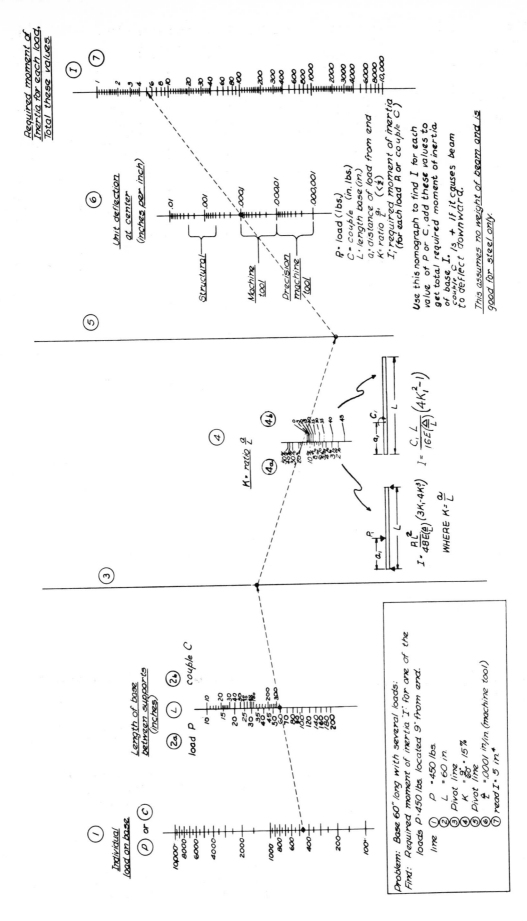

TABLE 3 - VALUES OF CONSTANTS (A and B) FOR SIMPLIFIED FORMULAS (16 and 17)

K	A	B	K	A	B	K	A	B
0	0	2.083×10^{-9}	.17	3.045×10^{-10}	1.842×10^{-9}	.34	5.002×10^{-10}	1.120×10^{-9}
.01	$.2083 \times 10^{-10}$	2.083	.18	3.588	1.813	.35	6.101	1.063
.02	.4166	2.080	.19	3.768	1.783	.36	6.204	1.003
.03	.6243	2.076	.20	3.944	1.750	.37	6.301	.9425
.04	.8312	2.070	.21	4.118	1.715	.38	6.392	.8900
.05	1.038	2.063	.22	4.268	1.680	.39	6.477	.8158
.06	1.244	2.053	.23	4.453	1.642	.40	6.556	.7500
.07	1.449	2.043	.24	4.616	1.603	.41	6.627	.6825
.08	1.653	2.030	.25	4.774	1.563	.42	6.692	.6133
.09	1.855	2.016	.26	4.928	1.520	.43	6.750	.5425
.10	2.056	2.000	.27	5.079	1.476	.44	6.801	.4700
.11	2.355	1.983	.28	5.224	1.430	.45	6.844	.3958
.12	2.452	1.963	.29	5.364	1.381	.46	6.880	.3221
.13	2.647	1.942	.30	5.500	1.333	.47	6.898	.2425
.14	2.847	1.920	.31	5.631	1.282	.48	6.928	.1633
.15	3.031	1.896	.32	5.756	1.209	.49	6.940	.0825
.16	3.219	1.870	.33	5.876	1.176	.50	7.000	0

the individual properties of the section (I_n):

For each force

$$I_n = \frac{P_n L^2}{48 E \left(\frac{\Delta}{L}\right)} (3 K_n - 4 K_n^3) \quad \dots \dots \dots \dots (14)$$

For each couple

$$I_n = \frac{C_n L}{16 E \left(\frac{\Delta}{L}\right)} (4 K_n^2 - 1) \quad \dots \dots \dots \dots (15)$$

where:

$$K_n = \frac{a_n}{L}$$

The two formulas have been simplified into the formulas given below in which the expression K_n now produces a constant (A or B) which is found in Table 3.

For each force

$$I_n = \frac{P_n L^2 A_n}{\left(\frac{\Delta}{L}\right)} \quad \dots \dots \dots \dots \dots \dots (16)$$

For each couple

$$I_n = \frac{C_n L B_n}{\left(\frac{\Delta}{L}\right)} \quad \dots \dots \dots \dots \dots \dots (17)$$

The value of K_n is equal to the ratio a_n/L, where a_n is the distance from the point at which the specific force or couple is applied to the nearest point of support. L is the span or length of beam between supports. From the value of K for any given load (P), the substitute constant A or B is obtained from Table 3.

When a force is applied to the member, use the constant A and substitute into the first formula. When a couple is applied to the member, use the constant B and substitute into the second formula.

A shorter method would be to make use of the nomograph in Figure 33.

10. INFLUENCE LINE FOR REACTIONS

Maxwell's Theorem of Reciprocal Deflections may be used to find the reactions of a continuous beam or frame, and is especially adaptable to model analysis.

Consider the continuous beam represented by the diagram at Figure 34a. The problem here is to find the reactions of the supports for various positions of the load (P_x).

According to Maxwell's theorem, the deflection of a beam at any given point due to a load on the beam at some other point, equals the deflection when the load was first applied if the load is shifted to the point where the deflection was first measured.

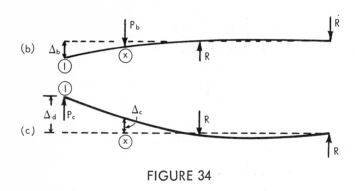

FIGURE 34

Figures 34b and 34c constitute a simple reversal of points at which the pressure is applied. This concept supplies a very useful tool for finding influence lines for reactions, deflections, moments, or shear. In this case, the interest is in reactions.

By observation of Figures 34b and 34c, in order to bring Δ_d at point 1 of (c) equal to Δ_b at point 1 of (b), the load (P_c) at point 1 of (c) must be reduced by the ratio: Δ_b/Δ_d. When this state of equality is reached, point 1 is supported and the reaction at this point is:

$$R_1 = P_c \frac{\Delta_b}{\Delta_d}$$

Since $P_c = P_b$ and $\Delta_b = \Delta_c$:

$$\boxed{R_1 = P_b \frac{\Delta_c}{\Delta_d}} \quad \dots\dots\dots\dots\dots\dots\dots\dots\dots\dots\dots \quad (18)$$

This means that if the model beam (as in Fig. 34c) is displaced in the same direction and at the same point as the reaction in question, the resulting deflection curve becomes the plot of the reaction as the load is moved across the length of the beam.

This is called an "influence curve". Considering the conditions of the real beam represented by Figure 34a, the reaction (R_1) at point 1 due to a load (P_x) at point x will be proportional to the ratio of the two ordinates at points x and 1 of the deflection curve.

This relationship is illustrated by the diagrams, Figure 34b and 34c, where:

$$P_b \Delta_c = P_c \Delta_b$$

and, if $P_c = P_b$, then $\Delta_b = \Delta_c$

In other words the deflection at point 1 (Δ_b) due to the load (P_b) at point x, equals the deflection at point x (Δ_c) due to the same amount of load (P_c) applied to point 1. There is a similar relationship between an applied load or moment and the resulting rotation of a real beam.

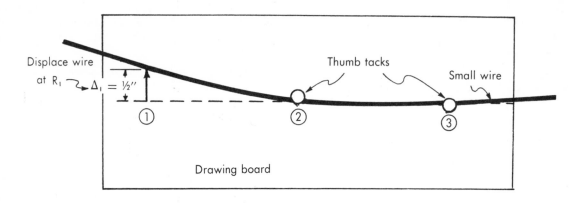

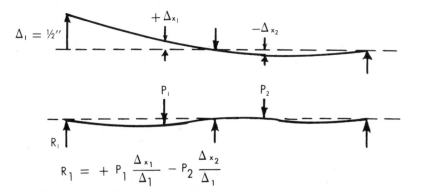

FIGURE 35

In other words:

$$R_1 = P_x \frac{\Delta_x}{\Delta_1}$$ . . . . (19)

For continuous beams of constant cross-section, a wire model may be set up on a drawing board, with the wire beam supported by thumb tacks spaced so as to represent the supports on the real beam. See Figure 35. A load diagram of the real beam is shown at the bottom. Notice that the thumb tacks used for supports of the wire must be located vertically so as to function in the opposite direction to reactions on the real beam.

The point of the model beam at the reaction in question (R_1) is raised upward some convenient distance, for example ½" or 1", and the deflection curve of the wire beam is traced in pencil. This is shown immediately below the model.

The final value for the reaction (R_1) is equal to the sum of the actual applied forces multiplied by the ratio of their ordinates of this curve to the

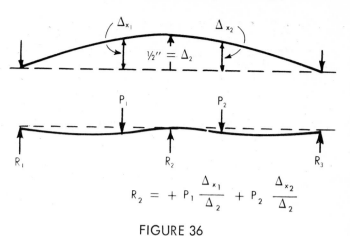

$$R_2 = + P_1 \frac{\Delta_{x_1}}{\Delta_2} + P_2 \frac{\Delta_{x_2}}{\Delta_2}$$

FIGURE 36

original displacement at R_1.

The influence curve for the central reaction (R_2) may also be found in the same manner. See Figure 36. Deflection curve of the wire model is shown first and then the load diagram of the real beam.

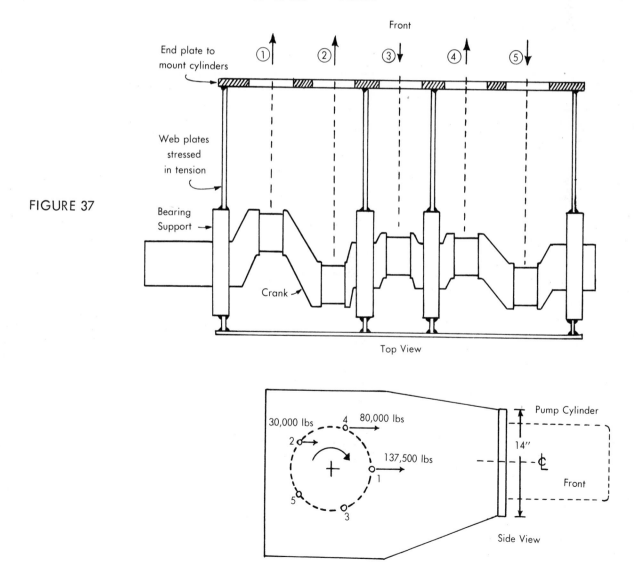

FIGURE 37

Top View

Side View

Problem 4

A housing for a 5-piston pump has 4 bearing supports for the crank. The cylinder head plate is attached to these crank bearing supports by means of 4 web plates. Treating the cylinder end plate as a 4-span continuous beam, loaded with a combination of 5 concentrated loads from the pump cylinders, it is necessary to find the reactions of this "beam" since these resulting reactions are transferred into the 4 web plates and will determine their thickness.

The pumping cycle sequence is (1), (4), (2), (5), and (3). It is assumed that the force exerted by the piston at the end of the stroke (1) is 137,500 lbs; at the next position (4) the force is 80,000 lbs; and at the start of the stroke (2) the force is 30,000 lbs. The other two positions are in the exhaust stroke.

The reactions on the web plates which support the end plate are found by comparing the ordinates of the deflection curve of a wire representing the beam. See Figure 38, where the critical dimensions appear on the (upper) load diagram.

For the end web plates, reactions R_1 and R_4, displace the end of the wire a given amount as shown. The portion of each applied load (P) to be transferred to the end web plate (reaction R_1), is proportional to the ordinate of the deflection curve under the load (P) and the given displacement at R_1.

For the interior web plates, reactions R_2 and R_3, displace the wire a given amount at R_2. From the ordinates of this deflected wire, determine the ratios of each applied load (P) for the reaction at R_2.

The complete computation of forces on the web plates appears in Table 4, based on the loads at every ⅕ of revolution. The fatigue K factor is also computed.

Assuming the selection of T-1 steel, the thickness of the web plates can then be found. Using fatigue allowables for T-1 butt weld in tension for 2,000,000 cycles, find:

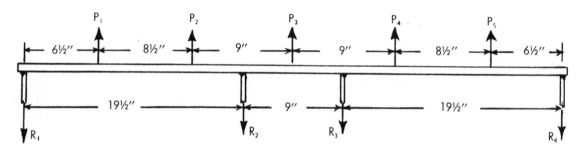

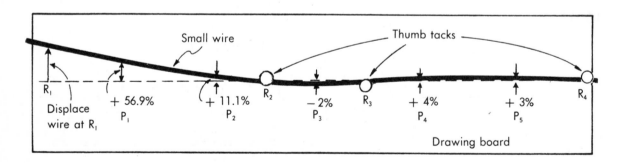

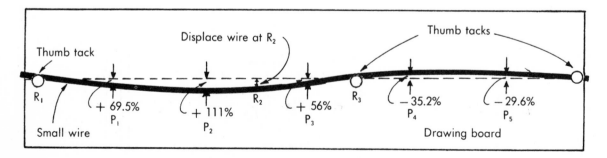

FIGURE 38

TABLE 4 – COMPUTATION OF FORCES ON WEB PLATES (FIG. 37)

| | | cylinder | | | | |
		1	2	3	4	5
one complete cycle	A	137,500	30,000	--	80,000	--
	B	--	80,000	--	137,500	30,000
	C	--	137,500	30,000	--	80,000
	D	30,000	--	80,000	--	137,500
	E	80,000	--	137,500	30,000	--
Values for R_1		+.569	+.111	-.02	+.04	+.03
Values for R_2		+.695	+1.11	+.56	-.352	-.296

End web plate, R_1

A $\quad(+.569)(137,500) \quad + \quad (.111)(30,000) \quad + \quad (.04)(80,000) \quad = + \ 84,770$ lbs
B $\quad(+.111)(80,000) \quad + \quad (.04)(137,500) \quad + \quad (.03)(30,000) \quad = + \ 15,280$
C $\quad(+.111)(137,500) \quad - \quad (.02)(30,000) \quad + \quad (.03)(80,000) \quad = + \ 17,060$
D $\quad(+.569)(30,000) \quad - \quad (.02)(80,000) \quad + \quad (+03)(137,500) \quad = + \ 19,595$
E $\quad(+.569)(80,000) \quad - \quad (.02)(137,500) \quad + \quad (.04)(30,000) \quad = + \ 43,970$

Maximum force is + 84,770 lbs

The ratio of minimum to maximum force is $K = \dfrac{\min}{\max} = \dfrac{15,280}{84,770} = +.18$

Interior web plate, R_2

A $\quad(+.695)(137,500) \quad + \quad (1.11)(30,000) \quad - \quad (.352)(80,000) = + \ 100,700$ lbs
B $\quad(+1.11)(80,000) \quad - \quad (.352)(137,500) \quad - \quad (.296)(30,000) = + \quad 31,520$
C $\quad(+1.11)(137,500) \quad + \quad (.56)(30,000) \quad - \quad (.296)(80,000) \quad = + \ 145,750$
D $\quad(+.695)(30,000) \quad + \quad (.56)(80,000) \quad - \quad (.296)(137,500) \quad = + \quad 24,950$
E $\quad(+.695)(80,000) \quad + \quad (.56)(137,500) \quad - \quad (.352)(30,000) \quad = + \ 123,040$

Maximum force is + 145,750 lbs

The ratio of minimum to maximum force is $K = \dfrac{\min}{\max} = \dfrac{24,950}{145,750} = + \ \underline{.171}$

Thickness of end web plates

allowable stress--

$$\sigma = \frac{16,500}{1 - .8K}$$

$$= \frac{16,500}{1 - .8(+.18)}$$

$$= 19,300 \text{ psi}$$

and, since--

$$P = t\,W\,\sigma$$

$$t = \frac{P}{W\,\sigma}$$

$$= \frac{84,770}{(14)(19,300)}$$

$$= .314'' \text{ or use } \tfrac{5}{16}'' \text{ plate}$$

Thickness of interior web plates

allowable stress--

$$\sigma = \frac{16,500}{1 - .8K}$$

$$= \frac{16,500}{1 - .8(+.171)}$$

$$= 19,100 \text{ psi}$$

and since--

$$P = t\,W\,\sigma$$

$$t = \frac{P}{W\,\sigma}$$

$$= \frac{145,750}{(14)(19,100)}$$

$$= .545'' \text{ or use } \tfrac{9}{16}'' \text{ plate}$$

T-1 fatigue allowables from "Fabrication and Design of Structures of T-1 Steel", by Gilligan and England, United States Steel Corporation.

11. INFLUENCE LINE FOR DEFLECTION

In like manner, the use of a wire model based on Maxwell's Theorem of Reciprocal Deflection is useful in finding the deflections of a beam under various loads or under a moving load.

If a 1-lb load is placed at a particular point on a beam, the resulting deflection curve becomes the plot of the deflection (Δ) at this point as the 1-lb load is moved across the length of the beam. This is called the influence line for deflection at this particular point.

> Problem 5

To determine the deflection of the overhung portion of this trailer, Figure 39, under the various loads. Assume a cross-section moment of inertia (I) of 2×11.82 in.^{4}.

Using the standard beam formula for this type of beam, the deflection of the free (right) end is determined for a 1-lb load placed at that point:

$$\Delta_{end} = \frac{P\,a^2}{3\,E\,I}\,(L + a)$$

$$= \frac{1\#\,(120)^2}{3\,(30 \times 10^6)\,(2 \times 11.82)}\,(360 - 120)$$

$$= 3.25 \times 10^{-3} \text{ inches}$$

A wire model of this beam is held at the two supports (trailer hitch and the wheel assembly) with

TABLE 5 - INCREMENTAL DEFLECTIONS OF REAL BEAM

POINT	LOAD (LBS)	ORDINATE x 10^{-3}	DEFLECTION AT FREE END (IN.)
0	100	0	0
3'	150	− .60	− .030
8'	300	−1.06	− .318
15'	400	−1.60	− .640
21'	750	−1.56	−1.170
23'	750	−1.36	−1.020
28'	375	− .70	− .262
33'	150	+ .70	+ .105
37'	325	+2.00	+ .650
40'	100	+3.25	+ .325
Total	3300 lbs		−2.360"

thumb tacks on a drawing board. The outer end is displaced an amount equal to 3.25 on a suitable scale. The deflection curve is traced in pencil from this displaced wire beam. The ordinates of this resulting deflection curve become the actual deflections at the free end as the 1-lb load is moved across the length of the beam.

Multiplying each of the loads on the real beam by the ordinate at that point gives the deflection at the free end caused by each load on the real beam. See Table 5. Summing these incremental deflections gives the total deflection:

$$\Delta = \underline{2.36'' \text{ upward}}$$

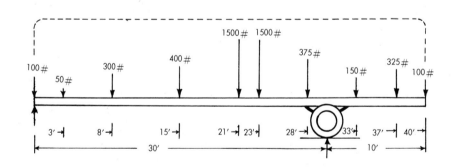

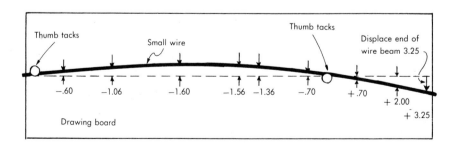

FIGURE 39

Shear Deflection in Beams

1. NATURE OF SHEAR DEFLECTION

Shear stresses in a beam section cause a displacement or sliding action on a plane normal to the axis of the beam, as shown in the right hand view of Figure 1. This is unlike the deflection resulting from bending in a beam, which is shown in the left hand view of Figure 1.

Normally deflection due to shear in the usual beam is ignored because it represents a very small percentage of the entire deflection. Figure 2 shows that the deflection due to shear increases lineally as the length of the beam increases, whereas the deflection due to bending increases very rapidly

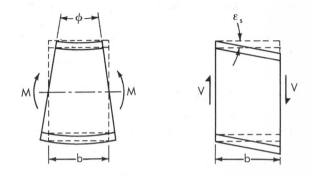

Fig. 1 Deflection in beam caused by bending moment, left, and by shear, right.

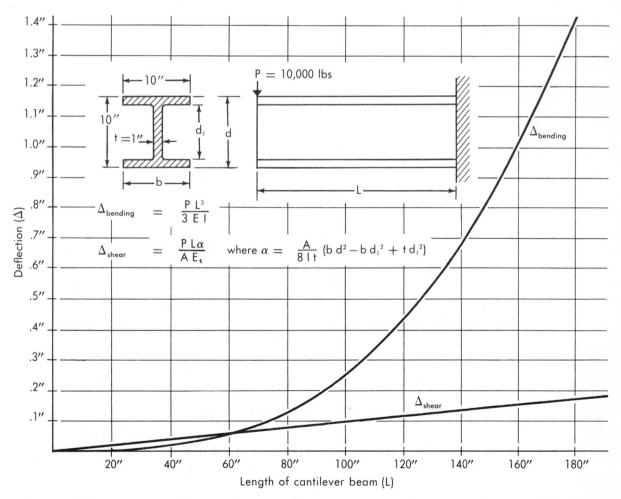

$$\Delta_{bending} = \frac{P L^3}{3 E I}$$

$$\Delta_{shear} = \frac{P L \alpha}{A E_s} \quad \text{where } \alpha = \frac{A}{8 I t} (b d^2 - b d_1^2 + t d_1^2)$$

Fig. 2 Deflection caused by shear increases linearly as length of beam, but that caused by bending increases as the third power of beam length.

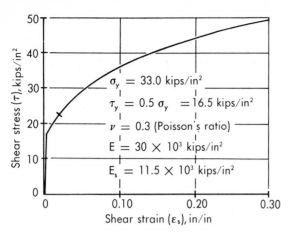

Fig. 3   Shear stress-strain diagram.

as a third power of the length of the beam. For this reason the deflection due to shear is not an important factor except for extremely short spans where deflection due to bending drops off to a very small value.

The deflection due to shear is dependent entirely on the shear distribution across the cross-section of the member and also the value of the shear stress (τ). Figure 3 shows the shear stress-strain diagram which is similar to the usual stress-strain diagram, although the shear yield strength is much lower than the tensile yield strength of the same material. After the shear yield strength is reached, the shear strain (ϵ_s) increases rapidly and the shear strength increases because of strain hardening.

2. DETERMINING SHEAR DEFLECTION

The theory of deflection caused by shear stress is rather simple. However, the actual determination of the shear stresses and their distribution across the beam section (which two factors cause the deflection) is more difficult. In all cases, some kind of a form factor (α) must be determined, and this is simply a matter of expressing the distribution of shear stress throughout the web of the section. Since there is practically no shear stress in the flange area, this particular area has negligible effect on the deflection due to shear (Δ_s).

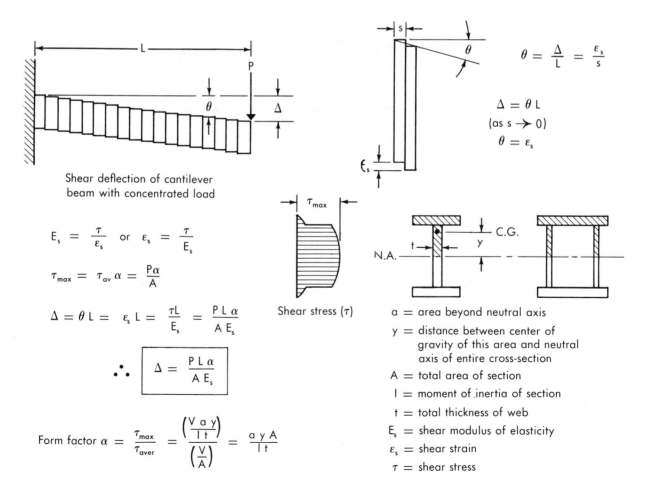

Shear deflection of cantilever beam with concentrated load

$$E_s = \frac{\tau}{\epsilon_s} \quad \text{or} \quad \epsilon_s = \frac{\tau}{E_s}$$

$$\tau_{max} = \tau_{av} \, \alpha = \frac{P \alpha}{A}$$

$$\Delta = \theta \, L = \epsilon_s \, L = \frac{\tau L}{E_s} = \frac{P L \alpha}{A E_s}$$

$$\therefore \quad \boxed{\Delta = \frac{P L \alpha}{A E_s}}$$

$$\theta = \frac{\Delta}{L} = \frac{\epsilon_s}{s}$$

$$\Delta = \theta \, L$$
(as $s \to 0$)
$$\theta = \epsilon_s$$

Shear stress (τ)

$$\text{Form factor } \alpha = \frac{\tau_{max}}{\tau_{aver}} = \frac{\left(\frac{V a y}{I t}\right)}{\left(\frac{V}{A}\right)} = \frac{a y A}{I t}$$

a = area beyond neutral axis
y = distance between center of gravity of this area and neutral axis of entire cross-section
A = total area of section
I = moment of inertia of section
t = total thickness of web
E_s = shear modulus of elasticity
ϵ_s = shear strain
τ = shear stress

Fig. 4   Form factor for shear deflection in built-up beams.

The following formulas are valid for several types of beams and loading:

Simply supported beam; uniform load (w)

$$\Delta_s = \frac{w\,L^2\,\alpha}{8\,A\,E_s}$$ . . . . (1)

Simply supported beam; concentrated load (P)

$$\Delta_s = \frac{P\,L\,\alpha}{4\,A\,E_s}$$ . . . . (2)

Cantilever beam; uniform load (w)

$$\Delta_s = \frac{w\,L^2\,\alpha}{2\,A\,E_s}$$ . . . . (3)

Cantilever beam; concentrated load (P)

$$\Delta_s = \frac{P\,L\,\alpha}{A\,E_s}$$ . . . . (4)

where:

P = total load, lbs
A = area of entire section
E_s = modulus of elasticity in shear
  (steel = 12,000,000 psi)
w = distributed load, lbs/linear in.

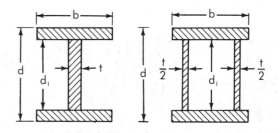

Fig. 5   Beam sections for which Eq. 5 applies.

The slope of the deflection curve (θ) is equal at each cross-section to the shearing strain (ϵ_s) at the centroid of this cross-section. α is a factor with which the average shearing stress (τ_{av}) must be multiplied in order to obtain the shearing stress (τ_{max}) at the centroid of the cross-sections.

On this basis, the form factor (α) for an I beam or box beam would be:

$$\alpha = \frac{A}{8\,I\,t}\,(b\,d^2 - b\,d_1^2 + t\,d_1^2)$$ . . . . (5)

where Figure 5 applies. Don't compute area (A) in this formula because it will cancel out when used in the formulas for shear deflection.

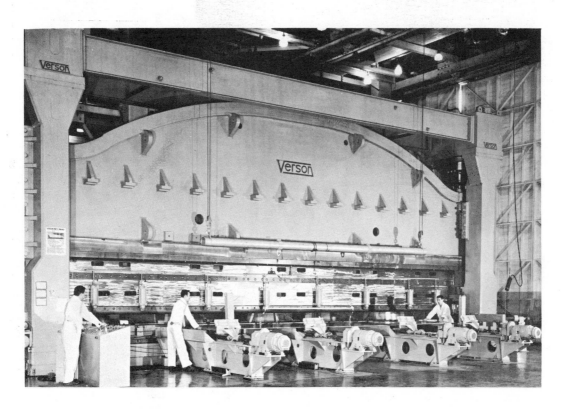

Steel weldments play an important part in modern high-tonnage press brakes. Shear deflection must be computed as part of the over-all deflection on the main slide.

Redesign of eyeletting machine permitted use of short-run stampings and all-welded frame. Machine has improved appearance, long service life and manufacturing cost only 1/3 that of previous design.

Fresh approach to design resulted in nut tapper being entirely arc welded structurally. Driving 79 spindles, the machine depends heavily on high rigidity for superior performance.

Rear view of nut tapping machine shows rib bracing on head for increased stiffness. Base incorporates thick-plate members welded up for needed rigidity.

Deflection of Curved Beams

1. DESIGN APPROACH

A symmetrical beam forming a single continuous arc, for example, is comparable to two equal cantilever beams connected end to end. Thus, the prediction of deflection in a curved beam can be approached in a manner similar to finding the deflection in a straight cantilever beam.

2. AREA MOMENT METHOD FOR CURVED CANTILEVER BEAM

In Sect. 2.9, Figures 22 to 25, the area moment method was used to find the deflection of a straight cantilever beam. This same method may be extended to a curved cantilever beam of variable section.

As before, the beam is divided into 10 segments of equal length (s) and the moment of inertia (I_n) is determined for each segment. See Figure 1.

The moment applied to any segment of the beam is equal to the applied force (P) multiplied by the distance (X_n) to the segment, measured from and at

right angles to the line passing through and in the same direction as the load (P).

This moment (M_n) applied to the segment causes it to rotate (θ_n), and —

$$\theta_n = \frac{M_n}{E\,I_n} \dots\dots\dots\dots\dots\dots\dots\dots\dots\dots\dots (1)$$

The resulting deflection (Δ_n) at the point of the beam where the deflection is to be determined is equal to the angle of rotation of this segment (θ_n) multiplied by the distance (Y_n) to the segment, measured from and at right angles to the line passing through and in the same direction as the desired deflection (Δ).

$$\Delta_n = \frac{M_n Y_n s}{E\,I_n} = \frac{P X_n Y_n s}{E\,I_n} \dots\dots\dots\dots\dots (2)$$

The distances (X_n and Y_n) and the moment of inertia (I_n) are determined for each of the 10 segments and placed in table form. In most cases,

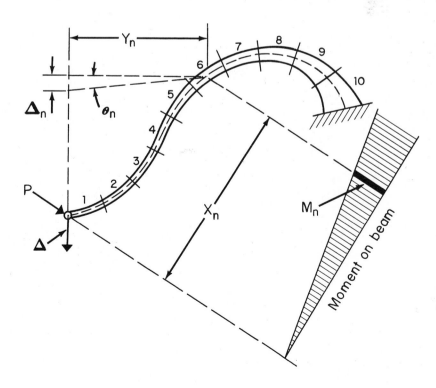

Fig. 1 To find deflection of curved cantilever beam of variable section, first divide it into segments of equal length.

the deflection to be determined is in line with the applied force so that these two distances are equal and the formula becomes--

$$\Delta_n = \frac{P X_n^2 s}{E I_n} \quad \dots \dots \dots \dots \dots \dots \dots \dots \dots (3)$$

The values of X_n^2/I_n are found and totaled. From this the total deflection (Δ) is found:

$$\Delta = \frac{P s}{E} \sum \frac{X_n^2}{I_n} \quad \dots \dots \dots \dots \dots \dots \dots \dots (4)$$

Problem 1

The total vertical deflection (Δ) is needed on a curved beam that will carry a maximum load (P) of 100,000 lbs. See Figure 2. Given the segment length $(s) = 10''$ and the various values of X_n and I_n, complete the computation.

Segment	X_n	I_n	$\dfrac{X_n^2}{I_n}$
1	5"	119 in.⁴	.21
2	15	216	1.04
3	23	358	1.48
4	29	550	1.53
5	32	800	1.28
6	32	800	1.28
7	29	550	1.53
8	23	358	1.48
9	15	216	1.04
10	5	119	.21
			$\sum \dfrac{X_n^2}{I_n} = \underline{11.08}$

$$\Delta = \frac{P s}{E} \sum \frac{X_n^2}{I_n}$$

$$= \left(\frac{100,000 \times 10}{30,000,000} \right) 11.08$$

$$= \underline{0.369''}$$

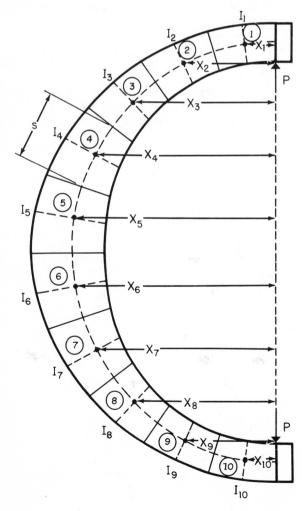

Deflection of Curved Beams

Solving for deflection

by using formula $\Delta = \dfrac{P s}{E} \sum \dfrac{X_n^2}{I_n}$

first calculate value of X_n^2/I_n

by using stiffness nomograph

graphically find value of $P X_n^2/E I_n$

for use in formula $\Delta = s \sum \dfrac{P X_n^2}{E I}$

Segment	X_n	I_n	
1			
2			
3			
4			
5			
6			
7			
8			
9			
10			
		$\sum =$	

Fig. 2   For deflection of simple curved beam, use Eq. 4 or nomograph, Fig. 3

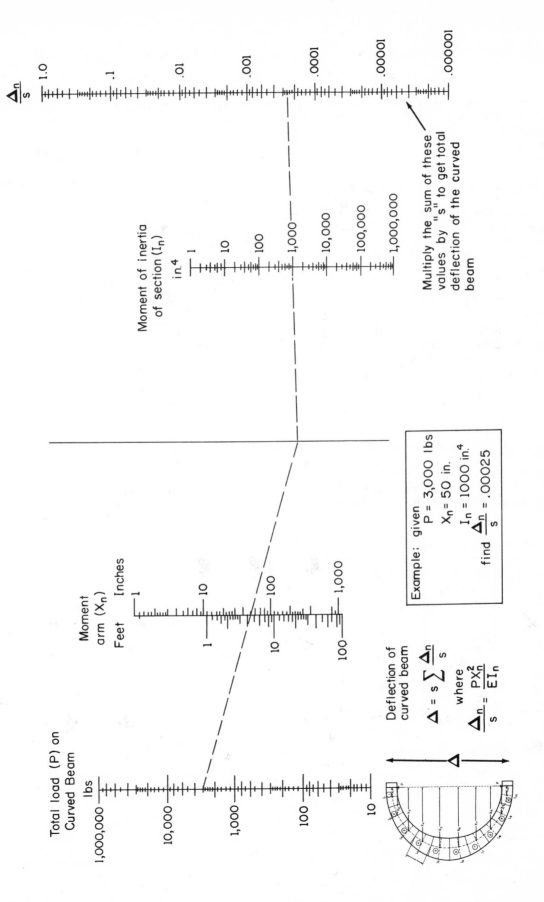

FIG. 3 DEFLECTION OF CURVED BEAM
(Stiffness Nomograph)

$\dfrac{\Delta_n}{s}$

Moment of inertia of section (I_n) in.^{4}

Multiply the sum of these values by "s" to get total deflection of the curved beam

Moment arm (X_n)

Feet   Inches

Total load (P) on Curved Beam

lbs

Example: given
$P = 3{,}000$ lbs
$X_n = 50$ in.
$I_n = 1000$ in.^{4}
$\dfrac{\Delta_n}{s} = .00025$
find $\dfrac{\Delta_n}{s}$

Deflection of curved beam

$\Delta = s \sum \dfrac{\Delta_n}{s}$

where

$\dfrac{\Delta_n}{s} = \dfrac{P X_n^2}{E I_n}$

Continuation of Problem 1 ......

It is readily seen that in the case of a beam that is symmetrical above and below the center of curvature, the value of X_n^2/I_n need be computed for only the first five segment sections. The remaining five will be of same value in reverse order.

3. SIMPLIFICATION USING NOMOGRAPH

By using the stiffness nomograph, Figure 3, the computation can be considerably shortened with no significant loss of accuracy. The nomograph is based on the modified formula:

$$\Delta = s \sum \frac{P X_n^2}{E I_n} \quad \dots\dots\dots\dots\dots\dots\dots(5)$$

Readings are obtained from the nomograph for PX_n^2/EI_n for each segment and entered in the last column of the table. These are then added and their sum multiplied by s to give the total vertical deflection.

Problem 2

Use the same beam example as in Problem 1, the same values for P, s, X_n and I_n, and the same form of table. Complete the computation.

Segment	X_n	I_n	$\dfrac{P X_n^2}{E I_n}$
1	5	119	.0006
2	15	216	.0036
3	23	358	.0048
4	29	550	.0050
5	32	800	.0043
6	32	800	.0043
7	29	550	.0050
8	23	358	.0048
9	15	216	.0036
10	5	119	.0006
		$\sum \dfrac{P X_n^2}{E I_n} =$	.0366

$$\Delta = s \sum \frac{P X_n^2}{E I_n}$$
$$= 10 \times .0366$$
$$= \underline{0.366''}$$

4. DEFLECTION OF "C" FRAMES

Many "C" frames resemble a series of straight sections rather than a curved beam. The preceding method for curved beams may be used to compute the deflection, or a better method might be to break the frame down into its several straight sections and compute the total deflection as in Figure 5.

After review of the procedure given in Figure 5, return to Problem 3, below, a practical problem in "C" frame deflection.

Problem 3

A 600-ton press is essentially a "C" frame, Figure 4. With the conditions specified in the drawing, compute the maximum vertical deflection.

Deflection due to axial elongation of upright

$$\Delta_a = \frac{P L_2}{A_2 E}$$
$$= \frac{(1,200,000)(112.62'')}{(615)(30 \times 10^6)}$$
$$= .00732''$$

Deflection due to bending

$$\Delta_b = \frac{P L_1^2 L_2}{2 E I_2}$$
$$= \frac{(1,200,000)(63.64)^2(112.62)}{2(30 \times 10^6)(317,400)}$$
$$= .0288''$$

$$\Delta_c = \frac{P L_1^3}{3 E I_1}$$
$$= \frac{(1,200,000)(63.64)^3}{3(30 \times 10^6)(185,100)}$$
$$= .01503''$$

Deflection due to shear

$$\Delta_d = \frac{P L_1 \alpha}{A_1 E_s}$$
$$= \frac{(1,200,000)(63.64)(2.9)}{(555)(12 \times 10^6)}$$
$$= .0332''$$

Total vertical deflection (bending + shear)

$$\Delta_T = \Delta_a + 2(\Delta_b + \Delta_c + \Delta_d)$$
$$= .0073 + 2(.0288 + .0150 + .0332)$$
$$= \underline{.161''}$$

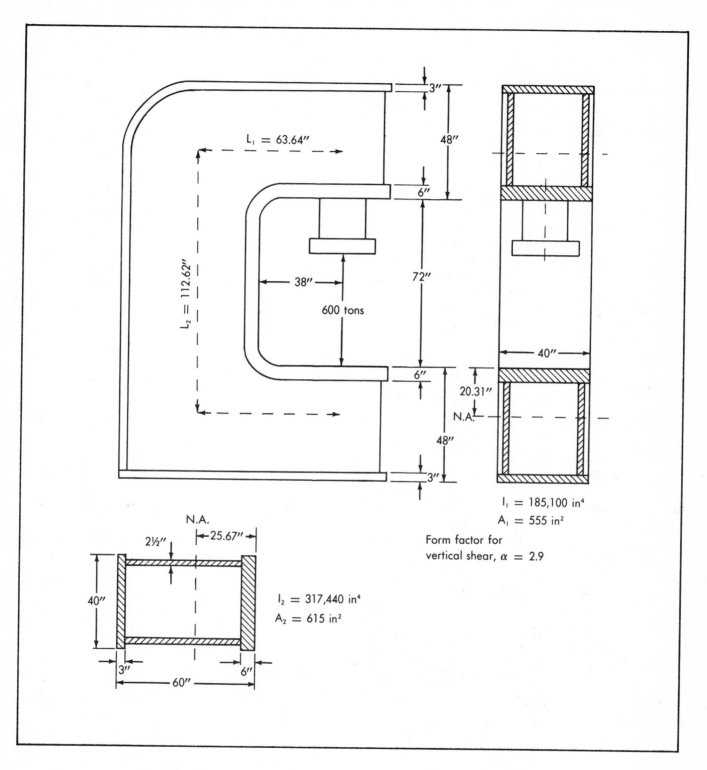

Fig. 4   Press of essentially "C" frame construction. See Problem 2.

FIG. 5 FINDING DEFLECTION OF "C" FRAME

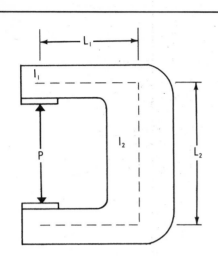

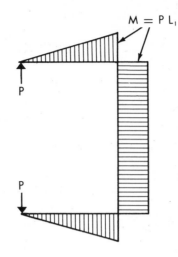

Deflection Due to Axial Elongation of Upright

$$\Delta_a = \frac{P L_2}{A_2 E}$$

Deflection Due to Bending

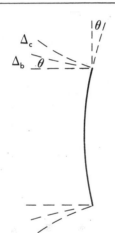

$$2\theta = \frac{(P L_1)L_2}{E I_2}$$

Due to rotation of vertical member

$$\Delta_b = \theta L_1 \qquad \text{or} \qquad \boxed{\Delta_b = \frac{P L_1^2 L_2}{2 E I_2}}$$

Due to acting as a cantilever beam

$$\Delta_c = \frac{\frac{1}{2}(P L_1)(L_1)(\frac{2}{3} L_1)}{E I_1} \qquad \text{or} \qquad \boxed{\Delta_c = \frac{P L_1^3}{3 E I_1}}$$

Deflection Due to Shear

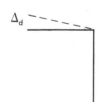

*Form factor $\alpha = \dfrac{\tau_{max}}{\tau_{aver}} = \dfrac{a\,y\,A}{I\,t}$

for I or box beam section

$$\alpha = \frac{A}{8 t I}\,(b\,d^2 - b\,d_1^2 + t\,d_1^2)$$

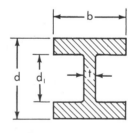

$$\boxed{\Delta_d = \frac{P L_1\,\alpha}{A_1 E_s}}$$

*See preceding Section on Shear Deflection

Total Vertical Deflection (Bending + Shear)

$$\boxed{\Delta_t = \Delta_a + 2\,(\Delta_b + \Delta_c + \Delta_d)}$$

Buckling of Plates

1. CAUSES OF BUCKLING

Buckling of flat plates may be experienced when the plate is excessively stressed in compression along opposite edges, or in shear uniformly distributed around all edges of the plate. This necessitates establishment of values for the critical buckling stress in compression (σ_{cr}) and in shear (τ_{cr}).

2. BUCKLING OF PLATES IN EDGE COMPRESSION

The critical compressive stress of a plate when subject to compression (σ_{cr}) can be found from the following:

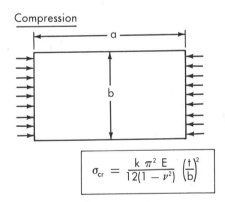

$$\sigma_{cr} = \frac{k\ \pi^2\ E}{12(1-\nu^2)}\left(\frac{t}{b}\right)^2$$

FIGURE 1

where:

E = modulus of elasticity in compression (Steel = 30,000,000 psi)

t = thickness of plate, inches

b = width of plate, inches

a = length of plate, inches

ν = Poisson's ratio (for steel, usually = 0.3)

k = constant; depends upon plate shape b/a and support of sides. When the ratio of plate width to length (b/a) is .20 or less, it can be ignored and the following values of k apply:

Values of k for Buckling Formula (Compression)	
1. one side simply supported, the other free	k = 0.425
2. one side fixed, the other free	k = 1.277
3. both sides simply supported	k = 4.00
4. one side simply supported, the other fixed	k = 5.42
5. both sides fixed	k = 6.97

It is usually more practical to assume the sides simply supported, that is (No. 1) k = 0.425 or (No. 3) k = 4.00.

If the resulting critical stress (σ_{cr}) from this formula is below the proportional limit(σ_p), buckling is said to be elastic and is confined to a portion of the plate away from the supported side; this does not mean complete collapse of the plate at this stress. This is represented by the portion of the curve B to D in Figure 2. If the resulting value (σ_{cr}) is above the proportional limit (σ_p), indicated by the portion of the curve A to B, buckling is said to be inelastic. Here, the tangent modulus (E_t) must be used in some form to replace Young's or secant modulus (E) in the formula for determining σ_{cr} .

Since the value of the tangent modulus (E_t) varies with the stress (σ), the solution of the formula in this case is difficult, being a trial and error method. For all practical purposes this problem can be simplified by limiting the maximum value of the critical buckling stress (σ_{cr}) resulting from the formula, to the yield strength (σ_y).

3. BUCKLING STRESS CURVES

According to "Design Manual for High Strength Steels" by Priest and Gilligan, present day testing indicates that the curve pattern of Figure 2 represents the actual buckling stress of flat plates in edge compression. Values indicated on this typical curve are for ASTM A-7 (mild) steel, having a yield strength of 33,000 psi.

The horizontal line (A to B) is the limit of the

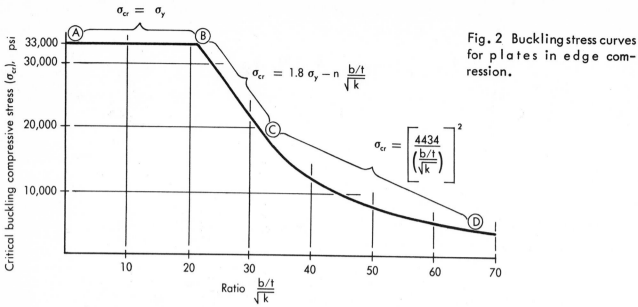

$$\sigma_{cr} = \sigma_y$$

Fig. 2 Buckling stress curves for plates in edge comression.

Critical buckling compressive stress (σ_{cr}) for A-7 steel having $\sigma_y = 33,000$ psi

yield strength(σ_y). Here σ_{cr} is assumed equal to σ_y.

The curve from B to C is expressed by--

$$\sigma_{cr} = 1.8 \, \sigma_y - n\frac{(b/t)}{\sqrt{k}}$$

where:

$$n = \frac{\sqrt{\sigma_y^3}}{4770}$$

The curve from C to D is 75% of the critical buckling stress formula, Figure 1, or:

$$\sigma_{cr} = .75\frac{k\,\pi^2\,E}{12\,(1-\nu^2)}\left(\frac{t}{b}\right)^2$$

$$= \left[\frac{4434}{\frac{b/t}{\sqrt{k}}}\right]^2$$

TABLE 1 – BUCKLING STRESS FORMULAS (COMPRESSION)

Portion of Curve	Factor $\dfrac{b/t}{\sqrt{k}}$	Critical Buckling Compressive Stress (σ_{cr}) Determined by
A to B	0 to $\dfrac{3820}{\sqrt{\sigma_y}}$	$\sigma_{cr} = \sigma_y$
B to C	$\dfrac{3820}{\sqrt{\sigma_y}}$ to $\dfrac{5720}{\sqrt{\sigma_y}}$	$\sigma_{cr} = 1.8\,\sigma_y - n\dfrac{b/t}{\sqrt{k}}$ where: $n = \dfrac{\sqrt{\sigma_y^3}}{4770}$
C to D	$\dfrac{5720}{\sqrt{\sigma_y}}$ and over	$\sigma_{cr} = \left[\dfrac{4434}{\frac{b/t}{\sqrt{k}}}\right]^2$

All of this is expressed in terms of the factor $\dfrac{b/t}{\sqrt{k}}$ See Table 1.

Factors needed for the formulas of curves in Figure 2, for steels of various yield strengths, are given in Table 2.

Figure 3 is just an enlargement of Figure 2, with additional steels having yield strengths from 33,000 psi to 100,000 psi.

For any given ratio of plate width to thickness (b/t), the critical buckling stress (σ_{cr}) can be read directly from the curves of this figure.

TABLE 2 - FACTORS FOR BUCKLING FORMULAS

Yield Strength of Steel σ_y psi	$\left(\dfrac{b/t}{\sqrt{k}}\right)$ for Point B $= \dfrac{3820}{\sqrt{\sigma_y}}$	$\left(\dfrac{b/t}{\sqrt{k}}\right)$ for Point C $= \dfrac{5720}{\sqrt{\sigma_y}}$	$n = \dfrac{\sqrt{\sigma_y^3}}{4770}$
33,000	21.0	31.5	1260
35,000	20.4	30.6	1370
40,000	19.1	28.6	1680
45,000	18.0	27.0	2000
50,000	17.1	25.6	2340
55,000	16.3	24.4	2700
60,000	15.6	23.4	3080
70,000	14.4	21.6	3470
80,000	13.5	20.2	4740
90,000	12.7	19.1	5660
100,000	12.1	18.1	6630

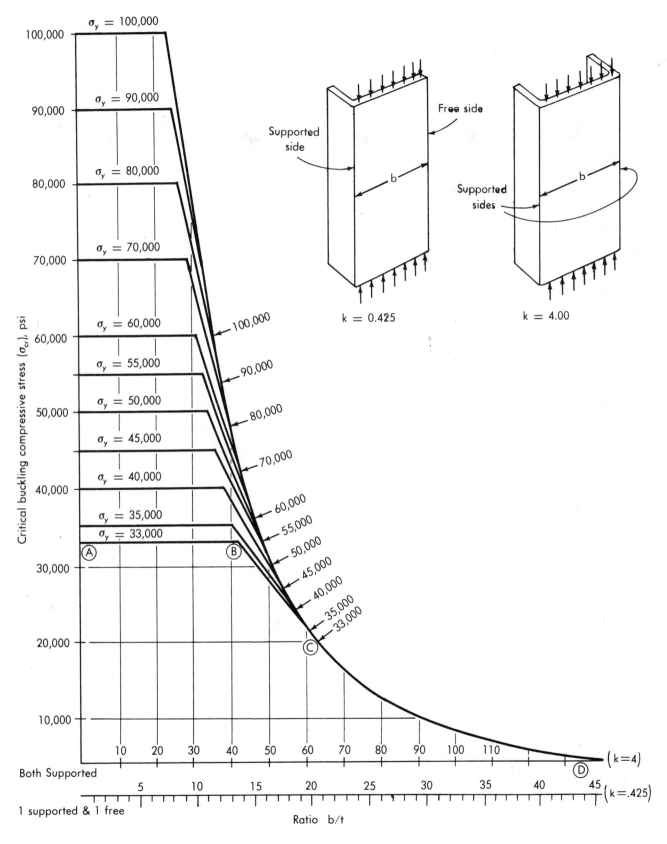

Fig. 3 Buckling stress curves (plates in edge compression) for various steels.

TABLE 3 - LIMITING VALUES OF b/t (CODE)

Side Conditions	Yield Strength σ_y psi	AISC	AASHO	AREA
One simply supported; the other free	33,000	13 & 16	12	12
	50,000	11 & 13	-	-
Both simply supported	33,000	44	40	40
	50,000	36	34	32

AISC – American Institute of Steel Construction
AASHO – American Association of State Highway Officials
AREA – American Railway Engineers Association

TABLE 4 - USUAL LIMITING VALUES OF b/t

Yield Strength σ_y psi	One Edge Simply Supported; the Other Edge Free	Both Edges Simply Supported
33,000	13.7	42.0
35,000	13.3	40.8
40,000	12.5	38.2
45,000	11.7	36.0
50,000	11.1	34.2
55,000	10.6	32.6
60,000	10.1	31.2
70,000	9.4	28.8
80,000	8.8	27.0
90,000	8.3	25.4
100,000	7.9	24.2

4. FACTOR OF SAFETY

A suitable factor of safety must be used with these values of b/t since they represent ultimate stress values for buckling.

Some structural specifications limit the ratio b/t to a maximum value (point B) at which the critical buckling stress (σ_{cr}) is equal to the yield strength (σ_y). By so doing, it is not necessary to calculate the buckling stress. These limiting values of b/t, as specified by several codes, are given in Table 3.

In general practice, somewhat more liberal values of b/t are recognized. Table 4, extended to higher yield strengths, lists these limiting values of b/t.

5. EFFECTIVE WIDTH OF PLATES IN COMPRESSION

The 20" × 1/4" plate shown in Figure 4, simply supported along both sides, is subjected to a compressive load.

Under these conditions, the critical buckling compressive stress (σ_{cr}) as found from the curve (σ_y) = 33,000 psi) in Figure 3 is --

$$\sigma_{cr} = 12,280 \text{ psi}$$

This value may also be found from the formulas in Table 1.

Since the ratio $\dfrac{b/t}{\sqrt{k}}$ is 40.0 and thus exceeds the value of 31.5 for point C, the following formula must be used--

$$\sigma_{cr} = \left[\frac{4434}{\frac{b/t}{\sqrt{k}}}\right]^2 = \left[\frac{4434}{40}\right]^2$$

$$= 12,280 \text{ psi}$$

At this stress, the middle portion of the plate would be expected to buckle, Figure 5. The compressive load at this stage of loading would be--

$$P = A\sigma = (20" \times 1/4") \, 12,280$$

$$= 61,400 \text{ lbs}$$

The over-all plate should not collapse since the portion of the plate along the supported sides could still be loaded up to the yield point (σ_y) before ultimate collapse.

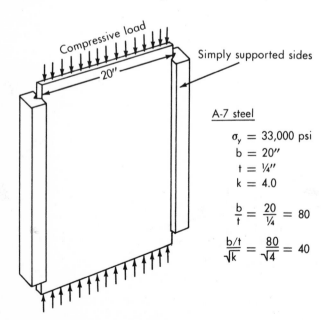

A-7 steel

$\sigma_y = 33,000$ psi
$b = 20"$
$t = 1/4"$
$k = 4.0$

$\dfrac{b}{t} = \dfrac{20}{1/4} = 80$

$\dfrac{b/t}{\sqrt{k}} = \dfrac{80}{\sqrt{4}} = 40$

FIGURE 4

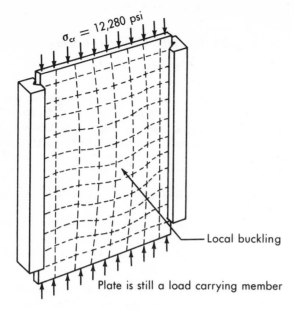

Local buckling

Plate is still a load carrying member

FIGURE 5

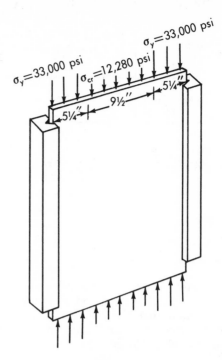

FIGURE 6

This portion of the plate, called the "effective width" can be determined by finding the ratio b/t when (σ_{cr}) is set equal to yield strength (σ_y) or point B.

From Figure 3 we find--

$$\frac{b}{t} = 42.0$$

or from Table 2 we find--

$$\frac{b/t}{\sqrt{k}} = 21.0$$

Since k = 4.0 (both sides simply supported), the ratio--

$$\frac{b}{t} = 21.0 \sqrt{k}$$

$$= 42.0$$

Since the plate thickness t = ¼" width, b = 42.0 t or b = 10.5"

This is the effective width of the plate which may be stressed to the yield point (σ_y) before ultimate collapse of the entire plate.

The total compressive load at this state of loading would be as shown in Figure 6.

The total compressive load here would be --

$$P = A_1 \sigma_1 + A_2 \sigma_2$$

$$= (10½ \times ¼)(33,000) + (9½ \times ¼)(12,280)$$

$$= \underline{115,800 \text{ lbs}}$$

Shear

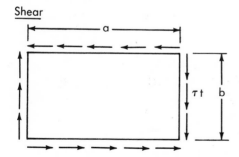

$$\tau_{cr} = \frac{k \pi^2 E}{12(1 - \nu^2)} \left(\frac{t}{b}\right)^2$$

FIGURE 7

where:

E = modulus of elasticity in compression (Steel ≐ 30,000,000 psi)

t = thickness of plate, inches

b = width of plate, inches

a = length of plate, inches (a is always the larger of the plate's dimensions)

ν = Poisson's ratio (for steel, usually = 0.3)

k = constant; depends upon plate shape b/a and edge restraint, and also accounts for the modulus of elasticity in shear (E_s)

TABLE 5 - BUCKLING STRESS FORMULAS (SHEAR)

Portion of Curve	Factor $\dfrac{b/t}{\sqrt{k}}$	Critical Buckling Shear Stress (τ_{cr}) Determined by
A to B	0 to $\dfrac{3820}{\sqrt{\tau_y}}$	$\tau_{cr} = \tau_y$
B to C	$\dfrac{3820}{\sqrt{\tau_y}}$ to $\dfrac{5720}{\sqrt{\tau_y}}$	$\tau_{cr} = 1.8\,\tau_y - n\dfrac{b/t}{\sqrt{k}}$ where: $n = \dfrac{\sqrt{\tau_y^3}}{4770}$
C to D	$\dfrac{5720}{\sqrt{\tau_y}}$ and over	$\tau_{cr} = \left[\dfrac{4434}{\dfrac{b/t}{\sqrt{k}}}\right]^2$

Another method makes no allowance for the central buckled portion as a load carrying member, it being assumed that the load is carried only by the supported portion of the plate. Hence the total compressive load would be--

$$P = A_1\,\sigma_1$$
$$= (10\tfrac{1}{2} \times \tfrac{1}{4})\,(33{,}000)$$
$$= \underline{86{,}600 \text{ lbs}}$$

6. BUCKLING OF PLATES UNDER SHEAR

The critical buckling shearing stress (τ_{cr}) of a plate when subject to shear forces (τt) may be expressed by the formula in Figure 7 (similar to that used for the critical buckling stress for plates in edge compression).

Values of k for Buckling Formula (Shear)

1. simply supported edges, $k = 5.34 + 4(b/a)^2$
2. fixed edges, $k = 8.98 + 5.60(b/a)^2$

It is usual practice to assume the edges simply supported.

Shear yield strength of steel (τ) is usually considered as $\dfrac{1}{\sqrt{3}}$ of the tensile yield strength (σ_y), or $.58\,\sigma_y$.

According to "Design Manual for High Strength Steels" by Priest & Gilligan, U. S. Steel Corp., the actual buckling shear stress (τ_{cr}) of flat plates in shear may be represented by the curve pattern in Figure 8. This specific curve is that of A-7 (mild) steel.

The curve is expressed in terms of $\left(\dfrac{b/t}{\sqrt{k}}\right)$. See Table 5. Comparison of Figure 8 and Table 5 with Figure 1 and Table 2 reveals the parallelism of critical buckling stress for compression (σ_{cr}) and for shear (τ_{cr}).

Figure 9 is just an enlargement of Figure 8, with additional steels having yield strengths from 33,000 psi to 100,000 psi. Factors needed for the formulas of curves in Figure 9 are given in Table 6.

For any value of $\left(\dfrac{b/a}{\sqrt{k}}\right)$ the critical buckling shear stress (τ_{cr}) can be read directly from the curves of this figure.

A suitable factor of safety must be used with these values since they represent ultimate stress values for buckling.

By holding the ratio of $\left(\dfrac{b/a}{\sqrt{k}}\right)$ to the value at point B, $\tau_{cr} = \tau_y$ and it will not be necessary to compute the critical shear stress (τ_{cr}). Assuming the edges are simply supported, the value of $k = 5.34 + 4(b/a)^2$. Then using just the three values of b/a as 1 (a square panel), ½ (the length twice the width of panel) and zero (or infinite length), the required b/t value is obtained from Table 7 for steels of various yield strengths. The plate thickness is then adjusted as necessary to meet the requirement.

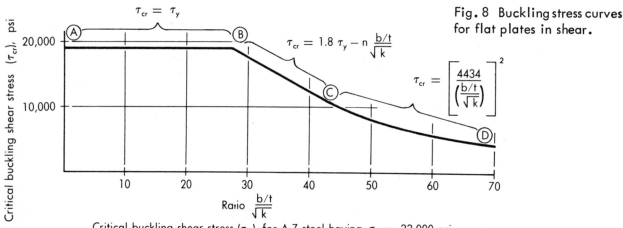

Fig. 8 Buckling stress curves for flat plates in shear.

Critical buckling shear stress (τ_{cr}), for A-7 steel having $\sigma_y = 33{,}000$ psi

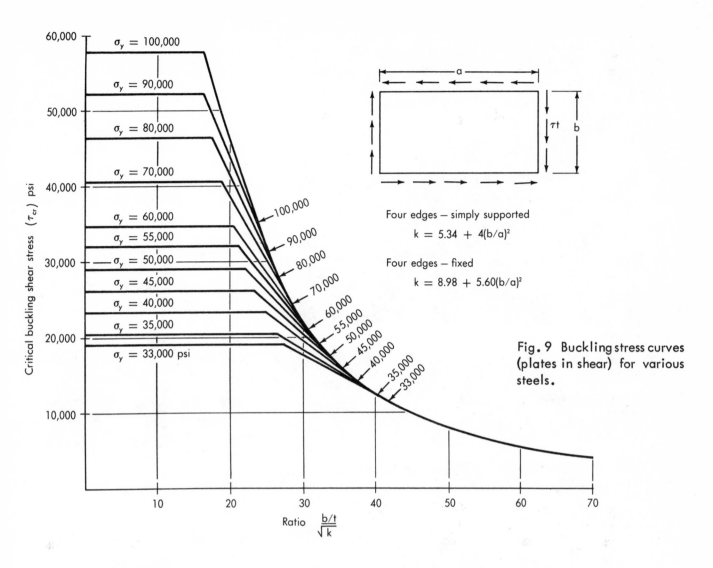

Four edges — simply supported

$$k = 5.34 + 4(b/a)^2$$

Four edges — fixed

$$k = 8.98 + 5.60(b/a)^2$$

Fig. 9 Buckling stress curves (plates in shear) for various steels.

TABLE 6 – FACTORS FOR BUCKLING FORMULAS (SHEAR)

Yield Strength of Steel σ_y psi	Corresponding Shearing Yield Strength $\tau_y = .58\,\sigma_y$ psi	$\dfrac{b/t}{\sqrt{k}}$ for point B $= \dfrac{3820}{\sqrt{\tau_y}}$	$\dfrac{b/t}{\sqrt{k}}$ for point C $= \dfrac{5720}{\sqrt{\tau_y}}$	$n = \dfrac{\sqrt[2]{\tau_y^3}}{4770}$
33,000	19,100	27.6	41.4	550
35,000	20,300	27.6	40.2	610
40,000	23,200	25.1	37.6	740
45,000	26,100	23.6	35.4	880
50,000	29,000	22.4	33.6	1030
55,000	31,900	21.4	32.1	1200
60,000	34,800	20.5	30.7	1360
70,000	40,600	19.0	28.4	1680
80,000	46,400	17.7	26.6	2100
90,000	52,200	16.7	25.1	2500
100,000	58,000	15.9	23.8	2920

TABLE 7 – MAXIMUM VALUES OF b/t TO AVOID FORMULAS

	Maximum Values of b/t to Hold τ_{cr} to τ_y (Panels with simply supported edges)		
Tensile Yield Strength σ_y psi	b/a = 1 (square panel)	b/a = 1/2 (panel with length twice the width)	b/a = 0 (panel with infinite length)
33,000	84.5	69.6	63.9
35,000	82.0	67.6	62.0
40,000	76.7	63.2	58.0
45,000	72.3	59.6	54.7
50,000	68.6	56.5	51.9
55,000	65.4	53.9	49.5
60,000	62.6	51.6	47.4
70,000	58.0	47.8	43.9
80,000	54.2	44.7	41.0
90,000	51.1	42.1	38.7
100,000	48.5	40.0	36.7

Truck design is in constant state of evolution. Welding plays a vital role in design flexibility and short delivery cycles, essential to contractors' schedules.

Both power shovels and trucks are exposed to high impact loads. Plate weldments can be accurately designed to withstand such loads, while higher-strength steels are widely used for low weight-to-strength ratios.

Designing for Impact Loads

1. NATURE OF IMPACT LOADING

Impact loading results not only from actual impact (or blow) of a moving body against the machine member, but is any sudden application of the load. It may occur in any of the following methods:

1. A direct impact, usually by another member or an external body moving with considerable velocity, as in a pile driver or a punch press.

2. Sudden application of forces, without a blow being involved.

   (a) The sudden creation of a force on a member, as during the explosive stroke in an engine.

   (b) The sudden moving of a force onto a member, as when a heavily loaded train or truck wheel moves rapidly over the floor of a bridge.

3. The inertia of a member resisting high accelerations or decelerations such as rapidly reciprocating levers, or when the machine is subjected to earthquake shocks or explosions in warfare.

From this, it will be observed that impact loading does not necessarily involve movement of a mass through a considerable distance. This is easily demonstrated: a bar resting on a weighing scale is lifted just clear of it and then released, showing that the force generated is momentarily greater than the static load. The same result is experienced when a lift truck rolls onto a weighing platform; here there is absolutely no striking of one body against the other. Yet, the loading phenomena are essentially the same. Perhaps the term "energy load" should be substituted for "impact load".

2. BASIC PHYSICAL LAWS

The analysis and solution of impact problems develop from a few basic laws and principles. These are reviewed briefly here, in linear terms, and are then summarized in Table 1, in both linear and angular terms.

● Velocity (V) is the rate at which a physical body changes position in space:

$$V = \frac{d}{t}$$

where:

d = distance through which the body moves during unit of time

t = time interval during which distance is measured (usually one second)

● Acceleration (a) and deceleration is the rate at which the velocity changes relative to time:

$$a = \frac{V - V_o}{t}$$

where:

V = final velocity, at moment when motion of the body is no longer considered

V_o = original velocity, at moment when motion of the body is first considered

t = elapsed time between moments when velocities V and V_o are determined

● Velocity of a falling body is--

$$V = \sqrt{2 g h}$$

where:

g = acceleration of gravity (386.4"/sec²)

h = height of fall

● Newton's first law: A body remains at rest or uniform motion unless acted upon by an external force.

● Newton's second law: An external force acting on a body accelerates the body in the direction of the force, and the acceleration is directly proportional to the force.

● In other words, force produces acceleration (a). In the application of this to impact forces on a member, the reverse is used, i. e. accelerating or decelerating a member produces a resisting force (F) on that member.

● Inertia is the property of a body which tends to resist a change in its state of rest or motion when an external force is applied.

$$F = \frac{W}{g} \, a$$

where W = weight of member, lbs

1

TABLE 1 - BASIC LAWS USED IN ANALYSIS OF IMPACT

	Linear	Angular
Mass	① $M = \dfrac{W}{g}$	⑩ $I = \dfrac{W}{g} r^2$ r = radius of gyration
Force	② F	⑪ $T = F d$ d = perpendicular distance from center of rotation to line of force
Velocity	③ $V = \dfrac{d}{t}$	⑫ $\omega = \dfrac{\theta}{t} = 2 \pi RPM = \dfrac{V}{r}$ r = radius of point for which ω is to be found
Acceleration	④ $a = \dfrac{V - V_o}{t}$	⑬ $\alpha = \dfrac{\omega - \omega_o}{t}$
Force of Impact	⑤ $F = \dfrac{W}{g} a$	⑭ $T = I\alpha$
Impulse	⑥ $F t$	⑮ $T t$
Momentum	⑦ $\dfrac{W}{g} V$	⑯ $I \omega$
Kinetic Energy	⑧ $\dfrac{W}{2g} V^2$	⑰ $\dfrac{I \omega^2}{2}$
Work	⑨ $F d$	⑱ $T \theta$

• Mass (M) is the quantity of matter in a body and is a measure of its inertia to change in velocity.

$$M = \frac{W}{g}$$

• Weight (W) is the force due to gravity exerted on a body toward the center of the earth.

• Momentum is the product of mass and velocity:

$$= \frac{W}{g} V$$

• Impulse is the product of a force and the time interval of its action:

$$= F t$$

• Impulse equals change in momentum:

$$F t = \frac{W}{g}(V_2 - V_1)$$

• Kinetic energy (E_k) is the amount of work which a body can do by virtue of its motion:

$$E_k = \frac{W}{2g} V^2$$

• Potential energy (E_p) is the amount of work which a body can do by virtue of its position (h = height of falling body):

$$E_p = W h$$

or state of strain:

$$E_p = \frac{\sigma \epsilon}{2} = \frac{\sigma^2}{2 E} \text{ (within elastic limit)}$$

3. APPROACH TO DESIGN PROBLEM

In many cases it is extremely difficult to evaluate impact forces quantitatively. The analysis of the problem is generally more of a qualitative nature and requires recognition of all of the factors involved and their inter-relationship.

There are two general methods to select from in designing members to withstand impact loads:

1. Estimate the maximum force exerted by the moving body on the resisting member by applying an impact factor. Consider this force to be a static load and use in standard design formulas.

2. Estimate the energy (kinetic energy $E_k = \dfrac{W V^2}{2 g}$) that is absorbed by the resisting member, and from this value determine the stresses or deformation by formulas for impact loads on members. This method is preferred for more accurate results.

The dimensions of the resisting member and the properties of the material in the member that give it maximum resistance to an energy load, are quite different from those that give the member maximum resistance to a static load. A metal may have good tensile strength and good ductility under static loading, and yet fracture if subjected to a high-velocity blow.

4. IMPACT FORCES

A body striking a member produces a force on the member because of its deceleration to zero velocity.

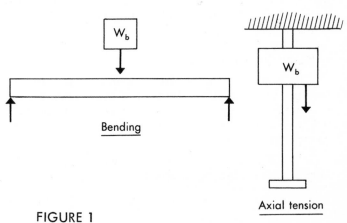

FIGURE 1

Force can then be expressed as -

$$F = \frac{W_b}{g} a$$

where:

W_b = weight of the body, lbs

a = deceleration of the body

g = acceleration of gravity (386.4 in/sec^2)

Fortunately the member will deflect slightly and allow a certain time (t) for the velocity (V) of the body (W_b) to come to rest, thereby reducing this impact force (F). Since this time interval (t) is not known, the above formula cannot be used directly to find the force (F). However, it is possible to solve for this force by finding the amount of kinetic energy (E_k) or potential energy (E_p) that must be absorbed by the member.

$$E_k = \frac{W_b}{g} V^2 \text{ or } E_p = W_b h$$

This energy (E_k) or (E_p) is then set equal to the energy (U) absorbed by the member within a given stress (σ), see Table 3.

5. INERTIA FORCES

When a member is accelerated or decelerated, a force (F) must be applied to it. See Figure 2.

$$F = \frac{W_m}{g} a$$

where W_m = weight of the member

Since the weight of the member (W_m) and the acceleration (a) may be known, the resulting inertia force (F) may be found from the above formula.

6. IMPACT PROPERTIES OF MATERIAL

The two most important properties of a material

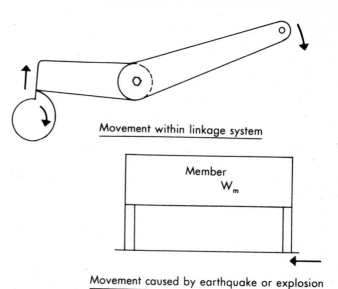

Movement within linkage system

Member W_m

Movement caused by earthquake or explosion

FIGURE 2

that indicate its resistance to impact loading, are obtained from the stress-strain diagram (Fig. 3).

The <u>modulus of resilience</u> (u) of a material is the energy it can absorb per unit volume when stressed to the proportional limit. This is represented on the tensile stress-strain diagram by the area under the curve defined by the triangle OAB, having its apex A at the elastic limit. For practicality let the yield strength (σ_y) be the altitude of the right triangle and the resultant strain (ϵ) be the base. Thus:

$$\boxed{u = \frac{\sigma_y^2}{2 E}} \dots \dots \dots \dots \dots \dots \dots \dots \dots \dots \dots (1)$$

The modulus of resilience represents the capacity of the material to absorb energy within its elastic range, i.e. without permanent deformation. Since the absorption of energy is actually a volumetric

FIGURE 3

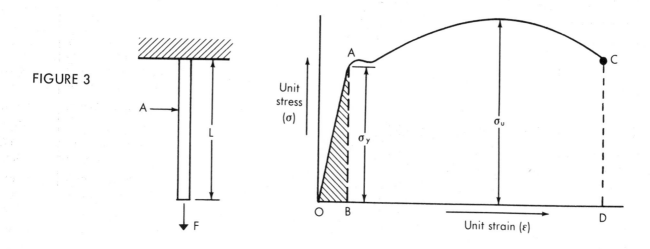

property, the u in (in.-lbs/in.³) = u in psi.

When impact loading exceeds the elastic limit (or yield strength) of the material, it calls for toughness in the material rather than resilience.

The ultimate energy resistance (u_u) of a material indicates its toughness or ability to resist fracture under impact loading. This is a measure of how well the material absorbs energy without fracture. A material's ultimate energy resistance is represented on the stress-strain diagram by the total area OACD under the curve. Here point A is at the material's yield strength (σ_y) and point C at its ultimate strength (σ_u). For ductile steel, the ultimate energy resistance is approximately--

$$u_u = A_{OACD} = \frac{\sigma_y + \sigma_u}{2} \epsilon_u \quad \dots \dots \dots \dots (2)$$

where:

ϵ_u = ultimate unit elongation, in./in.

Since the absorption of energy is actually a volumetric property, u_u in (in.-lbs/in.³) = u_u in psi.

Impact properties of common materials are charted in Table 2.

The maximum energy that can be absorbed by the member is affected by the member's dimensions. See left-hand sketch in Figure 3. Hence, the ultimate energy load is essentially Eq. 3.

$$U_u = \frac{\sigma_y + \sigma_u}{2} \epsilon_u A L \quad \dots \dots \dots \dots (3)$$

The total energy that can be absorbed elastically (without deformation) by the member is given as U by the various formulas of Table 3.

7. PROPERTIES OF SECTION

A glance at Table 3 will show that the property of the section which is needed to withstand impact loads or to absorb energy is the following:

$$\frac{I}{c^2}$$

In other words we are looking not only for high moment of inertia (I), but I/c^2. This is very important because as moment of inertia (I) increases with deeper sections, the distance from the neutral axis to the outer fiber (c) increases along with it, and it increases as the square. It is very possible that this increase in impact strength will not be as great as was expected.

TABLE 2 – IMPACT PROPERTIES OF COMMON DESIGN MATERIALS

Material	σ_y Tensile Proportional limit lbs/in.²	σ_u Tensile Ultimate Strength lbs/in.²	E Tensile Modulus of Elasticity lbs/in.²	ϵ_u Ultimate Unit Elongation in./in.	u Tensile Modulus of Resilience in.-lbs/in.³	u_u Toughness – Ultimate Energy Resistance in-lbs/in.³
Mild Steel	35,000	60,000	30×10^6	0.35	20.4	16,600
Low Alloy (under ¾") (¾ to 1½") (over 1½ to 4")	50,000 46,000 42,000	70,000 67,000 63,000	30×10^6 30×10^6 30×10^6	.18 .19 .19	41.6 35.2 29.4	
Medium carbon steel	45,000	85,000	30×10^6	0.25	33.7	16,300
High carbon steel	75,000	120,000	30×10^6	0.08	94.0	5,100
T-1 Steel	100,000	115,000 to 135,000	30×10^6	0.18	200.0*	about 9,400
Alloy Steel	200,000	230,000	30×10^6	0.12	667.0	22,000
Gray Cast Iron	6,000	20,000	15×10^6	0.05	1.2	70
Malleable Cast Iron	20,000	50,000	23×10^6	0.10	17.4	3,800

*Based on integrator-measured area under stress-strain curve.

TABLE 3 - IMPACT FORMULAS FOR COMMON MEMBER-LOAD CONDITIONS

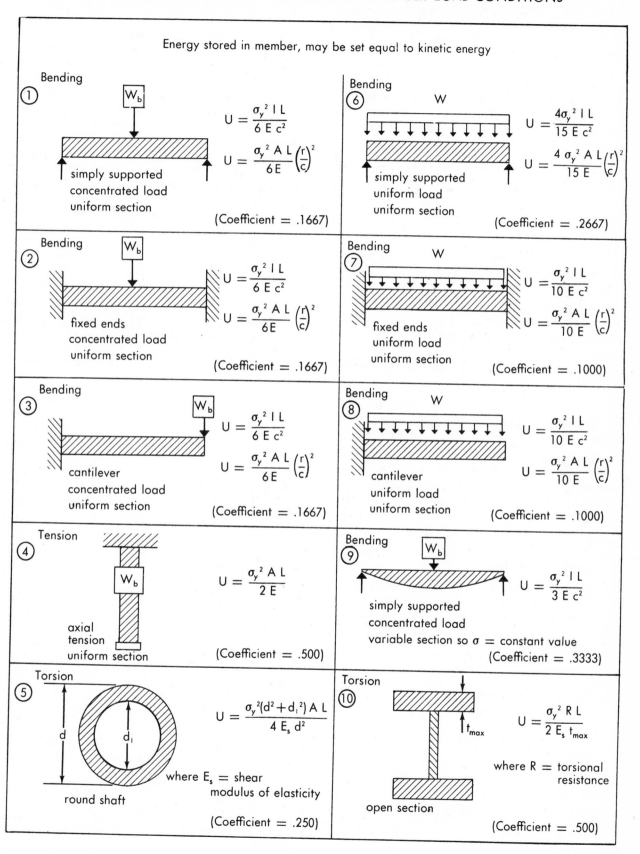

Energy stored in member, may be set equal to kinetic energy

Bending

① simply supported concentrated load uniform section

$$U = \frac{\sigma_y^2\, I\, L}{6\, E\, c^2}$$

$$U = \frac{\sigma_y^2\, A\, L}{6\, E}\left(\frac{r}{c}\right)^2$$

(Coefficient = .1667)

Bending

⑥ simply supported uniform load uniform section

$$U = \frac{4\sigma_y^2\, I\, L}{15\, E\, c^2}$$

$$U = \frac{4\, \sigma_y^2\, A\, L}{15\, E}\left(\frac{r}{c}\right)^2$$

(Coefficient = .2667)

Bending

② fixed ends concentrated load uniform section

$$U = \frac{\sigma_y^2\, I\, L}{6\, E\, c^2}$$

$$U = \frac{\sigma_y^2\, A\, L}{6\, E}\left(\frac{r}{c}\right)^2$$

(Coefficient = .1667)

Bending

⑦ fixed ends uniform load uniform section

$$U = \frac{\sigma_y^2\, I\, L}{10\, E\, c^2}$$

$$U = \frac{\sigma_y^2\, A\, L}{10\, E}\left(\frac{r}{c}\right)^2$$

(Coefficient = .1000)

Bending

③ cantilever concentrated load uniform section

$$U = \frac{\sigma_y^2\, I\, L}{6\, E\, c^2}$$

$$U = \frac{\sigma_y^2\, A\, L}{6\, E}\left(\frac{r}{c}\right)^2$$

(Coefficient = .1667)

Bending

⑧ cantilever uniform load uniform section

$$U = \frac{\sigma_y^2\, I\, L}{10\, E\, c^2}$$

$$U = \frac{\sigma_y^2\, A\, L}{10\, E}\left(\frac{r}{c}\right)^2$$

(Coefficient = .1000)

Tension

④ axial tension uniform section

$$U = \frac{\sigma_y^2\, A\, L}{2\, E}$$

(Coefficient = .500)

Bending

⑨ simply supported concentrated load variable section so σ = constant value

$$U = \frac{\sigma_y^2\, I\, L}{3\, E\, c^2}$$

(Coefficient = .3333)

Torsion

⑤ round shaft

$$U = \frac{\sigma_y^2(d^2 + d_1^2)\, A\, L}{4\, E_s\, d^2}$$

where E_s = shear modulus of elasticity

(Coefficient = .250)

Torsion

⑩ open section

$$U = \frac{\sigma_y^2\, R\, L}{2\, E_s\, t_{max}}$$

where R = torsional resistance

(Coefficient = .500)

Problem 1

For example, suppose there is a choice between these two beams:

Section Property	Beam A 12" WF 65# Beam	Beam B 24" WF 76# Beam
I	533. 4 in.^{4}	2096. 4 in.^{4}
c	6. 06 in	11. 96 in.
Steady load strength $S = \dfrac{I}{c}$	$\dfrac{533.4}{6.06} = 88.2$ in.^{3}	$\dfrac{2096.4}{11.96} = 175$ in.^{3}
Impact load strength $\dfrac{I}{c^2}$	$\dfrac{533.4}{(6.06)^2} = 14.5$ in.^{2}	$\dfrac{2096.4}{(11.96)^2} = 14.6$ in.^{2}

Under a steady load, beam B has a section modulus (S) twice that of beam A with a weight of only 1.17 times greater.

Under an impact load, beam B has no increase in strength, it is the same as beam A, and there would be no advantage in changing.

8. IMPROVING ENERGY ABSORPTION CAPACITY

The basic rule for the design of members for maximum energy absorption is to have the maximum volume of the member subjected to the maximum allowable stress. This means--

1. For any given cross-section, have the maximum amount of the area stressed to the maximum allowable. In the case of beams, place the greatest area of the section in the higher stressed portion at the outer fibers.

2. Choose sections so the member will be stressed to the maximum allowable stress along the entire length of the member.

Example (see sketch), a member subjected to axial tension. The entire cross-section is uniformly stressed to the maximum value and the entire length of the member is subjected to maximum stress.

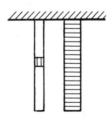

Example (see sketch), a variable depth beam designed for constant bending stress along its entire length. Although the cross-section at any

point is not uniformly stressed to the maximum value, the outer fiber is stressed to the maximum value for the entire length of the member.

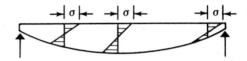

As an illustration, notice in Table 3 that the member in tension (No. 4) has 3 times the energy absorption capacity as the simple beam with a concentrated load (No. 1); this is a coefficient of ½ as against ⅙. This is because the tensile member (No. 4) has its entire cross-section uniformly stressed to maximum as well as for its full length. In contrast, beam No. 1 is not uniformly stressed throughout its cross-section, the maximum bending stress being at the outer fibers; nor is it stressed to maximum for its entire length, the bending stress decreasing away from the centerline, being zero at the two ends.

Notice in Table 3, that by decreasing the depth of the beam (No. 9) so as to have the same maximum bending stress along the entire length of the beam, the energy absorbing capacity of the beam has been doubled. This is a coefficient of ⅓ for beam No. 9 versus ⅙ for beam No. 1.

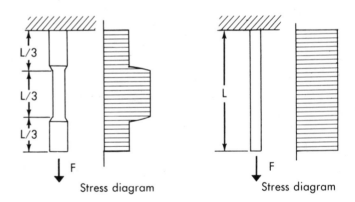

FIGURE 4

The two tensile bars in Figure 4 have equal strength under steady loads; yet, the uniform bar on the right has much more energy absorbing ability and can withstand a greater impact load.

Consider two beams of equal section, shown in Figure 5:

(1) For a steady load, doubling the length of the beam will double the resulting bending stress.

(2) For an impact load, doubling the length of the beam will reduce the resulting impact stress to 70.7% of the original.

Consider two beams made from identical bars, Figure 6:

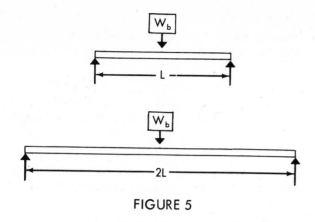

FIGURE 5

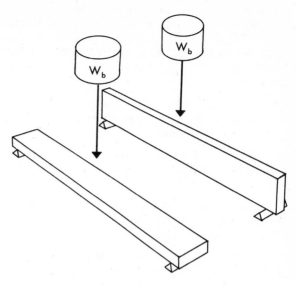

FIGURE 6

(1) For the same rectangular bar, both beams can theoretically absorb the same amount of energy and are just as strong under impact loading.

(2) The property of the section which determines this is I/c^2 and this is constant for a given rectangular area regardless of its position.

Summary

1. The property of the section which will reduce the impact stress in tension is increased volume (AL).

2. The property of the section which will reduce the impact stress in a simple beam is:

$$\text{increased} \sqrt{\frac{I\,L}{c^2}} \text{ or } = \frac{r}{c}\sqrt{A\,L}$$

3. In a simple beam, a decrease in length (L) will decrease the static stress, but will increase the stress due to impact.

4. In a simple tensile bar of a given uniform cross-section, increasing the length (l) will not alter the static stress yet it will decrease the stress due to impact.

9. NOTCH EFFECT ON ENERGY ABSORBING CAPACITY

In Figure 7, diagrams e and f represent the energy absorbed per unit length of member. The total energy absorbed is measured by the area under this diagram.

For example, assume the notch produces a stress concentration of twice the average stress (diagram d). Then for the same maximum stress, the average stress in the rest of the member will

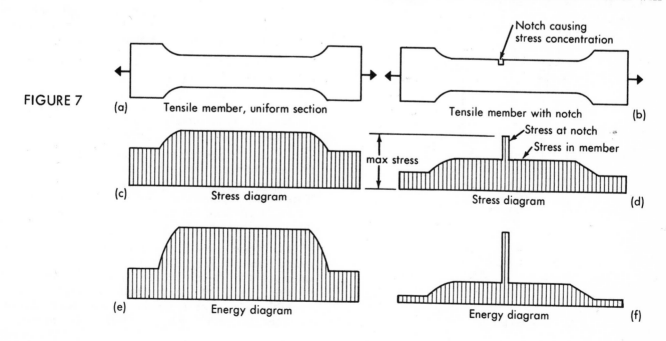

FIGURE 7

(a) Tensile member, uniform section

(b) Tensile member with notch — Notch causing stress concentration

(c) Stress diagram — max stress

(d) Stress diagram — Stress at notch / Stress in member

(e) Energy diagram

(f) Energy diagram

be reduced to ½ and the energy absorbed will be ¼ (diagram f) of the energy which would be absorbed if no notch were present (diagram e). For a stress concentration of three times the average stress, the energy absorbing ability of the member will be ⅑ , etc.

Notched bar impact test results are of very limited value to the design engineer, and in fact can at times be misleading:

(a) The test is highly artificial in respect to severe notch condition and manner of load condition.

(b) The results can be altered over a wide range by changing size, shape of notch, striking velocity, and temperature.

(c) The test does not simulate a load condition likely to be found in service.

(d) The test does not give quantitative values of the resistance of the material to energy loads.

10. REDUCTION IN ENERGY STRESS DUE TO INERTIA OF RESISTING MEMBER

In the formulas, Table 3, the mass of the member (M_m) has been neglected. Naturally some energy is lost due to the inertia of the member and less energy is left to stress the member. With heavy members this becomes more effective.

11. REDUCTION IN ENERGY STRESS BY SPRING SUPPORT OF RESISTING MEMBER

The use of energy absorbing devices such as springs, rubber pads, or hydraulic cushions will absorb some of the kinetic energy and thereby reduce the energy absorbed by the member.

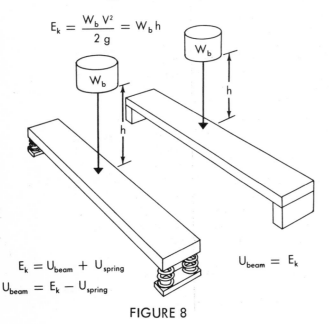

$$E_k = \frac{W_b V^2}{2 g} = W_b h$$

$$E_k = U_{beam} + U_{spring}$$

$$U_{beam} = E_k - U_{spring}$$

$$U_{beam} = E_k$$

FIGURE 8

12. GUIDES TO DESIGNING FOR IMPACT

Under impact loading the member is required to absorb a certain amount of kinetic or potential energy. It is important to:

1. Design the member as an energy absorbing system, that is to have the maximum volume of material stressed to the highest working stress; this increases the energy absorbed.

2. For any given cross-section of the member, have the maximum area subjected to the maximum allowable stress. Stress the entire length of the member to this maximum.

3. Reduce stress concentrations to a minimum and avoid abrupt changes in section.

4. Use the impact formulas (Table 3) as a guide to the proper design of the member rather than as an actual determination of the impact stress or impact deformation.

5. In general with steel, as the speed of loading is increased, the yield strength has a noticeable increase.

6. Material should have a high modulus of resilience $u = \sigma_y^2/2E$. This is the energy absorbed per unit volume. Although a lower modulus of elasticity (E) appears to be helpful, materials of lower (E) generally have correspondingly lower values of yield strength(σ_y), and this latter value is more important because it is squared. Therefore steels with higher yield strengths have higher values of modulus of resilience and are better for impact.

7. The material should have sufficient ductility to relieve the stress in any area of high stress concentration.

8. The material should have high fatigue strength, although this is not considered to be so important as high yield strength.

9. Place material so that the direction of hot rolling (of sheet or bar in steel mill) is in line with impact force, because the impact strength in this direction is higher than if impact occurs at right angles with the direction of rolling.

10. It is important to restrict the weight of the member and yet maintain proper rigidity of the member for its particular use or service. This means light-weight, well-stiffened members having sufficient moment of inertia (I) should be used.

11. Where required to build in protection against inertia forces caused by the rapid movement of the member due to earthquakes, explosions, etc., it is important to decrease the possible acceleration and/or deceleration of this member through some form of flexible support.

Designing for Fatigue Loads

1. ENDURANCE LIMIT

When the load on a member is constantly varying in value, or is repeated at relatively high frequency, or constitutes a complete reversal of stresses with each operating cycle, the material's endurance limit must be substituted for the ultimate strength where called for by the design formulas.

Under high load values, the variable or fatigue mode of loading reduces the material's effective ultimate strength as the number of cycles increases. At a given high stress value, the material has a definite service or fatigue life, expressed as N cycles of operations. Conversely, at a given number of service cycles the material has a definite allowable fatigue strength.

The endurance limit is the maximum stress to which the material can be subjected for a given service life.

2. NATURE OF FATIGUE LOADING

Fatigue failure is a progressive failure over a period of time which is started by a plastic movement within a localized region. Although the average unit stresses across the entire cross-section may be below the yield point, a non-uniform distribution of these stresses may cause them to exceed the yield point within a small area and cause plastic movement. This eventually produces a minute crack. The localized plastic movement further aggravates the non-uniform stress distribution, and further plastic movement causes the crack to progress. The stress is important only in that it causes the plastic movement.

Any fatigue test usually shows considerable scatter in the results obtained. This results from the wide range of time required before the initial crack develops in the specimen. Once this has occurred, the subsequent time to ultimate failure is fairly well confined and proceeds in a rather uniform manner.

The designer when first encountering a fatigue loading problem will often use the material's endurance limit or fatigue strength value given in his engineering handbook, without fully considering what this value represents and how it was obtained. This procedure could lead to serious trouble.

There are many types of fatigue tests, types of loading, and types of specimens. Theoretically the fatigue value used by the designer should be determined in a test that exactly duplicates the actual service conditions. The sample used should preferably be identical to the machine member, the testing machine should reproduce the actual service load, and the fatigue cycle and frequency should be the same as would be encountered in actual service. For example, if the actual problem is a butt weld in tension, the allowable fatigue strength used in the design must come from data obtained from loading a butt weld in axial tension on a pulsating type of fatigue testing machine, with the same range of stress.

3. ANALYZING THE FATIGUE LOAD

Figure 1 illustrates a typical fatigue load pattern, the curve representing the applied stress at any given moment of time.

There are two ways to represent this fatigue load:

1. As a mean or average stress (σ_m) with a superimposed variable stress (σ_v).

2. As a stress varying from a maximum value (σ_{max}) to a minimum (σ_{min}). Here, the cycle can be represented by the ratio —

$$K = \frac{\sigma_{min}}{\sigma_{max}}$$

FIGURE 1

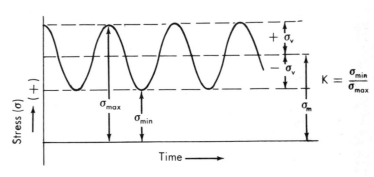

One approach to this problem is to let the variable stress (σ_v) be the ordinate and the steady or mean stress (σ_m) be the abscissa. When the mean stress (σ_m) is zero, see Figure 2, the variable stress (σ_v) becomes the value for a complete reversal of stress (σ_r). This value would have to be determined by experimental testing, and becomes point b in the diagram. When there is no variation in stress, i.e. a steady application of stress, σ_v becomes zero, and the maximum resulting mean stress (σ_m) is equal to the ultimate stress for a steady load (σ_u); this becomes point a.

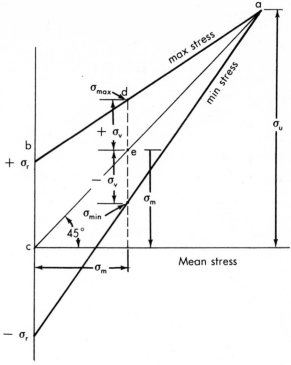

FIGURE 3

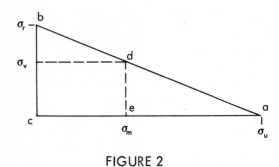

FIGURE 2

where:

   σ_r = fatigue strength for a complete reversal of stress

   σ_v = variable stress which is superimposed upon steady stress

   σ_u = ultimate strength under steady load
   (Some set σ_u equal to the yield strength, σ_y.)

   σ_m = mean stress (average stress)

A line connecting points b and a will indicate the relationship between the variable stress (σ_v) and the mean stress (σ_m) for any type of fatigue cycle, for a given fatigue life (N). This straight line will yield conservative values; almost all of the test data will lie just outside of this line.

From similar triangles it is found that--

$$\frac{\sigma_v}{\sigma_r} + \frac{\sigma_m}{\sigma_u} = 1$$

A Goodman diagram, Figure 3, is constructed from Figure 2 by moving point a vertically to a height equal to σ_u; in other words, line a-c now lies at a 45° angle.

It can be shown by similar triangles that the same relationship holds:

$$\frac{\sigma_v}{\sigma_r} + \frac{\sigma_m}{\sigma_u} = 1$$

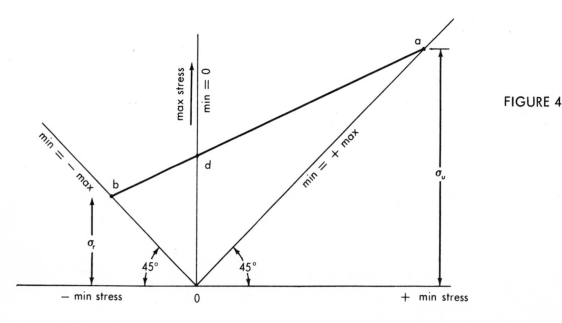

FIGURE 4

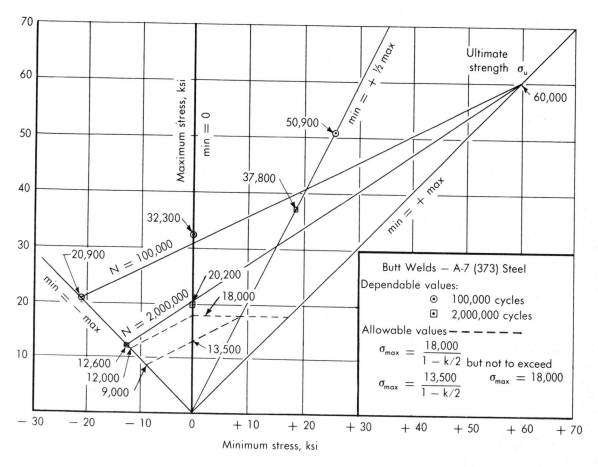

FIGURE 5

The Goodman diagram of Figure 3 may be modified so that the ordinate becomes the maximum stress (σ_{max}) and the abscissa becomes the minimum stress (σ_{min}); see Figure 4. It can be proved that all three diagrams yield the same results. The American Welding Society (Bridge Specification) uses this last type of diagram to illustrate their fatigue data test results.

If the maximum stress (σ_{max}) lies on line a-b, this value is found to be--

$$\sigma_{max} = \frac{2\,\sigma_r\,\sigma_u}{\sigma_u + \sigma_r - K(\sigma_u - \sigma_r)}$$

where $K = \dfrac{\sigma_{min}}{\sigma_{max}}$

The next diagram, Figure 5, is constructed with the values for complete reversal(σ_r) and the ultimate strength (σ_u) for butt welds in tension. The fatigue data from test results are also plotted. Notice the values lie on or slightly above these straight lines for service life (N) of 100,000 cycles and that of 2 million cycles.

These "dependable values" have been reduced to some extent below the minimum values obtained in the test. A factor of safety is applied to obtain al-

lowable values; these are shown by dotted lines. This is expressed as a formula along with a value which should not be exceeded. In this case, the maximum allowable is 18,000 psi. This formula represents the slanting line, but a maximum value must be indicated so that it is not carried too far.

Figure 6 illustrates several types of fatigue cycles, with corresponding K values to be used in the fatigue strength formulas.

4. ALLOWABLE MAXIMUM STRESS

Fatigue strength formulas, for determining the allowable maximum stress for a given service life of N cycles, are presented in Table 1 for A-7 mild steel and in Table 2 for T-1, quenched and tempered high yield strength steel.

Required fatigue life or number of cycles will vary but usually starts at several hundred thousand cycles. It is assumed that by the time the value of several million cycles is reached, the fatigue strength has leveled off and further stress cycles would not produce failure. For any particular specimen and stress cycle there is a relationship between the fatigue strength (σ) and fatigue life (N) in number of cycles before failure. The following empirical formula may be used to convert fatigue strengths from one fatigue life to another:

$$\sigma_a = \sigma_b \left(\frac{N_b}{N_a}\right)^k$$

where:

σ_a = fatigue strength for fatigue life N_a

σ_b = fatigue strength for fatigue life N_b

N_a = fatigue life for fatigue strength σ_a

N_b = fatigue life for fatigue strength σ_b

The constant (k) will vary slightly with the specimen; however, 0.13 has been widely used for butt welds and 0.18 for plate in axial loading (tension and/or compression).

The curve in Figure 7 illustrates the general increase in fatigue life when the applied fatigue stress is reduced. As an example, in this case, reducing the fatigue stress to 75% of its normal value will in general increase the fatigue life about nine times.

TABLE 1 – ALLOWABLE FATIGUE STRESS
for A7, A373 And A36 Steels And their Welds

	2,000,000 cycles	600,000 cycles	100,000 cycles	But Not to Exceed
Base Metal In Tension Connected By Fillet Welds But not to exceed ➤	① $\sigma = \dfrac{7500}{1 - 2/3\,K}$ psi P_t	③ $\sigma = \dfrac{10,500}{1 - 2/3\,K}$ psi P_t	⑤ $\sigma = \dfrac{15,000}{1 - 2/3\,K}$ psi P_t	$\dfrac{2\,P_c}{3\,K}$ psi
Base Metal Compression Connected By Fillet Welds	② $\sigma = \dfrac{7500}{1 - 2/3\,K}$ psi	④ $\sigma = \dfrac{10,500}{1 - 2/3\,K}$ psi	⑥ $\sigma = \dfrac{15,000}{1 - 2/3\,K}$ psi	P_c psi $\dfrac{P_c}{1 - \frac{K}{2}}$ psi
Butt Weld In Tension	⑦ $\sigma = \dfrac{16,000}{1 - \frac{8}{10}K}$ psi	⑪ $\sigma = \dfrac{17,000}{1 - \frac{7}{10}K}$ psi	⑮ $\sigma = \dfrac{18,000}{1 - \frac{K}{2}}$ psi	P_t psi
Butt Weld Compression	⑧ $\sigma = \dfrac{18,000}{1 - K}$ psi	⑫ $\sigma = \dfrac{18,000}{1 - .8K}$ psi	⑯ $\sigma = \dfrac{18,000}{1 - \frac{K}{2}}$ psi	P_c psi
Butt Weld In Shear	⑨ $\tau = \dfrac{9,000}{1 - \frac{K}{2}}$ psi	⑬ $\tau = \dfrac{10,000}{1 - \frac{K}{2}}$ psi	⑰ $\tau = \dfrac{13,000}{1 - \frac{K}{2}}$ psi	13,000 psi
Fillet Welds ω = Leg Size	⑩ $f = \dfrac{5100\,\omega}{1 - \frac{K}{2}}$ lb/in.	⑭ $f = \dfrac{7100\,\omega}{1 - \frac{K}{2}}$ lb/in.	⑱ $f = \dfrac{8800\,\omega}{1 - \frac{K}{2}}$ lb/in.	$8800\,\omega$ lb/in.

Adapted from AWS Bridge Specifications.   K = min/max

P_c = Allowable unit compressive stress for member.

P_t = Allowable unit tensile stress for member.

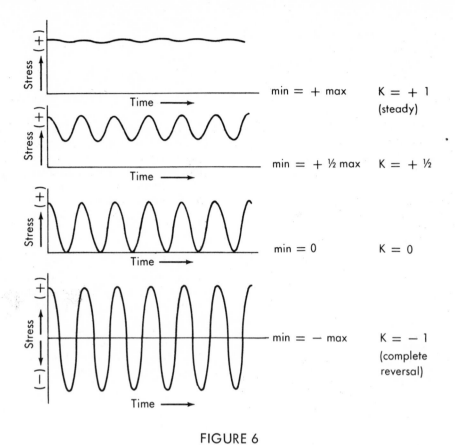

FIGURE 6

TABLE 2 - ALLOWABLE FATIGUE STRESS
for Quenched & Tempered Steels of High Yield Strength
And their Welds

	2,000,000 cycles	600,000 cycles	100,000 cycles	But Not to Exceed
Base Metal In Tension-Not Adjacent to Welds	① $\sigma = \dfrac{29,000}{1-.65K}$ psi	② $\sigma = \dfrac{33,000}{1-.60K}$ psi	③ $\sigma = \dfrac{39,500}{1-.50K}$ psi	$\sigma = 54,000$ psi
Butt Weld In Tension	④ $\sigma = \dfrac{16,500}{1-.80K}$ psi	⑤ $\sigma = \dfrac{21,000}{1-.75K}$ psi	⑥ $\sigma = \dfrac{31,000}{1-.60K}$ psi	$\sigma = 54,000$ psi
Fillet Weld ω = leg size	⑦ $f = \dfrac{6,360\,\omega}{1-.80K}$ lbs/in.	⑧ $f = \dfrac{9,900\,\omega}{1-.75K}$ lbs/in.	⑨ $f = \dfrac{14,500\,\omega}{1-.60K}$ lbs/in.	$f = 26,160\,\omega$ lbs/in.

Above values adapted from "The Fabrication and Design of Structures
of T-1 Steel" by Gilligan and England, United States Steel Corporation.

Problem 1

Test data indicates a fatigue life of $N_a = 1,550,000$ cycles when the member is stressed to $\sigma_a = 30,000$ psi. What would be the fatigue strength at a life of $2,000,000$ cycles?

Since:

$$\frac{\sigma_a}{\sigma_b} = \left(\frac{N_b}{N_a}\right)^k \quad \text{(For butt welds, k = 0.13)}$$

or: $\quad \dfrac{\sigma_b}{\sigma_a} = \left(\dfrac{N_a}{N_b}\right)^k$

and:

$$\frac{\sigma_b}{30,000} = \left(\frac{1,550,000}{2,000,000}\right)^{.13} = (0.775)^{.13}$$

Using logarithms* for the right hand side:

$= 0.13(\log 0.775) = 0.13(9.88930 - 10)$

$= 1.285609 \quad -1.3 \quad$ (add 8.7 to left side and sub-

$+ 8.7 \qquad\quad -8.7 \quad$ tract 8.7 from right side)

$\overline{\quad 9.985609 \quad -10.0}$

---

* A log-log slide rule could be used to find the value of 0.775 raised to the 0.13 power.

The anti-log of this is 0.96740; hence:

$$\frac{\sigma_b}{30,000} = 0.96740$$

$$\sigma_b = 30,000 \times 0.96740$$

$$= \underline{29,020} \text{ psi (at } N_b = 2,000,000 \text{ cycles)}$$

The nomograph, Figure 8, further facilitates such conversion and permits quickly finding the relative allowable stress for any required fatigue life provided the fatigue strength at some one fatigue life is known and that the constant k value has been established. Conversely, the relative fatigue life can be readily found for any given stress and any constant (k).

5. RELATIVE SEVERITY OF FATIGUE PROBLEM

In Figure 9, the allowable fatigue stress is the vertical axis (ordinate) and the type of fatigue stress cycle (K=min/max) is the horizontal axis (abscissa).

The extreme right-hand vertical line (K = +1) represents a steady stress. As we proceed to the left, the severity of the fatigue cycle increases; finally at the extreme left-hand axis (K = −1)

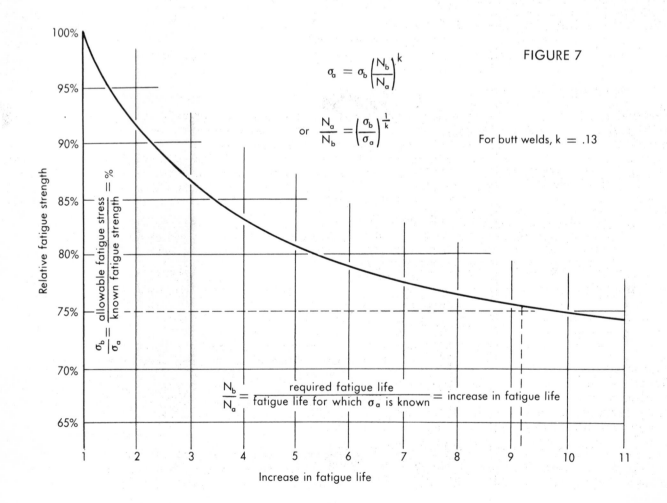

$$\sigma_a = \sigma_b \left(\frac{N_b}{N_a}\right)^k$$

or $\quad \dfrac{N_a}{N_b} = \left(\dfrac{\sigma_b}{\sigma_a}\right)^{\frac{1}{k}}$

For butt welds, k = .13

FIGURE 7

$$\frac{N_b}{N_a} = \frac{\text{required fatigue life}}{\text{fatigue life for which } \sigma_a \text{ is known}} = \text{increase in fatigue life}$$

Relative fatigue strength

$\sigma_b = \dfrac{\text{allowable fatigue stress}}{\text{known fatigue strength}} = \%$

Increase in fatigue life

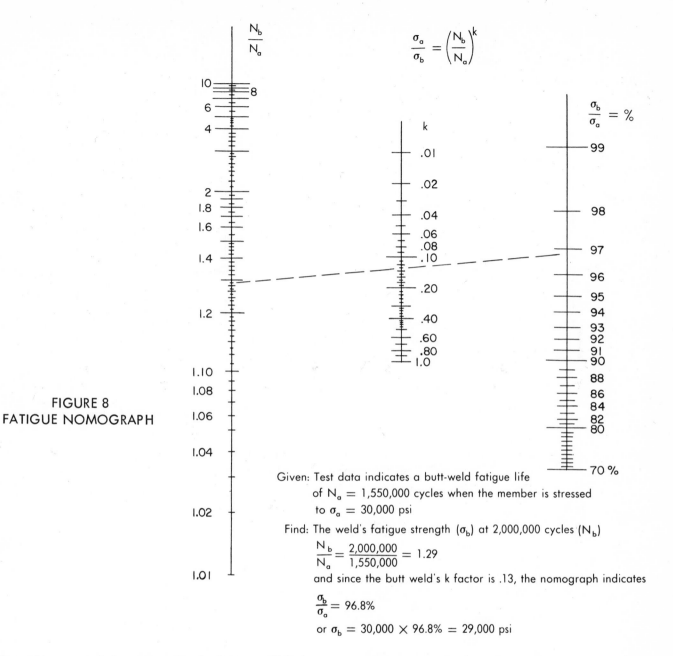

$$\frac{\sigma_a}{\sigma_b} = \left(\frac{N_b}{N_a}\right)^k$$

FIGURE 8
FATIGUE NOMOGRAPH

Given: Test data indicates a butt-weld fatigue life
of $N_a = 1,550,000$ cycles when the member is stressed
to $\sigma_a = 30,000$ psi

Find: The weld's fatigue strength (σ_b) at 2,000,000 cycles (N_b)

$$\frac{N_b}{N_a} = \frac{2,000,000}{1,550,000} = 1.29$$

and since the butt weld's k factor is .13, the nomograph indicates

$$\frac{\sigma_b}{\sigma_a} = 96.8\%$$

or $\sigma_b = 30,000 \times 96.8\% = 29,000$ psi

there is a complete reversal of stress. This is just one method of illustrating fatigue stress conditions. The important thing to be noticed here is that actual fatigue strength or allowable fatigue values are not reduced below the steady stress condition until the type of cycle (K = min/max) has progressed well into the fatigue type of loading.

In the case of 2 million cycles, the minimum stress must drop down to ½ of the maximum stress before there is any reduction of allowable strength. In the case of 100,000 cycles, the minimum stress can drop to zero before any reduction of allowable strength takes place. Even at these levels, the member and welds would be designed as though they were subjected to a steady load. The stress cycle must extend into a wider range of fluctu-

ation before it becomes necessary to use lower fatigue allowables.

In other words, a fatigue problem occurs only if—

1. Stress is very high,
2. Anticipated service extends for a great number of cycles,
3. Stress fluctuates over a wide range.

And it generally requires all three of these situations occuring simultaneously to produce a critical fatigue condition worthy of consideration.

The allowable fatigue strength values obtained from the formulas in Table 1 take all three of these into consideration, and it is believed they will result in a conservative design.

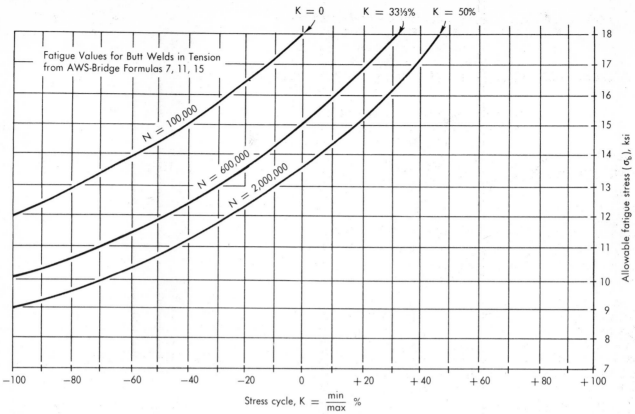

Fig. 9 Severity of fatigue depends on stress value and range of fluctuation, as well as service life.

TABLE 3 – FATIGUE STRENGTH OF BUTT WELDS
Summary of Results, Using 7/8-In. Carbon-Steel Plates

Description of Specimen	Fatigue Strength in 1000's of psi					
	Tension to an Equal Compression		0 to Tension		Tension to Tension 1/2 as Great	
	N = 100,000	N = 2,000,000	N = 100,000	N = 2,000,000	N = 100,000	N = 2,000,000
As Welded	22.3	14.4	33.1	22.5	53.3	36.9
Reinforcement On Stress Relieved	21.3	15.1	31.9	23.7		37.6
Reinforcement Machined Off Not Stress Relieved	28.9		48.8	28.4		43.7
Reinforcement Machined Off Stress Relieved	24.5	16.6	49.4	27.8		42.6
Reinforcement Ground Off Not Stress Relieved	26.8		44.5	26.3		
Plain Plate Mill Scale On	27.7	17.1	49.8	31.6		50.0
Plain Plate Mill Scale Machined Off and Surface Polished			59.6			
Butt Weld. Reinforcement and Mill Scale Machined Off and Surface Polished			53.9			

TABLE 4 – EFFECT OF TRANSVERSE ATTACHMENTS ON FATIGUE STRENGTH

$K = \dfrac{min}{max.} = -1$			
100,000 CYCLES	25,800 psi	25,400 psi	22,900 psi
2,000,000 CYCLES	22,800 psi	18,900 psi	13,100 psi

6. COMBINED FATIGUE STRESSES

Several formulas are available for this consideration but very little actual testing has been done on this. In many cases there is not very good agreement between the actual test and the formulas.

1. Principal-stress theory —

$$\sigma_e = \frac{\sigma_x + \sigma_y}{2} + \tfrac{1}{2}\sqrt{(\sigma_x - \sigma_y)^2 + 4\,\tau_{xy}^2}$$

2. Maximum shear-stress theory —

$$\sigma_e = \sqrt{(\sigma_x - \sigma_y)^2 + 4\,\tau_{xy}^2}$$

3. Shear-stress-invariant theory —

$$\sigma_e = \sqrt{\sigma_x^2 - \sigma_x\sigma_y + \sigma_y^2 + 3\,\tau_{xy}^2}$$

4. Combined bending and torsion. Findley corrected shear-stress theory for anistrophy —

$$\sigma_e = \sqrt{\sigma_x^2 + \left(\frac{\sigma_b}{\tau}\right)^2 \tau_{xy}^2}$$

where σ_b/τ is the ratio of fatigue strength in pure bending to that in pure tension.

5. Combined tensile stresses. Gough suggests —

$$\frac{\sigma_x^2}{\sigma_{ox}^2} + \frac{\sigma_y^2}{\sigma_{oy}^2} = 1$$

where:

σ_{ox} = fatigue strength in (x) direction

σ_{oy} = fatigue strength in (y) direction

σ_x and σ_y = applied stresses

7. INFLUENCE OF JOINT DESIGN

Any abrupt change of section along the path of stress flow will reduce the fatigue strength. It is not welding that effects a reducing of the fatigue strength but the resultant shape or geometry of the section. It is for this reason that fillet welds have lower fatigue strength, simply because they are used in lap joints and all lap joints including riveted joints have lower fatigue strength.

By means of Table 3, we can see that removing the reinforcement of a butt weld increases its fatigue strength to that of unwelded plate, also that stress relieving the weld has no appreciable effect on its fatigue strength.

Table 4 illustrates the effect of transverse fillet welds upon the fatigue strength of plate; this is ⅝″ plate.

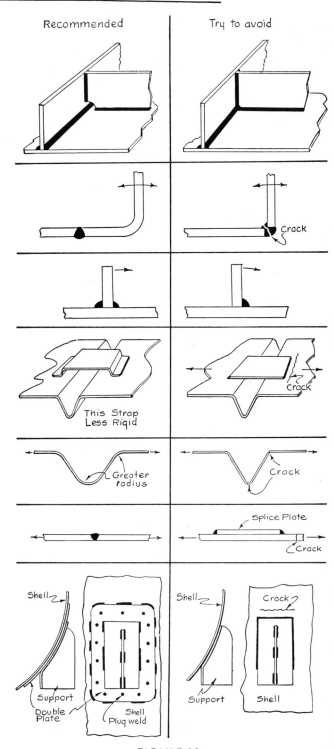

FIGURE 10

The attachment causes an abrupt change in section, and this reduces the fatigue strength of the plate. It is believed these results could be duplicated by machining these joints out of solid plate, without any welding.

Figure 10 presents some general recommendations on joint design when fatigue loading is a problem.

8. GUIDES TO DESIGNING FOR FATIGUE LOADING

1. In general, a machine is stressed to the full maximum value for only a portion of its fatigue life or cycles. For most of its fatigue life, the machine is stressed to a much lower value, and not to its full rated capacity; hence, most fatigue loading is not as severe as it may first appear.

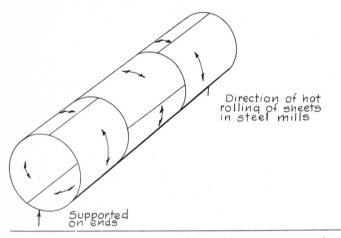

Direction of hot rolling of sheets in steel mills

Supported on ends

Recomended method if fatigue or impact Loading

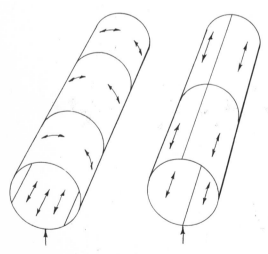

Direction of hot rolling of sheets in steel mills
Recomend at least on bottom half or third, or whole tank, sheets be run lengthwise with tank

Fig. 11 Grain direction of sheet or plate should be in line with force, for greater fatigue strength

Consider actual stress rather than average stress.

Reduce if possible the range of stress without increasing the maximum or average stress.

2. Fatigue loading requires careful fabrication, smooth transition of sections.

Avoid attachments and openings at locations of high stress.

Avoid sharp corners.

Use simple butt weld instead of lap or T fillet weld.

Grinding the reinforcement off of butt welds will increase the fatigue strength. This weld will have about the same fatigue strength as unwelded plate. Grinding, however, should not be specified unless essential, since it does add to the final unit cost.

Avoid excessive reinforcement, undercut, overlap, lack of penetration, roughness of weld.

Avoid placing weld in an area which flexes.

Stress relieving the weld has no appreciable effect upon fatigue strength.

Difficulties are sometimes caused by the welds being too small, or the members too thin.

3. Under critical loading, place material so that the direction of rolling (of sheet in steel mill) is in line with force, because the fatigue strength may be higher in this direction than if placed at right angles with the direction of rolling. See Figure 11.

4. Where possible, form member into shape that it tends to assume under load, and hence prevent the resulting flexial movement.

5. Avoid operating in the critical or resonant frequency of individual member or whole structure to avoid excessive amplitude.

6. Perhaps consider prestressing a beam in axial compression. This will reduce the tensile bending stress and lessen chance for fatigue failure even though the compressive bending stress is increased to some extent.

7. Avoid eccentric application of loads which may cause additional flexing with each application of load.

8. Stiffeners decrease flexibility of member and result in better fatigue strength, unless it causes a more abrupt change of section. If the latter should happen, the stiffeners may do more harm than good.

9. A rigid frame type of structure or statically indeterminate type of structure may be better than a simple structure since the load is shared by other members; hence, the structure is less likely to collapse immediately if a fatigue failure starts in one member. This will result in a more gradual failure of one part, then another, and this would

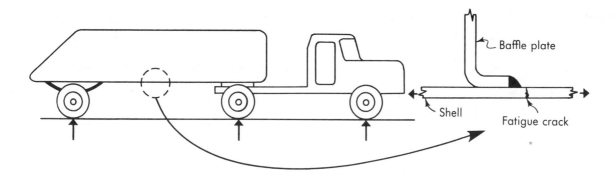

FIGURE 12

provide a better opportunity to notice that a fatigue failure is in progress.

10. Avoid biaxial and triaxial stresses, avoid restrained internal sections.

| Problem 2 |

Which type of steel should be selected for the following fatigue loads for minimum weight of material?

Case A

A built-up beam subjected to a complete reversal of a stress. The flange plates are subject to alternating tension and compression.

$$K = \frac{min}{max} = -1 \qquad N = 2,000,000 \text{ cycles}$$

From Tables 1 and 2, formulas for butt welds in tension:

A-7 Steel	T-1 Steel
$\sigma = \dfrac{16,000}{1 - \frac{1}{2}(-1)}$ psi $= 10,670$ psi	$\sigma = \dfrac{16,500}{1 - .8(-1)}$ psi $= 9,170$ psi

In this case, A-7 (mild steel) would be selected because it has about the same fatigue allowable as T-1 steel.

Case B

The web plates of a pump crankcase are connected to the face plate supporting the cylinders and bearings of the crankshaft. Compression is on the forward stroke only. Each web is subjected to axial tension only, and under the worse conditions drops to about 75% of the maximum tension, hence:

$$K = \frac{min}{max} = + .75 \qquad N = 2,000,000 \text{ cycles}$$

From Tables 1 and 2, formulas for butt welds in tension:

A-7 Steel	T-1 Steel
$\sigma = \dfrac{16,000}{1 - .375}$ psi $= 25,600$ psi (but not to exceed 18,000 psi — AWS-Bridge Spec)	$\sigma = \dfrac{16,500}{1 - .60}$ psi $= 41,200$ psi

In this case, T-1 steel would be selected because it has 2.29 times the allowable fatigue stress as A-7 (mild steel), and would require just 44% of the plate thickness and weight.

| Problem 3 |

After three years service a tank trailer is developing fatigue cracks in its 12-ga bottom shell, adjacent to an internal baffle plate. It is necessary to improve this so it will last for the expected life of the unit which is 20 years. See Figure 12.

Although the tank trailer is subject to bending, the bottom shell is mainly in tension. Fatigue data for butt welds in tension will be used.

$$\frac{\sigma_a}{\sigma_b} = \left(\frac{N_b}{N_a}\right)^{.13}$$

Here $\sigma = \dfrac{P}{A}$ or $= \dfrac{\text{force, lbs/in}}{\text{thickness}} = \dfrac{f}{t}$

So $\dfrac{f/t_a}{f/t_b} = \left(\dfrac{3 \text{ yrs}}{20 \text{ yrs}}\right)^{.13}$ or $\dfrac{t_b}{t_a} = \left(\dfrac{3}{20}\right)^{.13} = .782$

and $t_a = \dfrac{t_b}{.782} = \dfrac{(12 \text{ Ga} = .1046")}{.782}$

$= \underline{.1338"}$

or use 10-ga steel (t = .1345")

To avoid using the above fatigue formula, the curve in Figure 7 could be used. An extension in life of about 6⅓ times is desired. The curve indicates this can be obtained by reducing the fatigue stress to about 78% of the original. This reduction in stress could be obtained with a sheet thickness 1.28 times the original, or 10-gage.

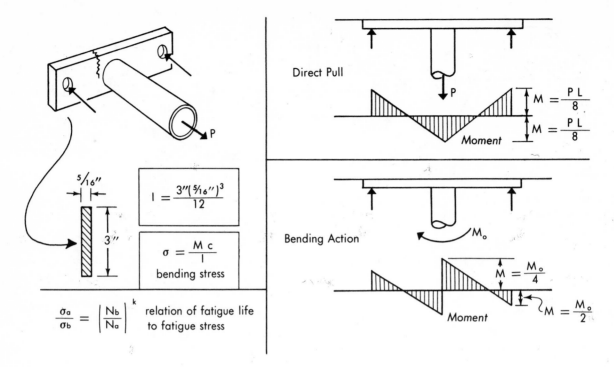

$$I = \frac{3''(\sfrac{5}{16}'')^3}{12}$$

$$\sigma = \frac{M\,c}{I}$$
bending stress

$$\frac{\sigma_a}{\sigma_b} = \left|\frac{N_b}{N_a}\right|^k \quad \begin{array}{l}\text{relation of fatigue life}\\\text{to fatigue stress}\end{array}$$

Direct Pull

$$M = \frac{P\,L}{8}$$

$$M = \frac{P\,L}{8}$$

Moment

Bending Action

$$M = \frac{M_o}{4}$$

$$M = \frac{M_o}{2}$$

Moment

FIGURE 13

Problem 4

A bracket (Fig. 13) on a farm implement machine is failing in fatigue after about 1 year in service. If we should increase the thickness of the bracket from $\sfrac{5}{16}''$ to $\sfrac{3}{8}''$, what extension in fatigue life can we expect?

From the above analysis of loading, it is apparent that fatigue failure is the result of the tensile stresses from both bending moments. For lack of fatigue data for plate in bending we shall use fatigue data for butt welds in tension:

$$\frac{\sigma_a}{\sigma_b} = \left(\frac{N_b}{N_a}\right)^{.13}$$

Since:

$$\sigma = \frac{M\,c}{I} = \frac{6\,M}{b\,t^2}$$

then, by substituting the bending moments into the left side of the above fatigue formula —

$$\frac{6\,M}{3''(\sfrac{3}{8}'')^2} \times \frac{3''(\sfrac{5}{16}'')^2}{6\,M} = \left(\frac{\sfrac{5}{16}''}{\sfrac{3}{8}''}\right)^2 = .695$$

$$.695 = \left(\frac{1\ \text{year}}{N_a}\right)^{.13}$$

and:

$$N_a = \frac{1\ \text{year}}{(.695)^{1/.13}} = \frac{1}{(.695)^{7.61}} = \frac{1}{.061}$$

$$= \underline{16.4\ \text{yrs}}$$

Designing for Improved Vibration Control

1. VIBRATION CONTROL AS DESIGN PROBLEM

The control of vibration is a design problem in machinery of many different types. In the past, the damping capacity of cast iron was considered to be an advantage in controlling vibration. Now, efficiently designed welded steel is known to have superior properties for coping with vibration problems found in many types of machine tools and other equipment. The damping capacity of cast iron is seldom used in the operating range in which it would be effective.

In recent years, there has been considerable research among machinery builders on the subject of vibration. Grinding machine manufacturers, in particular, have been concerned, since improved control of vibration results in increased operating speeds. New ideas about vibration and its control through the use of welded steel have come out of this recent research.

2. CONTRIBUTING FORCES

All members have a certain natural frequency. When struck once with an object, they will vibrate naturally at a given frequency.

A member also can be forced to vibrate at any frequency by striking it repeatedly. This is called forced frequency.

Whenever forced frequency equals natural frequency, the member becomes resonant and the amplitude of the vibration quickly builds up to a very high value, usually with disastrous results. Vibration becomes a problem only when the amplitude or height of vibration becomes excessive.

The damping property of a material is its ability to absorb the energy of the vibrating force. This is due, for the most part, to internal friction of the material.

Figure 1 shows the relative amplitude of vibration for a simple member when subjected to increased frequency of vibration. At resonant frequency, where the ratio of forced frequency to natural frequency is equal to 1, the amplitude is greatly increased. Theoretically, if there were no damping, the amplitude of vibration at this point would be infinitely high. For materials with greater damping capacity, the amplitude of vibration in the resonant frequency range is lower.

Fig. 1 Effect of damping capacity on amplitude of vibration. Damping reduces amplitude in resonant frequency range.

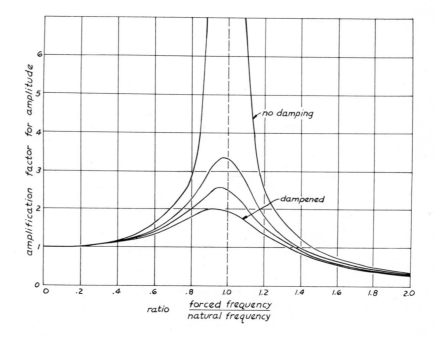

3. VIBRATION PROBLEMS

Vibration problems may be summarized with the following facts:

1. Excessive amplitude of vibration is the cause of the problem.

2. The amplitude of vibration becomes excessive in the resonant or critical frequency range.

3. Resonant or critical frequency is reached when the forced vibration equals the natural frequency of the member.

4. Damping capacity limits amplitude in the resonant range.

This means that the solution to a vibration problem would rest in either:

1. Changing the forced frequency, preferably to a lower frequency. This usually means a change in motor or operating speed.

2. Changing the natural frequency of the member, preferably to a higher frequency.

3. Increasing the damping capacity through efficient steel design.

4. NATURAL FREQUENCY OF MEMBER

In starting up a machine from zero speed, it is better if the machine does not have to pass through its critical speed or frequency. This means, if the natural frequency of the member is to be changed, it would be better to move it up to a still higher value.

In order to make any change in the natural frequency of a member, it would be well to study the factors involved in the vibration of a simple beam, Figure 2. What is learned from this can be applied to larger and more complicated members.

FIGURE 2

The natural frequency can be expressed by this formula:

$$f_n = k \sqrt{\frac{E\,I}{A\,L^4}}$$

where:

E = modulus of elasticity of the member

I = moment of inertia of the section

A = area of cross-section of member

L = unsupported length of the member

and where k is a constant which depends on how the member is supported. Usually, in the case of welded steel, the value of k is dropped from consideration while adjusting other components of the equation.

From this basic equation for a simple vibrating member, it is seen that the natural frequency can be increased by:

1. Increasing the moment of inertia (I) of the member.

2. Using a material having a higher modulus of elasticity (E).

3. Reducing the cross-sectional area (A) of the member (similar to weight).

4. Reducing the unsupported length (L) of the member.

Whenever a steel weldment is designed from an

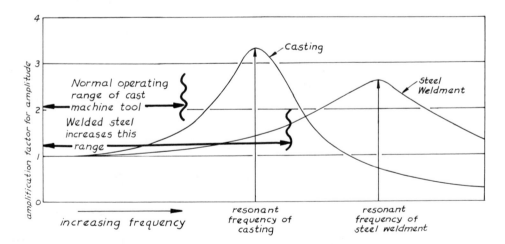

Fig. 3 Steel increases the efficient operating range of a machine, since its higher modulus of elasticity means higher natural frequency.

existing gray-iron casting, three things happen. The steel weldment--

1. Has a higher modulus of elasticity (E), 2½ times as much as gray iron.

2. Requires less moment of inertia (I) for the same stiffness, 40% of that for gray iron.

3. Requires less area (A) for the same stiffness, 40% of that for gray iron.

The results of these three changes upon the natural frequency (f_n) of the member is:

$$f_n = k\sqrt{\frac{E\,I}{A\,L^4}}$$

$$= \sqrt{\frac{(2.5)\,(0.40)}{(0.40)}}$$

$$= 1.58$$

The natural frequency of the equivalent steel member should be 1.58 times the natural frequency of the gray-iron member; in other words, the natural frequency has been increased 58%. Simply changing from gray-iron castings to steel weldments has given a 58% greater operating range. This is illustrated in Figure 3.

In addition, it is very simple to add stiffeners to steel weldments, so that the unsupported length (L) of panel or member is greatly reduced. Notice that the addition of a single stiffener, which cuts the unsupported length to half, will increase the natural frequency of the panel four times. This is a very easy method to move the natural frequency far away from the operating frequency.

5. DAMPING CAPACITY

It has been argued that gray iron has superior damping capacity over steel. This is true only if both are stressed the same amount. This is shown in Figure 4.

When both materials are stressed the same amount (see vertical line D), this would indicate that gray iron has about three times the damping capacity of steel. However, in an efficient redesign of a casting to a steel weldment, where the redesign is based upon equal stiffness, the steel member is always stressed more than the corresponding casting.

Steel, having a higher modulus of elasticity, requires less moment of inertia for the same stiffness and, as a result, has a lower section modulus. Therefore, for the same load, the steel member will have a corresponding higher stress. Because of its higher stress, its relative damping capacity will increase.

It can be shown in the case of a vertical member, such as the side of a base (see A, Fig. 4) in which the depth remains unchanged, that the steel is stressed 2½ times that of the corresponding casting, this will indicate a damping capacity 5.3 times that

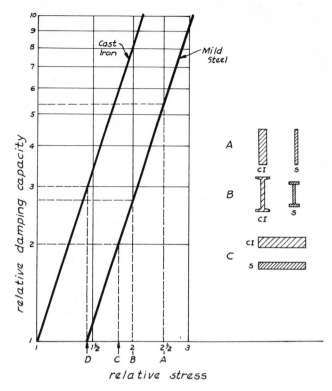

Fig. 4 Equivalent designs in steel are always stressed higher than cast-iron sections, for the same load, and thus have greater damping capacity.

of the casting. In the case of a similar type of section (see B, Fig. 4), the stress is 2.0 times that of the corresponding casting and indicates a damping capacity 2.7 times that of the casting. Even in the case of a top flat panel of a base in which the width remains constant (see C, Fig. 4), the stress in the steel is 1.84 times that of the casting and indicates a damping capacity two times that of the casting.

These are not difficult steel sections to make nor unusual conditions; they represent every-day, normal steel redesigns from cast construction having equal stiffness.

6. EFFECT OF WEIGHT ON VIBRATION

Normally the over-all dimensions of a member must remain unchanged in any redesign. If the weight is to be reduced, this is usually accomplished by means of thinner sections. In general, if the shape and outside dimensions remain unchanged, then the moment of inertia (I) of this section will vary as the thickness, or as the weight of the member. A reduction in weight would, therefore, mean a corresponding reduction in the moment of inertia of the section.

The effect of reducing the weight of a member is shown in Figure 5. Although the natural frequency of the member would remain unchanged, the resulting

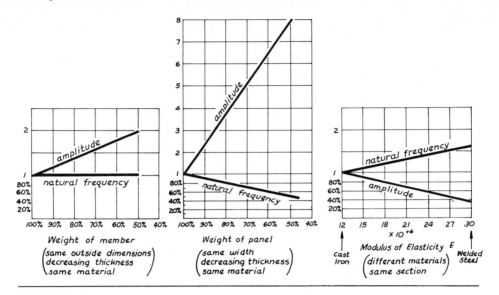

Fig. 5 Curves illustrate what happens to vibration in a steel weldment as the weight is reduced to where the design becomes more efficient.

amplitude of vibration would increase with decreased weight because of the loss of moment of inertia (I). For example, a simple reduction in weight of 50% (and moment of inertia) without changing the material, would result in double the amplitude of vibration (Fig. 5, left).

Merely reducing the weight of a flat panel would cause a still greater vibration problem (Fig. 5, center). The natural frequency is lowered and the amplitude is greatly increased. Reduced natural frequency means that the member will have a much narrower range in which to operate and there will be a greater possibility of it being operated at resonant frequency. At resonant frequency, the amplitude of vibration would be abnormally high and would prevent the machine from having any useful purpose.

It is important to emphasize that this is caused by the reduction in moment of inertia and not directly by the reduction in weight. It is possible to change from a heavy cast member to a lighter welded-steel member and have less amplitude of vibration and higher natural frequency.

If welded steel were used in place of the gray iron casting, in other words, a different material with a greater modulus of elasticity ($E_{c.i.}$=12,000,000 psi to E_{st} = 30,000,000 psi), then, for the same section, the natural frequency will be higher (1.58 times) and the amplitude of vibration will be lower (40%). This is shown in Figure 5, right.

If the redesign from the casting to welded steel is made for equivalent stiffness or rigidity, as is usually done in machine tools, the increased modulus of elasticity (E) would allow a corresponding decrease in the required moment of inertia (I). This would reduce the weight to 40% without any increase in amplitude of vibration over that of the casting.

7. ADVANTAGES OF STEEL

Experience has proved that efficient steel weldments weigh less than corresponding castings and this reduced weight should not create vibration problems. On the contrary, steel has superior properties for designing where vibration is an important consideration:

1. Steel can have a damping capacity equal to or greater than cast iron because an equivalent steel design under the same load is stressed higher.

2. The reduced section of the steel equivalent design has a greater modulus of elasticity; hence, reduced amplitude of vibration and, therefore, higher natural frequency. This means a greater operating range.

3. The design flexibility of welded steel makes it easy to shorten unsupported lengths by means of stiffeners and to make other changes that increase natural frequency and decrease amplitude, even after the machine has been fabricated, machined and tested.

8. NOISE CONTROL

The pitch of noise resulting from vibration depends on the frequency, and the volume depends on the amplitude. A noise problem is solved as a vibration problem: changing the frequency through stiffeners or stamping or breaking into smaller panels to reduce unsupported length. Sprayed-on coatings or cemented fiber materials will increase damping of very thin sections. See Figure 6.

9. EXAMPLES OF STEEL DESIGN

Various design ideas for minimizing vibration are illustrated in Figure 7.

Welding the ends of a member rigid, as shown at A in Figure 7, reduces the amplitude by 80% over a simply-supported member. Punching holes in a stiffening panel, B, reduces the area and increases the panel's natural frequency. Flanging a long panel, C, increases its stiffness and its natural frequency. Closed sections or diagonal bracing, D, increases torsional resistance (R), which increases the frequency and reduces the angle of vibration. Small tack-welded stiffeners, E, increase natural frequency and, when placed at 45°, add resistance to twist.

Figures 8, 9, and 10 illustrate machines that have been designed to improve operating characteristics by minimizing vibration.

The welded printing press illustrated in Figure 8 is used in color printing for a popular magazine

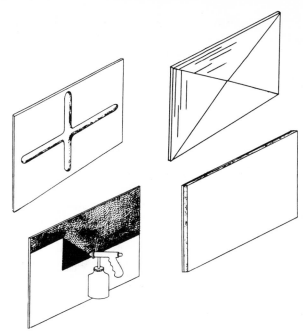

Fig. 6 Methods of achieving noise control.

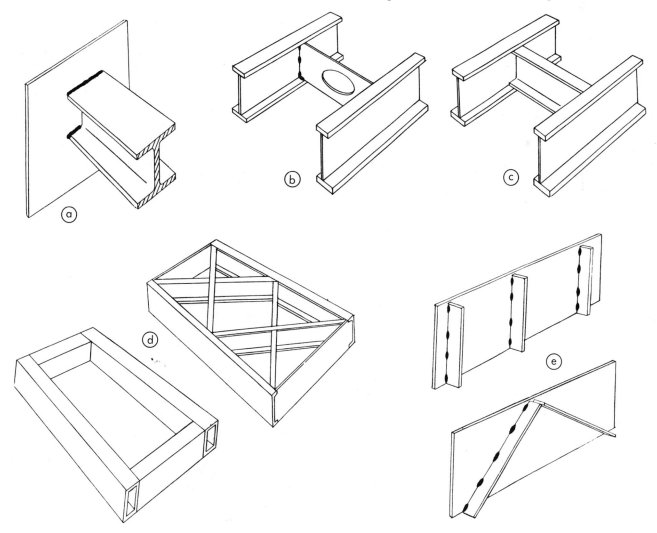

Fig. 7 A few design ideas for control of vibration.

with a circulation over one million. Color register and high speed are important. The welded press has resulted in substantial reductions in operating cost through its improved rigidity and, hence, better register at higher speeds.

In the design of a welded-steel bed for a new internal grinding machine, Figure 9, the engineers developed a high degree of functional rigidity, while making a significant weight reduction. The machine is used for internal grinding of inner rings for large ball bearing assemblies. The new welded-steel bed weighs only 1788 lbs, against 1829 lbs for a cast-iron bed on the previous design. However, the swing of the new machine was increased from 9" to 12"; so, in view of the higher capacity, a fairer comparison is on a unit weight basis, the figures being 149 lbs against 203 lbs, or a 26% saving. The cost of the welded bed was also substantially less than the former cast-iron design.

Comparative vibration tests on the old and new versions of the grinder were made by running production lots of bearing rings. The new design reduced grinding time from 13 to 8 sec; lowered size variation from 0.00040" to 0.00015", and improved surface finish from 21 to 10 micro-inches rms.

A leading grinder company, in its 10-year experience with welded design of precision grinding machines, has demonstrated convincingly the advantages of steel in vibration control. Figure 10 shows a rotary surface grinder which has a welded steel base and column. It is designed for maximum rigidity with minimum weight.

After numerous experiments, company engineers found that a fabricated base can be made just as rigid and just as free from resonance as any cast-iron base. Also, it was sometimes difficult to rib a cast-iron base because of resulting blind pockets which can cause blow-holes or spongy material because of trapped gas, and from which dirt can never be cleaned properly. No such difficulties were encountered in fabricating the base of welded steel. Ribs can be placed quite close together, exactly where they are required, without any damage whatever to the structure of the metal.

The original fabricated-base grinder after nine years of continuous service had required no maintenance of any of the wearing surfaces, which are part of the fabrication.

Every machine built by this manufacturer is analyzed thoroughly according to a standard inspection pattern with a vibration analyzer. This instrument enables the engineers to detect vibration in any part of the machine and also to detect and correct any source of vibration in the machine.

Fig. 8 Welded-steel printing press makes nearly 3 times the impressions per hour made by predecessor design. Color registry is better because rigidity has reduced vibration.

Fig. 9   The welded-steel bed design of this internal grinder develops high functional rigidity while reducing weight.

Fig. 10   For over 10 years, welded-steel bases on this line of precision grinders have provided better vibration control.

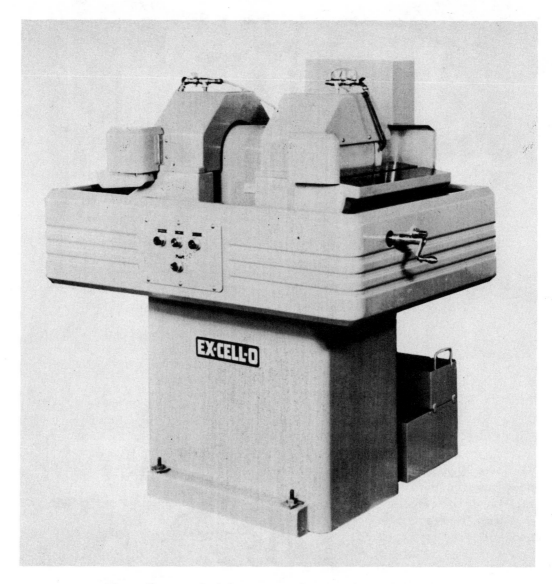

The influence of vibration control on grinder performance is well known. In recent years, builders of grinding machines have successfully adopted welded steel construction to help meet increasingly higher quality requirements for ground surfaces.

Dimensional Stability

1. STABILITY OF STEEL

Occasionally there has been some concern as to whether a properly stress-relieved weldment will stay put after being machined and placed in service. Apparently the thought was that in time some of the residual or locked-in stresses would be relieved slightly, resulting in subsequent movement of the weldment.

Every bit of engineering data indicates that welded steel will remain "dead" to any movement throughout time, unless acted upon by some type of applied force.

2. THE NATURE OF CREEP

Some metals, including steel, will have a continuous increase in movement (strain) when stressed over a period of time. This is called "creep". However, it is necessary to stress the member to a rather high value (of the order of the yield strength) and also at elevated temperatures (several hundred $^{\circ}$F) to achieve this effect.

This is indicated by the curves shown in Figure 1, for low-carbon steel.

If these curves could be projected further down the temperature scale, the creep rate at 500°F would be somewhere below $\frac{1}{10} \times 10^{-8}$ in./in./hr for a stress of about

$$\sigma = 10,000 \text{ psi}$$

$$\text{This creep rate} = \frac{\epsilon \text{ (strain)}}{t \text{ (time)}}$$

For a time period of 25 years (t = 50,000 working hrs), the resulting creep strain would be--

$$\epsilon = (\frac{1}{10} \times 10^{-8}) (50,000 \text{ hrs})$$
$$= .00005 \text{ in./in.}$$

To get a better idea of this indicated strain, it would be equivalent to the elastic strain resulting from a stress of

$$\sigma = \epsilon E = (.00005 \text{ in./in.}) (30 \times 10^6)$$
$$= 1500 \text{ psi}$$

Even though this is for a high temperature of 500°F, it would be negligible.

The above data indicates that "creep" as such, because of its high stress and high temperature re-

quirement, would not be a factor in the dimensional stability of a steel weldment when operating under standard conditions.

3. RESIDUAL STRESSES

It is possible to have tensile residual stresses in the weld area of the order of the steel's yield strength. In order to balance out these tensile stresses, there will always be some areas stressed in compression. After sufficient movement (distortion) of the member has taken place to cause this

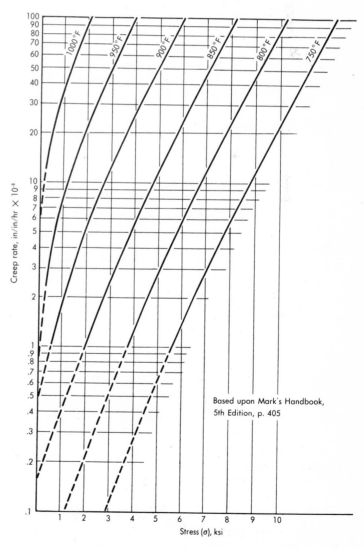

Fig. 1 Influence of temperature and stress on creep rate.

1

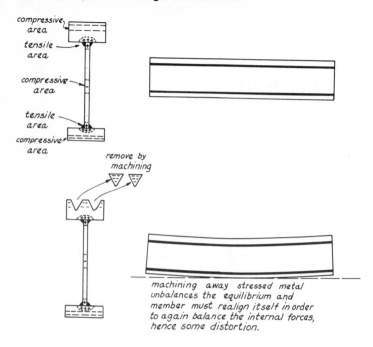

machining away stressed metal
unbalances the equilibrium and
member must realign itself in order
to again balance the internal forces,
hence some distortion.

Fig. 2 Weldment should be stress-relieved prior to any subsequent machining.

balance, there should be no further movement of the member.

If a considerable amount of stressed material is subsequently machined out, either tensile area in the weld area, or compressive area in some other part of the section, there will be a new unbalance of the

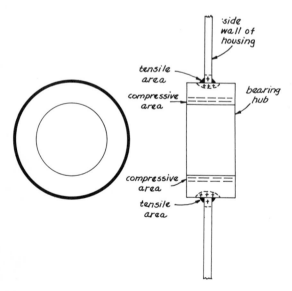

Inside diameter of hub is in compression and prevents hub from further shrinking.

When hub is bored out this metal stressed in compression is removed and hub will contract to a smaller diameter.

Fig. 3 Contraction of hub during machining can be avoided by stress relieving the weldment.

stresses. A corresponding movement of the member must then take place to rebalance these stresses. The result in this case is that the member gradually moves as machining progresses. This movement gradually decreases with lighter machine cuts. See Figure 2.

To avoid this difficulty, the weldment should be stress-relieved before machining.

A hub for a bearing support is shown in Figure 3. The hub is welded into the side wall of the housing. The two large circumferential fillet welds tend to shrink and assume a smaller circumference and diameter.

Here, the inner diameter of the hub will resist this movement and, therefore, is stressed in compression. After welding, the hub is bored out and much of the compressive area is removed. This will allow the weld area to shrink, becoming a smaller diameter. As the machining progresses, the hub will become smaller. Unless this is stress-relieved before machining, it will be necessary to machine out the hub with many light cuts, the movement becoming less and less with each cut.

4. STRESS-RELIEVING

Stress-relieving is a process whereby residual or locked-up stresses are reduced. Although this is usually done by heat, it can also be accomplished by mechanical methods. Some steel weldments are in fact "stress-relieved" by tumbling them, end over end, across the floor of the fabricating shop. Undoubtedly this could be just as effective as the conventional method by heating.

The usual method is to carefully place the weldment in a special furnace, and heat to a tempera-

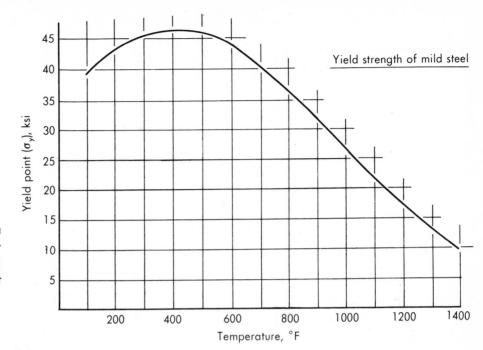

Fig. 4 Stresses in a weldment are relieved by plastic yielding of the metal when heated to sufficient temperature.

ture of about 1100°F. It is held at this temperature for a period approximately equal to 1 hr/in. of thickness, after which it is furnace cooled.

Heating the weldment to a given temperature will lower the yield strength of the steel to a much lower value. See the curve, Figure 4.

When the yield strength is reduced to a value below the residual stress, the temporarily "weakened" weldment will yield plastically and thus relieve most of the stresses. In general, these stresses cannot be relieved much lower than the value of the yield point of the steel at the temperature to which it was heated.

The above curve, Figure 4, may also be used to give the maximum value of any residual stresses resulting from a given stress-relieving treatment.

It is necessary to properly support the weldment in the furnace during stress-relieving.

Holes should be provided (flame cut or drill) to allow air in a totally enclosed section to escape during heating; otherwise it is possible to blow the weldment open.

The weldment must be heated up slowly and uniformly, and just as carefully cooled. Thicker sections, because of their greater mass, will lag in temperature change, as compared to the thinner sections. On heating, thinner sections will expand more, because of their higher temperature and, if restrained around their edges by thicker sections, may buckle until the thicker sections catch up to them during the holding or soaking time. On cooling, thicker sections will cool last, and shrink last; this usually places them in tension and the

thinner sections in compression. This is in addition to any residual stresses resulting from welding.

When there is quite a difference in thickness of parts of a weldment, it becomes more necessary to use a slower rate of heating, and a slower rate of cooling.

5. BOWING PROBLEM

A problem sometimes encountered by engineers is the lengthwise bowing of a member due to a non-uniform temperature distribution throughout its cross-section.

Consider the section in Figure 5, which could represent a long weldment, completely machined and in service. Assume that the ambient temperature has increased slightly and at one instant the

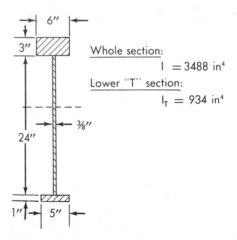

Whole section:
$$I = 3488 \text{ in}^4$$
Lower "T" section:
$$I_T = 934 \text{ in}^4$$

Fig. 5 Cross-section of long weldment.

Compressive force applied to flange of built-up member

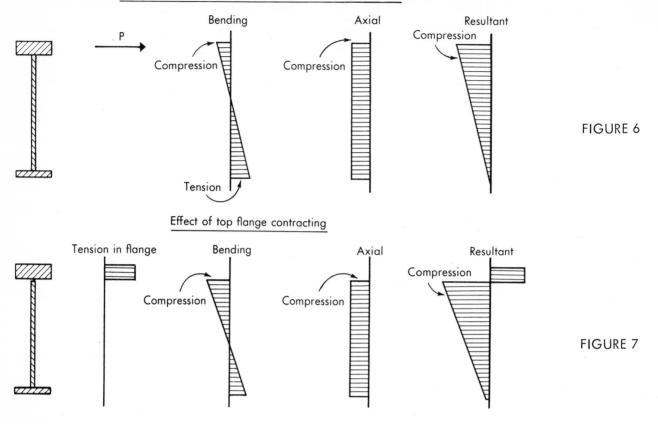

FIGURE 6

Effect of top flange contracting

FIGURE 7

Top flange 1°F cooler: $e = 240'' \times 7 \times 10^{-6} \times 1°F = .00168''$

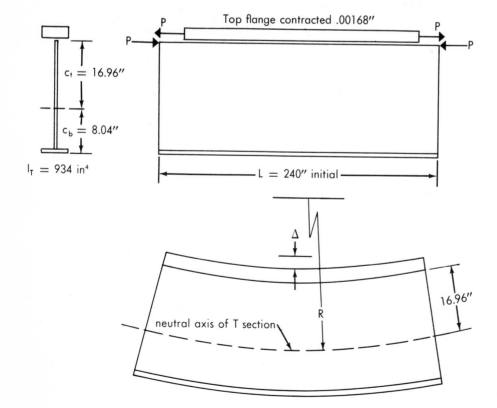

Top flange contracted .00168''

$c_t = 16.96''$

$c_b = 8.04''$

$I_T = 934$ in^4

L = 240'' initial

16.96''

neutral axis of T section

Fig. 8 Non-uniform temperature distribution in I-beam causes bowing of the beam. In this case the top flange, being 1°F cooler than remaining cross-section, contracts and applies an axial force, resulting in deflection.

top flange is one degree cooler than the rest of the section because of its greater thickness. This will cause the top flange to contract, tending to force the member to bow length-wise.

In the conventional problem, an external force (P) is applied to the member. In this case it is an axial force applied at the ends of the top flange, Figure 6, where the resulting stress from this eccentric force is shown. Here the moment of inertia (I) of the entire cross-section will resist this bowing or bending reaction.

In our problem, the force (P) is applied by the contracting top flange, Figure 7, so that it does not supply any resisting action. Here the resisting moment of inertia (I) comes from the cross-section of the remaining "T" section only. This of course

has a much smaller value and as a result the "T" will tend to bow or bend easier than if the force (P) is applied externally.

Notice (Fig. 5) the moment of inertia of the entire section is $I = 3488$ in.[4] while that of the "T" section is only $I_T = 934$ in.[4]

The top flange, if separated from the "T" section, would contract .00168" as shown in the upper view of Figure 8.

By applying an axial tensile force (P) to the top flange, pulling it out, while applying an equal compressive force (P) to the inside edge of the "T" section to push it in so both meet as in the lower view of Figure 8, it is possible to solve for the force (P) and the resulting bowing or deflection (Δ) of a member.

COMPUTATION FOR SOLVING FOR BOWING (Δ), FIGURE 8

Top flange

Since $P = \sigma A_f$ and $\sigma = \dfrac{P}{A_f}$

and $E = \dfrac{\sigma}{\epsilon}$ and $\epsilon = \dfrac{\sigma}{E}$

then contraction or extension in the top flange is —

$e_f = \epsilon L = \dfrac{\sigma L}{E} = \dfrac{P L}{A_f E}$

Resisting "T" section

$M = P \times$ moment arm

$= P (16.96 + 1.5) = 18.46\,P$

Contraction due to pure bending

$L_{NA} = L_{initial} = 240''$

$L_{inside} = L_{NA}\left(\dfrac{R - c_t}{R}\right)$

| R = radius of curvature to neutral axis of "T" section |

$= 240\left(\dfrac{R - 16.96}{R}\right) = 240 - \dfrac{4070}{R}$

and $e = 240 - L_{inside}$

$= 240 - \left(240 - \dfrac{4070}{R}\right) = \dfrac{4070}{R}$

Contraction due to axial compression (P)

$e = \dfrac{P L}{A_T E}$

Total contraction (axial and bending) of inner face of "T" section due to shrinkage of top flange

$e_T = \dfrac{P L}{A_T E} + \dfrac{4070}{R}$

Since $\dfrac{I}{R} = \dfrac{M}{E\,I_T}$ and $M = 18.46\,P$

then

$e_T = \dfrac{P L}{A_T E} + \dfrac{75,130\,P}{E\,I_T}$

and recalling the extension of the top flange when pulled by "T" section is —

$e_f = \dfrac{P L}{A_f E}$

Therefore, in summary

$e_T + e_f = .00168''$ or

$\dfrac{P L}{A_f e} + \dfrac{P L}{A_T E} + \dfrac{75,130\,P}{E\,I_T} = .00168''$

where $A_f = 3'' \times 6'' = 18$ in.[2] $L = 240''$

$A_T = 14$ in.[2] $I_T = 934$ in.[4]

$E = 30 \times 10^6$

Rewriting the preceding formula and then substituting —

$\dfrac{P}{E}\left(\dfrac{L}{A_f} + \dfrac{L}{A_T} + \dfrac{75,130\,P}{I_T}\right) = .00168''$

$\therefore P = \dfrac{.00168\,E}{\dfrac{L}{A_f} + \dfrac{L}{A_T} + \dfrac{75,130}{I_T}}$

$= \dfrac{(.00168)(30 \times 10^6)}{\dfrac{240}{18} + \dfrac{240}{14} + \dfrac{75,130}{934}}$

$= \underline{455\ \text{lbs}}$

Since the moment of the resisting "T" section can now be found —

$M = 18.46\,P$

$= 18.46\,(455)$

$= \underline{8,400\ \text{in.-lbs}}$

the deflection of beam with constant bending moment is —

$\Delta = \dfrac{M L^2}{8\,E\,I_T}$

$= \dfrac{(8400)(240)^2}{8\,(30 \times 10^6)(934)}$

$= \underline{.002''}$

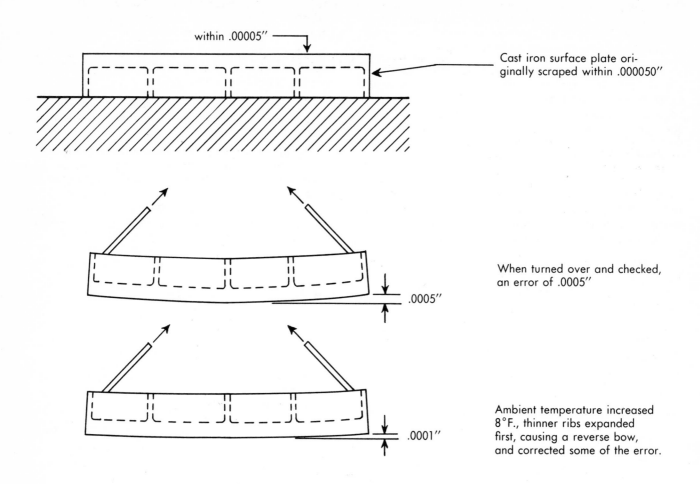

within .00005"

Cast iron surface plate originally scraped within .000050"

When turned over and checked, an error of .0005"

.0005"

Ambient temperature increased 8°F., thinner ribs expanded first, causing a reverse bow, and corrected some of the error.

.0001"

Fig. 9 Temperature change may bow casting due to non-uniform stress.

The preceding example would indicate that on long, narrow weldments requiring extreme stability in operation, it would be necessary to either (1) insure constant temperature, or (2) provide a design which is symmetrical as far as massive sections are concerned. With the latter provision, expansion or contraction of these sections is balanced about the neutral axis and the member will remain straight and unaffected by temperature changes.

In other words, if there is a combination of thick and thin areas in the cross-section of a weldment, the center of gravity of the thick areas should coincide with the center of gravity of the thin areas.

This problem is not limited to steel weldments but could occur with rolled shapes, castings, or with any type of material.

To illustrate this, a cast iron surface plate, Figure 9, had been hand scraped to within .000050". After turning it over and checking, it was found to have an error of .0003". One hour later this error had increased to .0005". Later when the ambient temperature had increased 8°F, the error had dropped back to .0001". It was found that the ribs, being thinner than the top portion, heated up quicker and thus expanded, bowing the surface plate in the opposite direction and correcting for the error.

A similar surface plate made of welded steel and of box construction, Figure 10, had an accuracy of within .0001" even when heated 10°F. This was because any uneven expansion was balanced on both sides of the neutral axis.

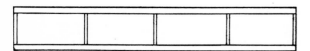

Welded steel surface plate does not bow with temperature change, because plate is symmetrical about neutral axis

FIGURE 10

Elastic Matching

1. ANGULAR DEFLECTION OF CONNECTING MEMBERS

Elastic matching is a term used when two connecting members are designed so that their angular deflections are equal. This means they will remain aligned regardless of the value of the loading applied.

Consider the following roller, Figure 1, supported by two fixed bearings (not self-aligning bearings).

This roller will always deflect somewhat, regardless of how large and rigid it is.

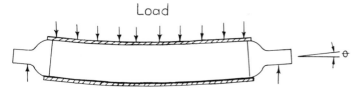

FIGURE 1

The bearing support will not tilt, because the uniform bearing pressure is centered about the center of gravity of the support.

The end of the roller will tilt with any loading and the bearing will remain horizontal, Figure 2. This will produce wear and shorter bearing life.

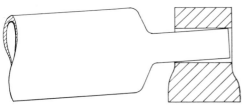

FIGURE 2

2. COMPENSATING FOR ANGULAR DEFLECTION

By shifting the bearing support slightly off the center of the bearing, Figure 3, the bearing force is applied to the support with a slight eccentricity. This results in a bending moment, which causes the bearing to tilt slightly.

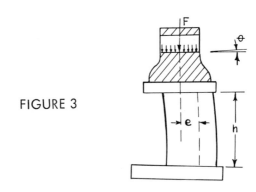

FIGURE 3

It is then possible to calculate the proper moment of inertia (I) of the bearing support so that the bearing will tilt at the same angle as the ends of the roller under any loading, Figure 4. Both will always be in perfect alignment.

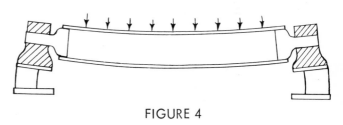

FIGURE 4

| Problem 1 |

Consider the steel roll, Figure 5. Its face is 100" long, and it has two stub ends each 18" long. The main portion of the roll is 24" diameter, and the stub ends are 8" diameter. In addition to the weight of the roll itself, there is a uniform roll pressure of 10 lbs/in. along the face of the roll. It is supported on each end by bearings which are not self-aligning. Because the roll deflects slightly, the stub ends are not in alignment with the bearings; the bearings overheat, and their life is rather short. It is desired to design the bearing supports so they will tilt slightly under load and line up perfectly with the end of the roller shaft.

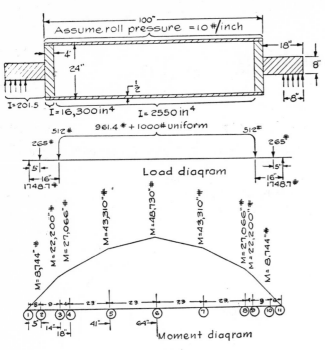

FIGURE 5

Here the moments about Point 1 are:

$M_2 = 1748.7(5) = +8,744$ in.-lbs

$M_3 = 1748.7(14) - 256(9) = +22,200$ in.-lbs

$M_4 = 1748.7(18) - 256(13) - 512(2) - 40(2)$
$\quad = +27,066$ in.-lbs

$M_5 = 1748.7(41) - 256(36) - 512(25) - 270(13.5)$
$\quad - 240.4(11.5) = +43,310$ in.-lbs

$M_6 = 1748.7(64) - 256(59) - 512(48) - 500(25)$
$\quad - 480.7(23) = +48,730$ in.-lbs

The total angle (in radians) between the tangents at Points 1 and 11 is equal to the sums of the areas of the moment diagram, divided by their corresponding EI (E = 30,000,000 psi):

$$\theta = \frac{2 \cdot \frac{1}{2}(8744)(5)}{E(201.5)} + \frac{2 \cdot \frac{1}{2}(22,200 + 8,744)(9)}{E(201.5)}$$

$$+ \frac{2(27,066 + 22,200)(4)}{2E(16,300)} + \frac{2(43,310 + 27,066)(23)}{2E(2550)}$$

$$+ \frac{2(48,730 + 43,310)(23)}{2E(2550)}$$

$\theta = .0001027$ radians, or one end $\theta = \underline{.0000513 \text{ radians}}$

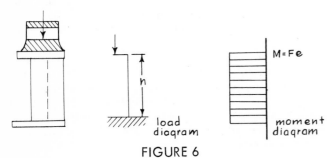

FIGURE 6

Then, considering each of the two bearing supports, Figure 6:

$$\theta = \frac{F e h}{E I}$$

where:

$\theta = .0000513$ radians

$F = 1748.7$ lbs

$e = 1''$

$h = 30''$

Here a certain value is assumed for the eccentricity (e=1"). The eccentricity (e) is the distance of the center of bearing pressure or bearing load to the center of gravity of the support.

It is now possible to solve for the required moment of inertia (I) which will cause the bearing support to tilt the same angle as the end of the shaft, regardless of the value of the applied load:

$$I = \frac{F e h}{E \theta}$$

$$= \frac{(1748.7)(1'')(30)}{(30,000,000)(.0000513)}$$

$$= 34.1 \text{ in.}^4$$

The bearing support is then dimensioned so as to provide the required moment of inertia (I=34.1 in.⁴).

Or we can suggest a certain section for the support, Figure 7, having a given moment of inertia (I) and solve for the required eccentricity (e) which will allow the bearing support to tilt at the same angle as the shaft:

$$e = \frac{I E \theta}{F h}$$

20" × 85#I	8" × 8" ×31#WF	8" std pipe
$I_y = 47.0$	$I_y = 37.0$	$I = 63.35$
e = 1.38"	e = 1.08	e = 1.86"
A = 24.8 sq in	A = 9.12 sq in.	A = 7.27 sq in.

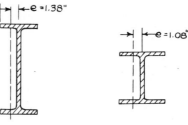

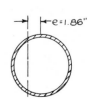

FIGURE 7

Any of the three rolled sections in Figure 7, with its corresponding value for the eccentricity (e) will produce a bearing support which will allow the bearing to tilt at the same angle as the end of the shaft, for any loading. A support height of 30" has been assumed.

Designing for Torsional Loading

1. NATURE OF TORSIONAL LOADING

Torsional loading is the application of a force that tends to cause the member to twist about its structural axis. This type of loading is associated with axles, spindles and other rotating members.

It is less recognizable in well-supported bases, for example, on which are mounted rotating members. And, it may be experienced merely as the result of an eccentric static load.

Torsion is usually referred to in terms of torsional moment or torque (T), which is basically the product of the externally applied force and the moment arm or force arm. The moment arm is the distance of the centerline of rotation from the line of force and perpendicular to it. This distance often equals the distance from the member's center of gravity to its outer fiber (radius of a round shaft, for example), but not always.

The principal deflection caused by torsion is measured by the angle of twist, or by the vertical movement of one corner of the frame or base.

2. IMPROVING TORSIONAL RESISTANCE

A machine tool base, for example, is generally designed by assuming the base to be supported at each end. However, after it is made, it is usually supported along its entire length on a good foundation. As a result, bending stresses and deflections are low. A motor drive mounted on the base tends to twist the base. While a good foundation supports bending loads, it contributes little in preventing the base from twisting.

Other steps, therefore, must be taken to design against twisting or torsional loads.

Steel, in rolled structural shapes or built-up sections, is very efficient in resisting torsion.

When a cast iron beam (A, in Fig. 1) is replaced with a steel beam (B), weight per foot can be reduced, in this example from 122.5 to 96.9 lbs, to achieve the same torsional resistance. Using a steel closed box section (C), weight can be further reduced to 25.5 lbs/ft, an over-all reduction in weight of approximately 80%.

With steel, torsionally rigid sections are easily developed by the use of stiffeners. Castings, on the other hand, are restricted because of difficulties in coring, need for draft, etc.

Here are the three basic rules for designing machinery members to make the best use of steel where torsional loads are a problem:

1. Use closed sections where possible.
2. Use diagonal bracing.
3. Make rigid end connections.

3. POLAR MOMENT OF INERTIA

When a round shaft is subjected to a twisting or torsional moment (torque), the resulting shear stress in the shaft is--

$$\tau = \frac{T c}{J} \quad \dots\dots\dots\dots\dots\dots\dots\dots\dots (1)$$

where:

τ = shear stress, psi

c = distance from center of section to outer fiber

T = torque, in.-lbs

J = polar moment of inertia of section, in.^{4}

$= I_x + I_y = 2I$

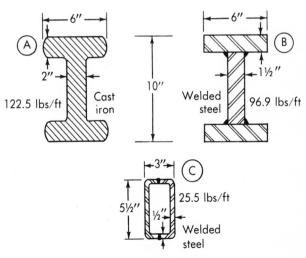

FIGURE 1

The angular twist of a round shaft is —

$$\theta = \frac{T L}{E_s J} \quad \dots\dots\dots\dots\dots\dots\dots\dots\dots\dots\dots(2)$$

where:

θ = over-all angular twist of shaft, in radians
   (1 radian = 57.3° approx.)

L = length of shaft, in inches

E_s = modulus of elasticity in shear
   (steel E_s = 12,000,000 psi)

In most cases, the designer is interested in holding the torsional moment within the material's elastic limit. Where the torsional strength of a round shaft is required (i.e. the stress it can take without failure), the polar section modulus is J/c, and the allowable torque is thus--

$$T = \tau_u \frac{J}{c}$$

where, lacking test data, the ultimate shear strength of steel (τ_u) is assumed to be in the order of 75% of the material's ultimate tensile strength.

TABLE 1 - TORSIONAL PROPERTIES OF VARIOUS SECTIONS

Section	Shear Stress	(for steel) R-torsional Resistance
	$\tau = \frac{16\,T}{\pi\,d^3}$	$R = .0982\,d^4$
	$\tau = \frac{16\,T\,d_2}{\pi\,(d_2{}^4 - d_1{}^4)}$	$R = .0982\,(d_2{}^4 - d_1{}^4)$
	$\tau = \frac{3\,T}{\pi\,d\,t^2}$	$R = 1.0472\,t^3 d$
	$\tau = \frac{4.8\,T}{d^3}$	$R = .1406\,d^4$
	$\tau = \frac{T}{\alpha\,b\,d^2}$	$R = \beta\,b\,d^3$

for solid rectangular sections	$\frac{b}{d} =$	1.00	1.50	1.75	2.00	2.50	3.00	4.00	6	8	10	∞
	α	.208	2.31	.239	.246	.258	.267	.282	.299	.307	.313	.333
	β	.141	.196	.214	.229	.249	.263	.281	.299	.307	.313	.333

Section	Shear Stress	(for steel) R-torsional Resistance
	mid-length short side $\tau = \frac{T}{2t\,(b-t)\,(d-t_1)}$ mid-length long side $\tau = \frac{T}{2t_1\,(b-t)\,(d-t_1)}$	$R = \frac{2\,t\,t_1\,(b-t)^2\,(d-t_1)^2}{b\,t + d\,t_1 - t^2 - t_1{}^2}$ $R = \frac{2\,t\,(b-t)^2\,(d-t)^2}{b+d-2t}$ if all plates same thickness $R = t\,(b-t)^3$ if square
Use this for diagonal bracing	single brace	$R = 3.54\,I$
	double brace	$R = 10.6\,I$

I of diagonal brace

The above three formulas are true for solid round or tubular round shafts. For non-circular sections the shear stresses are not uniform, and therefore the standard torsional formulas no longer hold.

4. TORSIONAL RESISTANCE

Values of torsional resistance (R)--stiffness factor--have been established for various standard sections and provide more reliable solutions to torsional rigidity problems. Values of R are expressed in inches to the fourth power.

Table 1 shows the formulas for shear stress and torsional resistance of various sections. The formulas for solid rectangular sections call for values, of α and β, which are derived from the ratio of section width (b) to depth (d), as shown in the table.

Actual tests show that the torsional resistance (R) of an open section made up of rectangular areas, nearly equals the sum of the torsional resistances of all the individual rectangular areas. For example, the torsional resistance of an I beam is approximately equal to the sum of the torsional resistances of the two flanges and web (Fig. 2).

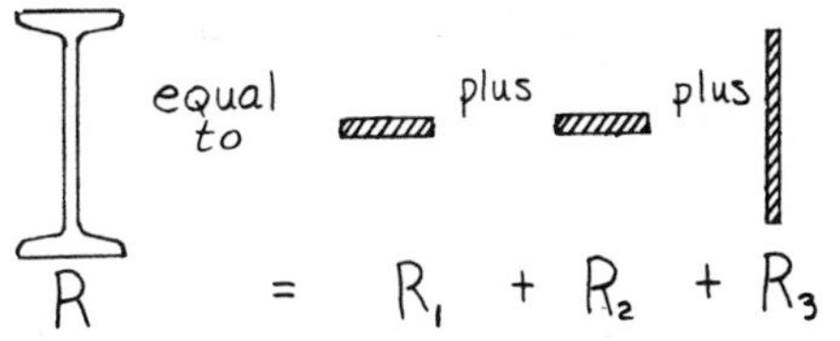

equal to plus plus

$$R = R_1 + R_2 + R_3$$

FIGURE 2

Figure 3 shows the results of twisting an I beam made of three equal plates. Calculated values of twist by using the conventional polar moment of inertia (J) and the torsional resistance (R) are compared with the actual results. This shows greater accuracy by using torsional resistance (R).

Angle of twist		
all loadings identical	t=.055	t=.055
Conventional method **J** polar moment of inertia	.065°	.007°
Method using **R** Torsional Resistance	21.8°	7.3°
Actual twist	22°	9.5°

FIGURE 3

Angle of twist					
	a	b	c	d	e
all loadings identical	t=.060	t=.060	t=.060	t=.060	t=.060
Conventional method **J** polar moment of inertia	.01°	.006°	.04°	.04°	.045°
Method using **R** Torsional Resistance	9.5°	9.7°	10°	.04°	.06°
Actual twist	9°	9.5°	11°	too small to measure	too small to measure

FIGURE 4

This means that the torsional resistance of a flat plate is approximately the same whether it is used as such or is formed into an angle, channel, open tube section, etc. This is illustrated in Figure 4. Samples of different sections made of 16-gage steel are subjected to torsion. The flat section twists 9°. The same piece of steel formed into a channel (b) twists 9½°. When rolled into a tube with an open seam (c), it twists 11°.

When the same section is made into a closed section (d) by placing a single tack weld in the middle of the open seam, the torsional resistance increases several hundred times. When the tube becomes a closed section, the torsional stresses are distributed more evenly over the total area, thus permitting a greater load.

Notice the error in using polar moment of inertia (J) for the angle of twist of open sections, and the good agreement by using torsional resistance (R).

Design Rule No. 1: USE CLOSED SECTIONS WHERE POSSIBLE

The solid or tubular round closed section is best for torsional loading since the shear stresses are uniform around the circumference of the member.

Next to a tubular section, the best section for resisting torsion is a closed square or rectangular tubular section.

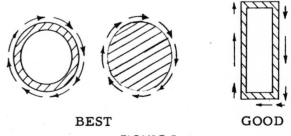

BEST   GOOD

FIGURE 5

The poorest sections for torsional loading are open sections, flat plates, angle sections, channel sections, Z-bar sections, T-bar sections, I-beam sections, and tubular sections which have a slot.

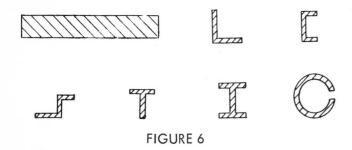

FIGURE 6

After the R values of all areas in a built-up section have been added together, their sum is inserted into the following formula or a modification of it:

$$\theta = \frac{T L}{E_s R} \quad \dots \dots \dots \dots \dots \dots \dots \dots \dots \dots (3)$$

Torque (T) in in.-lbs may be obtained from one of the formulas in Table 2, such as—

$$T = \frac{63,000 \times HP}{RPM}$$

or $T = P e$

TABLE 2 - FORMULAS FOR DETERMINING SAFE TORQUE UNDER VARIOUS CONDITIONS

Based on tangential load:
$$T = P e$$

Based on horsepower transmitted:
$$T = \frac{63,030 \times HP}{RPM}$$

Based on strength of shaft:
$$T = \frac{.19635 \, S_s \, (d_2^4 - d_1^4)}{d_2}$$

where $S_s = 15,000$

$$T = \frac{2945 \, (d_2^4 - d_1^4)}{d_2}$$

Based on safe twist of shaft (.08°/ft):
$$T = 137 \, (d_2^4 - d_1^4)$$

Based on fillet weld leg size around shaft or hub:
$$T = \frac{3781}{d + \omega} \left[(d + \omega)^4 - d^4 \right]$$

Based on butt weld size around hub:
$$T = 20,420 \, d^2 \, t$$

where:

HP = horsepower

RPM = speed of revolution

P = applied force, lbs

e = moment arm of force (the perpendicular distance from the center of rotation to the line of force)

Problem 1

As an example, consider the torsional resistance of a closed round tube and one that is slotted. The tube has an O.D. of 4", an I.D. of 3", a length of 100", and is subjected to a torque of 1000 in.-lbs.

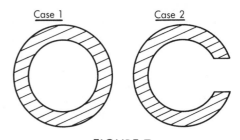

FIGURE 7

Case 1

From Table 1, the torsional resistance of the closed round tube is found to be—

$$R = 0.0982 \, (d_2^4 - d_1^4)$$
$$= 0.0982 \, (4^4 - 3^4)$$
$$= \underline{17.19 \text{ in.}^4}$$

and the angular twist is —

$$\theta = \frac{T L}{E_s R}$$
$$= \frac{(1000)(100)}{(12 \times 10^6)17.19}$$
$$= 0.000485 \text{ radians, or } \underline{0.0278°}$$

Case 2

From Table 1, the torsional resistance of the slotted round tube is found to be—

$$R = 1.0472 \, t^3 \, d$$
$$= 1.0472 \, (½)^3 \, 3½$$
$$= \underline{0.459 \text{ in.}^4}$$

and the angular twist is —

$$\theta = \frac{T L}{E_s R}$$
$$= \frac{(1000)(100)}{(12 \times 10^6).459}$$
$$= 0.018 \text{ radians, or } \underline{1.04°}$$

Thus, the tube without the slot is many times more rigid than the slotted tube.

Problem 2

Two 6" × 2" × 10½-lb channels are to be used in making a 100"-long frame, which will be subjected to a torque of 1000 in.-lbs. In what relationship to each other will these channels offer the greatest resistance to twist?

Case 1

These two channels when separated but fastened together by end plates do not have much torsional resistance.

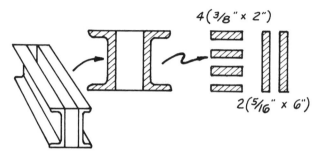

4 (3/8" × 2")

2 (5/16" × 6")

FIGURE 8

From Table 1, the value of R for each of the flanges is found to be--

$R_1 = 0.0306$ in.^{4}

and that of each web is —

$R_2 = 0.0586$ in.^{4}

and thus the total angular twist is —

$$\theta = \frac{1000 \times 100}{(12 \times 10^6)(4 \times .0306 + 2 \times .0586)}$$

$= 0.0348$ radians, or $\underline{2.0°}$

Case 2

When these two channels are securely fastened back to back, there is suitable resistance to any slip or movement due to horizontal shear. Here the two webs are considered as one solid web, and the top and bottom flanges are considered solid.

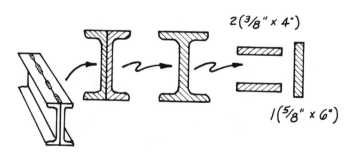

2 (3/8" × 4")

1 (5/8" × 6")

FIGURE 9

From Table 1, the value of R for each of the two composite flanges is found to be--

$R_1 = 0.066$ in.^{4}

and that of the composite web is —

$R_2 = 0.459$ in.^{4}

and thus the total angular twist is —

$$\theta = \frac{1000 \times 100}{(12 \times 10^6)(2 \times .066 + .459)}$$

$= 0.0141$ radians, or $\underline{0.81°}$

which is much less than in Case 1.

Case 3

If these two channels were welded toe to toe to form a box section, the torsional resistance would be greatly increased.

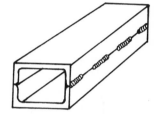

FIGURE 10

From Table 1, the value of R for a box section is found to be--

$$R = \frac{2\, t\, t_1\, (b - t)^2\, (d - t_1)^2}{b\, t + d\, t_1 - t^2 - t_1^2}$$

$$= \frac{2\,(\tfrac{3}{8})\,(\tfrac{5}{16})\,(6 - \tfrac{3}{8})^2\,(4 - \tfrac{5}{16})^2}{(6)\,(\tfrac{3}{8}) + (4)\,(\tfrac{5}{16}) - (\tfrac{3}{8})^2 - (\tfrac{5}{16})^2}$$

$= 30.94$ in.^{4}

and the angular twist is —

$$\theta = \frac{1000 \times 100}{(12 \times 10^6)\, 30.94}$$

$= 0.00027$ radians, or $\underline{0.015°}$

which is far less than in Case 2, which in turn was much better than Case 1.

Problem 3

A 6" standard pipe has been used for the main front support of an earth-moving scraper. Its main requirement is to resist the torsional load within an allowable angular twist.

It is desired to replace this pipe section (Fig. 11) with a fabricated square box section (Fig. 12) having the same over-all dimensions. In the box section, b = d = 2 r_m = 6.345 in.

Determine the required thickness of plate for this box section to hold it within the same angular twist. Assume bending resistance is sufficient.

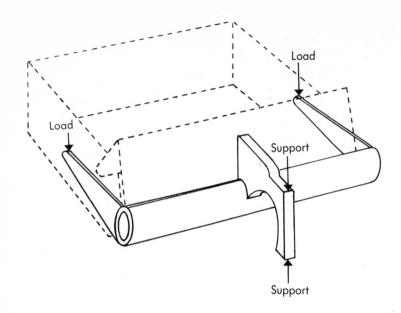

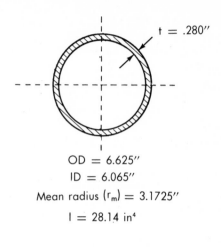

t = .280''

OD = 6.625''
ID = 6.065''
Mean radius $(r_m) = 3.1725''$
I = 28.14 in⁴

FIGURE 11

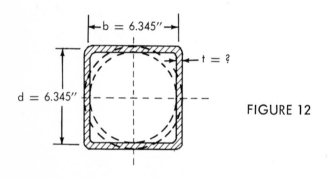

b = 6.345''

d = 6.345''

t = ?

FIGURE 12

The torsional resistance of the pipe, treated as a line, (see Sect. 2.3, Table 6), is--

$$R_{pipe} = 2 \, t \, \pi \, r_m^3$$

$$= 2(.280) \, \pi \, (3.1725)^3$$

$$= 56.18 \text{ in.}^4$$

If the appropriate formula from Table 1 is used, the answer obtained will be nearly the same:

$$R_{pipe} = .0982 \, (d_2^4 - d_1^4)$$

$$= .0982 \, (1926.39 - 1353.08)$$

$$= 56.30 \text{ in.}^4$$

The actual value from a steel handbook is --

$$R_{pipe} = J = I_x + I_y$$

$$= 28.14 + 28.14$$

$$= 56.28 \text{ in.}^4$$

The torsional resistance of the box section, also treated as a line, is —

$$R_{box} = \frac{2 \, t \, b^2 \, d^2}{b + d}$$

$$= \frac{2 \, t \, (6.345)^2 \, (6.345)^2}{6.345 + 6.345} = t \, (6.345)^3$$

$$= R_{pipe} = 56.18 \text{ in.}^4$$

$$\therefore \quad t \, (6.345)^3 = 56.18 \text{ in.}^4$$

and $t = \dfrac{56.18}{(6.345)^3}$

$$= .22'' \text{ or use } \tfrac{1}{4}'' \text{ } \mathbb{P}L$$

5. MAXIMUM SHEAR STRESS IN BUILT-UP SECTIONS

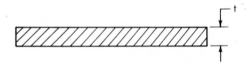

t

FIGURE 13

The maximum shear stress of a rectangular section in torsion lies on the surface at the center of the long side.

For the maximum shear stress on a narrow rectangular section or section element--

$$\tau = \phi \, t \, E_s = \frac{T \, t}{R}$$

where:

ϕ = unit angular twist of whole section (each element twists this amount), in radians/linear inch of member

t = thickness of rectangular section

R = torsional resistance of entire member, not necessarily just this one flat element

This formula can be used for a flat plate, or the flat plate of a built-up section not forming a closed section (i.e. channel, angle, T- or I-beam section).

In such a built-up open section, the unit angular

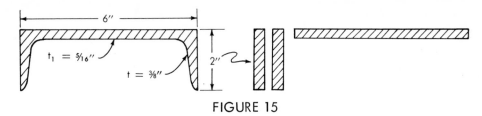

FIGURE 15

twist (ϕ) of the whole member is first found:

$$\phi = \frac{\theta}{L}$$

and then the maximum shear stress in the specific rectangular element.

Shear stresses tend to concentrate at re-entrant corners. In this case, the maximum stress value should be used and is--

$$\tau_{max} = \tau \left(1 + \frac{t}{4a} \right)$$

where a = inside corner radius.

FIGURE 14

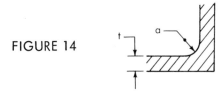

| Problem 4 |

A 6" × 2" × 10½-lb channel is subjected to a torque of T = 1000 in.-lbs. Find the shear stress along the web. See Figure 15.

Applying the formula for rectangular sections from Table 1, find the torsional resistance of each of the two identical 2" × ⅜" flanges (R_1) and of the 6" × ⁵⁄₁₆" web (R_2):

$$R_1 = .0306 \text{ in.}^4$$
$$R_2 = .0586 \text{ in.}^4$$
$$\therefore \quad R = 2R_1 + R_2$$
$$= 2(.0306) + .0586$$
$$= .1208 \text{ in.}^4$$

Then:

$$\tau = \frac{t\,T}{R}$$
$$= \frac{⁵⁄₁₆ \times 1000}{.1208}$$
$$= 2,580 \text{ psi}$$

| Problem 5 |

Two 6" × 2" × 10½-lb channels are welded toe to toe, to form a short box section. This is subjected to a torque of T = 100,000 in.-lbs. Find the horizontal shear stress at the toes and the amount of groove welding required to hold these channels together for this torsional load. See Figure 16.

From Table 1, the shear stress at mid-length of the short side is found to be--

$$\tau = \frac{T}{2t\,(b - t)(d - t_1)}$$

$$= \frac{100,000}{2\,(.375)\,(6 - .375)\,(4 - .3125)}$$

$$= 6420 \text{ psi}$$

The horizontal shear force is then - -

$$f = \tau\,t$$
$$= 6420 \times .375$$
$$= 2410 \text{ lbs/linear inch}$$

Since weld metal is good for 13,000 psi in shear, the throat or depth of the continuous butt weld must be--

$$f = \tau_{weld}\,t$$
$$2410 = 13,000\,t$$
or $$t = \frac{2410}{13,000}$$
$$= .185" \text{ or } ³⁄₁₆"$$

The groove weld connecting the channels must have a throat depth of at least ³⁄₁₆". Of course, if the torsional load is applied suddenly as an impact load, it would be good practice to add a safety factor to the computed load. This would then necessitate a deeper throat for the butt weld.

FIGURE 16

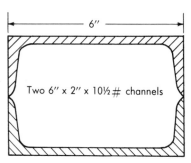

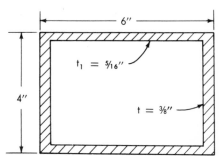

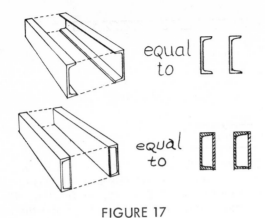

FIGURE 17

6. BUILT-UP FRAMES

The principles of torsion which determine the best sections for resisting twist apply to built-up frames. Just as the torsional resistance of the section is equal to the total of the resistances of its individual areas, so is the torsional resistance of a frame approximately equal to the total resistance of its individual parts.

The torsional resistance of the frame whose longitudinal members are two channels would be approximately equal to twice the torsional resistance of each channel section, Figure 17. The distance between these members for purpose of this example is considered to have no effect. Since the closed section is best for resisting twist, the torsional resistance of this frame could be greatly increased by making the channels into rectangular box sections through the addition of plate.

Problem 6

A frame is made of two 6" standard pipes, spaced 24" between centers, and having a length of 60". This frame supports a 10-hp motor running at 1800 rpm and driving a pump. Find the approximate twist of the frame under the load.

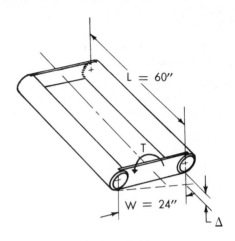

FIGURE 18

The 6" standard pipe has O.D. = 6.625" and I.D. = 6.065". In finding the torsional resistance of each tube:

$$R = .0982 \, (d_2^4 - d_1^4)$$
$$= .0982 \, (6.625^4 - 6.065^4)$$
$$= 56.30 \text{ in.}^4$$

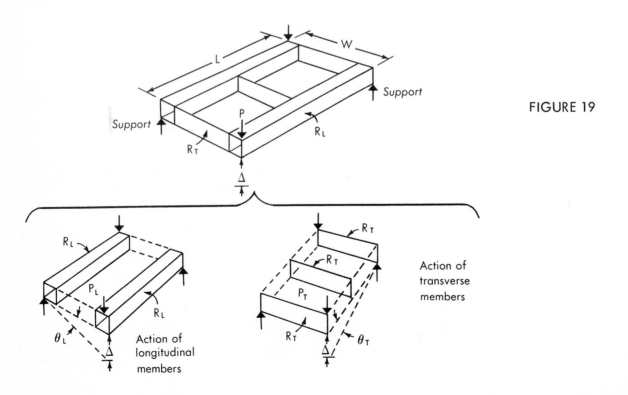

FIGURE 19

The torque is easily found:

$$T = \frac{63{,}030 \times HP}{RPM}$$

$$= \frac{63{,}030 \times 10}{1800}$$

$$= 350 \text{ in.-lbs}$$

Then, adding together the R of each tube, the angular twist is—

$$\theta = \frac{T L}{E_s R}$$

$$= \frac{350 \times 60}{(12 \times 10^6)(2 \times 56.30)}$$

$$= 0.0000156 \text{ radians, or } \underline{0.00089°}$$

Maximum deflection in the frame is the vertical displacement (Δ), which is the product of angular twist (θ) and frame width (W) between centers:

$$\Delta = \theta W$$

$$= 0.0000156 \times 24''$$

$$= \underline{0.00037''}$$

7. DEFLECTION OF BUILT-UP FRAMES

In analyzing the resistance and strength of a built-up frame against twisting, consider the torque applied as two forces in the form of a couple at each end of the frame. In this manner, it is seen that these same forces apply a torque transverse to the frame as well as longitudinal to it.

This helps to show that the over-all resistance against twisting is the sum of the resistances of all the members, longitudinal as well as transverse. It is usually more convenient to express the resulting angular twist in terms of vertical deflection of the frame corner which receives the vertical load.

The longitudinal members are now considered to make up a frame of their own. When the vertical force (P_L) applied at the corner reaches the proper value, the frame will deflect vertically the given distance (Δ) and each longitudinal member will twist (θ_L). The same separate analysis is also made of the transverse members.

By observation we find—

$$\Delta = \theta_L W = \theta_T L$$

Then:

$$(1) \quad \theta_L = \frac{\Delta}{W} \quad \text{and} \quad \theta_T = \frac{\Delta}{L}$$

Using the common formula for angular twist —

$$\theta_L = \frac{T_L L}{E_s n_L R_L} \quad \text{and} \quad \theta_T = \frac{T_T W}{E_s n_T R_T}$$

and combining this with Formula (1) above —

$$\frac{\Delta}{W} = \frac{T_L L}{E_s n_L R_L} \quad \text{and} \quad \frac{\Delta}{L} = \frac{T_T W}{E_s n_T R_T}$$

TABLE 3 - TORSIONAL RESISTANCE OF FRAME AND VARIOUS SECTIONS

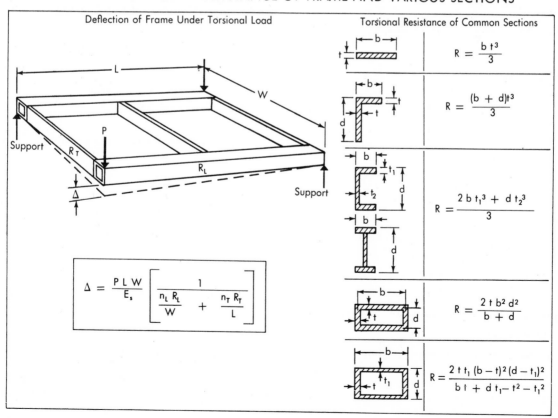

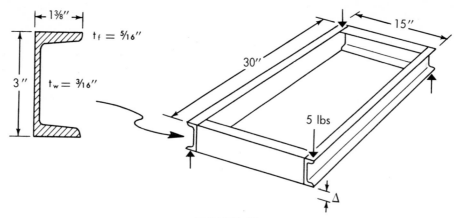

FIGURE 20

Then:

(2) $\quad T_L = \dfrac{\Delta E_s n_L R_L}{W L}$ and $T_T = \dfrac{\Delta E_s n_T R_T}{W L}$

Since the applied torque is —

$T_L = P_L W$ and $T_T = P_T L$

$\therefore \quad P_L = \dfrac{T_L}{W}$ and $P_T = \dfrac{T_T}{L}$

and combining this with Formula (2) above —

$P_L = \dfrac{\Delta E_s n_L R_L}{W^2 L}$ and $P_T = \dfrac{\Delta E_s n_T R_T}{W L^2}$

Since the external force (P) applied at the corner is the sum of these two forces:

$$P = P_L + P_T = \dfrac{\Delta E_s n_L R_L}{W^2 L} + \dfrac{\Delta E_s n_T R_T}{W L^2}$$

$$= \dfrac{\Delta E_s}{W L}\left(\dfrac{n_L R_L}{W} + \dfrac{n_T R_T}{L}\right)$$

$$\therefore \quad \boxed{\Delta = \dfrac{P L W}{E_s}\left[\dfrac{1}{\dfrac{n_L R_L}{W} + \dfrac{n_T R_T}{L}}\right]} \quad \ldots\ldots\ldots\ldots\ldots(4)$$

where:

L = length of whole frame, in.

W = width of whole frame, in.

R_L = torsional resistance of longitudinal member, in.[4]

R_T = torsional resistance of transverse member, in.[4]

n_L = number of longitudinal members

n_T = number of transverse members

P = load applied at corner, lbs

E_s = modulus of elasticity in shear (steel: 12×10^6), psi

Δ = vertical deflection, in.

It can be seen that the torque on a given member is actually produced by the transverse forces supplied by the cross members attached to them. These same forces subject the cross members to bending.

In other words, the torque applied to a member equals the end moment of the cross member attached to it. There is some deflection due to bending of all the members, and this would slightly increase the over-all deflection of the frame. For simplicity this has been neglected in this analysis.

Problem 7

To illustrate the use of the preceding deflection formula, consider a frame 15" wide and 30" long, made of standard 3" channel, Figure 20. Find the vertical deflection of the unsupported corner when under a load of 5 lbs.

Using the appropriate formula from Table 3, torsional resistance of the U channel cross-section is--

$$R = \dfrac{2 b t_1^3 + d t_2^3}{3} = \dfrac{2 b t_f^3 + d t_w^3}{3}$$

$$= \dfrac{2(1.375)(.3125)^3}{3} + \dfrac{3(.1875)^3}{3}$$

$$= .0346 \text{ in.}^4$$

Substituting actual values into formula #4:

$$\Delta = \dfrac{P L W}{E_s}\left[\dfrac{1}{\dfrac{n_L R_L}{W} + \dfrac{n_T R_T}{L}}\right]$$

$$= \dfrac{(5)(30)(15)}{(12 \times 10^6)}\left[\dfrac{1}{\dfrac{2(.0346)}{15} + \dfrac{2(.0346)}{30}}\right]$$

$$= .027"$$

The actual deflection when tested was —

$\Delta = .030"$

8. BRACING OF FRAMES

The two main stresses on a member under torsional loading are (1) transverse shear stresses and

(2) longitudinal shear stresses.

These two stresses combine to produce diagonal tensile and compressive stresses which are maximum at 45°. At 45°, the transverse and longitudinal shear stresses cancel each other. Therefore, there is no twisting stress or action on a diagonal member placed at 45° to the frame.

In a frame made up of flat members, the transverse shear stresses cause the longitudinal members to twist. The longitudinal shear stresses cause the cross braces and end members to twist.

On a diagonal member at 45° to axis of twist, the transverse and longitudinal shear stress components are opposite in direction to each other and cancel out, but in line with this member they combine to produce diagonal tensile and compressive stresses which tend to cause bending rather than twisting. See Figure 21.

Since these two shear stresses cancel out, there is no tendency for a diagonal member placed in this direction to twist.

The diagonal tensile and compressive stresses try to cause this diagonal member to bend; but being very resistant to bending, the diagonal member greatly stiffens the entire frame against twisting.

The two steel bases in Figure 22 look alike when

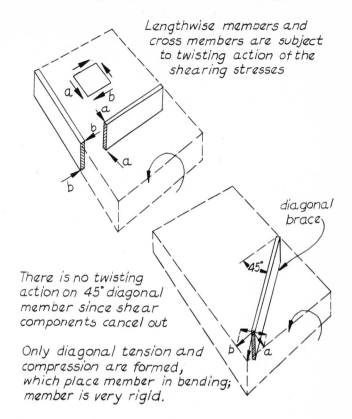

Lengthwise members and cross members are subject to twisting action of the shearing stresses

diagonal brace

There is no twisting action on 45° diagonal member since shear components cancel out

Only diagonal tension and compression are formed, which place member in bending; member is very rigid.

FIGURE 21

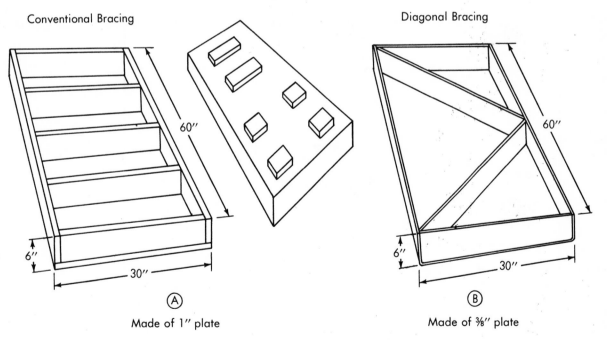

Conventional Bracing

Diagonal Bracing

60″

60″

6″

6″

30″

30″

Ⓐ

Ⓑ

Made of 1″ plate

Made of ⅜″ plate

FIGURE 22

Cost Saving with Base B:
　　Materials (352 lbs vs 877 lbs, steel) 60%
　　Welding (247″ vs 552″) 78%
　　Preparation (shearing, braking and assembly
　　　　vs flame-cutting and assembly) 42%
　　And, a <u>Total</u> Cost Saving of 54%

covered by a top panel. They have approximately the same resistance to twisting, but the one on the right weighs only 40% as much as the other and costs only 45.8% as much. The reason for this is diagonal bracing.

Design Rule No. 2:   USE DIAGONAL BRACING

Stiffening the Braces

Previous experience in designing longitudinal side members for bending is now used to design these diagonal members.

It is important that the diagonal members have a high moment of inertia to provide sufficient stiffness so there will be no failure from local buckling, under severe torsional loads.

Since the diagonal brace is not subjected to any twisting action, it is not necessary to use a closed box section.

For short diagonal braces, use a simple flat bar. The top and/or bottom panel of the frame will stiffen this to some extent (Fig. 23). As the unsupported length of the diagonal brace becomes longer, it may become necessary to add a flange (Fig. 24). This is done by flanging one edge of the brace or using an angle bar or T section. The flange of the brace may also be stiffened to keep it from buckling.

For open frames with no flat panel, it is better to use a channel or I beam section having two flanges (Fig. 25).

FIGURE 23

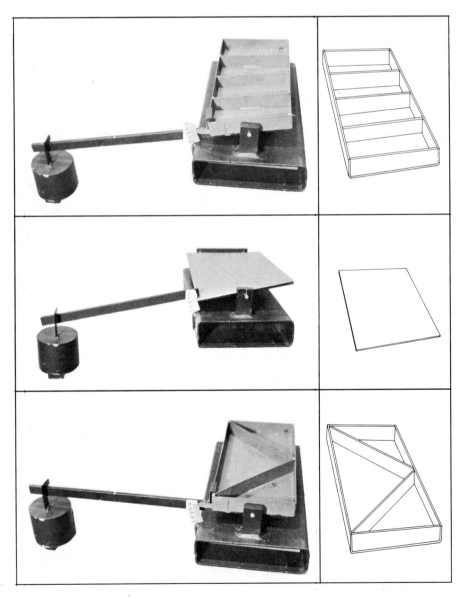

FIGURE 26

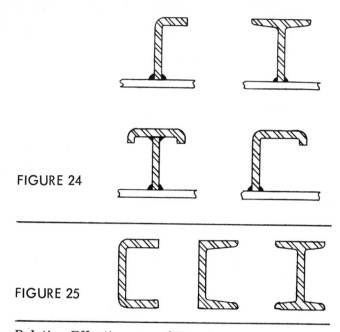

FIGURE 24

FIGURE 25

Relative Effectiveness of Bracing

Tests were made on scale models of typical machine bases to illustrate increase in resistance to twist as a result of the diagonal bracing.

The top base in Figure 26 has conventional cross bracing at 90° to side members. It twisted 9°.

The above base is little better in resistance to twist than a flat sheet of the same thickness, as shown in the middle. The plain sheet twisted 10°.

The bottom base has diagonal braces at 45° with side members. It twisted only ¼°. It is 36 times as resistant to twisting as the first base, yet uses 6% less bracing material.

9. DIAGONAL BRACING (Double)

(See Figure 27)

An approximate indication of the angular twist of a frame using double diagonal bracing (in the form of an X) may be made by the following procedure. Here each brace is treated as a beam.

$$\Delta = \frac{(2\,F)\,Y^3}{48\,E\,I}$$

$$\theta = \frac{\Delta}{\tfrac{1}{2}\,L} = \frac{2\,\Delta}{L} = \frac{F\,Y^3}{12\,E\,I\,L}$$

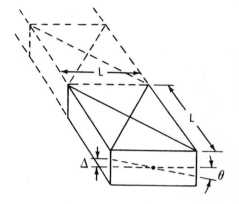

FIGURE 28

Since $T = F\,L$, then $F = \dfrac{T}{L}$

$$\therefore \quad \theta = \frac{T\,Y^3}{12\,E\,I\,L^2}$$

Since $Y = \sqrt{2}\,L$

$$\theta = \frac{T\,(\sqrt{2})^3\,L^3}{12\,E\,I\,L^2} = \frac{\sqrt{2}\,T\,L}{6\,E\,I}$$

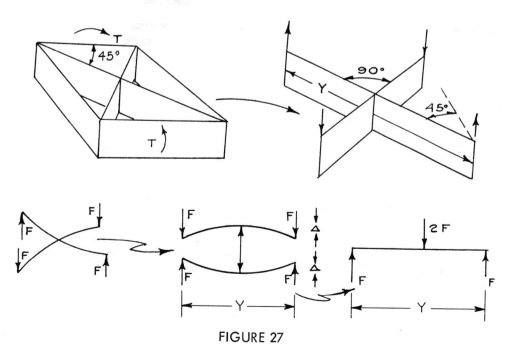

FIGURE 27

also $\theta = \dfrac{T L}{E_s R}$ Hence $\dfrac{\sqrt{2}\, T L}{6 E I} = \dfrac{T L}{E_s R}$

and $R = \dfrac{6 E I}{\sqrt{2}\, E_s}$

Since for steel $E = 30 \times 10^6$, and $E_s = 12 \times 10^6$

$$\boxed{R = 10.6\ I}$$

which appeared in Table 1.

Therefore: For a double diagonal brace use R = 10.6 I and substitute this value into the standard formula:

$$\theta = \dfrac{T L}{E_s R}$$

to get the frame's angular twist (radians).

Practical examples of various types of bracing are included in Section 4.3 on Designing Braces and Stiffeners.

Problem 8

Two ¼" × 10" plates, 40" long, spaced 20" apart to make a frame 40" long, are subjected to a torque of T = 1000 in.-lbs. Find the relative angular twist on the frame, when using conventional and diagonal bracing.

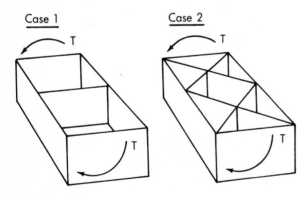

FIGURE 29

Case 1 (Conventional bracing)

Here the torsional resistance of the plate section is known, from Table 3, to be--

$$R = \dfrac{b t^3}{3}$$

$$\therefore\ R = 2\,\dfrac{(10)\,(.25)^3}{3}$$

$$= .104 \text{ in.}^4 \text{ (both sides)}$$

The total angular twist is then —

$$\theta = \dfrac{T L}{E_s R}$$

$$= \dfrac{(1000)\,(40)}{(12 \times 10^6)\,(.104)}$$

$$= .0321 \text{ radians or } \underline{1.84°}$$

Case 2 (Diagonal bracing)

Since this is "double" bracing, the Table 1 formula for this type of frame is used--

R = 10.6 I

First find the moment of inertia for the cross-section of a brace, which is a simple rectangle, assuming the brace also is ¼" × 10":

$$I = \dfrac{b\, d^3}{12}$$

where b = the <u>section width</u> (plate thickness), and d = the <u>section depth</u>

$$I = \dfrac{.25\,(10)^3}{12}$$

$$= 20.83 \text{ in.}^4$$

then substituting into the formula for R--

$$R = 10.6\,(20.83)$$
$$= 221 \text{ in.}^4$$

The angular twist on the frame is then--

$$\theta = \dfrac{T L}{E_s R}$$

$$= \dfrac{(1000)\,(40)}{(12 \times 10^6)\,(221)}$$

$$= .0000152 \text{ radians or } \underline{.00087°}$$

10. TORSIONAL RESISTANCE NOMOGRAPHS

Several nomographs helpful to the solution of torsional problems, appear in Section 4.1, "How to Design Machine Bases." The first of these gives the moment of inertia required to resist a given bending load. The second provides the torsional resistance of a proposed design. The third gives the resulting angular twist of the member or frame.

11. END CONNECTIONS OF TORSION MEMBERS

When a member having an open section is twisted, the cross-section warps (see b, in Fig. 30) if ends of the member are free. The flanges of these members not only twist, but they also swing outward (see c), allowing the member to twist more. If the ends of the flanges can be lock-

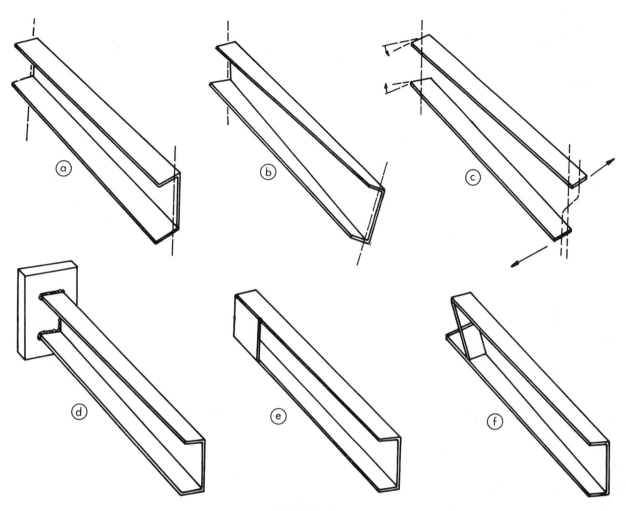

FIGURE 30

ed in place in relation to each other, this swinging will be prevented.

> Design Rule No. 3: MAKE RIGID END CONNECTIONS

There are several methods of locking the flanges together. The simplest is to weld the end of the member to the supporting member as in (d). If the supporting member is then neither thick enough nor rigid enough, a thin, square plate may be welded to the two flanges at the end of the member (e). Another method is to use diagonal braces between the two flanges at the two ends of the member (f).

Either of these methods reduce the angular twist by about ½.

12. MEMBRANE ANALOGY

Membrane analogy is a very useful method to understand the behavior of open sections when sub-jected to torsion. To make use of this method, holes are cut into a thin plate making the outline of various shaped sections. A membrane material such as soap film is spread over the open surface and air pressure is applied to the film. The mathematical expressions for the slope and volume of this membrane or film covering the openings representing different cross-sections are the same as the expressions for the shear stresses and torsional resistance of the actual member being studied. It is from this type of analysis that formulas for various types of open sections subjected to torsion have been developed and confirmed.

If several outlines are cut into the thin plate and the same pressure applied to each membrane, the following will be true:

1. The volumes under the membranes will be proportional to the torsional resistances of the corresponding sections.

2. The slope of the membrane's surface at any

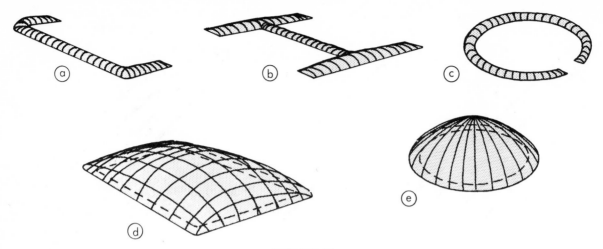

FIGURE 31

point is proportional to the shear stress of the section at this point.

3. A narrow section (thin plate) has practically the same torsional resistance regardless of the shape of the section it is formed into. Notice a, b, and c in Figure 31. For a given area of section, the volume under the membrane remains the same regardless of the shape of the section.

It is possible to determine the torsional resist-ance of these open sections by comparing them with a standard circle on this same test plate whose torsional resistance can readily be calculated.

By comparing the membrane of the slotted open tube, (c) in Figure 31, to that of the membrane of the closed tube (e), it is readily seen why the closed tube is several hundred times more resistant to twist, when it is remembered that the volume under the membrane is proportional to the torsional resistance.

Welded steel slide for 500-ton press incorporates diagonal bracing for tor-sional stiffness; span between .housings is 240".

How to Design Machine Bases

1. REQUIREMENTS

Bases for all types of machines and for such sub-assemblies as power drive units are usually critical to the machine's performance. The problem is essentially one of rigidity under a bending load, and the base cross-section must have sufficient moment of inertia to resist the bending load without excessive deflection.

Deflection of bases subject to bending loads is complex; see Sect. 2.9, Topic 9, relative to "Designing a base to resist bending". Most bases have more than two loads, and it is necessary to consider each and to sum them in determining total required moment of inertia. Likewise, members of the base must be considered separately as to their contribution to the total resistance to deflection; i.e. longitudinal side members and cross members and/or braces.

Rotational forces and eccentric static, impact or cyclic loads usually create an additional problem of torsion, or deflection by angular twist. The principal measures taken by the designer to improve torsional resistance are (1) diagonal bracing; (2) closed sections in longitudinal members; and (3) rigid end connections. See Sect. 3.6, Topics 7, 8 and 9, relative to the deflection of built-up frames and the effects of bracing.

Intermediate stiffeners, particularly diagonal braces, are important to lessening the unsupported span of the top panel, thereby increasing its resistance to localized deflection under bending.

Excessive deflection of a base may cause angular misalignment, especially troublesome in the case of mechanically coupled power drive components and of shafts in bearings. It may result in high vibration and eccentric loading of rotating members, excessive bearing wear, and impaired quality of work performed. See Sect. 3.3 on Vibration Control.

In the case of machine tools, deflection may cause tool chatter and premature tool failure, inability to hold dimensional tolerances, and tapered surfaces. In other types of machinery, deflection has comparable effects on quality.

2. ADVANTAGES OF STEEL

Steel is the best material economically for building bases. It is inherently much more rigid than gray cast iron, for example. The behavior of steel members under loading conditions can be accurately predetermined, and improvements are easily made to meet changing service conditions.

In the past the lead time required in making patterns, pouring the machine base, and aging the castings has been a serious deterrent to model changes and to short delivery cycles for many machinery builders. The efficient use of welded steel eliminates these problems.

3. BASIC DESIGN APPROACH

The design of a steel base on the basis of loading, closely follows that of a simple built-up frame as discussed in previous sections. The main principles are reviewed in the following problem.

Problem 1

To design a base or foundation for an engine, driving an electric generator. The total weight of the engine and the generator is 25 tons or 50,000 lbs. Functionally, the base should be about 24" high, 36" wide and 200" long. Not only must the base have sufficient strength, but it must be rigid. The designer considers that the unit deflection, i.e. total deflection in inches of a member divided by its length in inches, (Δ/L) should not exceed .0001 in./in.

1

<u>Design the cross-section of longitudinal members</u>

Assume the base to be supported on each end as a beam, uniformly loaded, and design a cross-section having sufficient moment of inertia to hold the unit deflection of the beam to within .0001 in./in.

Using the beam diagrams, find the required moment of inertia (I):

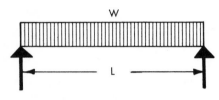

W

L

FIGURE 1

where:

$W = 50,000$ lbs
$L = 200"$
$E = 30,000,000$ psi

$$\frac{\Delta}{L} = .0001 \text{ in./in.}$$

Since:

$$\Delta = \frac{5\,W\,L^3}{384\,E\,I}$$

$$I = \frac{5\,W\,L^3}{384\,E\,\Delta} = \frac{5\,W\,L^2}{384\,E\left(\frac{\Delta}{L}\right)}$$

$$= \frac{5(50,000)\,(200)^2}{384\,(30,000,000)\,(.0001)}$$

$$= 8,675 \text{ in.}^4 \text{ (total of both sides)}$$

or:

$I = \underline{4,338 \text{ in.}^4}$ on each side member

To build up a steel section which will have this required moment of inertia, the unit properties table will be helpful. See Sect. 2.3, Tables 2, 3, 4 and 5.

It is decided to use an I section, having a depth of 24". Since:

$$I = I_u\,d^4$$

$$I_u = \frac{I}{d^4} = \frac{4338}{24^4}$$

$$= .01305 \text{ in.}^4$$

Using the unit properties for stiffness of an I section, it is found this value can be obtained from an I section having a width of ½ the depth and a thickness of 4½% of the depth. For unit properties, see Lower Table 3 in Sect. 2.3. Thus the following sections will provide the required moment of inertia in the longitudinal members:

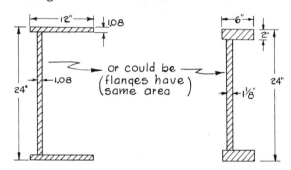

FIGURE 2

The decision then is to use a built-up I section, as shown here:

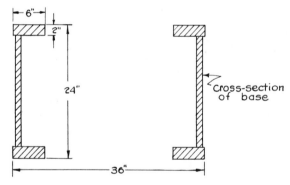

FIGURE 3

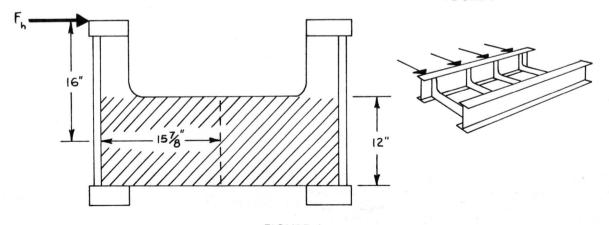

FIGURE 4

Design the cross members

The next step is to design the cross member joining the main side members of the base. The dimensions, Figure 4, are established on the basis of over-all considerations.

Even though there is no applied horizontal loading on the base, the base should be capable of withstanding an assumed horizontal force; for example, $\frac{1}{5}$ of the vertical load.

$\frac{1}{5}$ of 50,000 lbs = 10,000 lbs

Having decided to use 4 cross members, F_h = 2500 lbs per member.

Considering only the main portion of the cross member (extending the full distance from side to side) as two beams joined end to end, from beam diagrams:

FIGURE 5

where:

P = 2500 lbs
e = 16"
L = 15⅞"
E = 30,000,000 psi

$\frac{\Delta}{L}$ = .0001 in./in.

Since:

$$\Delta = \frac{P e L^2}{2 E I}$$

$$I = \frac{P e L^2}{2 E \Delta} = \frac{P e L}{2 E}\left(\frac{L}{\Delta}\right)$$

$$= \frac{2500\,(16)\,(15⅞)}{2\,(30,000,000)\,(.0001)}$$

$$= \underline{105.8 \text{ in.}^4}$$

Now the steel cross member must be built up to have this value, with a depth of 12". Since:

$I = I_u\, d^4$

$I_u = \dfrac{I}{d^4} = \dfrac{105.8}{12^4}$

$= .0051 \text{ in.}^4$

Using the unit properties for stiffness of an I section, it is found this value can be obtained from an I section having a width of ½ the depth, and a thickness of 2% of the depth. See Lower Table 3, Section 2.3.

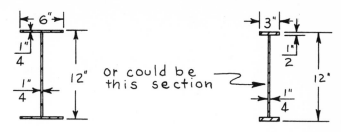

FIGURE 6

The next step is to check the resultant upper portion of this cross member; a horizontal cross-section of this is similar to an I beam. Its outer flange is a portion of the longitudinal member's web; its web is the web of the cross member; and its inner flange is a continuation of the cross member's top flange.

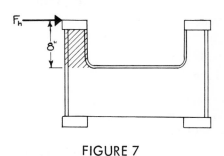

FIGURE 7

From beam diagrams:

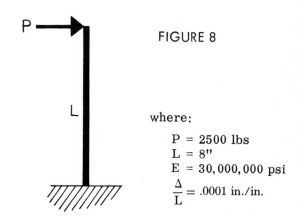

FIGURE 8

where:

P = 2500 lbs
L = 8"
E = 30,000,000 psi
$\frac{\Delta}{L}$ = .0001 in./in.

Since:

$$\Delta = \frac{P L^3}{3 E I}$$

$$I = \frac{P L^3}{3 E \Delta} = \frac{P L^2}{3 E}\left(\frac{L}{\Delta}\right)$$

$$= \frac{2500\,(8)^2}{3\,(30,000,000)\,(.0001)}$$

$$= \underline{17.8 \text{ in.}^4} \text{ required}$$

From Figure 9:

d = 5"
t = 5% of d

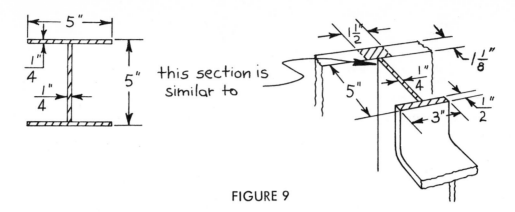

FIGURE 9

Because of the 6" width of the top longitudinal flange, it is desirable to hold the depth here to 5".

Using the appropriate unit properties table:

$I_u = .02562$

$I = I_u d^4$

$= .02562 \times 5^4$

$= \underline{16.0 \text{ in.}^4}$

Hence section is OK, close enough to the 17.8 in.^{4} required inertia in view of only part of side plate being considered in flange.

Check the base for resistance to twisting

The final step is to check the torsional resistance of the base, and to modify it if necessary.

Power transmitted = 1000 HP
Speed = 800 RPM

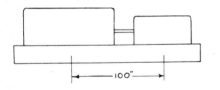

FIGURE 10

$T = \dfrac{63,024 \times HP}{RPM}$

$= \dfrac{(63,024)(1000)}{(800)}$

$= 78,780 \text{ in.-lbs.}$

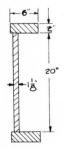

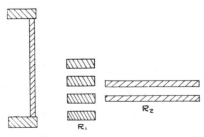

FIGURE 11

From Section 3.6 on Torsion, the torsional resistance of a built-up open section is known to equal the sum of the torsional resistances of its rectangular areas. Considering the longitudinal side members, follow Table 1 of Section 3.6:

(1) $R_1 = \beta b d^3$ (See Figure 11)

where:

$\beta = .263$

$b = 6"$

$d = 2"$

$\therefore R_1 = .263(6)(2)^3$

$= 12.62 \text{ in.}^4$

(2) $R_2 = \beta b d^3$ (See Figure 11)

where:

$\beta = .333$

$b = 20"$

$d = 1\frac{1}{8}"$

$\therefore R_2 = .333(20)(1\frac{1}{8})^3$

$= 9.49 \text{ in.}^4$

The total resistance of the two side members to twisting is —

$R = 4R_1 + 2R_2$

$= 4(12.62) + 2(9.49)$

$= \underline{69.46 \text{ in.}^4}$

and the angular twist will be —

$\theta = \dfrac{T L}{E_s R}$

$= \dfrac{(78,780)(100)}{(12 \times 10^6)(69.46)}$

$= .0095 \text{ radians or } \underline{.54°}$

If this is believed to be excessive, diagonal braces can be used or the two side members can be boxed in.

FIG. 12 – REQUIRED MOMENT OF INERTIA
For Each Load or Couple on the Base

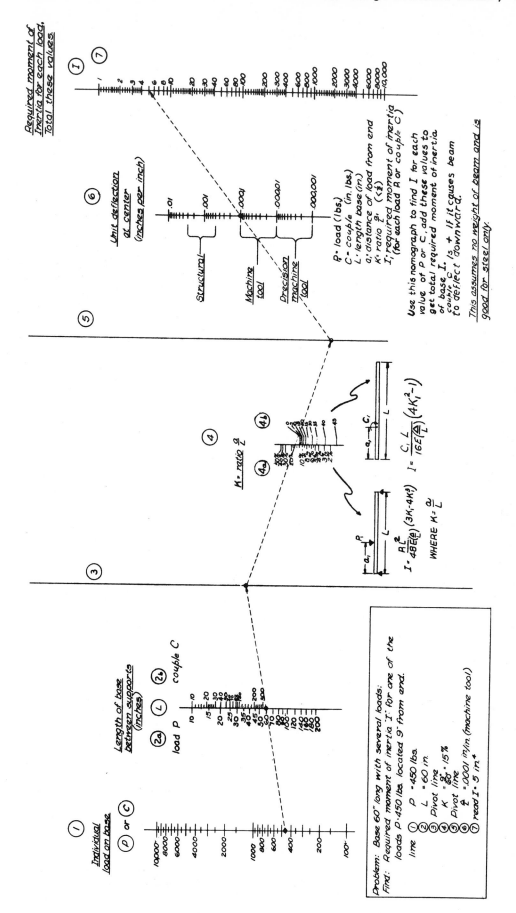

FIG. 13 – TORSIONAL RESISTANCE OF BASE MEMBER

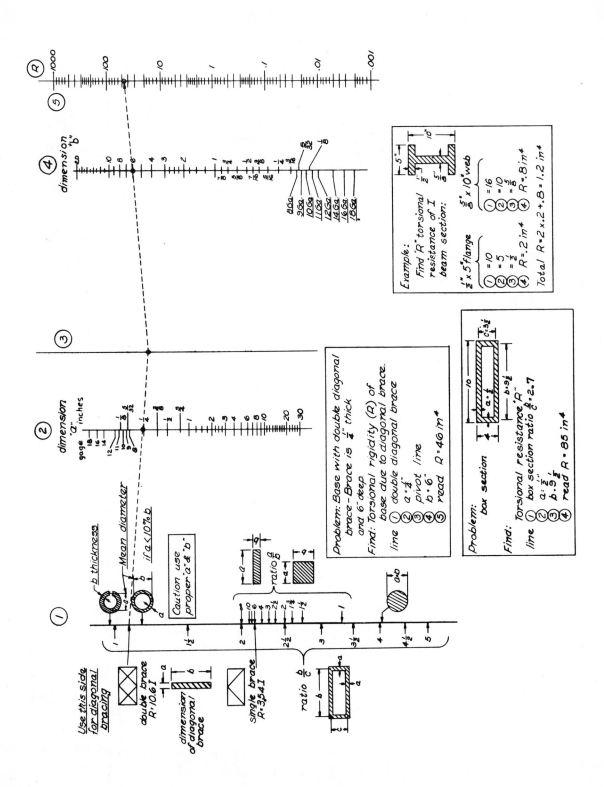

4. USE OF NOMOGRAPHS

The basic design procedure is modified so that equally reliable designs may be developed more quickly by using the nomographs presented herein.

Step 1: Design base to resist bending

For simplicity, only the deflection at the middle of the base is considered. Most bases have more than two loads. Each load causes a certain deflection at the middle of the base, and the total deflection at this point equals the sum of the deflections produced by the individual loads acting on the base.

Further, each load requires the base to have a certain moment of inertia in order to maintain an established allowable unit deflection. Hence, the required moment of inertia of the base equals the sum of the moments of inertia obtained by considering each load to act separately on the base, one at a time.

The first nomograph, Figure 12, gives the moment of inertia (I) required of the frame to resist a given load.

Here:

Line 1 = Each individual load on the base (P) in lbs or couple (C) in in.-lbs
Line 2 = Length of the base between end supports (L), in.
Line 3 = Pivot line
Line 4 = Ratio a/L, the distance of the load from the closest end support divided by the length of base between supports. (This ratio never exceeds 50%.)
Line 5 = Pivot line
Line 6 = Allowable unit deflection of the base (Δ/L) ,in./in. This is the designer's idea of the deflection which may be allowed at the middle of the base, divided by the length of the base. As a guide this scale has been marked off into three basic ranges for various classes of service requirements.
Line 7 = The answer to be read from this graph: the required moment of inertia (I) for the particular load, in.[4]

These moments of inertia are added together to give the required total moment of inertia of the base. The cross-section of the base will be determined by this value.

Step 2: Strengthen base to resist twisting

The base design tentatively proposed on the basis of providing the required moment of inertia, as determined by the first nomograph, will probably have to be checked for its resistance to twisting. Most bases are subjected to some kind of torque.

The cause of vertical deflection is often misinterpreted; and ignoring the torque problem, the longitudinal members are sometimes made heavier

without any appreciable decrease in the deflection. A base may be sufficiently resistant to deflection by bending, and yet have very low torsional resistance.

The second nomograph, Figure 13, permits the designer to quickly find the torsional resistance of a proposed design. The total torsional resistance equals the sum of the resistances offered separately by the members.

On this nomograph:

Line 1 = Type of section, or element of a built-up section. Observe caution as to meaning of letter symbols. For a solid rectangular section use the ratio of width (a) divided by thickness (b); for a hollow rectangular section use width (b) divided by depth (c).
Line 2 = Dimension (a), in.
Line 3 = Pivot line
Line 4 = Dimension (b), in.
Line 5 = Torsional resistance of the section (R), in.[4] These values for each element are added together to give the total torsional resistance of the section, and the resistances of the sections are added to give the total torsional resistance of the frame or base. This is used in the design formula for angular twist, or in the next nomograph, Figure 14.

In the case of a member having a built-up cross-section, such as a T or I beam, read the Figure 13 nomograph for the R value of each element or area making up the section. Start at vertical Line 1 in the nomograph, using the scale to the right of it that expresses the rectangular element's a/b ratio. In the case of solid squares or rounds, and closed or open round tubes, go directly to the point on the scale indicated by the visual representation of the cross-section.

Notice that the meaning of a and b varies. In the case of a rectangular element, a is the longer dimension; but in the case of a hollow rectangle, a is the wall or plate thickness. The value of a and b on Lines 1, 2 and 4 must correspond, according to the type of section or element for which torsional resistance (R) is sought.

For hollow rectangular sections (of uniform wall or plate thickness), use the scale along the left of vertical Line 1 that expresses the ratio b/c. Here b = the section's width and c = its depth.

Numerous conditions may cause a torsional load to be applied to the member or base. Usually it will be similar in nature to one of the following situations:

1. A given horsepower (HP) transmitted through a gear reducer at a given speed (RPM) will produce a certain torque (in.-lbs) on the supporting base.

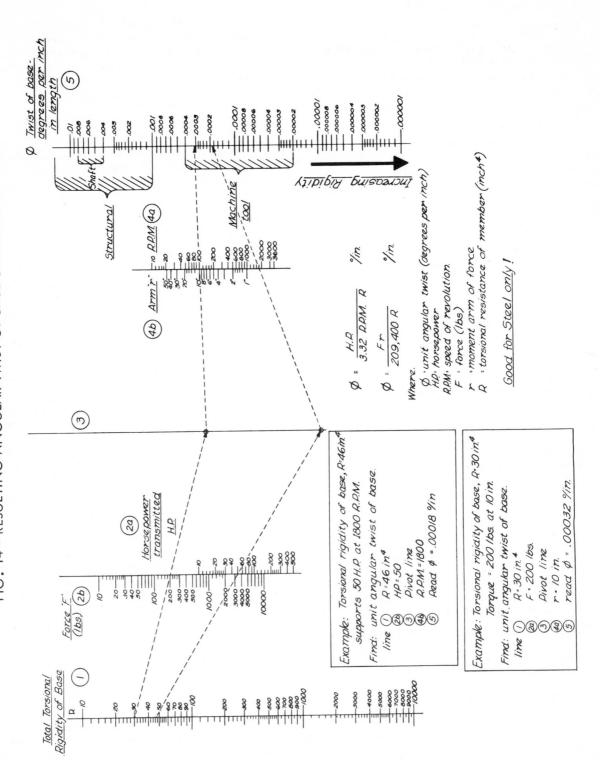

FIG. 14 – RESULTING ANGULAR TWIST OF BASE UNDER LOAD

2. A given tool pressure (lbs) in a lathe acting on a given radius of work (inches) will produce a certain torque (in.-lbs) on the base.

Having evaluated the conditions producing torque and having obtained the total torsional resistance of the member or base by using the preceding nomograph, Figure 13, the resulting angular twist of the member or base can be determined. The third nomograph, Figure 14, can be used for this purpose.

On this nomograph:

Line 1 = Total torsional resistance of the base (R), in.[4].

Line 2a = Horsepower (HP) transmitted to the base

Line 2b = Force which causes torsion (F) lbs

Line 3 = Pivot line

Line 4a = Speed (RPM) of the machine part which applies the torsional load to the base

Line 4b = Radius or torque arm, distance of axial centerline from point at which force is applied, in.

Line 5 = Resultant unit angular twist (ϕ), degrees/in. in length of base.

If the torsional load is caused by a given horsepower transmitted to the base at a given RPM, use Lines 2a and 4a. If the torsional load is applied by a given force acting on a given radius, use Lines 2b and 4b in the nomograph.

The allowable unit angular twist is what the designer knows or assumes will provide acceptable performance of the base for the given application. As a guide, the values along vertical Line 5 of the nomograph are grouped according to the commonly accepted range for several classes of application.

If use of these nomographs (Figs. 13 and 14) shows a torsional resistance (R) or subsequently an angular twist (ϕ) which is considered inadequate, the base may have to be strengthened and the resultant structure rechecked.

Stiffening the base against twisting is achieved (1) by closing in of an open section, in the case of the longitudinal side members, and/or (2) by using diagonal bracing. On the second nomograph (Fig. 13), go directly to the point along left side of Line 1 indicated for the type of bracing employed and on Lines 2 and 4 let a = thickness of the brace and b = depth of the brace.

Step 3: Design top panel to resist localized bending between stiffeners

Frequently the flat top panel of the proposed base will not be thick enough to support a given load, even though the section of which it is a part has sufficient moment of inertia (I) to properly resist bending as determined by Step 1. Rather than increase the thickness of this panel, it is usually preferable and

more economical to add stiffeners to reduce the unsupported length of panel.

The fourth nomograph (Fig. 15) enables the designer to quickly determine the required spacing of stiffeners to maintain the unit deflection within an allowable limit.

Consider only the panel portion between stiffeners, whether triangular or rectangular. Diagonal bracing will result in a triangular pattern. Conventional cross-members will result in a rectangular pattern.

On this nomograph:

Line 1 = Concentrated bending load (P) on the panel, lbs

Line 2 = Thickness of panel, in.

Line 3 = Pivot line

Line 4 = Allowable unit deflection (Δ/a), in.

Line 5a = For triangular panel--maximum length of side a, in.

Line 5b = For rectangular panel--use this as a pivot line

Line 6 = For rectangular panel--width a of base, in.

Line 7 = For rectangular panel--ratio of b/a, where b is maximum spacing between stiffeners, in.

For a triangular panel pattern, read the answer on Line 5.

For a rectangular panel pattern, read the answer on Line 7 as a percentage of the base width.

Problem 2

To design a new base for a motor and speed reducer unit on the basis of loading. The weights of the equipment are known, as are the HP and RPM of the motor. Steel is selected because of its superior rigidity and its economy.

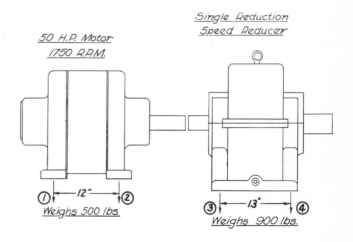

FIGURE 16

FIG. 15 – REQUIRED SPACING OF STIFFENERS OF FLAT PANELS

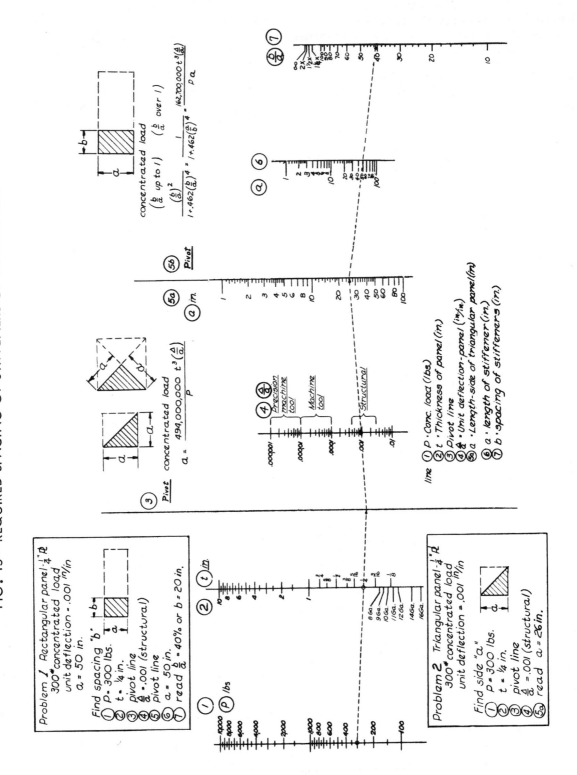

The following three steps will result in a welded steel design to meet load and service requirements:

1. Design base to resist bending.
2. Strengthen base to resist twisting.
3. Design top panel to resist localized bending between stiffeners.

These steps are illustrated in Figure 17.

Step 1: Design base to resist bending

First find the required moment of inertia (I) of the base, which should be about 60" long and 30"

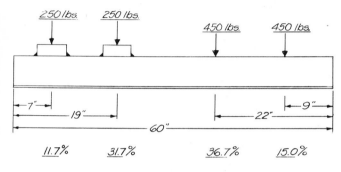

FIGURE 18

wide. Distribution of the loads relative to the nearest end of the base is diagrammed:

Use the first nomograph (Fig. 12), treating the base as a beam simply supported on the ends and loaded with the maximum weight of the motor and the reducer. Determine a minimum moment of inertia (I) required to hold the unit deflection within the desired value, in this case .0001 in./in.

From Nomograph No. 1

Load	Line 1 P, lbs	Line 2 L, in.	Line 4 K, %	Line 6 Δ/L in./in.	Line 7 I, in.^{4}
1	250	60	11.7	.0001	2.2
2	250	60	31.7	.0001	5.0
3	450	60	36.7	.0001	10.0
4	450	60	15.0	.0001	5.0

Total Required I = 22.2 in.^{4}

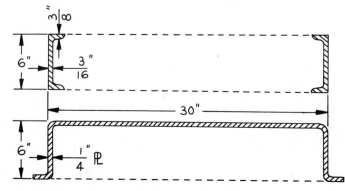

FIGURE 19

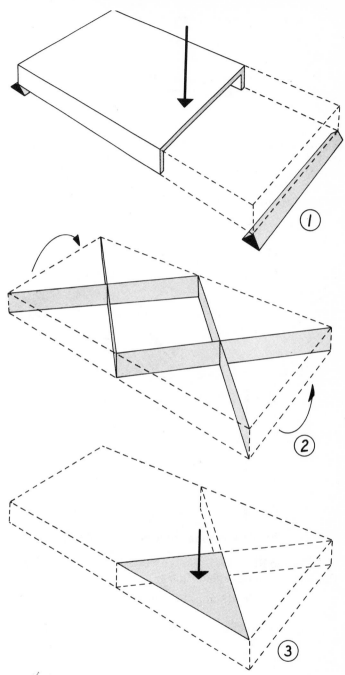

Fig. 17 The 3 major steps in base design.

Consulting a steel handbook we find that two 6" × 2½" × 8.2 lb channels will provide this value, since each channel has a moment of inertia of 13 in.^{4}

I = 2 × 13

= 26 in.^{4}

Using this as a guide, it is decided to form up the base from a continuous ¼" plate which can be assumed to have an equal or greater moment of inertia. See Figure 19, to the left.

Step 2: Strengthen base to resist twisting

This step is divided into two parts:

1. Using nomograph, Figure 13, find torsional resistance of base and, if insufficient, add bracing.

2. Using nomograph, Figure 14, find resulting angular twist resulting from the load and, if excessive, strengthen further.

Treating the proposed base as a section composed of solid rectangles, a quick check shows that this base does not have sufficient resistance to twist (R = .24 in.⁴). Therefore, it is decided to try ¼" diagonal braces to stiffen the base, tack-welding them in place.

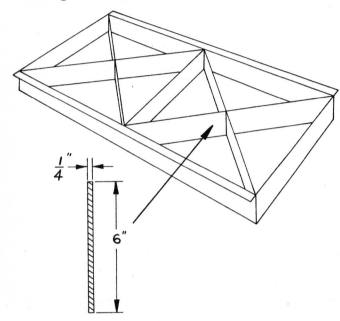

Fig. 20   Use heavier braces for greater R.

The modified base design is again checked, using the same nomograph, Figure 13:

Line 1.   Double-diagonal braced base
Line 2.   a = ¼"
Line 3.   Pivot line
Line 4.   b = 6"
Line 5.   Read R = 46 in.⁴

Since the torsional resistance of the rest of the base is very small (R = .24 in.⁴), it is not added to the value of the diagonal brace.

The stiffened base can be further checked by checking it for resultant angular twist, using the nomograph, Figure 14:

Line 1.   R = 46"
Line 2.   HP = 50
Line 3.   Pivot line
Line 4.   RPM = 1800
Line 5.   Read φ = .0002°/in. (unit angular twist).

This corresponds to a vertical uplift (Δ = φW) of .006" at the corner if base is not anchored down.

This amount of twist is considered allowable for this type of application.

Step 3: Design top panel to resist localized bending between stiffeners

Since the greatest load is 900 lbs, and is supported at 4 points, it is assumed that 300 lbs would be the maximum load concentrated at the center of any one panel area between stiffeners. The unit deflection of the triangular panel will be held to a maximum of .001 in./in.

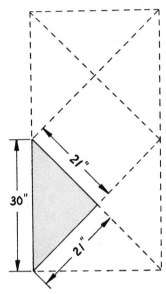

Fig. 21   Checking top panel stiffness.

Using the nomograph, Figure 15, find the maximum dimensions of the triangular panel:

Line 1.   P = 300 lbs
Line 2.   t = ¼"
Line 3.   Pivot line
Line 4.   The allowable unit deflection (Δ/a) = .001 in./in.
Line 5a. Read a = 26"

The proposed stiffened base (Fig. 22) with a = 21" is well on the safe side.

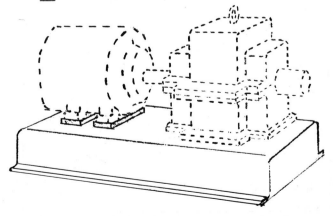

Fig. 22   Stiffened base for motor and reducer.

5. CONVERTING FROM A CASTING TO A STEEL WELDMENT

In converting directly from a casting to a steel weldment, some designers have found the Equivalent Sections approach very helpful. Section 1.4 presents a full discussion of converting a base by this method. Several nomographs are available for that express purpose.

6. DESIGN AND FABRICATING IDEAS

The following examples of welded steel base designs incorporate many ideas on efficient use of steel and on economical fabrication. Since the base is normally one of the largest components of a machine, it offers the opportunity for greatest cost saving.

Example 1 Base for Drilling and Tapping Machine

The designer of this base for a multiple-spindle drilling and tapping machine put special emphasis on achieving minimum weight, without sacrificing needed rigidity. The basic loading is that of compression and tension. See Figure 23.

Directly below each spindle position is a square section which would support this load and also give the best section to resist twisting. By combining all of these sections together, the engineer was able to take advantage of double diagonal bracing throughout the whole base. This greatly stiffens the top panel in addition to being resistant to twist.

The exploded view illustrates the method of assembling, giving the greatest accessibility for welding at all times. Brake forming is used to

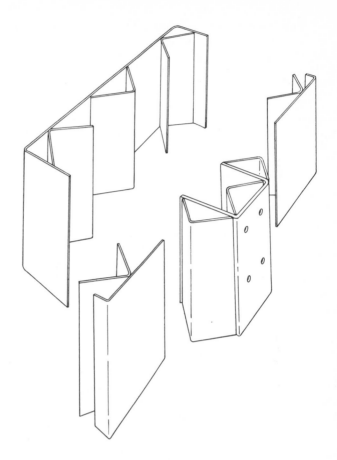

Fig. 24 Method of assembling base.

advantage. Many of these diagonal members are welded to the side sections as subassemblies, and then the entire unit slipped together with very little welding required to tie the whole base together.

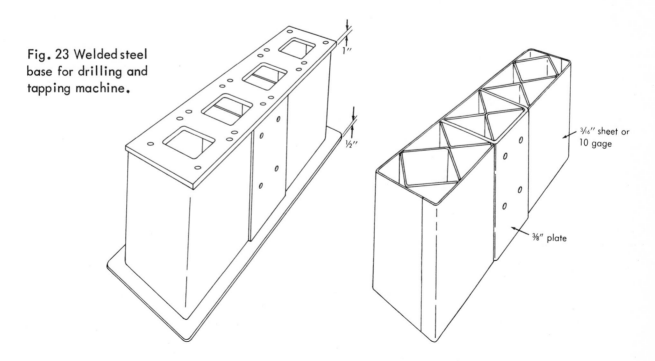

Fig. 23 Welded steel base for drilling and tapping machine.

The front panel, which must have added strength to support ways upon which a table is to be fastened, is made of ⅜" plate, sheared and bent into a "U" shape. The remainder of the side panels can be made of 3/16" or 10-gage material.

The unit price per pound for fabrication is low, since the cost consists largely of shearing thin plates, bending these to shape, and intermittently welding them together. The top and bottom plates are flame-cut to size. The result is a lightweight but very rigid base.

| Example 2 | Bed for Packaging Machine

This cast iron bed was used to support packaging machinery. It was a rather expensive casting because of the amount of coring required. Because it was used in dairies, it had to be smooth and easy to clean, free from any pockets where milk might easily collect. There were six leveling screws. Converting this to a welded steel design proved to be advantageous.

A closed box type of section can be used for both the longitudinal members and the cross members. This type of construction offers very high resistance to twisting, something lacking in the previous cast iron design. The box section's top and bottom flanges develop a high resistance to bending. The members will be simple to fabricate and weld, and will result in the closed construction required for sanitary reasons.

The six supports for leveling the base can be made of thick-walled tube sections welded into the side members; or, solid 4" × 4" pieces of steel can be used, with the side and cross members welded into them (as shown).

Side and cross members can be made of ¼"

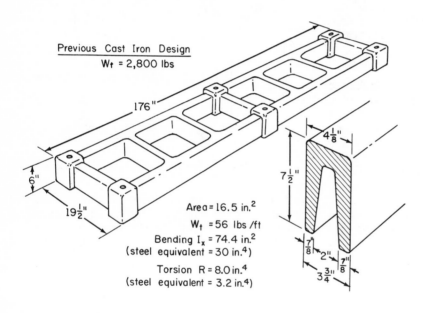

Previous Cast Iron Design
W_t = 2,800 lbs

176"

6"

19½"

4⅛"

7½"

⅞" 2" ⅞"

3¾"

Area = 16.5 in.²
W_t = 56 lbs /ft
Bending I_x = 74.4 in.²
(steel equivalent = 30 in.⁴)

Torsion R = 8.0 in.⁴
(steel equivalent = 3.2 in.⁴)

Fig. 25 Conversion to steel weldment for bed of packaging machine.

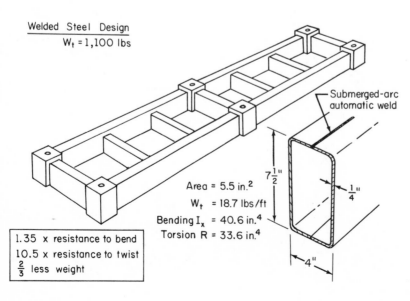

Welded Steel Design
W_t = 1,100 lbs

Submerged-arc automatic weld

7½"

¼"

4"

Area = 5.5 in.²
W_t = 18.7 lbs /ft
Bending I_x = 40.6 in.⁴
Torsion R = 33.6 in.⁴

1.35 x resistance to bend
10.5 x resistance to twist
⅔ less weight

steel plate, sheared to size, brake-formed into channel sections, and then slipped into a simple fixture and automatically submerged-arc welded. These members are also available from the mill as hot-rolled rectangular sections at about the same price as other hot-rolled sections.

Making the cross members slightly less in depth (about ½") than the longitudinal members produces an easy to weld fillet joint. All of these pieces can then be dropped into a simple fixture and manually welded together. Placing the fixture on a positioner will permit making manual welds in the flat position for maximum welding speed.

| Example 3 | Lathe Bed

This welded-steel lathe bed combines into one integral unit the bed, chip pan and pedestals which are separate units in the conventional engine lathe design. Casting limitations which dictated previous designs did not apply to the new design. As a result, the depth of the bed structure is almost double what it would be in a conventional design.

Since the front wall must resist most of the force of the cutting loads, it was extended down to the floor and kept solid. The chip pan must extend considerably to the front and rear of the bed to perform its function adequately. This member contributes significantly to the horizontal rigidity of the bed when combined as an integral unit.

The torsional rigidity of a lathe bed is also extremely important. Preliminary model studies and final analysis showed that pyramid-shaped reinforcing ribs would result in high torsional stiffness. These ribs also form the walls of chip disposal chutes in the bed and effectively tie the heavy rails forming the bed ways to the front and rear walls.

The original objective was to have several times more rigidity than a conventional cast iron bed. The design approach, when combined with the increased modulus of elasticity of steel over cast iron, actually netted an 18-fold increase in the rigidity of the bed without increasing the machine weight. Exhaustive testing proved this high degree of rigidity has solved the vibration damping problem.

| Example 4 | Pump Base

The cast iron pump base shown in Figure 27 weighed 2600 lbs. In addition to the cost of the unmachined castings, there was a high initial pattern cost, occasional repairs to the pattern, insurance, storage cost, time in getting the pattern out of storage, etc. The company cost reduction committee selected this particular casting to investigate for possible cost reduction.

The casting's walls were 1" thick. They estimated that making the base of welded steel plate would reduce the walls to about ⅜". The service department revealed that a few of the castings had

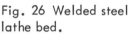

Fig. 26 Welded steel lathe bed.

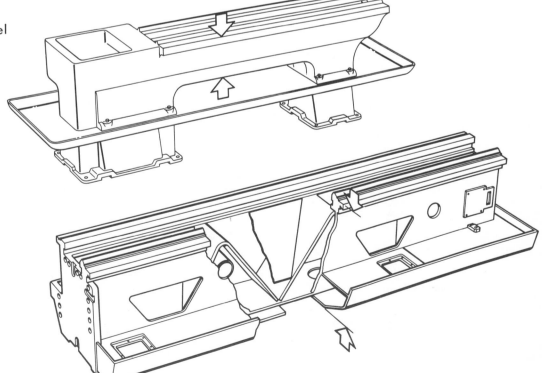

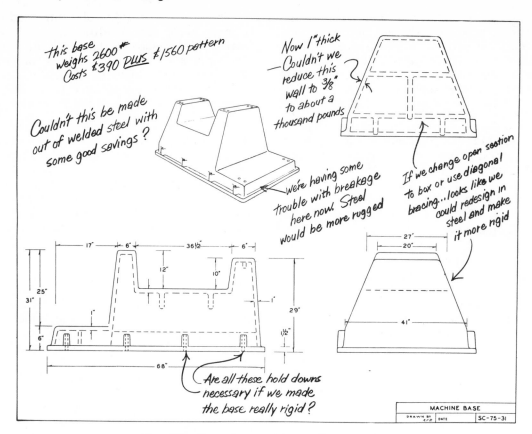

Fig. 27   Pump base subject of cost study.

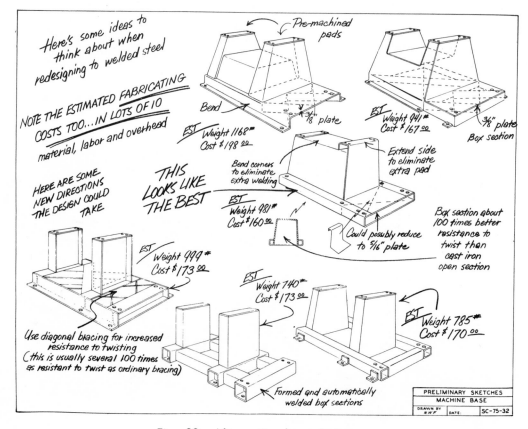

Fig. 28   Alternative base designs.

broken when dropped in the field. It was recognized that a welded steel unit would be more rugged.

Because of the difficult coring problem, the bottom of the casting was open. Closing this in was not economical, even though it would have greatly increased the torsional resistance and strength of the unit. Closed box sections or diagonal bracing were suggested for the proposed welded steel unit. Someone questioned the necessity for all eight hold-down lugs if the welded unit resulted in a more rigid section.

Six different designs which would fulfill all the requirements were developed, Figure 28. These are shown along with the estimated fabricating cost

for ten units.

The methods committee made a careful study of each proposed design from the standpoint of estimated cost, appearance, ease of fabrication with the equipment available in the plant, obtainability of the required material without difficulty or delay, predicted service performance of the unit as well as possible maintenance required, etc. Subsequently the design shown at center, having highest cost-reduction potential, was selected for a test run.

Other Design and Fabricating Ideas

Figure 29 illustrates various other welded-steel base designs and features that may be suggestive to the designer according to his specific problem.

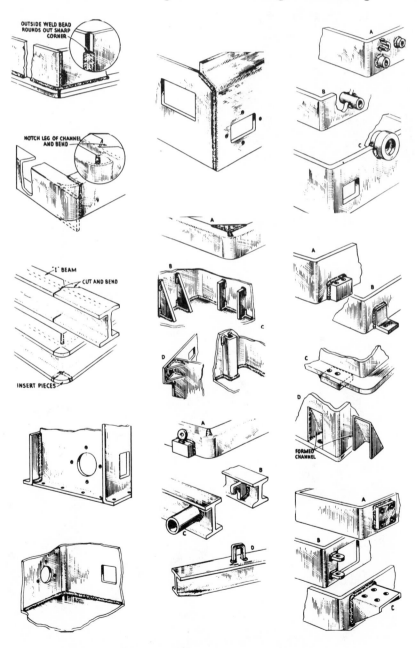

Fig. 29   Design ideas for base details.

Partial redesign may produce substantial savings through use of composite construction — steel plates and castings welded together.

Interior reinforcing ribs of 1/4" plate contribute to 57% weight advantage of this welded steel base, as compared with cast iron equivalent. For an undercutting facer used in mining, the stiffened welded base cost only half as much as cast base.

How to Design Flat Tables

1. BASIC PROBLEMS

Many machinery components, and other products, are essentially a flat table. A machine tool table is especially critical because its rigidity determines how well relationships can be maintained between reference surfaces and the tool spindle centerline, and thus directly affects the quality of work produced. But even a loading ramp must have limited deflection so that a high pitch caused by excessive curvature will not slow up the movement of materials handling trucks.

The design of machine tool tables, vacuum chucks, loading ramps, and comparable products in welded steel demands a sound approach to ensure the completed structure adequately resists bending and twisting. Providing required hold-down slots in table surfaces, for example, removes material from the cross-section, further complicating the design problem. Suggestions that follow will help the designer solve these problems.

2. MACHINE TOOL TABLES

Flat tables for modern machine tools usually have little depth in comparison to their large surface area. Thus, an assembly of relatively thin, arc-welded steel sections must depend on the arrangement of its component parts to develop sufficient rigidity to resist bending and twisting.

In the following illustrations, three common methods for achieving this result are shown. In each case, a thin plate is bent along its edge to form the top panel and two sides. In the first assembly, Figure 1, T-sections are used to obtain the desired resistance to bending in one direction, and flat bars connecting the flanges of the T-sections produce the needed rigidity in the other direction. This design is the most common and widely

used due to the ease with which it can be fabricated using existing standard structural shapes. However, this design lacks resistance to twisting.

In the alternate design, Figure 2, channel sections are joined to the top plate to form box sections. The design in Figure 3 employs diagonal bracing. Either diagonal bracing or box sections provide a tremendous increase in torsional resistance as compared to the T-section assembly. This increased torsional resistance is achieved without sacrificing resistance to bending.

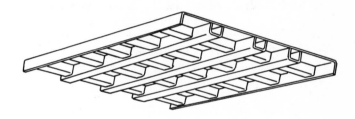

FIGURE 2

FIGURE 3

Nevertheless, any one of these three designs (Figs. 1, 2 or 3) will show improved performance over a cast iron counterpart. This has been verified with tests made by a planer manufacturer on their new welded steel tables. The welded facing planer table was supported at three corners and the sag of the fourth corner was measured, Figure 4. Total deflection was 0.014", only 20% of the 0.070" deflection measured by the same test on the previously used cast iron table. The increased rigidity of the welded table permitted a machining tolerance of 0.001" to be maintained on surface flatness. In addition, the designer used the better physical properties of steel to effect a 20% weight reduction - from a 410-lb casting to a 320-lb weldment.

FIGURE 1

FIGURE 4

Efficient Bracing

The following illustrations demonstrate two simple techniques for economical diagonal bracing. Both approaches are designed to minimize the number of component parts and the amount of welding necessary to join them into the desired assembly. The slotted flat strips, Figure 5, nest together and

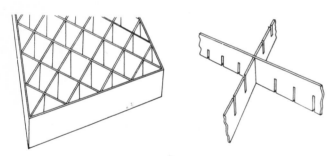

FIGURE 5

require only a few short fillet welds to hold them in position. In Figure 6, flat strip has been pre-formed on a bend brake into a continuous zig-zag pattern. The bracing is completed by arc welding them at their contacting surfaces. Both approaches have specific manufacturing advantages.

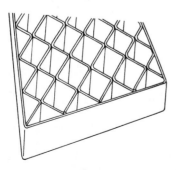

FIGURE 6

3. VACUUM CHUCKS

Designing vacuum chucks for welded steel construction poses problems that parallel those encountered with welded table designs. To maintain alignment of very thin flat sections while various grinding or machining operations are carried out, the designer must execute the chuck design to effectively use steel's physical properties and place the steel where it can best accomplish its function.

Two vacuum chucks illustrated here were designed for the aircraft industry to hold wing and skin panels to the tables of high-speed, planer-type milling machines. They demonstrate two types of welded design. Advantages accruing from welding include a major reduction in construction cost, reduction of finish machining allowance for chuck surface approximating 50% as compared to cast iron, greater flexibility, and over-all versatility in design.

The welded steel universal vacuum chuck, Figure 7, was fabricated in three sections. Modified V-section longitudinal ribs produced the desired rigidity while maintaining minimum chuck depth.

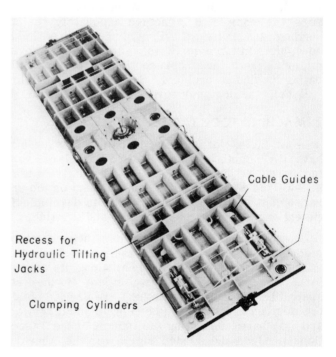

FIGURE 7

Another approach to vacuum chuck design is found in Figure 8. Diagonal bracing was accomplished with welded channels forming box-section ribs. This almost square chuck requires only corner support from the machine table.

4. FLAT TABLES WITH KEYWAYS

Many flat tables must incorporate keyway slots extending their entire length for fastening hold-

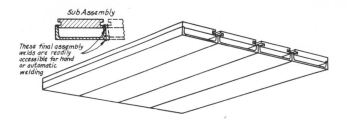

FIGURE 11

FIGURE 8

flat bars to standard structural shapes. In Figures 10 and 11, the slots are premachined into the heavier surface plates of these designs. This is not required in the designs of Figures 9 and 12. Controlling welding and using correct welding sequence procedures in the subassembly operations and the final assembly will minimize distortion and reduce stock removal during final surface machining. Selection from among these four designs would be based primarily on production facilities.

down attachments. This greatly weakens the table unless special effort is made to tie the unit together. Different designs have been developed which produce the desired rigidity and still permit accessibility for economically welding the components of the assembly to obtain unitized construction. These sketches illustrate various design approaches that have satisfactorily answered the problem. Note how each design effectively places the weld in a readily accessible position.

The designs in Figures 9 and 10 combine properly spaced flat plate strips with formed sections. Those in Figures 11 and 12 join properly positioned

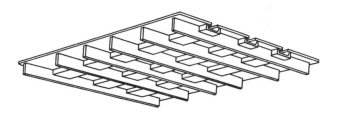

FIGURE 12

5. LOADING RAMPS

Minimum weight and resistance to bending and twisting are basic design requirements for loading ramps. To produce a satisfactory design, however, selling requirements not only demand that the ramp function effectively but also be low cost.

One design approach analyzes the ramp's torsional resistance by measuring the deflection of the ramp under torsional loading. This demonstrates the ramp's ability to distribute a corner load more equally among all the supporting members and reflects the ramp's rigidity.

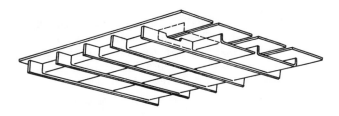

FIGURE 9

Various standard structural sections can be used for the component parts of the assembly and range from flat plate through rectangular box sections. Flat plate would seem to be the simplest design solution and most economical to produce. However, the necessity for economy in weight as well as manufacturing cost complicates the problem and requires the designer to integrate material, quantity, cost, shape, and placement while keeping production costs down.

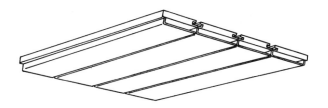

FIGURE 10

The formula for calculating the deflection (Δ) of an unsupported corner of a rectangular frame supported at the other three corners is given in Table 1.

TABLE 1 – TORSIONAL RESISTANCE OF FRAME AND TYPICAL SECTIONS

Deflection of Frame Under Torsional Load	Torsional Resistance of Common Sections

$$\Delta = \frac{P\,L\,W}{E_s}\left[\frac{1}{\dfrac{n_L\,R_L}{W} + \dfrac{n_T\,R_T}{L}}\right]$$

$$R = \frac{b\,t^3}{3}$$

$$R = \frac{(b + d)t^3}{3}$$

$$R = \frac{2\,b\,t_1{}^3 + d\,t_2{}^3}{3}$$

$$R = \frac{2\,t\,b^2\,d^2}{b + d}$$

$$R = \frac{2\,t\,t_1\,(b - t)^2\,(d - t_1)^2}{b\,t + d\,t_1 - t^2 - t_1{}^2}$$

where:

    L = length of whole frame, in.

    W = width of whole frame, in.

    R_L = torsional resistance of longitudinal member, in.[4]

    R_T = torsional resistance of transverse member, in.[4]

    n_L = number of longitudinal members

    n_T = number of transverse members

    P = load applied at corner, lbs

    E_s = modulus of elasticity in shear (steel: 12×10^6), psi

    Δ = vertical deflection, in.

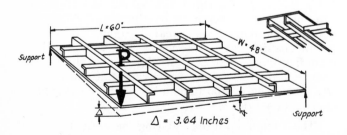

FIGURE 13

The formulas for calculating torsional resistance (R) of some standard structural shapes are found in Table 1.

One manufacturer's initial design incorporated 2″ × 3″ × 3/16″ standard rolled angles running full width, Figure 13. Longitudinal angles were custom cut to fit, and welded to the laterals. Using the standard frame deflection formula, it was determined the unsupported corner of a ramp having the indicated dimensions, when subjected to a load (P) of only 100 lbs, would deflect about 3.64″.

Here, the torsional resistance of the plate can be included with that of the longitudinal members to give the total resistance:

$$R_{plate} = \frac{b\,t^3}{3}$$

$$= \frac{48\,(.25)^3}{3}$$

$$= .25 \text{ in.}^4$$

$$R_{stiffener} = \frac{(b + d)\,t^3}{3}$$

$$= \frac{(2 + 3)\,1.875^3}{3}$$

$$= .011 \text{ in.}^4$$

$$\Delta = \frac{P L W}{E_s}\left[\frac{1}{\frac{n_L R_L}{W} + \frac{n_T R_T}{L}}\right]$$

$$= \frac{100 (60) (48)}{(12 \times 10^6)}\left[\frac{1}{\frac{3 (.011) + .25}{48} + \frac{4 (.011)}{60}}\right]$$

$$= \underline{3.64''}$$

In an effort to improve the design and reduce costs, the manufacturer replaced the angles with 2″ × 3″ × 10-gage formed channel sections, Figure 14. (Depth of lateral channels were made ¼″ less, or 2.75″, to permit fillet welds entirely.) These U sections when welded to the top plate, form box sections that add greatly to the torsional resistance of the entire ramp.

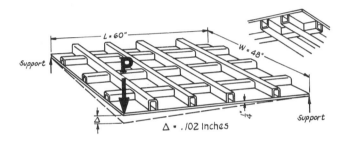

FIGURE 14

Where, even disregarding the plate's contribution to total R:

$$R_T = \frac{2 t b^2 d^2}{b + d}$$

$$= \frac{2 (.1345) (2)^2 (3)^2}{2 + 3}$$

$$= 1.94 \text{ in.}^4$$

$$R_L = \frac{2 t b^2 d^2}{b + d}$$

$$= \frac{2 (.1345) (2)^2 (2.75)^2}{2 + 2.75}$$

$$= 1.71 \text{ in.}^4$$

$$\Delta = \frac{P L W}{E_s}\left[\frac{1}{\frac{n_L R_L}{W} + \frac{n_T R_T}{L}}\right]$$

$$= \frac{100 (60) (48)}{(12 \times 10^6)}\left[\frac{1}{\frac{3 (1.71)}{48} + \frac{4 (1.94)}{60}}\right]$$

$$= \underline{.102''}$$

Deflection (Δ) with this new design is thus reduced to .102″, making it 36 times more rigid than the original angle design. In addition, manufacturing costs were reduced by simplifying cutting, fitting and welding procedures.

Weld fabrication of large platforms, using proper stiffeners, provides required strength and rigidity while keeping weight to a minimum.

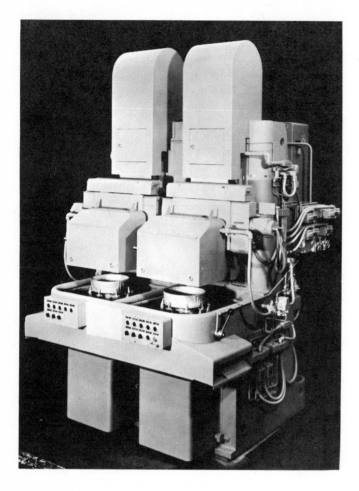

Welded steel base for precision machine tool incorporates diagonal bracing for maximum rigidity with minimum material.

How to Brace or Stiffen a Member

1. BRACES AND STIFFENERS

The efficient use of materials is the first essential to low-cost product designs. One way to achieve such efficiency is to use lighter-gage sheet or plate that is easily sheared and formed, and to add stiffeners as necessary for the required strength and/or rigidity.

When a frame is reinforced by the addition of members cross-wise or diagonal to the members, the modification is commonly referred to as bracing and the added members as braces. When a flat panel is strengthened or stiffened by the addition of ribs or diaphragms, the added members are commonly referred to as stiffeners.

The two terms--braces and stiffeners--are often used interchangeably, probably because the same member often serves the dual function of bracing the frame against torsion and of stiffening the top panel against deflection under a bending load. Design techniques are inter-related.

2. HOW STIFFENERS ARE USED

When stiffeners are used properly, they permit the utilization of smaller member sections, while maintaining the required strength and rigidity. Here are some of the ways stiffeners are used in efficient designs for welded steel:

1. Rigid stiffeners or diaphragms enable a panel to support a greater bending load by reducing its unsupported length. This assumes a diaphragm welded at the ends and having sufficient depth to give proper support.

2. Stiffeners added to a flexible panel increase the combined moment of inertia, reduce its deflection and increase its strength under a bending load.

3. Stiffeners added to webs of beams and portions of frames stiffen the web against buckling from diagonal compressive forces.

4. Stiffeners or braces placed at 45° on a panel, or at 45° to side members of a frame, greatly increase its resistance to twist.

5. Stiffeners added to a flat panel increase its resistance to buckling from edge compression; this is due to the increase in radius of gyration.

3. REDUCING PANEL SPAN

Frequently, the top panel of a weldment will not be thick enough to support a given load, even though the entire section of which it is a part has sufficient moment of inertia to properly resist over-all bending.

Rather than increase the thickness of this panel, it is usually preferable to add stiffeners or diaphragms to reduce the unsupported length of the panel.

The chart, Figure 2, shows how the top panel thickness may be reduced by attaching stiffeners or diaphragms. These are welded to the side members. The horizontal axis is the ratio of the panel's length to its width; the vertical axis is the relative thickness of the panel with stiffeners. The chart is for panels with one to five stiffeners.

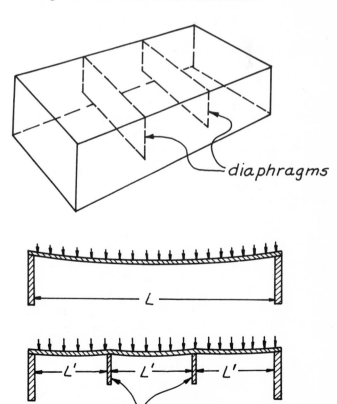

FIGURE 1

1

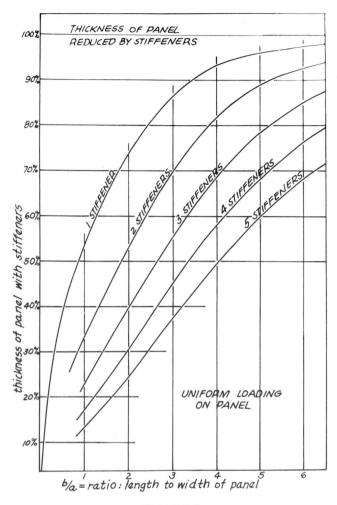

FIGURE 2

hand vertical Line 7, read the ratio of stiffener spacing to width of panel. If a very low ratio indicates the stiffeners will be too close together for fabrication economy, the panel thickness must be increased.

4. INCREASING PANEL RIGIDITY

A second use of stiffeners is to stiffen a panel, regardless of how flexible or rigid the stiffeners are. These will increase the stiffness of the whole panel by increasing the moment of inertia (I) of the member panel sections.

The usual method is to consider a section of the panel having a width equal to the distance between centers of the stiffeners. In this manner, just one stiffener will be included in the panel section. The resulting moment of inertia (I) of the stiffener and the section of the panel may be found from the following formula:

$$I = I_s + \frac{A_p t^2}{12} + \frac{A_s A_p d^2}{A_s + A_p} \dots\dots\dots\dots(1)$$

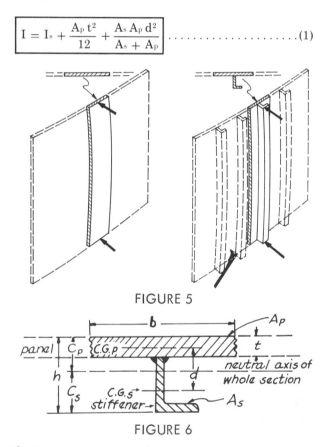

FIGURE 5

FIGURE 6

where:

  b = distance between stiffeners, in.

*d = distance between center of gravity of panel and that of stiffener, in.

A_p = cross-sectional area of plate within distance b, in.^{2}

*A_s = cross-sectional area of stiffener, in.^{2}

  t = thickness of panel, in.

*I_s = moment of inertia of stiffener, in.^{4}

*Data obtained from any steel handbook

For example, a 1" thick top panel having a length twice the width (b/a = 2) with a uniform load, can be reduced to about ¾" if just one stiffener is added, and results in the same deflection or equivalent stiffness. If two stiffeners are added, this thickness need be only ½".

Nomographs, Figures 3 and 4, give the required spacing of stiffeners, for any condition, of either a uniform or a concentrated load.

The Nomograph, Figure 3, applies to panels wherein the area between stiffeners will be triangular in shape. Use this when either single or double diagonal stiffeners are to be added. Note that vertical Line 4 represents the unit deflection (Δ/a), in./in., considered by the designer to be allowable for the specific application. For guidance, the ranges of allowable deflection for several classifications are marked off. On right-hand vertical Line 5, read the dimension a which geometrically controls spacing of the stiffeners.

The Nomograph, Figure 4, applies to panels wherein the area between stiffeners will be rectangular in shape. Use this when conventional transverse stiffeners are to be added. On right-

FIG. 3 – STIFFENING OF FLAT PANELS

(Diagonal)

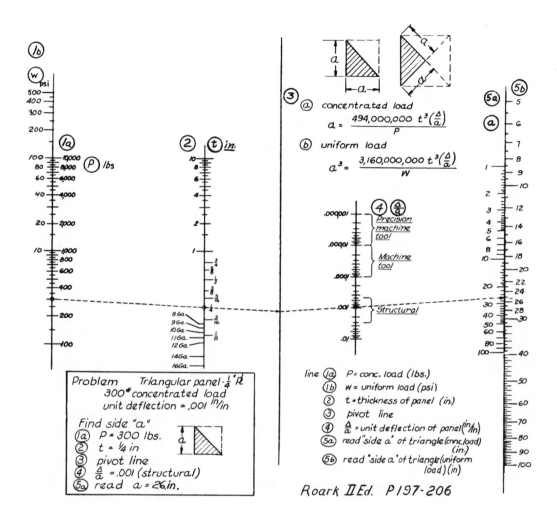

Roark ⅡEd. P197-206

In figuring the maximum bending stress in this built-up section, the following distances to the outer fibers must be known.

$$c_p = \frac{A_s d}{A_s + A_p} + \frac{t}{2} \quad \dots \dots \dots \dots \dots (2)$$

$$c_s = h - c_p = h - \frac{t}{2} - \frac{A_s d}{A_s + A_p} \quad \dots \dots \dots (3)$$

where:

c_p = distance from neutral axis of whole section to outer fiber of plate, in.

c_s = distance from neutral axis of whole section to outer fiber of stiffener, in.

The panel section may then be treated as a simply supported beam and be designed with sufficient moment of inertia (I) to withstand whatever load is applied. Use a 1" wide strip of this panel, and use uniform load of (w) lbs per linear inch; if entire width of panel (b), use uniform pressure of (p) psi.

Figure 7 (page 5) illustrates the technique of treating a panel section as a beam under three different conditions. Formulas for finding maximum deflection, bending moment, and vertical shear are given, with p being the pressure in psi against the panel.

FIG. 4 – STIFFENING OF FLAT PANELS

(Transverse)

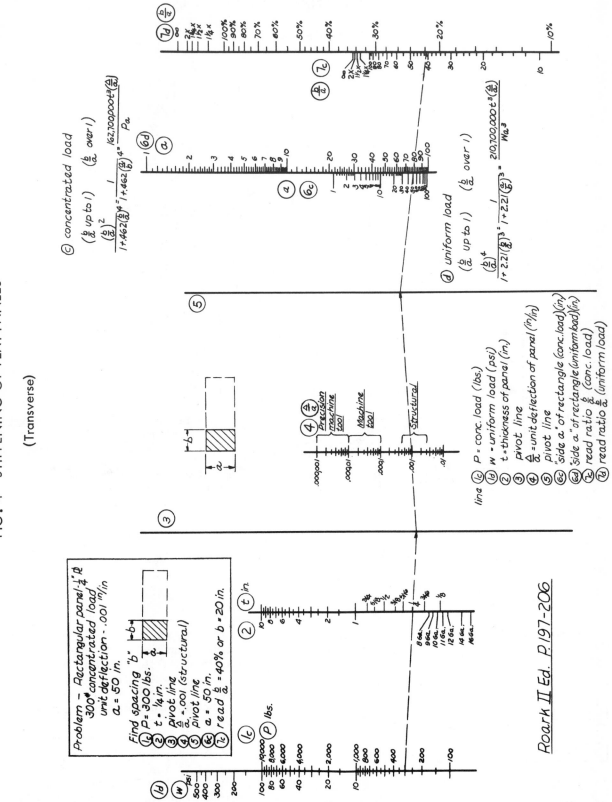

Roark II Ed. P.197-206

FIG. 7 - PROPERTIES OF PANEL SECTION TREATED AS A BEAM

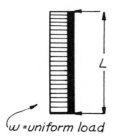

w = uniform load

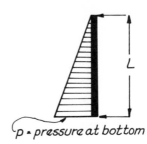

p = pressure at bottom

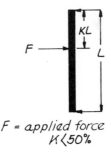

F = applied force
K < 50%

Condition A

$$\Delta_{max} = \frac{5\,p\,b\,L^4}{384\,E\,I} \quad \dots (4)$$

$$M_{max} = \frac{p\,b\,L^2}{8} \quad \dots (5)$$

$$V_{max} = \frac{p\,b\,L}{2} \quad \dots (6)$$

Condition B

$$\Delta_{max} = 0.00652\,\frac{p\,b\,L^4}{E\,I} \quad \dots (7)$$

$$M_{max} = 0.0642\,p\,b\,L^2 \quad \dots (8)$$

$$V_{max} = \frac{p\,b\,L}{3} \quad \dots (9)$$

Condition C

$$\Delta_{max} = \frac{F\,L^3\,K}{27\,E\,I}\sqrt{3\,(1-K^2)^3} \quad \dots (10)$$

$$M_{max} = F\,L\,K\,(1-K) \quad \dots (11)$$

$$V_{max} = F\,(1-K) \quad \dots (12)$$

(With reference to Figure 7)

If due to weight of liquid or granular material:

p = h d = .006944 H D
p = .0361 h s = .4335 H s

where:

  h = height of liquid or material, in.
  H = height of liquid or material, ft
  s = specific gravity of liquid or material, lbs/cu in.
  d = density of liquid or material, lbs/cu in.
  D = density of liquid or material, lbs/cu ft.

The maximum stress in the outer fibers of either the panel or the stiffener may be found by using the corresponding value of $\underline{c}$ and the maximum moment (M_{max}) in the following formulas:

For the panel

$$\sigma_p = \frac{M_{max}\,c_p}{I} \quad \dots (13)$$

For the stiffener

$$\sigma_s = \frac{M_{max}\,c_s}{I} \quad \dots (14)$$

5. STIFFENING WEB SECTION

Stiffeners can also be used to give proper support against buckling from diagonal compressive stresses in a section subjected to high shear forces. All vertical shear stresses have an equal value of horizontal shear stress. These two stresses combine to form a diagonal compressive stress and a diagonal tensile stress. For thin, deep web sections, a high diagonal compressive stress might cause the web to buckle, unless it is properly stiffened.

Stiffeners on just one side of the web will satisfy the need to resist web buckling. These stiffeners are frequently used on beams, as well as on the horizontal portions of frames subject to the high shear reactions such as presses.

Intermediate Stiffeners

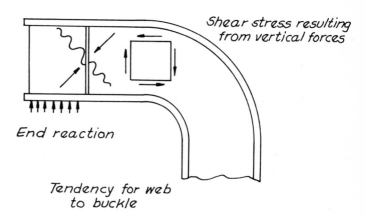

Shear stress resulting from vertical forces

End reaction

Tendency for web to buckle

FIGURE 8

6. RESISTING TORSION

Conventional cross stiffeners on a panel do not offer any resistance to twisting. However, if these stiffeners are placed at 45°, they will greatly in-

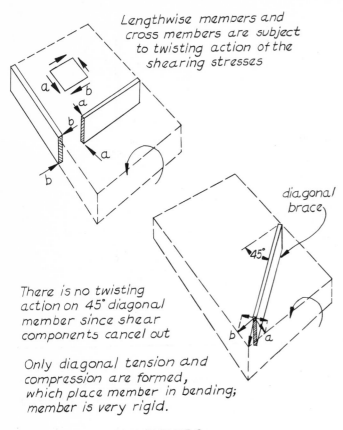

Lengthwise members and cross members are subject to twisting action of the shearing stresses

diagonal brace

45°

There is no twisting action on 45° diagonal member since shear components cancel out

Only diagonal tension and compression are formed, which place member in bending; member is very rigid.

FIGURE 9

crease the torsional resistance of a panel. There is no twisting action on the 45° stiffeners because the two components from the longitudinal and transverse shear stresses are equal and opposite and, therefore, cancel out.

7. RIGIDITY VS. STRENGTH

It is possible to reinforce a plate with stiffeners and reduce its strength even though the rigidity of the section is increased, Figure 10.

Section A consists of a ¾" × 15" plate without any stiffeners. The designer feels that this section should have increased stiffness and therefore decides to add 6 stiffeners, ¼" × ⅜", to this original plate as shown in B.

Notice that the addition of the stiffeners increases the section's moment of inertia (I) by 34%. More important, however, is the fact that the strength of this section as measured by section modulus (S) has been reduced to 67% of the original plate. This is because the strength or section modulus of a section is equal to the moment of inertia divided by the distance of the neutral axis to the outer fiber (c).

In this particular case although the moment of inertia has increased 34%, the distance of the outer

fiber has doubled; thus, the distance to the outer fiber in the original plate (A) is ⅜", while the distance to the outer fiber in the built-up section (B) is ¾". We must realize that the addition of material to a section does not always increase its strength even though the stiffness does increase.

	Relative Values		
	I	S	W_t
Ⓐ	1.00	1.00	1.00
Ⓑ	1.34	.67	1.05

$$S = \frac{I}{c} = \frac{1.34}{2.00} = .67$$

Theoretically this means that section B could only be loaded up to 67% that of section A for the same stress at the outer fiber. Fortunately, mild steel is ductile enough so that under the same load, although section B might have 50% greater stress, it would ultimately exceed the yield point. The resulting plastic flow in the stiffener would allow the remainder of the plate to be stressed up to its yield point; hence no harm would be done.

There are two places where this theoretical consideration would have to be considered. The first would be if the material were brittle such as cast iron, then of course section A would be recommended. The second example would be in the case of fatigue loading where quite often the fatigue strength of a material is below the yield point. This means that even with ductile mild steel, under certain fatigue conditions the fatigue strength would be reached before the yield point and therefore no plastic flow could take place to relieve this higher stress at the outer fiber of the stiffener. In this particular case stiffeners as illustrated in section B should not be used. Stiffeners could be used if of sufficient size that the section modulus is not reduced below the original value of the plate alone.

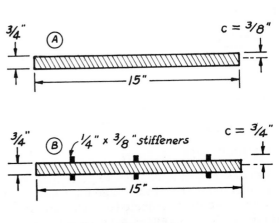

FIGURE 10

8. WELD SIZE

The leg size of the continuous fillet weld required to join a stiffener to the panel may be found from the following formula:

$$\omega = \frac{V\,a\,y}{9600\,I\,n}$$

where:

ω = leg size of continuous fillet weld, in.
V = total shear on section at a given position along the beam, lbs
a = area held by weld, in.^{2}
y = distance between center of gravity of the area and neutral axis of whole section, in. = $c_p - \frac{1}{2}t$
I = moment of inertia of whole section, in.^{4}
n = number of continuous welds joining the stiffener to the panel

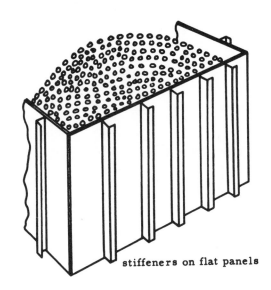

stiffeners on flat panels

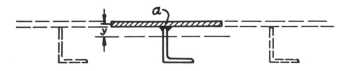

FIGURE 11

If intermittent fillet welds are to be used, calculate the continuous fillet weld leg size expressed as a decimal, and divide this by the actual leg size of intermittent fillet weld used. When expressed as a percentage this will give the amount of intermittent weld to be used per unit length. For convenience, Table 1 has various intermittent weld lengths and distance between centers for a given percentage of continuous weld.

TABLE 1 - INTERMITTENT WELDS

Percent of Continuous Weld	Length of Intermittent Welds and Distance Between Centers		
75%		3 – 4	
66			4 – 6
60		3 – 5	
57			4 – 7
50	2 – 4	3 – 6	4 – 8
44			4 – 9
43		3 – 7	
40	2 – 5		4 – 10
37		3 – 8	
33	2 – 6	3 – 9	4 – 12
30		3 – 10	
25	2 – 8	3 – 12	
20	2 – 10		
16	2 – 12		

Large roller mill for tile industry makes effective use of weldments. Performance of mill requires high base rigidity to resist torsional forces developed by the dual drive. Diagonal bracing of welded steel base offers this security at low cost.

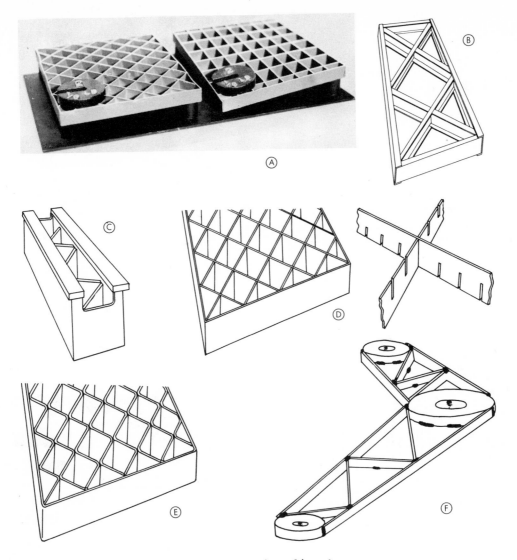

Fig. 12 Examples of bracing.

9. BRACING FRAME AGAINST TWIST

Sometimes when it becomes desirable to reduce the thickness of the top panel, the designer overlooks the torsional problem. Braces can be spaced so as to cut down the length of the unsupported span of the panel, and yet be arranged in a pattern so as to resist twist. Examples of this are shown in Figure 12.

A test on a scale model of a type bed from a flat bed printing press is illustrated at A. The model on the right has conventional bracing, that on the left has diagonal bracing. Each model is supported on three corners and is loaded on the fourth corner. Diagonal bracing greatly increases the resistance to twist.

Double diagonal bracing of the frame of a self-propelled farm combine, B, produced greater resistance against twisting.

The machine tool base at C has single diagonal bracing in the lower portion to give greater resistance to twist.

The underside of a welded steel base for a canmaking machine is shown at D. Double diagonal bracing was used because of the extreme resistance against twisting that was required.

In another method of producing double diagonal bracing, E, bracing is formed from steel strip in a bend brake.

The lever at F is from a packaging machine which must be rigid but light in weight. It makes use of single diagonal bracing.

Designers use this principle successfully on bases, tables, frames, brackets, levers, etc. By the use of arc welding the engineer has complete freedom of design and can economically use a pattern of braces which will produce the section properties required.

How to Design Steel Frames

1. INTRODUCTION

The design of built-up steel frames for use in machinery overlaps the discussion of other subjects in this text, and therefore will not be treated as comprehensively here. A machine base, for example, represents a particular class of frame. Most of the discussion on designing machine bases, Sect. 4.1, could be repeated here, but instead the designer is referred to that Section and to other passages cross-referenced in Sect. 4.1.

Of special value to the designer, Reference Section 7.4 at the back of this book contains numerous pages of frame diagrams and formulas. These, directly or by judicious adaptation, will cover a host of seemingly difficult design situations.

A few examples of frame design problems and their solutions are given here for the guidance of other designers in finding and developing a sound engineering approach to their problems.

Defining design objectives, and evaluating alternative proposed designs with respect to these objectives, should constitute the major challenge to which the mathematical procedure should be servant.

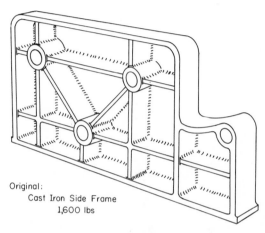

Original:
Cast Iron Side Frame
1,600 lbs

FIGURE 1

2. COMPARISON OF ALTERNATIVE DESIGNS

The first design can hardly be expected to be the best. Whatever one is accepted should be considered a compromise, to be used until time and experience and evolution of the art result in a redesign that is sufficiently superior to justify its use.

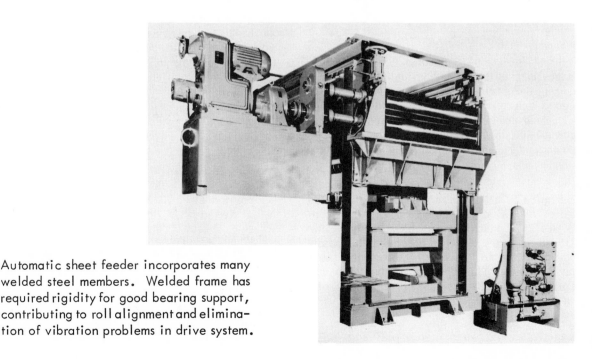

Automatic sheet feeder incorporates many welded steel members. Welded frame has required rigidity for good bearing support, contributing to roll alignment and elimination of vibration problems in drive system.

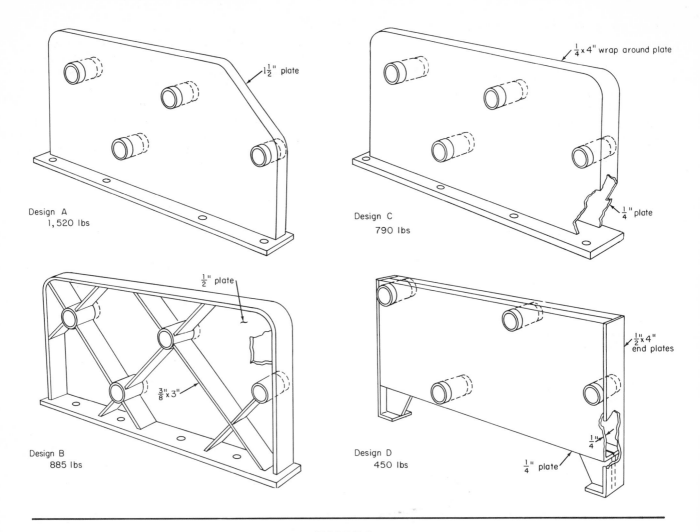

FIGURE 2

All-steel designs, fabricated by welding, lend themselves to economical modification and improvement between major model changes.

A frame is usually so large and heavy that a small percentage savings in weight is very important. A good example of this is illustrated in Figure 1. The original side frame as a gray iron casting weighed 1600 lbs. It can easily be converted into a strong, rigid and much lighter welded steel frame.

The evolution of a much more efficient design is shown in Figure 2. Perhaps the simplest fabricated steel frame is design A. This is flame-cut from 1½" plate. A 1" × 8" base plate is welded to it. Four thick-wall tubes are welded in place for the bearings; these could be solid round bar stock and later bored out to size. This frame weighs 1520 lbs, which represents a very low savings in weight. obviously, a better design is needed.

Design B is made of ½" plate, with three of its edges flanged over and two formed ½" plates inserted

for the corners. For additional torsional resistance, ⅜" by 3" flat bars are inserted at 45° to form diagonal bracing; these also tie into the bearing hubs and stiffen them. This frame weighs 885 lbs.

Design C uses two ¼" side plates flame-cut to shape. These are welded directly to the 1" × 8" base plate and joined all the way around the other three sides by a ¼" × 4" flat bar. Thick-walled tubing is inserted between the two side plates and welded in place to provide for the bearings and to tie the frame together. This produces an efficient box section for added torsional resistance. This weighs 790 lbs, an approximately 50% reduction in weight from the original design.

Design D is made of two ¼" side plates flanged top and bottom so as to form a box section when toe-welded together. End plates, ½" × 4", are bent at the bottom and with the added stiffener provide the feet of the frame. Thick-walled tubes are provided for the bearings. This final design weighs 450 lbs, an ultimate 72% savings in weight, while retaining the necessary rigidity and strength.

3. USE OF STANDARD SECTIONS

Many frames can be designed as a build-up of members having desirable section properties. Strength (S) and rigidity (I) of the section carry over to the well-designed frame and permit its being made lighter, stiffer, and more economically.

The most efficient sections for compressive or torsional loading are closed shapes, such as hollow rounds, squares and rectangles. Since these are available in a wide range of standard structural steel tubing and pipe, they can often be used advantageously. Steel handbooks catalog the properties of standard sections, making their selection relatively easy.

For large frames, similar sections can be fabricated from flat stock using press brake, bending rolls, and like equipment, and arc-welding the seams.

Problem 1

The frame in Figure 3 is part of a grain unloader for a box car. It supports a baffle, which is inserted into the car while the car is tilted, and directs the grain out through the car door and into a hopper below.

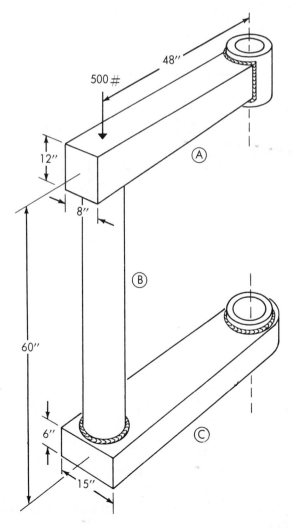

FIGURE 3

Because so many forces are applied to this frame and vary because of changing load conditions, it is difficult to make a complete analysis of this frame. However, it is possible to analyze portions of the frame under a given set of load conditions.

Assume this frame is simply supported by two bearings, loaded with the dead weight of the frame as well as the weight of the baffle. The baffle is inserted into the box car with the pressure of the grain against it. The frame is fixed or held at the lower connection. This results in--

1. A twisting action to the lower horizontal member. The torque equals the force on the baffle multiplied by the height of the baffle above the bottom member.

2. A twisting and bending action on the vertical pipe member.

The following analyses the strength and stiffness of the frame supporting a 500-lb vertical load and its own dead weight.

Excluding the hubs, this frame has three members: A, B, and C. Cross-section properties of these members are readily available.

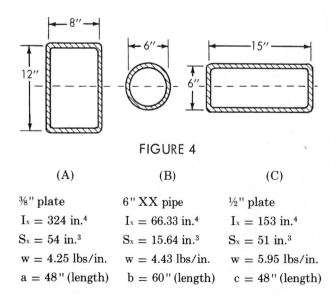

FIGURE 4

(A)	(B)	(C)
⅜" plate	6" XX pipe	½" plate
$I_x = 324$ in.^{4}	$I_x = 66.33$ in.^{4}	$I_x = 153$ in.^{4}
$S_x = 54$ in.^{3}	$S_x = 15.64$ in.^{3}	$S_x = 51$ in.^{3}
$w = 4.25$ lbs/in.	$w = 4.43$ lbs/in.	$w = 5.95$ lbs/in.
$a = 48$" (length)	$b = 60$" (length)	$c = 48$" (length)

Problem 1 continued . . . .

From our frame diagrams (See Reference Section at back of this book), the vertical shear on each member is--

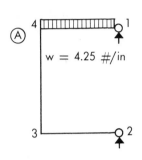

(A)

$$V = \frac{w\,a}{8} \left[\frac{\dfrac{5\,a}{I_a} + \dfrac{6\,b}{I_b}}{\dfrac{a}{I_a} + \dfrac{3\,b}{I_b} + \dfrac{a}{I_c}} \right]$$

$$= \frac{(4.25)\,(48)}{8} \left[\frac{\dfrac{5(48)}{324} + \dfrac{6(60)}{66.33}}{\dfrac{48}{324} + \dfrac{3(60)}{66.33} + \dfrac{48}{153}} \right]$$

$$= 49.6 \text{ lbs}$$

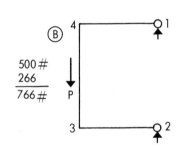

(B)

$$V = \frac{P}{2} \left[\frac{\dfrac{2\,a}{I_a} + \dfrac{3\,b}{I_b}}{\dfrac{a}{I_a} + \dfrac{3\,b}{I_b} + \dfrac{a}{I_c}} \right] \quad \begin{array}{l} \text{where } P = F + w\,b \\ = 500 + 4.43(60) \\ = 766 \end{array}$$

$$= \frac{766}{2} \left[\frac{\dfrac{2(48)}{324} + \dfrac{3(60)}{66.33}}{\dfrac{48}{324} + \dfrac{3(60)}{66.33} + \dfrac{48}{153}} \right]$$

$$= 361.5 \text{ lbs}$$

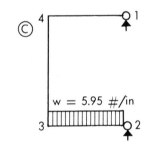

(C)

$$V = \frac{w\,a}{8} \left[\frac{\dfrac{8\,a}{I_a} + \dfrac{18\,b}{I_b} + \dfrac{3\,a}{I_c}}{\dfrac{a}{I_a} + \dfrac{3\,b}{I_b} + \dfrac{a}{I_c}} \right]$$

$$= \frac{(5.95)\,(48)}{8} \left[\frac{\dfrac{8(48)}{324} + \dfrac{18(60)}{66.33} + \dfrac{3(48)}{153}}{\dfrac{48}{324} + \dfrac{3(60)}{66.33} + \dfrac{48}{153}} \right]$$

$$= 207.5 \text{ lbs}$$

Total vertical shear--

$$V = 49.6 + 361.5 + 207.5$$
$$= 618.6 \text{ lbs}$$

Reactions at points of support

$$R_2 = V = +618.6 \text{ lbs}$$
$$R_1 = w_a\,a + P + w_c\,a - V_2$$
$$= (4.25)\,(48) + 766 + (5.95)\,(48) - 618.6$$
$$= 637.4 \text{ lbs}$$

Bending moments at corners

$$M_4 = \frac{w_a\,a^2}{2} - R_1\,a$$
$$= \frac{(4.25)\,(48)^2}{2} - (637.4)\,(48)$$
$$= -25,700 \text{ in.-lbs}$$

$$M_3 = \frac{w_c\,a^2}{2} - R_2\,a$$
$$= \frac{(5.95)\,(48)^2}{2} - (618.6)\,(48)$$
$$= -22,800 \text{ in.-lbs}$$

Bending stress in members

(A) $\sigma_a = \dfrac{M_4}{S_a} = \dfrac{25,700}{54} = 476 \text{ psi}$

(B) $\sigma_b = \dfrac{M_4}{S_b} = \dfrac{25,700}{15.64} = 1,640 \text{ psi}$

(C) $\sigma_c = \dfrac{M_3}{S_c} = \dfrac{22,800}{51} = 450 \text{ psi}$

These values are well below the allowable maximum stress.

Problem 1 continued . . . .

Then Check Fillet Weld Size Around Pipe (B) at Corner 4

Treating the weld as a line, its strength in bending expressed as section modulus is--

$$S_w = \frac{\pi d^2}{4} = \frac{\pi 6^2}{4}$$

$$= 28.4 \text{ in.}^2$$

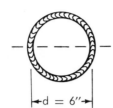

$$\therefore \quad f = \frac{M_4}{S_w} = \frac{25,700}{28.4}$$

$$= 905 \text{ lbs/in. of weld}$$

Since 9600 lbs is the accepted allowable load per linear inch for a fillet weld of 1" leg size, the minimum fillet weld leg size is--

$$\omega = \frac{905}{9600} = .095\text{"}$$

or $\quad \underline{\omega = \tfrac{3}{16}\text{"} \, \triangle \text{ fillet weld would be sufficient.}}$

Then Check Stiffness of Frame

Check vertical deflection (Δ) when P = 500 lbs is applied. Since we are only interested in the change between unloaded and loaded conditions, the weight of the frame is disregarded in using formulas.

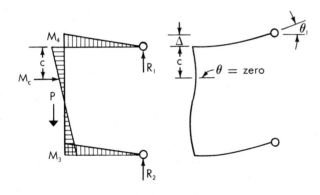

FIGURE 5

Vertical shear

$$V = \frac{P}{2} \left[\frac{\dfrac{2a}{I_a} + \dfrac{3b}{I_b}}{\dfrac{a}{I_a} + \dfrac{3b}{I_b} + \dfrac{a}{I_c}} \right]$$

$$= \frac{500}{2} \left[\frac{\dfrac{2(48)}{324} + \dfrac{3(60)}{66.33}}{\dfrac{48}{324} + \dfrac{3(60)}{66.33} + \dfrac{48}{153}} \right]$$

$$= 236.0 \text{ lbs}$$

Bending moments at the corners

From frame diagrams in the Reference Section:

$$M_4 = + R_1 a = + (P - V) a$$
$$= + (500 - 236)(48)$$
$$= + 12,700 \text{ in.-lbs}$$

$$M_3 = - V a = - (236)(48)$$
$$= - 11,300 \text{ in.-lbs}$$

Vertical distance to point on Member B where angle of deflection is zero

$$c = \frac{6 M_4 b - b \sqrt{36 M_4^2 - 12 (M_4 - M_3)(2M_4 + M_3)}}{6 (M_4 - M_3)}$$

here:

$$M_4 - M_3 = 12,700 - (- 11,300)$$
$$= 24,000$$

$$2 M_4 + M_3 = 25,400 + (- 11,300)$$
$$= 14,100$$

and:

$$c = \frac{6(12,700)(60) - 60 \sqrt{36(12,700)^2 - 12(24,000)(14,100)}}{6(24,000)}$$

$$= 20.35\text{"}$$

Bending moment at distance c

From similar triangles of moment diagram:

$$M_c = (M_3 - M_4) \frac{c}{b} + M_4$$

$$= (-11,300 - 12,700) \frac{20.35}{60} + 12,700$$

$$= + 4,560 \text{ in.-lbs}$$

Vertical deflection

The following corresponds to standard formula from Frame Diagrams in Reference Section:

$$\Delta = \left(\frac{M_c + M_4}{2} \right) \frac{c a}{E I_b} + \frac{1}{2} \frac{M_4 a}{E I_a} \frac{2 a}{3}$$

$$= \left(\frac{4560 + 12,700}{2} \right) \frac{(20.35)(48)}{(30 \times 10^6)(66.33)} + \frac{(12,700)(48)^2}{(30 \times 10^6)(324)(3)}$$

$$= .0052\text{"}$$

Angular deflection

$$\theta_1 = \left(\frac{M_c + M_4}{2} \right) \frac{c}{E I_b} + \frac{1}{2} \frac{M_4 a}{E I_a}$$

$$= \left(\frac{4560 + 12,700}{2} \right) \frac{(20.35)}{(30 \times 10^6)(66.33)} + \frac{(12,700)(48)}{2(30 \times 10^6)(324)}$$

$$= .00013 \text{ radians, or } \underline{.007°}$$

4. TORSIONAL RESISTANCE

In most cases there is some torque on the frame, and in many cases adequate torsional resistance is the primary design consideration. Section 3.6 discusses the torsional resistance of built-up frames in a comprehensive manner, but a sample problem is included here.

Problem 2

To check the torsional resistance and strength of the frame for a front-end loader, Figure 6, and to determine the size of the connecting weld on the cross-member. Here the width between centerlines of the longitudinal members is 34.75", and the latter are 82" long.

For simplicity, assume the frame to be as shown in Figure 7, with loading on the frame to be 17,000 lbs on one corner.

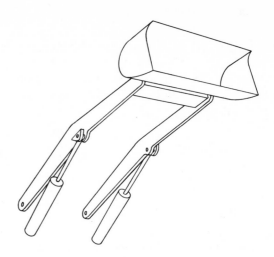

FIGURE 6

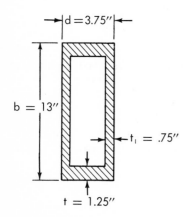

FIGURE 7

Torsional resistance of

Longitudinal members--

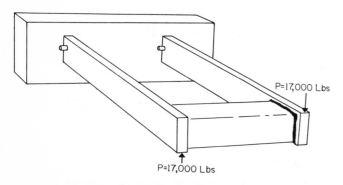

FIGURE 8

$$R_L = \frac{2 t t_1 (b - t)^2 (d - t_1)^2}{b t + d t_1 - t_1^2 - t^2}$$

$$= \frac{2 (1.25) (.75) (13.0 - 1.25)^2 (3.75 - .75)^2}{(13.0) (1.25) + (3.75) (.75) - (.75)^2 - (1.25)^2}$$

$$= 137.5 \text{ in.}^4, \text{ each member}$$

Torsional resistance of

Transverse member--

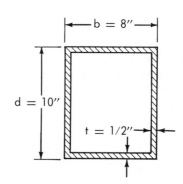

FIGURE 9

$$R_T = \frac{2 t (b - t)^2 (d - t)^2}{b + d - 2 t}$$

$$= \frac{2 (.5) (8 - .5)^2 (10 - .5)^2}{8 + 10 - 2 (.5)}$$

$$= 298.3 \text{ in.}^4$$

Then check the vertical deflection of the frame--

$$\Delta = \frac{P W L}{E_s \left(\frac{n_L R_L}{W} + \frac{n_T R_T}{L} \right)}$$

$$= \frac{(17,000) (34.75) (82)}{(12 \times 10^6) \left(\frac{2 \times 137.5}{34.75} + \frac{298.3}{82} \right)}$$

$$= .349"$$

and the angular twist of a longitudinal member--

$$\theta_L = \frac{\Delta}{W}$$

$$= \frac{.349}{34.75}$$

$$= .01004 \text{ radians, or } .57°$$

Shear stress in longitudinal member

Using the formula from Sect. 3.6, Topic 7 on torsional resistance of built-up frames, the applied torque on only one longitudinal member is--

$$T_L = \frac{\Delta\, E_s\, n_L\, R_L}{W\, L}$$

$$= \frac{(.349)(12 \times 10^6)(1)(137.5)}{(34.75)(82)}$$

$$= 202,500 \text{ in.-lbs, each member}$$

From Section 3.6, Table 1, the shear stress along the mid-section of the longitudinal member, on the short side of its cross-section is--

$$\tau = \frac{T_L}{2\, t\, (b - t)(d - t_1)}$$

$$= \frac{202,500}{2(1.25)(13 - 1.25)(3.75 - .75)}$$

$$= 2,300 \text{ psi}$$

and the shear stress at mid-section of the member, on the long side of its cross-section is--

$$\tau = \frac{T_L}{2\, t_1\, (b - t)(d - t_1)}$$

$$= \frac{207,500}{2\,(.75)(13 - 1.25)(3.75 - .75)}$$

$$= 3,800 \text{ psi}$$

Shear stress in transverse member

In a similar manner it is found that the applied torque on the transverse member is--

$$T_T = \frac{\Delta\, E_s\, n_t\, R_t}{W\, L}$$

$$= \frac{(.349)(12 \times 10^6)(1)(298.3)}{(34.75)(82)}$$

$$= 438,500 \text{ in.-lbs}$$

Since the cross-section of the transverse member is a hollow rectangle of uniform thickness, the shear stress at mid-length along either side of the section is--

$$\tau = \frac{T_T}{2\, t\, (b - t)(d - t)}$$

$$= \frac{438,500}{2(.5)(8 - .5)(10 - .5)}$$

$$= 6,160 \text{ psi}$$

Size of connecting fillet weld

Treating the weld as a line--

$$I_x = \frac{b\, d^2}{2} + \frac{d^3}{6} \qquad \text{(See Figure 10)}$$

$$= \frac{(8)(10)^2}{2} + \frac{(10)^3}{6}$$

$$= 566.7 \text{ in.}^3$$

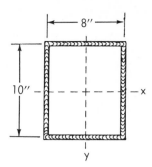

FIGURE 10

$$I_y = \frac{b^2\, d}{2} + \frac{b^3}{6}$$

$$= \frac{(8)^2 (10)}{2} + \frac{(8)^3}{6}$$

$$= 405.3 \text{ in.}^3$$

and the polar moment of inertia is —

$$J_w = I_x + I_y$$

$$= 566.7 + 405.3$$

$$= 972 \text{ in.}^3$$

Assuming just two vertical welds transfer vertical shear (V), the length of the weld is--

$$L_w = 2 \times 10 = 20"$$

Torsion on weld

From the standard design formula for torsion —

$$\tau = \frac{T\, c}{J} \text{ lbs/in.}^2 \text{ (stress)}$$

the corresponding formula for total weld force is obtained —

$$f_t = \frac{T\, c}{J} \text{ lbs/in. (force per linear inch of weld)}$$

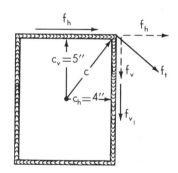

FIGURE 11

The horizontal component of this torque is —

$$f_h = \frac{T\, c_v}{J_w}$$

$$= \frac{(438,500)(5)}{972}$$

$$= 2,250 \text{ lbs/in.}$$

and the vertical components of this torque is —

$$f_v = \frac{T\,c_h}{J_w}$$

$$= \frac{(438,500)(4)}{972}$$

$$= 1,805 \text{ lbs/in.}$$

Vertical shear on weld

Since the vertical shear on the joint is--

$$V = P_T = \frac{T_L}{W}$$

$$= \frac{202,500}{34.75}$$

$$= 5,825 \text{ lbs}$$

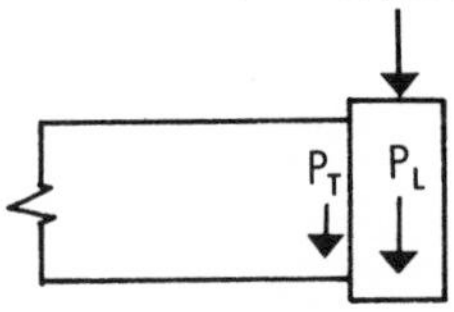

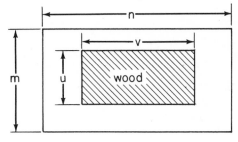

FIGURE 12

the resultant force on the vertical welds is —

$$f_{v_1} = \frac{V}{A_w}$$

$$= \frac{5,825}{20''}$$

$$= 292 \text{ lbs/in.}$$

Bending on weld

Since the bending moment on the joint is--

$$M = T_L$$

$$= 202,500 \text{ in.-lbs}$$

the resultant force on the weld is —

$$f_m = \frac{M\,c}{I_w}$$

$$= \frac{(202,500)(5)}{(566.7)}$$

$$= 1785 \text{ lbs/in.}$$

Resultant force on weld

Resolving combined forces on weld at point of greatest effect--

Transverse member

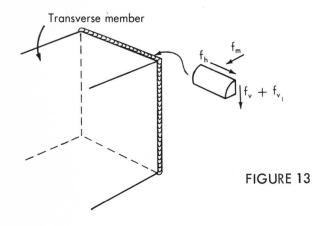

FIGURE 13

$$f_r = \sqrt{f_h{}^2 + f_m{}^2 + (f_v + f_{v_1})^2}$$

$$= \sqrt{2250^2 + 1785^2 + (1805 + 292)^2}$$

$$= 3560 \text{ lbs/in.}$$

Weld size

Since 9600 lbs is the accepted allowable load per linear inch of fillet weld having a 1" leg size, the minimum leg size for this application is--

$$\omega = \frac{3560}{9600} = .371''$$

or use ⅜" △ fillet weld.

5. ANALYSIS OF THE PROBLEM

Many types of machines present problems not immediately identifiable as to use of standard design formulas. However, any situation can be expressed mathematically and doing so is the only way to achieve an efficient design with accurately predetermined results.

| Problem 3 |

To design a steel platen for use in pressing layers of wood together while they are being glued, Figure 14.

FIGURE 14

Platen (m by n) applies pressure against layers of wood (u by v), the shaded area. A uniform pressure (p_m) is applied to the platen. It is desired that this will result in a uniform pressure (p_u) against the wood.

If this pressure against the wood (p_u) is to be held constant for all areas of wood, or panel sizes, the applied pressure on the platen (p_m) will vary as follows:

$$p_m\, m\, n = p_u\, u\, v$$

or:

$$\boxed{p_m = p_u\, \frac{uv}{mn}}$$

In Figure 15 the platen applies pressure over most of the area of the wood. The layers of wood will come out fairly flat.

In Figure 16, the much smaller wood panel size results in a considerable overhang of the platen. This causes the center of the platen to lift up off of

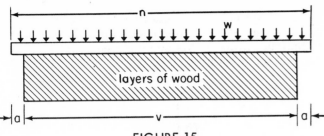

FIGURE 15

the surface of the wood and produces a concentrated force at the ends of the wood. With further downward travel of the platen, this condition of force will compress the wood panels more at the ends than at the center, and they will come out curved.

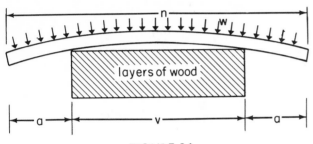

FIGURE 16

where:

$$w = p_m \, m = p_u \frac{u \, v}{n}$$

in lbs/linear in. of length (n)

The layers of wood cannot curve more than the platen; therefore, the vertical deflection of the platen at its center will be assumed to be a measure of the amount of curve of the wood. This deflection can be determined for any given size of wood panel:

$$\Delta_{\mathcal{L}} = \frac{w \, v^2}{384 \, E \, I} \, (5 \, v^2 - 24 \, a^2)$$

Since $n = 2a + v$, or $a = \dfrac{n - v}{2}$

$$\Delta_{\mathcal{L}} = \frac{w \, v^2}{384 \, E \, I} \, (v^2 - 12 \, n \, v + 6 \, n^2)$$

In order to hold this deflection (Δ) at center to a given value, the required stiffness or moment of inertia (I) of the platen is--

$$I = \frac{w \, v^2}{384 \, E \, \Delta} \, (v^2 - 12 \, n \, v + 6 \, n^2)$$

This formula is used if the length of the wood (v) is less than 0.523 of the length of the platen (n), in which case the center of the platen will ordinarily deflect upward. A positive value for moment of inertia (I) indicates an upward deflection. For an indicated downward deflection the platen would press uniformly against the wood and this formula would not be applicable.

Consider the following problem--

platen	plywood door
m = 50.0"	u = 25.0"
n = 98.0"	v = 46.0"

and the pressure against the wood surface is to be $p_u = 125$ psi. It is desired to hold the deflection of the wood and the platen to within 1/32".

Using the preceding formulas--

$$w = p_u \frac{u \, v}{n}$$

$$= 125 \frac{(25)(46)}{(98)}$$

$$= 1463 \text{ lbs/linear inch}$$

$$I = \frac{w \, v^2}{384 \, E \, \Delta} \, (v^2 - 12 \, n \, v + 6 \, n^2)$$

$$= \frac{(1463)(46)^2}{384 \, (30 \times 10^6)(1/32)} \, [46^2 - 12 \, (98)(46) + 6 \, (98)^2]$$

$$= \underline{48.5 \text{ in.}^4}, \text{ required}$$

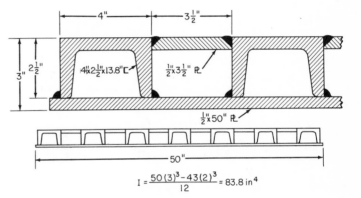

$$I = \frac{50(3)^3 - 43(2)^3}{12} = 83.8 \text{ in}^4$$

FIGURE 17

In the first design, Figure 17, seven 4" × 2½" × 13.8-lb channels are welded to a ½" × 50" surface plate. Six ½" × 3½" bars are welded in between the channels. This welding is done with automatic submerged-arc welder for maximum speed and minimum distortion. The resulting moment of inertia of this platen is I = 83.8 in.⁴, which is sufficient.

In an alternate design, Figure 18, twenty 2⅜" × 3" × 5.7-lb I beams are welded together. This results in a moment of inertia of I = 58 in.⁴ which also is sufficient.

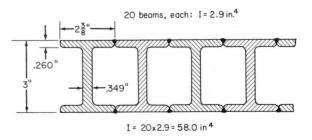

I = 20×2.9 = 58.0 in⁴

FIGURE 18

Rectangular stiffeners or chocks are placed within the channel sections (1st design) before welding to the steel plate; this provides stiffness in the transverse direction. The I beam sections (2nd design) could also be stiffened, although there wouldn't be as much access for welding the stiffeners in place.

Problem 4

To design a welded steel supporting frame for a fifth wheel assembly of a semi-trailer. The assumed maximum load on this frame is 20,000 lbs, applied vertically. There is also a horizontal force due to accelerating and braking.

One suggestion is to make this frame out of thin steel (viz. ¼") formed into channels and then welded into box sections. This results in a very efficient cross-section for the bending moments resulting from the load, and also gives a very stable section for any twisting or racking action.

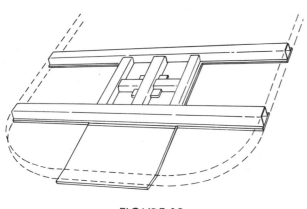

FIGURE 19

Thus, the entire assembly will take its share of the loading rather than simply loading one beam to its maximum. Two intersecting channel sections, which form box sections with the fifth wheel plate, intersect over the king pin and secure it better than many designs in which these stiffening members pass around the pin.

Section beyond central plate

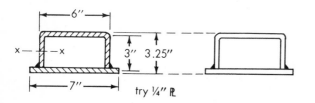

FIGURE 20

Assume the reference axis (x–x) to be midway of the built-up section's depth. Compute the moment of inertia (I) about this section's neutral axis, and the section modulus (S):

Element Area	d	A	M	I_x	
7 × .25	− 1.5"	1.75	− 2.625	+ 3.9375	−
.5 × 3	0	1.50	0	0	1.125
6 × .25	+ 1.5	1.50	+ 2.250	+ 3.375	−
Total		4.75	−.375	8.4375	

$$I_{NA} = I_x - \frac{M^2}{A}$$

$$= + 8.4375 - \frac{(-.375)^2}{4.75}$$

$$= 8.4079 \text{ in.}^4$$

Locating the neutral axis—

$$NA = \frac{M}{A} = \frac{-.375}{4.75} = -.079" \text{ (below x–x axis)}$$

$$c_{top} = 1.704"$$

$$c_{bottom} = 1.546"$$

the section modulus is thus —

$$S_{top} = \frac{8.4079}{1.704} = 4.93 \text{ in.}^3$$

$$S_{bottom} = \frac{8.4079}{1.546} = 5.44 \text{ in.}^3$$

Section at center

Here the 36" wide fifth wheel support plate adds an effective 11" to the bottom plate.

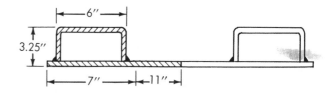

FIGURE 21

Element Area	d	A	M	I_x
1st total		4.75	− .375	+ 8.4375
add: 11 × .25	− 1.5	2.75	− 4.125	+ 6.1875
New total		7.50	− 4.5	+ 14.625

$$I_{NA} = 14.625 - \frac{(-4.5)^2}{7.50}$$

$$= 11.925 \text{ in.}^4$$

$$NA = \frac{4.5}{7.5} = -.60"$$

$$c_{top} = 2.225''$$

$$c_{bottom} = 1.025''$$

$$S_{top} = \frac{11.925}{2.225} = 5.36 \text{ in.}^3$$

$$S_{bottom} = \frac{11.925}{1.025} = 11.63 \text{ in.}^3$$

Diagramming the closed channel member as a beam

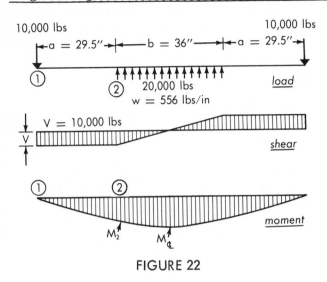

FIGURE 22

The bending moments at principal points of interest are--

$$M_{\mathfrak{C}} = (10,000)(47.5) - (10,000)(9)$$
$$= 385,000 \text{ in.-lbs}$$

$$M_2 = (10,000)(29.5)$$
$$= 295,000 \text{ in.-lbs}$$

Thus, the stress at midspan, distributed over the two parallel channels, is--

$$\sigma_{top} = \frac{M}{S_{top}} = \frac{385,000}{2(5.36)}$$
$$= 36,000 \text{ psi tension}$$

$$\sigma_{bottom} = \frac{M}{S_{bottom}} = \frac{385,000}{2(11.63)}$$
$$= 16,552 \text{ psi compression}$$

and at point (2) just beyond the edge of the fifth wheel support plate--

$$\sigma_{top} = \frac{M}{S_{top}} = \frac{295,000}{2(4.93)}$$
$$= 29,900 \text{ psi tension}$$

$$\sigma_{bottom} = \frac{M}{S_{bottom}} = \frac{295,000}{2(5.44)}$$
$$= 27,100 \text{ psi compression}$$

Summarizing the stresses

The maximum bending moment occurs at the centerline of the member and is equal to 385,000 in.-lbs. This results in a bending stress of 36,000 psi tension in the top fibers, and 16,552 psi compression in the bottom fibers.

The bending moment just beyond the fifth wheel plate is 295,000 in.-lbs. This represents a bending stress of 29,900 psi tension in the top fibers, and 27,100 psi compression in the bottom fibers.

Because of the magnitude of these stresses and the fatigue factors in this type application, the decision is to check the possibility of using T-1 steel.

Assuming the mean load of 20,000 lbs on the frame may rise to 25,000 lbs or decrease to 15,000 lbs, the ratio representing the fatigue cycle is--

$$K = \frac{min}{max} = \frac{+15,000}{+25,000} = +.60$$

For a service life of 2 million cycles, T-1 steel in tension will have an allowable fatigue strength (Sect. 3.2, Table 2) of--

$$\sigma = \frac{29,000}{1-.65K} = \frac{29,000}{1-.65(6)}$$
$$= 47,600 \text{ psi}$$

Note: Fatigue stress of T-1 in tension should not exceed 54,000 psi, and the computed allowable value of 47,600 is within this limit.

For the same service life, T-1 steel butt welds in tension will have an allowable fatigue strength of--

$$\sigma = \frac{16,500}{1-.80K} = \frac{16,500}{1-.80(.60)}$$
$$= 31,700 \text{ psi}$$

Note: Fatigue stress of T-1 butt welds in tension also should not exceed 54,000 psi, and the computed allowable value of 31,700 is within this limit. The allowable for a butt weld has been selected because in the future this frame may be fabricated by butt-welding two halves together.

Determining the weld size

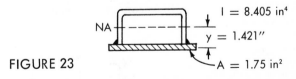

I = 8.405 in⁴

y = 1.421''

A = 1.75 in²

FIGURE 23

Here the horizontal shear force on the fillet weld, considering the fact that there are two closed-in channel members supporting the total load, is--

$$f = \frac{VAy}{I}$$

$$= \frac{(10,000)(1.75)(1.421)}{(8.405)}$$

$$= 2960 \text{ lbs/in. (two fillet welds)}$$

or f = 1480 lbs/in. (each fillet weld)

For mild steel, the allowable force on the fillet weld to assure a service life of 2 million cycles is—

$$f = \frac{5090\,\omega}{1 - .5\,K} = \frac{5090\,\omega}{1 - .5\,(.6)}$$

$$= 7300\,\omega \text{ lbs/in.}$$

and therefore the fillet weld leg size is —

$$\omega = \frac{1480}{7300}$$

$$= .203'' \underline{\text{ or between } \tfrac{3}{16}'' \text{ and } \tfrac{1}{4}''}$$

For T-1 steel, the allowable force on the fillet weld to assure a service life of 2 million cycles is—

$$f = \frac{6360\,\omega}{1 - .80\,K} = \frac{6360\,\omega}{1 - .8\,(.6)}$$

$$= 12,200\,\omega \text{ lbs/in.}$$

and therefore the minimum fillet weld leg size is —

$$\omega = \frac{1,480}{12,200}$$

$$= .121'' \text{ or } \tfrac{1}{8}''$$

Influence of horizontal force

The described design has been based on resisting the principal vertical force of 20,000 lbs. There is, of course, a horizontal force supplied by the truck in accelerating and also pulling the trailer up an inclined road. There could also be a horizontal force supplied in braking the unit if there should be a difference in braking power of truck and trailer.

Although these horizontal forces might be computed for various conditions, they will be of a lower value than the vertical force on which the design was made. Also, because of restricted height in which the frame must be placed, the frame has a much higher moment of inertia and section modulus about the vertical axis to resist these horizontal forces than it has about the horizontal axis to resist the vertical load of 20,000 lbs; so the design is on the safe side. For example, the critical section for any horizontal force would be just adjacent to the edge of the fifth wheel plate; the properties about the vertical axis are:

$I_y = 25.16$ in.^{4}
$S_y = 7.19$ in.^{3}

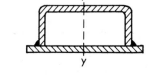

whereas the same properties about the horizontal axis are:

$I_x = 8.41$ in.^{4}
$S_x = 4.93$ in.^{3} (top)

For some idea of the limiting value of this possible horizontal force, assume the operator initially traveling at 60 miles/hr will apply all his brakes for a crash stop and come to rest within a distance of 350 ft.

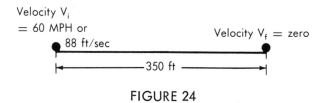

Velocity V_i = 60 MPH or 88 ft/sec

Velocity V_f = zero

350 ft

FIGURE 24

The average velocity is —

$$V_{av} = \frac{V_i + V_f}{2}$$

$$= \frac{88 + 0}{2}$$

$$= 44 \text{ ft/sec}$$

The time to come to rest is —

$$t = \frac{d}{V_{av}}$$

$$= \frac{350 \text{ ft}}{44 \text{ ft/sec}}$$

$$= 7.95 \text{ sec}$$

The rate of deceleration is —

$$a = \frac{V_i - V_f}{t}$$

$$= \frac{88 - 0}{7.95}$$

$$= 11.1 \text{ ft/sec}^2$$

The force required to decelerate the trailer is —

$$F = ma = \frac{W}{g}\,a$$

$$= \frac{40,000 \text{ lbs}}{32.2 \text{ ft/sec}} \, (11.1 \text{ ft/sec}^2)$$

$$= 13,800 \text{ lbs}$$

The greatest portion of this horizontal force will be supplied by the braking force of the trailer's tires, and only a portion might be transferred through the fifth wheel unit.

If just the truck were to supply the braking force, it would require a much longer distance to stop, thereby reducing this horizontal force.

Since it has already been established that the moment of inertia and section modulus being higher about the vertical axis would resist a higher transverse force, the finding that the horizontal force is less than the vertical force makes further computation unnecessary.

Columns, Legs or Feet

1. GENERAL

Columns, legs and feet are all supporting members which are loaded primarily in compression. Torsional loading may also be a problem, although good over-all machine design will generally result in good balance of forces on supporting members.

2. COLUMNS

Machine columns, as compression members, are ordinarily long enough to be considered long columns in which the slenderness ratio is a critical design factor. Section 2.5 on the Analysis of Compression fully discusses the mathematical approach to the design of long compression columns.

Figure 1 shows some simple columns built up from standard structural shapes. Each of these exploits the efficiency and the economy of a closed hollow section under compressive or torsional loading.

Fig. 1 Welding permits maximum economy in column design through optimum use of standard structural shapes and brake-formed sections.

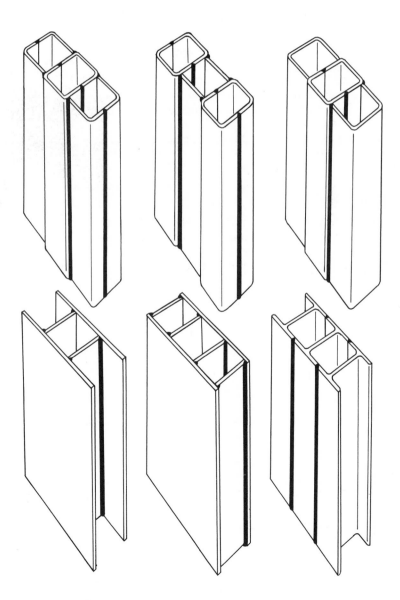

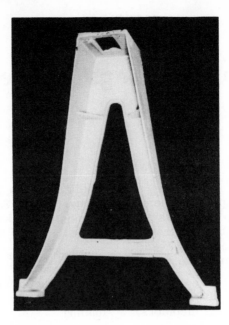

Fig. 2 Thin section was difficult to cast, right. Cost of the safer arc-welded steel leg, left, was only 51% of the casting.

3. LEGS

For aesthetic reasons, legs are not as common in machinery designs as they were in years past. However, legs are still needed on many portable machines and those used in the service trades. When used, legs often have a sufficiently low slenerness ratio that advantage can be taken of higher-strength steels. Sizeable savings in material are possible by using these steels in heavy-duty applications.

Light-gage steel legs

Light-gage steel sheet may be sheared; or, if production warrants, a simple low-cost die may be used to blank out the member. This would give smooth edges at the lowest possible cost.

Corners of the leg may be formed in a bend brake. This produces smooth round corners and eliminates much welding. Any part of the leg so formed adds stiffness to the leg.

With sheet steel, required holes may be quickly punched into the leg instead of being drilled as is required in a cast leg. Punching requires but a fraction of the drilling time.

In the example shown at the left in Figure 2, welded steel saved 30% in weight and 51% in total cost. The original casting, at right, shows a repaired lower cross brace which had broken in shop handling.

It is also easy to close a sheet metal leg into a box section and thereby greatly increase its torsional resistance when required on heavier loading.

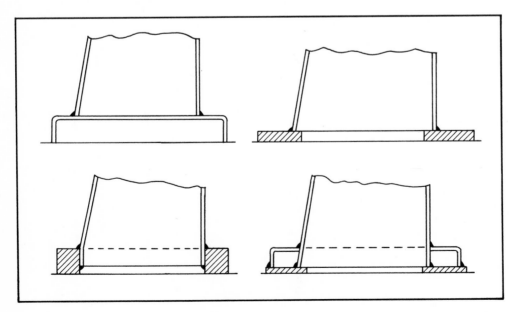

Fig. 3 Welded feet offer sound support to bases and columns.

4. FEET

Feet which are loaded in compression are considered short columns and failure, when it occurs, is by crushing. The higher-strength steels offer advantages here also.

By welding feet onto a machine base, column or frame, considerable saving can often be made in fabrication. Sometimes, however, it is simpler to flange outward the side panels of the base so as to be self-supporting.

The illustrations here, Figures 3 and 4, show various designs for adding feet to satisfy economy, functional or appearance objectives.

FIG. 4 DESIGN IDEAS FOR WELDED FEET

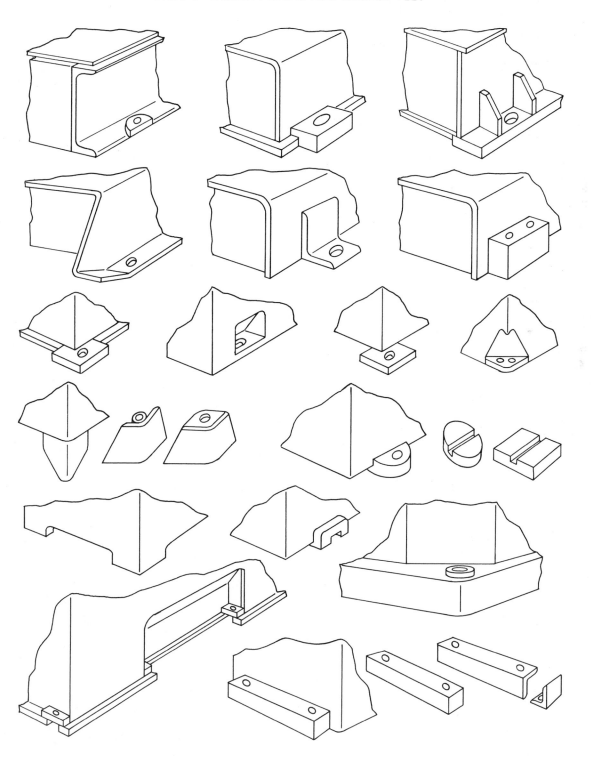

Vertical contour grinder makes effective use of steel weldments to meet high quality standards while keeping manufacturing costs to a minimum. Note the use of diagonal bracing in the column for extra rigidity.

Containers, Cylinders and Shells

1. SCOPE

This is a broad classification, covering many types of containers. However, principles and formulas relating to their design are best discussed as a single group. Some of these containers have flat surfaces; some have curved surfaces; some have both. Some carry steam, gasses, or pressurized fluids that exert uniform pressure in all directions; others carry bulk material such as grain, the weight of which exerts a varying horizontal pressure against the side walls.

The first requisite of a container is that it be tight. It must have sufficient strength to withstand the internal pressure to which it is subjected. In arc-welded construction, the joints are made as tight and strong as the plates joined. In large tanks built up from a number of plates or sheets, butt welds are customarily specified.

Rolled steel plate versus cast steel has hard, smooth, pitless inside surfaces that offer greater hydraulic efficiency, more resistance to corrosion and erosion. Whereas many castings must be sealed by vacuum impregnation with a resin in order to be used for container purposes, rolled steel plate is inherently sealed by its homogeneous metallurgy.

Many containers must be designed and fabricated according to the minimum requirements of certain

TYPES OF CONTAINERS		
Flat and/or Curved Surfaces		
tanks	chutes	crankcases and oil pans
boilers	mixing chambers	tumbling barrels
vats	steam chests	hydraulic cylinders
hoppers	accumulators	revolving driers
drums	dump cars	clamshell buckets
bins	annealing pots	pipe and piping systems
silos	stacks	oil well casings
		and many others

codes, for example ASME. Most containers have thin shells in comparison to their diameters and come under the classification of thin-wall shells.

2. ELEMENTS OF THE CONTAINER

The surfaces of any container must withstand pressure of some type, so it would be well to consider the strength and stiffness of various shapes and forms of plates under uniform pressure.

In analysis of a given container, the designer explodes it into its various elements and applies the corresponding formulas.

FLAT SURFACES OF CONTAINERS

3. GENERAL

Some containers are of box construction, made up entirely of flat surfaces. Other containers, many tanks for example, consist of a cylinder closed at each end by a flat plate.

Table 1 presents design formulas applicable to various flat plates subjected to internal pressure.

| Problem 1 |

Determine the required plate thickness of the following tank to hold water, Figure 1.

Since the varying pressure against side walls is due to the weight of a liquid:

$p = .4336 \text{ H s}$

$= .4336(6)(1)$

$= 2.6 \text{ psi}$

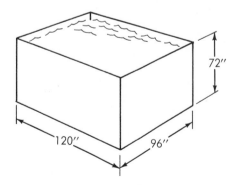

FIGURE 1

where:

H = the maximum height of the liquid, in feet

s = the specific gravity of the liquid

1

It is necessary to consider only the longest side plate, having the greatest span between supports: 120". The top edge is free, the other three are supported. This is recognized as condition 5B on Table 1.

Since the ratio of plate height to width is--

$$\frac{a}{b} = \frac{72}{120} = .6$$

values are estimated from Table 1 to be--

$$\beta = .14 \qquad \text{and } \gamma = .030$$

Then the required plate thickness is derived from the maximum stress formula:

$$\sigma_{max} = \frac{\beta\,p\,b^2}{t^2}$$

or, assuming an allowable stress of 20,000 psi —

$$t^2 = \frac{\beta\,p\,b^2}{\sigma}$$

$$= \frac{(.14)(2.6)(120)^2}{20,000}$$

$$= .262$$

$$\therefore \quad t = \sqrt{.262}$$

$$= .512", \text{ or use } \tfrac{1}{2}" \text{ ℞}$$

Checking the deflection of this plate —

$$\Delta_{max} = \frac{\gamma\,p\,b^4}{E\,t^3}$$

$$= \frac{(.030)(2.6)(120)^4}{(30 \times 10^6)(.5)^3}$$

$$= 4.3"$$

Since this deflection would be excessive, a stiffening bar must be added along the top edge of the tank to form a rectangular frame, Figure 2.

Tank with Top Edge Stiffener

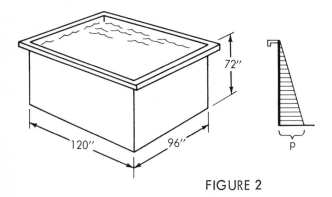

FIGURE 2

The modified tank now satisfies the condition 5A on Table 1, because the critical plate is supported on all four edges.

The ratio of plate height to width still being .6, values are estimated from Table 1 to be--

$$\beta = .102 \qquad \text{and } \gamma = .0064$$

Since the same maximum stress formula applies —

$$t^2 = \frac{\beta\,p\,b^2}{\sigma}$$

$$= \frac{(.102)(2.6)(120)^2}{20,000}$$

$$= .191$$

$$\therefore \quad t = \sqrt{.191}$$

$$= .437", \text{ or use } \tfrac{7}{16}" \text{ ℞}$$

Checking the deflection of this plate--

$$\Delta_{max} = \frac{\gamma\,p\,b^4}{E\,t^3}$$

$$= \frac{(.0064)(2.6)(120)^4}{(30 \times 10^6)(.4375)^3}$$

$$= 1.37"$$

It might be advisable to go back to the ½" plate thickness, still using the top edge stiffener, in which case the bending stress and deflection would be reduced to--

$$\sigma_{max} = 15,300 \text{ psi} \qquad \text{and } \Delta_{max} = .92"$$

There is another method of determining the bending stress and deflection. A description of this follows immediately.

Considering Plate Section as a Beam

A narrow section of the tank's side panel (width m = 1") can be considered as a beam, Figure 3, using formulas taken from Table 1 in the Reference Section on Beam Diagrams.

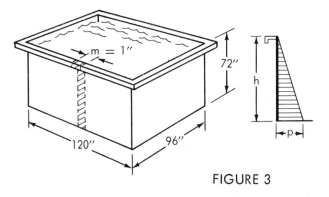

FIGURE 3

Since the maximum bending moment here is--

$$M_{max} = .0642\,p\,h^2\,m \text{ (with h expressed in inches)}$$

$$= .0642(2.6)(72)^2(1)$$

$$= 865 \text{ in.-lbs}$$

$$\sigma_{max} = \frac{M}{s} = \frac{M\,6}{t^2}$$

$$= 20,800 \text{ psi}$$

instead of the 15,300 psi obtained by considering the

Problem 1 continued on page 5

TABLE 1 – STRESS AND DEFLECTION, FLAT PLATES*
Subjected to Internal Pressure (p), psi

CIRCULAR PLATE

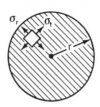

ELLIPTICAL PLATE

$$\alpha = \frac{b}{a}$$

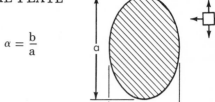

(1A) Edges supported; uniform load

At center:

$$(\text{max}) \; \sigma_r = \sigma_t = -\frac{1.24 \, p \, r^2}{t^2}$$

$$\Delta_{\text{max}} = -\frac{.695 \, p \, r^4}{E \, t^3}$$

(1B) Edges fixed; uniform load

At center:

$$\sigma_r = \sigma_t = -\frac{.488 \, p \, r^2}{t^2}$$

$$\Delta_{\text{max}} = -\frac{.1705 \, p \, r^4}{E \, t^3}$$

At edge:

$$(\text{max}) \; \sigma_r = \frac{3 \, p \, r^2}{4 \, t^2}$$

$$\sigma_t = \frac{.225 \, p \, r^2}{t^2}$$

(2A) Edges supported;
uniform load

At center:

$$(\text{max}) \; \sigma_b = -\frac{.3125 \, (2 - \alpha) \, p \, b^2}{t^2}$$

$$(\text{approx}) \; \Delta_{\text{max}} = \frac{(.146 - .1 \, \alpha) \, p \, b^4}{E \, t^3}$$

(2B) Edges fixed; uniform load

At center:

$$\sigma_a = -\frac{.075 \, p \, b^2 \, (10 \, \alpha^2 + 3)}{t^2 \, (3 + 2 \, \alpha^2 + 3 \, \alpha^4)}$$

$$\sigma_b = -\frac{.075 \, p \, b^2 \, (3 \, \alpha^2 + 10)}{t^2 \, (3 + 2 \, \alpha^2 + 3 \, \alpha^4)}$$

$$\Delta_{\text{max}} = -\frac{.1705 \, p \, b^4}{E \, t^3 \, (6 + 4 \, \alpha^2 + 6 \, \alpha^4)}$$

At edge:

$$(\text{Span a}) \; \sigma_a = \frac{1.5 \, p \, b^2 \, \alpha^2}{t^2 \, (3 + 2 \, \alpha^2 + 3 \, \alpha^4)}$$

$$\begin{array}{l}(\text{max}) \\ (\text{Span b})\end{array} \; \sigma_b = \frac{1.5 \, p \, b^2}{t^2 \, (3 + 2 \, \alpha^2 + 3 \, \alpha^4)}$$

SQUARE PLATE

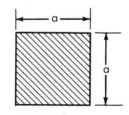

(3A) Edges supported (and held down);
uniform load

At center:

$$(\text{max}) \; \sigma_a = -\frac{.2870 \, p \, a^2}{t^2}$$

$$\Delta_{\text{max}} = -\frac{.0443 \, p \, a^4}{E \, t^3}$$

(3B) Edges fixed; uniform load

At center:

$$\sigma_a = -\frac{.166 \, p \, a^2}{t^2}$$

$$\Delta_{\text{max}} = -\frac{.0138 \, p \, a^4}{E \, t^3}$$

At midpoint of each edge:

$$(\text{max}) \; \sigma_a = +\frac{.308 \, p \, a^2}{t^2}$$

*After Roark, "Formulas for Stress and Strain".

Table 1 continued on following page

.. Table 1 continued

RECTANGULAR PLATES

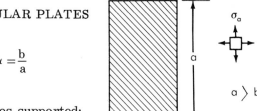

$$\alpha = \frac{b}{a}$$

(4A) Edges supported; uniform load

At center:

$$\sigma_a = -\frac{p\,b^2\,(.225 + .382\,\alpha^2 - .320\,\alpha^3)}{t^2}$$

$$(\text{max})\ \sigma_b = -\frac{.75\,p\,b^2}{t^2\,(1 + 1.61\,\alpha^3)} \quad \text{or} \quad = \frac{\beta\,p\,b^2}{t^2}$$

$$\Delta_{max} = -\frac{.1422\,p\,b^4}{E\,t^3\,(1 + 2.21\,\alpha^3)} \quad \text{or} \quad = -\frac{\gamma\,p\,b^4}{E\,t^3}$$

(4B) Edges fixed; uniform load

At center:

$$\sigma_a = -\frac{.054\,p\,b^2\,(1 + 2\,\alpha^2 - \alpha^4)}{t^2}$$

$$\sigma_b = -\frac{.75\,p\,b^2}{t^2\,(3 + 4\,\alpha^4)}$$

$$\Delta_{max} = -\frac{.0284\,p\,b^4}{E\,t^3\,(1 + 1.056\,\alpha^5)} \quad \text{or} \quad = -\frac{\gamma\,p\,b^4}{E\,t^3}$$

At midpoint of long edges:

$$(\text{max})\ \sigma_b = \frac{.5\,p\,b^2}{t^2\,(1 + .623\,\alpha^6)} \quad \text{or} \quad = \frac{\beta\,p\,b^2}{t^2}$$

At midpoint of short edges:

$$\sigma_a = \frac{.25\,p\,b^2}{t^2}$$

See the following sub-tables for values of β and γ:

$\frac{a}{b}$	1.0	1.1	1.2	1.3	1.4	1.5	1.6	1.7	1.8	1.9	2.0	∞
	For edges supported											
β	.2874	.3318	.3756	.4158	.4518	.4872	.5172	.5448	.5688	.5910	.6102	.7500
γ	.0443	.0530	.0616	.0697	.0770	.0843	.0906	.0964	.1017	.1064	.1106	.1422
	For edges fixed											
β	.3078	.3486	.3834	.4122	.4356	.4542	.4680	.4794	.4872	.4932	.4974	
γ	.0138	.0164	.0188	.0209	.0226	.0240	.0251	.0260	.0267	.0272	.0277	

(4C) All edges supported; varying load

Load increasing uniformly from zero at one edge to a maximum of (p) psi at opposite edge (triangular load)

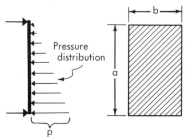

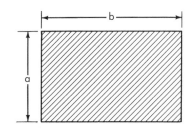

$$\sigma_{max} = \frac{\beta\,p\,b^2}{t^2}$$

$$\Delta_{max} = \frac{\gamma\,p\,b^4}{E\,t^3}$$

The following values apply to Condition 4C;

$\frac{a}{b}$	.25	.286	.333	.4	.5	.667	1.0	1.5	2.0	2.5	3.0	3.5	4.0
β	.024	.031	.041	.056	.080	.116	.16	.26	.32	.35	.37	.38	.38
γ	.00027	.00046	.00083	.0016	.0035	.0083	.022	.042	.056	.063	.067	.069	.070

Table 1 continued on facing page

. . Table 1 continued

(4D) Top edge free, other three edges supported; varying load

Load increasing uniformly from zero at top edge to a maximum of (p) psi at bottom edge (triangular load)

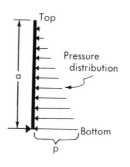

$$\sigma_{max} = \frac{\beta\,p\,b^2}{t^2}$$

$$\Delta_{max} = \frac{\gamma\,p\,b^4}{E\,t^3}$$

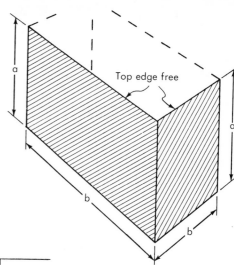

The following values apply to Condition 4D;

$\frac{a}{b}$	.5	.667	1.0	1.5	2.0	2.5	3.0	3.5	4.0
β	.11	.16	.20	.28	.32	.35	.36	.37	.37
γ	.026	.033	.040	.050	.058	.064	.067	.069	.070

. . . Problem 1 continued

entire plate width; and--

$$\Delta_{max} = \frac{.0625\,p\,h^4\,m}{E\,I}$$

$$= \frac{.0625\,(2.6)(72)^4\,(1)\,(12)}{(30 \times 10^6)\,(.5)^3}$$

$$= 1.39\,''$$

instead of the .92" obtained by considering the entire plate width.

This method of isolating a 1" strip of the panel and considering it as a beam will indicate greater bending stress and deflection than actually exists. The reason is that the stiffening effect of the surrounding panel has been neglected for simplicity.

The previous method of considering the entire panel is recommended for its accuracy and for a more efficient design wherever it can be applied.

Adding Another Stiffener

When a panel is divided into two parts by a large stiffener, it becomes a continuous panel, triangularly loaded with a rather high negative moment at the stiffener which acts as a support. There is no simple formula for this; therefore the method of considering a 1" strip will be used, and of course will result in a slightly greater stress value than actually exists.

The plate thickness in the tank being considered can probably be reduced by adding such a stiffener around the middle of the tank, Figure 4.

The first step is to locate the stiffener at the

height which will produce the minimum bending moment in the panel, both above and below the stiffener. (Again use formulas from Table 1 in the Reference Section on Beam Diagrams.) This dimension (a), the distance between the two stiffeners, is—

$$a = .57\,h = .57(72) = 41''$$

Then, at the middle stiffener--

$$M_{max} = .0147\,p\,h^2\,m$$
$$= .0147\,(2.6)(72)^2\,(1)$$
$$= 198\ \text{in.-lbs}$$

Trying $\frac{5}{16}''$ ℞ —

$$\sigma_{max} = \frac{M}{s} = \frac{M\,6}{t^2}$$

$$= \frac{(198)\,6}{(\frac{5}{16})^2}$$

$$= \underline{12{,}200\ \text{psi}} \qquad \text{OK}$$

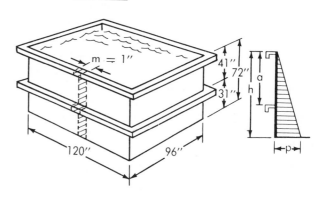

FIGURE 4

CONTAINER SURFACES FORMED BY A FIGURE OF REVOLUTION

4. STRESSES IN SHELL

The various container shapes illustrated in Table 2 are formed by a figure of revolution.

TABLE 2 - CONTAINER SURFACES FORMED BY A FIGURE OF REVOLUTION

THIN WALL CONTAINERS		
CONTAINER SHAPE	UNIT WALL SEGMENT	TENSILE STRESS FORMULAE
CYLINDER		$\sigma_{m_p} = \dfrac{p\, r_c}{2\, t_s}$ $\sigma_{c_p} = \dfrac{p\, r_c}{t_s}$
SPHERE		$\sigma_{m_p} = \sigma_{c_p} = \dfrac{p\, r_c}{2\, t_s}$
ANY FIGURE OF REVOLUTION		$\dfrac{\sigma_{c_p}}{r_{c_p}} + \dfrac{\sigma_m}{r_m} = \dfrac{p}{t_s}$ $\sigma_{m_p} = \dfrac{p\, r_c}{2\, t_s}$ $\sigma_{c_p} = \dfrac{p\, r_c}{t_s}\left(1 - \dfrac{r_c}{2\, r_m}\right)$
CONE		$\sigma_{m_p} = \dfrac{p\, r_c}{2\, t_s \cos \alpha}$ $\sigma_{c_p} = \dfrac{p\, r_c}{t_s \cos \alpha}$

In any of these containers, the internal pressure (p) along with the weight of the gas, liquid or other media within the container produces three types of tensile stresses in the container's shell. These are:

1. σ_{m_p} = tensile stress in the direction of a meridian. (A meridian is the curve formed by the intersection of the shell and a plane through the longitudinal axis of the container.) This stress is referred to as longitudinal stress.

2. σ_{c_p} = tensile stress in the direction of a tangent to a circumference. (A circumference is the curve formed by the intersection of the shell and a plane perpendicular to the longitudinal axis of the container.) This stress is referred to as tangential or circumferential stress but is commonly called the hoop stress.

3. σ_{r_p} = tensile stress in the radial direction.

For containers having relatively thin shells (generally considered as less than 10% of the mean

radius) and no abrupt change in thickness or curvature, the radial tensile stress (σ_{r_p}) and any bending stress may be neglected.

The biaxial tensile stresses (σ_{m_p}) and (σ_{c_p}) in thin-wall containers can be calculated with the basic formulas shown in Table 2, where:

t_s = thickness of shell, in.

r_c = mean radius of a circumference of the shell, in.

r_m = mean radius of the meridian of the shell, in.

p = internal pressure, psi

5. THICK-WALLED CONTAINERS

In thin-walled containers, the hoop stress is assumed to be uniformly distributed across the shell thickness without serious error occurring in stress calculations. However, in a thick-walled container generated by a figure of revolution the decreasing variance of hoop stress from the inner surface to the outer surface of the shell wall must be considered.

Table 3 presents formulas for calculating the stresses in two common thick-walled cylinders. In the first condition, the internal pressure parallel to the structural (longitudinal) axis is balanced by the external force against the moving piston and by the resistance of the cylinder's support, and the resultant longitudinal stress (σ_{m_p}) is zero. In the second condition, there is a longitudinal stress (σ_{m_p}).

TABLE 3 - STRESSES IN THICK-WALL CYLINDERS

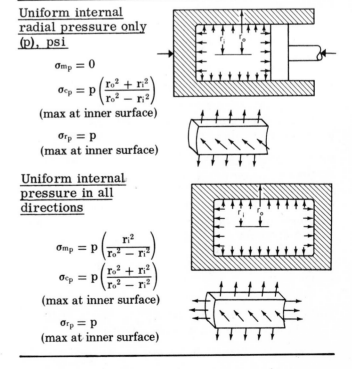

Uniform internal radial pressure only (p), psi

$\sigma_{m_p} = 0$

$\sigma_{c_p} = p\left(\dfrac{r_o^2 + r_i^2}{r_o^2 - r_i^2}\right)$
(max at inner surface)

$\sigma_{r_p} = p$
(max at inner surface)

Uniform internal pressure in all directions

$\sigma_{m_p} = p\left(\dfrac{r_i^2}{r_o^2 - r_i^2}\right)$

$\sigma_{c_p} = p\left(\dfrac{r_o^2 + r_i^2}{r_o^2 - r_i^2}\right)$
(max at inner surface)

$\sigma_{r_p} = p$
(max at inner surface)

UNFIRED PRESSURE VESSELS

6. ASME CODE - SECTION 8

Any pressure container of any importance undoubtedly must conform to the minimum requirements of the ASME, so it would be well to use ASME Section 8 "Unfired Pressure Vessels" as a guide. In general this covers containers for pressures exceeding 15 psi up to a maximum of 3,000 psi, and having a diameter exceeding 6".

Table 4 presents the formulas for calculating the minimum required wall thickness of cylindrical

shells and spherical shells, where:

p = internal pressure, psi

σ_a = allowable stress (See ASME Sec. 8, par USC-23)

E = joint efficiency (See ASME Sec. 8, par UW-12)

Table 5 presents the formulas for calculating the minimum required thickness of various types of heads. Turn to next page for Table 5.

TABLE 4 – WALL THICKNESS OF SHELLS
Subjected to Internal Pressure (p), psi
(ASME-8: Unfired Pressure Vessels)

CYLINDRICAL SHELLS (UG-27c and UA-1)	SPHERICAL SHELL (UG-27d and UA-3)
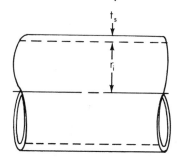	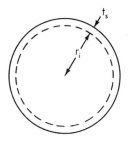
Thin shell — when $t_s < \frac{1}{2} r_i$ and $p < .385 \, \sigma_a E$ $t_s = \dfrac{p \, r_i}{\sigma_a E - .6 \, p}$	Thin shell — when $t_s < .356 \, r_i$ and $p < .665 \, \sigma_a E$ $t_s = \dfrac{p \, r_i}{2 \, (\sigma_a E - .1 \, p)}$
Thick shell — when $t_s > \frac{1}{2} r_i$ and $p > .385 \, \sigma_a E$ $t_s = r_i \, (\sqrt{Z} - 1)$ where $Z = \dfrac{\sigma_a E + p}{\sigma_a Z - p}$	Thick shell — when $t_s > .356 \, r_i$ and $p > .665 \, \sigma_a E$ $t_s = r_i \, (\sqrt[3]{Y} - 1)$ where $Y = \dfrac{2 \, (\sigma_a E + p)}{2 \, \sigma_a E - p}$

OTHER CONTAINERS

7. NON-CRITICAL CONTAINERS

Many containers are not critical from the standpoint of withstanding pressurized gases or of holding fluids without leakage. They may be designed to hold discrete objects which have considerable weight but exert low side pressure. Some of these containers are included in Figure 5, "Design Ideas."

8. SIMILAR STRUCTURES

Some structures are similar to conventional cylinders, but other conditions may require primary design consideration. One example follows:

> Problem 2

Determine the size and amount of plug welding necessary to hold a ½" thick steel liner to the ⅞" thick steel shell of a dryer, or kiln, Figure 6. The drum is 96" mean diameter and is fired from the outside. Under normal conditions the outer shell is at 850°F and the inner liner is at 750°F.

At 800°F (average temperature of the two), the coefficient of thermal expansion of the steel is 7.95×10^{-6} in./in./°F. The modulus of elasticity at this level is $E = 18.7 \times 10^6$ psi. Assume Poisson's ratio, $\nu = .3$

If liner and shell are free to move independently

Problem 2 continued on page 10

TABLE 5 - THICKNESS OF FORMED HEADS
Subjected to Internal Pressure (p) on Concave Side
(ASME-8: Unfired Pressure Vessels)

ELLIPSOIDAL HEAD
(UG-32d and UA-4c)

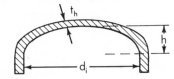

Standard head — where $h = d_i/4$

(h = minor axis: inside depth of head minus skirt)

$$t_h = \frac{p \, d_i}{2(\sigma_a E - .1 \, p)}$$

Head of other proportions

$$t_h = \frac{p \, d_i \, K}{2(\sigma_a E - .1 \, p)}$$

where:

$$K = \frac{1}{6}\left[2 + \left(\frac{d_i}{2h}\right)^2\right]$$

TORISPHERICAL HEAD
(UG-32e and UA-4d)

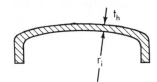

Standard head — where $r_k = .06 \, r_i$

(r_k = knuckle radius)

$$t_h = \frac{.885 \, p \, r_i}{\sigma_a E - .1 \, p}$$

Head of other proportions

$$t_h = \frac{p \, r_i \, M}{2(\sigma_a E - .1 \, p)}$$

where:

$$M = \frac{1}{4}\left[3 + \sqrt{\frac{r_i}{r_k}}\right]$$

HEMISPHERICAL HEAD
(UG-32f and UA-3)

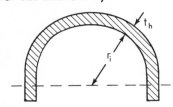

Thin head — when $t_h < .356 \, r_i$
and $p < .665 \, \sigma_a E$

$$t_h = \frac{p \, r_i}{2(\sigma_a E - .1 \, p)}$$

Thick head — when $t_h > .356 \, r_i$
and $p > .665 \, \sigma_a E$

$$t_h = r_i\left(\sqrt[3]{Y} - 1\right)$$

where:

$$Y = \frac{2(\sigma_a E + p)}{2 \, \sigma_a E - p}$$

FLAT HEAD (UG-34)

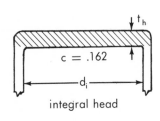

$c = .162$

integral head

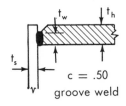

$c = .30$
lap weld

$r_{min} = 3 \, t_s$

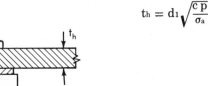

$c = .50$
groove weld

t_w = twice required thickness of spherical shell or $1.25 \, t_s$ and not greater than t_h

$$t_h = d_1\sqrt{\frac{c \, p}{\sigma_a}}$$

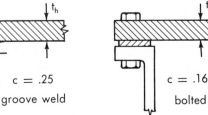

$c = .25$
groove weld

$c = .162$
bolted

FIG. 5 DESIGN IDEAS FOR WELDED SHEET METAL CONTAINERS

.. Problem 2 continued

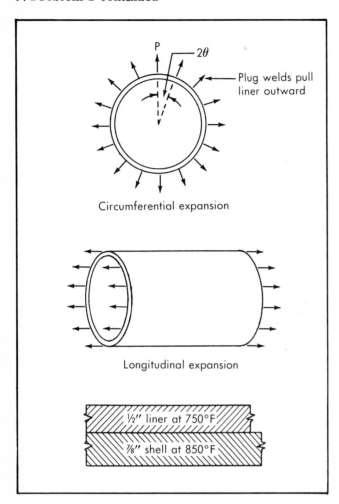

FIGURE 6

of each other, the difference in expansion of liner and shell is as represented in Figure 7.

But the liner and shell are attached, and must move together, as in Figure 8, and the effective movement would be at some intermediate point 2.

Poisson's Ratio

This is the ratio of circumferential (lateral) unit strain to longitudinal (meridian) unit strain, under the condition of uniform and uniaxial longitudinal stress within the proportional limit, Figure 9.

where:

under stress σ_c	under stress σ_L
$\dfrac{\varepsilon_2}{\varepsilon_1} = \nu = .3$	$\dfrac{\varepsilon_4}{\varepsilon_3} = \nu = .3$
$E = \dfrac{\sigma_c}{\varepsilon_1}$	$E = \dfrac{\sigma_L}{\varepsilon_3}$
$\therefore \varepsilon_1 = \dfrac{\sigma_c}{E}$	$\therefore \varepsilon_3 = \dfrac{\sigma_L}{E}$

Longitudinal stress (σ_L) as used here is equivalent to the meridian stress (σ_m) discussed previously.

Circumferential (lateral) strain is —

$$\varepsilon_c = \varepsilon_1 - \varepsilon_4 = \frac{\sigma_c}{E} - \nu \frac{\sigma_L}{E} \quad \dotfill (1)$$

and from this formula, the corresponding stress is —

$$\sigma_c = E\,\varepsilon_c + \nu\,\sigma_L \quad \dotfill (2)$$

Longitudinal strain is —

$$\varepsilon_L = \varepsilon_3 - \varepsilon_2 = \frac{\sigma_L}{E} - \nu \frac{\sigma_c}{E} \quad \dotfill (3)$$

and from this formula, the corresponding stress is —

$$\sigma_L = E\,\varepsilon_L + \nu\,\sigma_c \quad \dotfill (4)$$

From these, the following are derived:

$$\sigma_L = E\,\varepsilon_L + \nu\,(E\,\varepsilon_c + \nu\,\sigma_L)$$
$$= E\,\varepsilon_L + \nu\,E\,\varepsilon_c + \nu^2\,\sigma_L$$

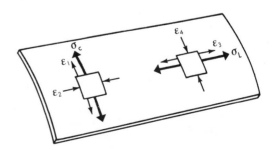

$7.95 \times 10^{-6} \times 100^{\circ}F = 7.95 \times 10^{-4}$ in./in.

FIGURE 7

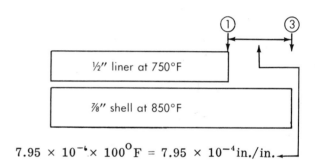

FIGURE 8

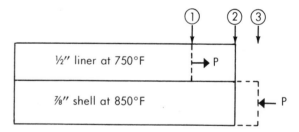

FIGURE 9

$$\therefore \boxed{\sigma_L = \frac{E(\varepsilon_L + \nu \varepsilon_c)}{1 - \nu^2}} \quad \dots\dots\dots\dots\dots (5)$$

$$\sigma_c = E \varepsilon_c + \frac{\nu E(\varepsilon_L + \nu \varepsilon_c)}{1 - \nu^2} \text{ or}$$

$$\therefore \boxed{\sigma_c = \frac{E(\varepsilon_c + \nu \varepsilon_L)}{1 - \nu^2}} \quad \dots\dots\dots\dots\dots (6)$$

In the present problem of expansion and contraction in both directions —

$$\varepsilon_c = \varepsilon_L = \varepsilon$$

$$\therefore \quad \sigma_L = \sigma_c = \frac{E \varepsilon (1 + \nu)}{1 - \nu^2} \text{ or}$$

$$= 1.43 \, E \varepsilon$$

Forces Resulting from Thermal Changes

Assuming a 1″ wide strip, the forces in liner and shell, if each is pulled in or out with a strain of 7.95×10^{-4} in./in. are as follows:

½″ liner:

$$\sigma_a = 1.43 \, E \varepsilon$$
$$= 1.43 \, (18.7 \times 10^6)(7.95 \times 10^{-4})$$
$$= 21{,}250 \text{ psi, and}$$

$$P_a = A_a \, \sigma_a$$
$$= (\tfrac{1}{2}'' \times 1'') \, 21{,}250 \text{ psi}$$
$$= 10{,}625 \text{ lbs (on 1″ wide strip)}$$

⅞″ shell:

$$\sigma_b = \sigma_a = 21{,}250 \text{ psi, and}$$

$$P_b = A_b \, \sigma_b$$
$$= (\tfrac{7}{8}'' \times 1'') \, 21{,}250 \text{ psi}$$
$$= 18{,}600 \text{ lbs (on 1″ wide strip)}$$

Diagram-Expansion and Forces

Points 1 and 3 from Figure 8 are diagrammed with the known expansion and forces P_a and P_b in order to locate the final position (point 2) of liner and shell when attached, Figure 10.

From similar triangles —

$(\alpha) \quad \dfrac{P}{x} = \dfrac{10{,}625}{7.95 \times 10^{-4}} \qquad$ or $\quad x = \dfrac{7.95 \times 10^{-4} \, P}{10{,}625}$

$(\beta) \quad \dfrac{P}{y} = \dfrac{18{,}600}{7.95 \times 10^{-4}} \qquad$ or $\quad y = \dfrac{7.95 \times 10^{-4} \, P}{18{,}600}$

$(\gamma) \quad$ and $x + y = 7.95 \times 10^{-4} \quad$ or $\quad y = 7.95 \times 10^{-4} - x$

Therefore:

(β) and $(\gamma) \quad y = \dfrac{7.95 \times 10^{-4} \, P}{18{,}600} = 7.95 \times 10^{-4} - x$

or $7.95 \times 10^{-4} \, P = 14.8 - 18{,}600 \, x$

or $18{,}600 \, x = 14.8 - 7.95 \times 10^{-4} \, P$

$$\therefore \quad x = \frac{14.8 - 7.95 \times 10^{-4} \, P}{18{,}600} = \frac{7.95 \times 10^{-4} \, P}{10{,}625}$$

or $(14.8)(10{,}625) - (7.95 \times 10^{-4})(10{,}625) \, P$
$$= (18{,}600)(7.95 \times 10^{-4}) \, P$$

$$\therefore \quad P = \frac{(14.8)(10{,}625)}{(7.95 \times 10^{-4})(18{,}600 + 10{,}625)}$$
$$= 6{,}760 \text{ lbs}$$

This could have been measured graphically from Figure 10 to avoid the above work.

And, the tensile (axial) stresses resulting are —

$$\sigma_a = \frac{P}{A_a} = \frac{6{,}760}{\tfrac{1}{2}'' \times 1''}$$
$$= \underline{13{,}520 \text{ psi}} \text{ (liner)}$$

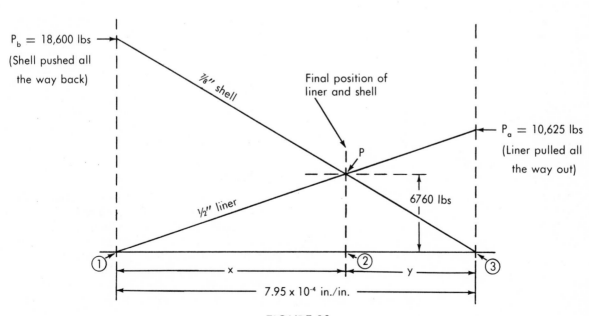

$P_b = 18{,}600$ lbs

(Shell pushed all the way back)

⅞″ shell

½″ liner

Final position of liner and shell

P

6760 lbs

$P_a = 10{,}625$ lbs

(Liner pulled all the way out)

① x ② y ③

7.95×10^{-4} in./in.

FIGURE 10

$$\sigma_b = \frac{P}{A_b} = \frac{6,760}{\frac{7}{8}'' \times 1''}$$

$$= 7,730 \text{ psi (shell)}$$

Stress in Plug Weld

The equivalent internal pressure (p) necessary to cause this stress in the liner is--

$$\sigma = \frac{p\,r}{t} \text{ or } p = \frac{\sigma\,t}{r} = \frac{(13,520)\,(\frac{1}{2})}{48}$$

$$= 141 \text{ psi}$$

If the plug welds are 4" apart —

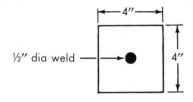

½" dia weld

FIGURE 11

$$P_{\text{plug weld}} = (4'' \times 4'')\,141$$

$$= 2256 \text{ lbs, or round it off to 2260 lbs}$$

The resultant tensile stress in each ½" dia plug weld is —

$$\sigma = \frac{P}{A} = \frac{2260}{\pi\,\dfrac{d^2}{4}} = \frac{2260}{\pi\,\dfrac{(\frac{1}{2})^2}{4}}$$

$$= \underline{11,500 \text{ psi}} \qquad \text{OK}$$

Treat a 4" width of this liner as a ring and determine the bending stresses due to the concentrated forces (P) applied by the plug welds at 4" circumferential intervals.

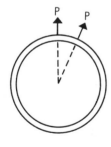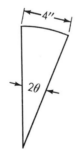

FIGURE 12

where:

$$2\,\theta = \left(\frac{4''}{\pi\,96''}\right)360°$$

$$= 4.774°$$

$$\theta = 2°\,23' = .041667 \text{ radians}$$

$$\cot\theta = 23.9861$$

Section modulus of ½" × 4" ring —

$$S = \frac{(4'')\,(\frac{1}{2}'')^2}{6} = \frac{1}{6}\,\text{in.}^3$$

Bending moment in ring —

> Roark "Formulas for Stress and Strain"
> II Ed., p 154, No. 9

$$M = \frac{P\,r}{2}\left(\frac{1}{\theta} - \cot\theta\right)$$

$$= \frac{(2260)\,(48'')}{2}\left(\frac{1}{.041667} - 23.9861\right)$$

$$= 754 \text{ in.-lbs}$$

Bending (tensile) stress in ring of liner —

$$\sigma = \frac{M}{S} = \frac{764}{\frac{1}{6}}$$

$$= 4,524 \text{ psi}$$

Tensile (axial) stress found previously in liner —

$$\sigma_a = 13,520 \text{ psi}$$

∴ Total tensile stress in the ½" liner is —

$$\sigma_{\text{total}} = \underline{18,044 \text{ psi}} \qquad \text{OK}$$

Alternatives

Although the work is not shown here, if the liner were decreased in thickness to ¼", the force (P) would be decreased to 4,125 lbs/in. Because of the thinner liner, the tensile stress in the liner (σ_a) would increase to 16,500 psi, and that in the shell (σ_b) would decrease to 4,720 psi. Using plug welds on 4" centers, the pull per weld would be decreased to 1,375 lbs. The bending stress in the liner due to these concentrated forces would increase to 11,020 psi, giving a total tensile stress in the liner of 27,520 psi.

As the distance between plug welds increases, the bending moment in the liner as well as the shell will increase. Using the original ½" thick liner, but increasing the distance between plug welds to 5" would increase the bending stress in the liner to 7,070 psi, and would result in a total tensile stress in the liner of 20,590 psi as against 18,044 psi when the welds were spaced at 4".

End Welds

We are concerned with movement in two directions, longitudinal and circumferential. The circumferential has already been discussed; the plug welds taking care of these forces. The longitudinal pull must be carried by transverse fillet welds at both ends of the liner. In the case of the ½" liner, these end welds must transfer a force of 6760 lbs/linear inch. This force in turn stresses the ½" liner to 13,520 psi which is required in order to elastically strain or elongate it along with the hotter and more rigid shell.

Based upon AWS, a ½" fillet weld has an allowable of 4800 lbs/linear inch. It is known that this same fillet weld when loaded transversely is ⅓ stronger. This would give us 1⅓ × 4800, or 6400 lbs/in. which is slightly less than the 6760 lbs/in. load. This means the fillet weld should not be the conventional 45° flat fillet, but must be very convex, maintaining a throat equivalent to the ½" thickness of the plate for a short distance and then gradually sloping down. See Figure 13.

As long as these two end connecting welds hold, the longitudinal tensile stress on the liner will be maintained throughout the length of the liner, and the plug welds will not contribute in any way to this transfer of force. In other words, the plug welds will be stressed only in tension, this tension result-

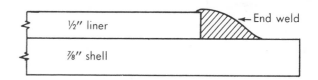

FIGURE 13

ing from forcing the liner to expand along its diameter or circumference.

We have considered the condition at the higher temperature level which occurs during the operation of the kiln. The lower temperature levels must also be checked. Undoubtedly there will be less difference in temperature between the liner and shell at the lower temperatures, but this advantage will be offset because the modulus of elasticity (E) will be higher.

Welded hopper costs less than bolted design. Stiffeners require minimum welding, thus the skip welds shown here are adequate.

Piggyback-trailer unloader presents some interesting framing problems. Welded steel construction is used extensively to eliminate points of high stress concentration, to transfer forces more uniformly, and to achieve maximum economy while meeting functional objectives.

The Design of Hangers and Supports For Shells and Similar Sections

1. BASIC FORCES AND STRESSES

Designing hangers or brackets for supporting a shell such as a pipe, tank or pressure vessel requires consideration of two important factors:

1. The additional stress of the support forces when combined with the working stress of the shell must not increase the stress in the shell above the allowable limit.

2. The support should not restrain the stressed shell so it becomes too rigid to flex under normal changes in working pressures or loads.

Many types of stresses are involved in any supporting structure. The more common types are the following:

1. The internal pressure of the gas or liquid in the shell, along with its weight, cause tangential (σ_{c_p}) and longitudinal (σ_{m_p}) tensile stresses in the shell.

2. Any radial force (F_1) acting on a section of the shell causes bending stresses in the ring of the shell (from the bending moment M_r) as well as axial tensile stresses (from the tensile force T), both of which act tengentially to the circumference of the shell.

3. The radial force (F_1) causes radial shear stresses in the shell, and the longitudinal force (F_2) causes longitudinal shear stresses, both adjacent to the hanger. These stresses usually will be low.

After proper analysis of the forces involved, the various stresses must be combined to determine the maximum normal stress (σ_{max} --tensile or compressive) and maximum shear stress (τ_{max}). If the resulting stresses are excessive, a simple study of the individual stresses will indicate what portion of the hanger is under-designed and should be strengthened.

For example, the bending stresses may be excessive, indicating that some type of stiffener ring should be attached to the shell between supports to substantially increase the moment of inertia of the shell section thereby decreasing the bending stress.

The following discussions identify and analyze the effect of various basic stresses and relate them to material thickness and curvature.

2. STRESSES IN SHELL FROM INTERNAL PRESSURE

As explained more fully in Sect. 4.6, internal pressure in a shell produces two tensile stresses of importance.

1. σ_{m_p} = tensile stress in the direction of the meridian. This is called the longitudinal stress.

2. σ_{c_p} = tensile stress in the direction of the tangent to the circumference. This stress is commonly called the hoop stress, but is also referred to as the tangential or circumferential stress.

THIN WALL CONTAINERS		
CONTAINER SHAPE	UNIT WALL SEGMENT	TENSILE STRESS FORMULAE
CYLINDER		$\sigma_{m_p} = \dfrac{p\, r_c}{2\, t_s}$ $\sigma_{c_p} = \dfrac{p\, r_c}{t_s}$
SPHERE		$\sigma_{m_p} = \sigma_{c_p} = \dfrac{p\, r_c}{2\, t_s}$
ANY FIGURE OF REVOLUTION		$\dfrac{\sigma_{c_p}}{r_c} + \dfrac{\sigma_m}{r_m} = \dfrac{p}{t_s}$ $\sigma_{m_p} = \dfrac{p\, r_c}{2\, t_s}$ $\sigma_{c_p} = \dfrac{p\, r_c}{t_s}\left(1 - \dfrac{r_c}{2\, r_m}\right)$
CONE		$\sigma_{m_p} = \dfrac{p\, r_c}{2\, t_s \cos\alpha}$ $\sigma_{c_p} = \dfrac{p\, r_c}{t_s \cos\alpha}$

1

The tensile stresses σ_{m_p} and σ_{c_p} can be calculated with the formulas presented in Table 2 of the preceding Section 4.6 and repeated here.

3. EFFECT OF HANGER OR SUPPORT WELDED TO SHELL

The force (P) applied to the hanger (see Figure 1) may be resolved into a radial component (F_1) and a longitudinal component (F_2) having the following values:

$$F_1 = P \cos \theta$$
$$F_2 = P \sin \theta$$

where θ is the angle between guy cable or support attached to the shell and the horizontal.

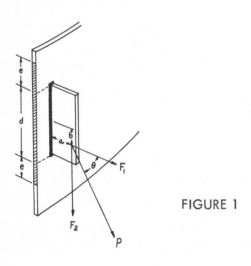

FIGURE 1

If these components are applied at some eccentricity (a and b), they will produce moments applied to the shell section by the hanger and having values:

$$M_1 = b F_1$$
$$M_2 = a F_2$$

Combining these values, observing proper signs, will give the total moment acting on the shell from the hanger:

$$M_h = M_1 + M_2$$

A study of stress distribution in the shell can be resolved into separate analyses of the radial and moment force distributions. Before analyzing these forces, however, the engineer should determine how much shell beyond the hanger is effective in resisting these forces.

The shell with stiffeners can be compared to a curved beam with an extremely wide flange, Figure 1. Von Karman* suggests that an effective

* "Analysis of Some Thin-Walled Structures", Von Karman, ASME paper AER-55-19C, Aer Eng, Vol. 5, No. 4, 1933.

RADIAL FORCE (f_a) DISTRIBUTION

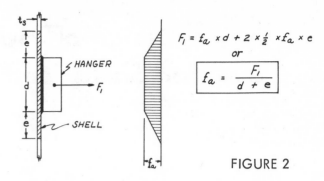

$$F_1 = f_a \times d + 2 \times \tfrac{1}{2} \times f_a \times e$$
or
$$\boxed{f_a = \frac{F_1}{d + e}}$$

FIGURE 2

width (e) of the flange on each side of the stiffening web is approximately--

$$\boxed{e = \frac{\sqrt{t_s\, r_c}}{2}}$$

where:

r_c = radius of shell curvature, inches

t_s = thickness of shell, inches

The value of "e" should be limited to a maximum of $12 t_s$.

The radial component (F_1) of the force (P) is applied directly to the shell. It is reasonable to assume that the radial forces applied to the additional shell width (e) would decrease linearly to almost zero at its outer limits. This assumed distribution of radial forces (f_a) due to the radial component (F_1) is sketched in Figure 2.

The value of f_a is equivalent to the force (lbs) on a 1" wide ring of the shell.

The longitudinal component (F_2) of the force (P) because of its eccentricity (a), and the radial component (F_1) because of its eccentricity (b), combine into moment M_h and apply radial forces to the shell having a distribution similar to that of bending forces, i.e. maximum at the outer fibers and zero along the neutral axis. The assumed distribution of the radial forces (f_b) due to the action of the applied moment is indicated in Figure 3.

RADIAL FORCE (f_b) DISTRIBUTION

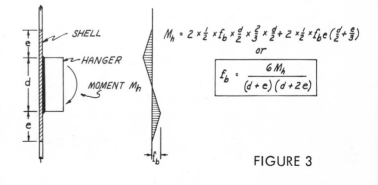

$$M_h = 2 \times \tfrac{1}{2} \times f_b \times \tfrac{d}{2} \times \tfrac{2}{3} \times \tfrac{d}{2} + 2 \times \tfrac{1}{2} \times f_b\, e \left(\tfrac{d}{2} + \tfrac{e}{3}\right)$$
or
$$\boxed{f_b = \frac{6 M_h}{(d + e)(d + 2e)}}$$

FIGURE 3

The value of f_b is equivalent to the force (lbs) on a 1" wide ring of the shell.

The resulting radial forces applied on the shell must be added, being careful to watch the signs:

$$f_1 = f_a + f_b$$

4. EFFECT OF ADDING STIFFENING RING TO SHELL

For additional stiffening of the shell at the support, rings may be welded to the shell. As before, the additional width of the shell on each side of the ring assumed to be effective in resisting these forces is--

$$e = \frac{\sqrt{t_s r_c}}{2}$$

with e not to exceed $12\, t_s$ on each side of the supporting ring.

The total radial force (F) applied to this built-up section is the radial force resulting from the longitudinal force (F_2), plus any radial force (F_1) applied at this point of support:

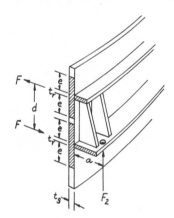

$$F = \frac{F_2 a}{d} + F_1$$

IN THIS CASE SINCE $F_1 = 0$

$$F = \frac{F_2 a}{d}$$

FIGURE 4

After determining the bending moment in this built-up ring resulting from the radial forces at the point of support, the moment of inertia (I) of this section is calculated. The bending stresses are then found and later combined with any other stresses.

5. EFFECT OF THESE FORCES UPON A SECTIONAL RING OF THE SHELL

Forces (f_1) normal to the shell set up tangential tensile forces (T) and bending moments (M_r) in the ring of the shell, Figure 5.

Stresses σ_{ct} and σ_{cb} are added to σ_{cp} to give $\sigma_c =$ total tangential (or circumferential) stress in a section of the critical shell ring.

The maximum shear stress is equal to ½ the difference of the two principal stresses (σ) having the greatest algebraic difference. See Sect. 2.7, Topic 2.

The following are typical examples that demonstrate the use of these formulas for calculating the stresses in a shell.

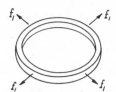

FIGURE 5

NOTE: FOR I INCH WIDE RING RADIAL FORCES ARE f_1; WHEN SECTION IS BUILT UP AS ILLUSTRATED IN PREVIOUS SKETCH, RADIAL FORCES ARE F.

THESE FORCES AND MOMENTS CAN BE TABULATED FOR VARIOUS SUPPORT CONFIGURATIONS:

TABLE I				
	FORMULA FOR TANGENTIAL TENSILE FORCE $T = K_1 f_1$		FORMULA FOR BENDING MOMENT M_r in ring $M_r = K_2 f_1 r_c$	
	VALUES FOR K_1		VALUES FOR K_2	
NUMBER OF HANGERS	AT HANGERS	HALFWAY BETWEEN HANGERS	AT HANGERS	HALFWAY BETWEEN HANGERS
2	0	0.500	+ 0.318	− 0.182
3	0.289	0.577	+ 0.188	− 0.100
4	0.500	0.707	+ 0.136	− 0.071
6	0.866	1.000	+ 0.089	− 0.045
8	1.207	1.306	+ 0.065	− 0.033
	RESULTING TENSILE STRESS $\sigma_{c_t} = \dfrac{T}{A}$		RESULTING BENDING STRESS $\sigma_{c_b} = \dfrac{M_r}{S}$	

where:

A = area of shell ring cross-section or built-up section

S = section modulus of the same section.

Problem 1

PART A: Four hangers are used for guying a smoke stack with its axis in the vertical position, Figure 6. Determine the total radial force acting on the shell as a result of the force (P) applied to the hangers.

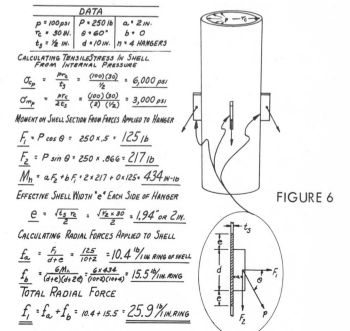

DATA		
p = 100 psi	P = 250 lb	a = 2 IN.
r_c = 30 IN.	θ = 60°	b = 0
t_s = ½ IN.	d = 10 IN.	n = 4 HANGERS

CALCULATING TENSILE STRESS IN SHELL FROM INTERNAL PRESSURE

$$\sigma_{c_p} = \frac{p r_c}{t_s} = \frac{(100)(30)}{\frac{1}{2}} = 6{,}000\ psi$$

$$\sigma_{m_p} = \frac{p r_c}{2 t_s} = \frac{(100)(30)}{(2)(\frac{1}{2})} = 3{,}000\ psi$$

MOMENT ON SHELL SECTION FROM FORCES APPLIED TO HANGER

$$F_1 = P \cos\theta = 250 \times .5 = \underline{125\ lb}$$

$$F_2 = P \sin\theta = 250 \times .866 = \underline{217\ lb}$$

$$M_h = aF_2 + bF_1 = 2 \times 217 + 0 \times 125 = \underline{434\ IN.-lb}$$

EFFECTIVE SHELL WIDTH "e" EACH SIDE OF HANGER

$$e = \frac{\sqrt{t_s r_c}}{2} = \frac{\sqrt{\frac{1}{2} \times 30}}{2} = \underline{1.94"\ or\ 2\,IN.}$$

CALCULATING RADIAL FORCES APPLIED TO SHELL

$$f_a = \frac{F_1}{d+e} = \frac{125}{10+2} = \underline{10.4\ \tfrac{lb}{IN.\ RING\ OF\ SHELL}}$$

$$f_b = \frac{6 M_h}{(d+e)(d+2e)} = \frac{6 \times 434}{(10+2)(10+4)} = \underline{15.5\ \tfrac{lb}{IN.\ RING}}$$

TOTAL RADIAL FORCE

$$f_1 = f_a + f_b = 10.4 + 15.5 = \underline{25.9\ \tfrac{lb}{IN.\ RING}}$$

FIGURE 6

PART B: With tangential tensile force (T) and bending moment (M_r) per 1" wide ring of this shell resulting from radial forces (f_1) applied to the four hangers, calculate the tensile (σ_{ct}) and bending (σ_{cb}) stresses at the hangers.

FIGURE 7

FROM TABLE I
$K_1 = 0.500$

FROM PART A
$f_1 = 25.9$ lb/in. ring

$$\underline{T = K_1 f_1 = .500 \times 25.9 = \underline{13} \text{ lb/1 in. ring}}$$

$$\underline{A \text{ (AREA OF 1" RING)} = W t_s = 1 \times 1\tfrac{1}{2} = \tfrac{1}{2} \text{ SQ. IN.}}$$

$$\sigma_{cT} = \frac{T}{A} = \frac{13}{\tfrac{1}{2}} = \underline{26 \text{ psi}} \text{ (SMALL CAN BE NEGLECTED)}$$

FROM TABLE I WE KNOW $M_r = K_2 f_1 r_c = .136 \times 26 \times 30 = \underline{106 \text{ IN.-lb.}}$

SECTION MODULUS $S = \dfrac{(1")(\tfrac{1}{2}")^2}{6} = \underline{\dfrac{1}{24} \text{ IN}^3}$

THEN $\underline{\sigma_{cb} = \dfrac{M_r}{S} = \dfrac{106}{\tfrac{1}{24}} = 2{,}544 \text{ psi}}$

Conclusion: Combining these stresses in the outer fiber of the shell adjacent to the hanger shows our analysis of the shear stress (τ_{max}) to be--

FIGURE 8

$\sigma_r = 0$
$\sigma_{mp} = 3{,}000 \text{ psi}$
$\sigma_c = \sigma_{cp} + \sigma_{cb} = 6{,}000 + 2{,}544 = 8{,}544 \text{ psi}$

THEN

$$\underline{\tau_{MAX} = \frac{8{,}544 - 0}{2} = 4{,}272 \text{ psi}}$$

STRESSES WITHIN REASON

DESIGN O.K.

Problem 2

PART A: Four hangers are used to support a vertical 12" stand pipe, Figure 9. Determine the total radial force acting on the shell as a result of the force (P) applied to the hangers.

DATA		
$p = 100$ psi	$P = 600$ lb.	$a = 5$ IN.
$r_c = 6.21$ IN.	$\theta = 90°$	$b = 0$
$t_s = .33$ IN.	$d = 3$ IN.	$n = 4$ HANGERS

CALCULATING TENSILE STRESS IN SHELL FROM INTERNAL PRESSURE

$\sigma_{cp} = \dfrac{p r_c}{t_s} = \dfrac{100 \times 6.21}{.33} = \underline{1{,}888 \text{ psi}}$

$\sigma_{mp} = \dfrac{p r_c}{2 t_s} = \dfrac{100 \times 6.21}{2 \times .33} = \underline{9.42 \text{ psi}}$

MOMENT ON SHELL SECTION FROM FORCES APPLIED TO HANGER

$F_1 = P \cos \theta = 600 \times 0 = \underline{0 \text{ lb.}}$

$F_2 = P \sin \theta = 600 \times 1 = \underline{600 \text{ lb.}}$

$M_h = a F_2 + b F_1 = 5 \times 600 + 0 \times 0 = \underline{3{,}000 \text{ lb.}}$

EFFECTIVE SHELL WIDTH "e" EACH SIDE OF HANGER

$\underline{e = \dfrac{\sqrt{t_s r_c}}{2} = \dfrac{\sqrt{.33 \times 6.21}}{2} = .72 \text{ IN.}}$

CALCULATING RADIAL FORCES APPLIED TO SHELL

$\underline{f_a = \dfrac{F_1}{d + e} = \dfrac{0}{3 + .72} = 0 \text{ lb/in. RING OF SHELL}}$

$\underline{f_b = \dfrac{6M}{(d+e)(d+2e)} = \dfrac{6 \times 3000}{(3+.72)(3+1.44)} = 1{,}090 \text{ lb/in. RING}}$

TOTAL RADIAL FORCE

$\underline{f_1 = f_a + f_b = 0 + 1{,}090 = 1{,}090 \text{ lb/in. RING OF SHELL}}$

FIGURE 9

PART B: With tensile force (T) and bending moment (M_r) per 1" wide ring of this shell resulting from radial forces (f_1) applied at the four hangers, calculate the tensile (σ_{ct}) and bending (σ_{cb}) stresses at the hangers.

FROM TABLE I
$K_1 = 0.500$

FROM PART A
$f_1 = 1{,}090$ lb/in. ring

$$\underline{T = K_1 f_1 = 0.500 \times 1{,}090 = \underline{545} \text{ lb/1 in. ring}}$$

$$\underline{A \text{ (AREA OF 1" RING)} = W t_s = 1 \times .33 = .33 \text{ SQ. IN.}}$$

$$\underline{\sigma_{cT} = \frac{T}{A} = \frac{545}{.33} = 1650 \text{ psi}}$$

FROM TABLE I WE KNOW $M_r = K_2 f_1 r_c = .136 \times 1{,}090 \times 6.21 = \underline{920 \text{ IN.-LB.}}$

SECTION MODULUS $S = \dfrac{(r')(.33)}{6} = .0181 \text{ IN}^3$

THEN $\underline{\sigma_{cb} = \dfrac{M_r}{S} = \dfrac{920}{.0181} = 50{,}800 \text{ psi} \text{ (EXCESSIVE)}}$

Since this bending stress in the ring of the shell is excessive, it is necessary to stiffen the shell in this region. To accomplish this, two ¼" × 2" ring stiffeners are added as illustrated, Figure 10.

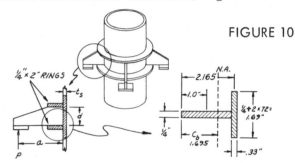

FIGURE 10

The effect of the bottom ring will be considered since it will apply radial tensile forces to the built-up ring and shell section. Using the method of finding moment of inertia by adding areas (Sect. 2.3), the properties of this section are as follows:

TABLE II					
RING SECTION	A	d	$M = Ad$	$I_x = Md$	I_g
$1.69 \times .33$	.557	+2.165	1.205	2.61	.005
$\tfrac{1}{4} \times 2.0$	.500	+1.0	.500	.50	.167
TOTAL	1.057		1.705	3.282	

THEN MOMENT OF INERTIA ABOUT NEUTRAL AXIS WILL BE

$$\underline{I_{NA} = I_x - \frac{M^2}{A} = 3.282 - \frac{1.705^2}{1.057} = 0.532 \text{ in.}^4}$$

AND NEUTRAL AXIS WILL BE

$$\underline{NA = C_b = \frac{M}{A} = \frac{1.705}{1.057} = +1.613 \text{ in.}}$$

The radial force (F) acting on the ring section and resulting from the vertical force (P) is--

$$\underline{F = \frac{F_2 a}{d} = \frac{600 \times 5}{3} = 1000 \text{ lb}}$$

FIGURE 11

PART C: Recalculation of the tensile (σ_{c_t}) and bending (σ_{c_b}) stresses at the hangers yields the following results:

FROM TABLE 1
$K_1 = 0.500$

THE NEW F
$F = 1,000$

$$T = K_1 F = 0.500 \times 1,000 = \underline{500\ lb.}$$

A (*TOTAL FROM TABLE 2*) $= \underline{1.057\ sq.in.}$

$$\sigma_{c_T} = \frac{T}{A} = \frac{500}{1.057} = \underline{473\ psi}$$

FROM TABLE 1 WE KNOW $M_r = K_2 F r_c = .136 \times 1,000 \times 6.21 = \underline{845\ in.-lb.}$

THEN $\sigma_{c_b} = \dfrac{M_r c}{I} = \dfrac{845 \times 1.695}{.532} = \underline{2,690\ psi}$

The hoop stress of $\sigma_{c_p} = 1,888$ psi in the shell will be assumed to be reduced when considered to be acting over the entire cross-section of the built-up ring section:

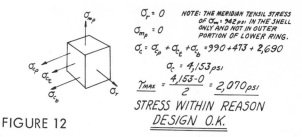

$\sigma_{c_p} = 1,888 \times \dfrac{\textit{AREA SHELL IN RING SECTION}}{\textit{AREA OF RING SECTION}}$

$\sigma_{c_p} = 1,888 \times \dfrac{1.69 \times .33}{1.057}$

$\sigma_{c_p} = \underline{990\ psi}$

Combining these stresses in the outer fiber of the lower ring, adjacent to the hanger, we find the maximum shear stress (τ_{max}) to be--

$\sigma_r = 0$
$\sigma_{m_p} = 0$

NOTE: THE MERIDIAN TENSIL STRESS OF $\sigma_m = 942$ PSI IN THE SHELL ONLY AND NOT IN OUTER PORTION OF LOWER RING.

$\sigma_c = \sigma_{c_p} + \sigma_{c_t} + \sigma_{c_b} = 990 + 473 + 2,690$

$\sigma_c = 4,153\ psi$

$\tau_{max} = \dfrac{4,153 - 0}{2} = 2,070\ psi$

STRESS WITHIN REASON
DESIGN O.K.

FIGURE 12

FIG. 13   TYPICAL HANGERS AND SUPPORTS

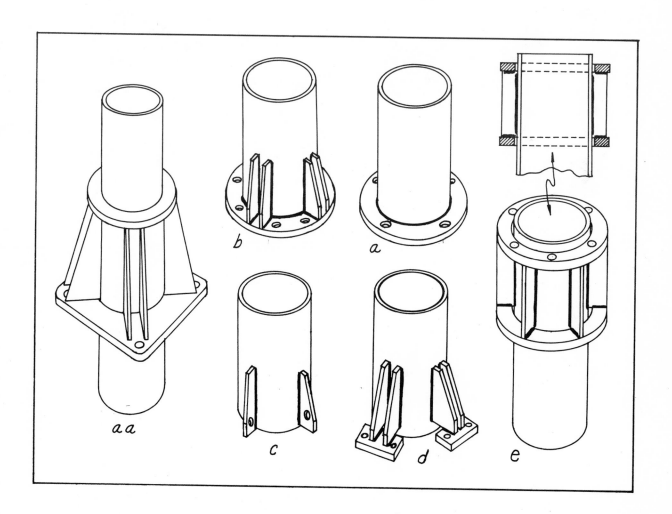

a a   *b*   *a*   *c*   *d*   *e*

Conversion of oil will service pump housing to all-welded high strength steel improved quality of material with higher physical properties, and achieved design flexibility, lower manufacturing costs, and lower weight.

How to Design Gear Housings

1. DESIGNING FOR GREATEST STRENGTH AND RIGIDITY

The cost of gear housings may be reduced as much as 50% by designing them for welded steel construction. These direct savings are possible because steel is 3 times stronger and 2 ½ times more rigid than gray cast iron. This means less material is required for a gear housing of required strength and rigidity. Where space or weight considerations are involved, it often means greater strength and rigidity than could otherwise be obtained. The result is a more compact, better looking, stronger gear housing at much less cost.

A 4-step sequence saves time and gives reliable results in designing a welded steel gear housing to meet the major design requirements:

1. Vertical stiffness of housing
2. Horizontal stiffness of housing
3. Torsional stiffness of housing
4. Compressive stiffness of housing

This procedure, plus the design freedom of welded steel fabrication, will result in the best service performance.

2. FORCES OF GEARING ON HOUSING

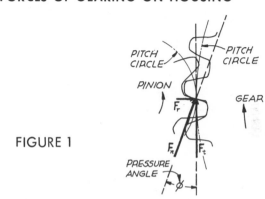

FIGURE 1

The load transmitted by plain spur gears is the normal pressure (F_n) between the contacting tooth surfaces, acting along the line of action normal to the tooth profile, Figure 1. This pressure gen-

FIG. 2 BASIC FORCES ON HOUSING FROM GEARING

The vertical reaction at the bearings caused by the weight of the shaft and the gears:

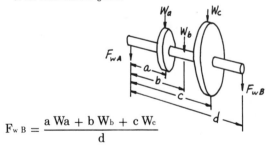

$$F_{wB} = \frac{a W_a + b W_b + c W_c}{d}$$

The horizontal reaction at the bearings caused by the radial force:

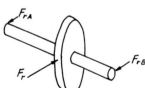

$$F_r = F_t \tan \phi$$
$$F_{rA} = F_{tA} \tan \phi$$
$$F_{rB} = F_{tB} \tan \phi$$

There is no end thrust from Herringbone gears since the end thrust from each half of the gear is equal and opposite in value to the other half:

The vertical reaction at the bearings caused by the tangential force:

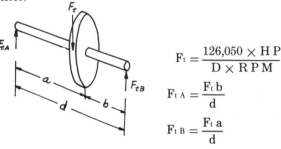

$$F_t = \frac{126,050 \times HP}{D \times RPM}$$
$$F_{tA} = \frac{F_t b}{d}$$
$$F_{tB} = \frac{F_t a}{d}$$

In the case of helical gears there is a side thrust applied at the pitch circle. This produces an end thrust on the shaft:

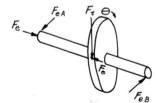

$$F_e = F_t \tan \theta$$

This also produces a couple on the bearing supports:

$$F_{eA} = F_{eB} = \frac{F_e D}{2 d}$$

erates several new forces on the tooth which are transmitted back to the bearings supporting the gear shaft, Figure 2. A more complete discussion of gear forces and gear design appears in Sect. 5.4.

A few of the symbols used in the design of gears and housings are--

HP = horse power transmitted

ϕ = pressure angle, usually $14\frac{1}{2}°$ or $20°$

D = pitch diameter of gear, inches

RPM = revolutions per minute of gear

θ = helix angle, if helical gear

a, b, c, etc. = positions of gears on shaft

A, B = points of force reaction

3. REQUIREMENTS OF HOUSING

Step 1: Vertical Stiffness of Housing

The cross-section of the housing must have sufficient moment of inertia (I_x) about the horizontal neutral axis to resist the bending moments of the vertical forces of the weights of the shaft and gears (F_w) and the tangential force of the gears (F_t) as well as the horizontal radial force of the gears (F_r).

Convert the horizontal radial forces into couples (C) by multiplying each force by the distance (y) from the point of its application to the neutral axis of the housing's side member.

Treat each vertical force and couple separately and use the nomograph, Figure 7, to find the required moment of inertia for each of these loads (I_n). See Sect. 2.9, Topic 9.

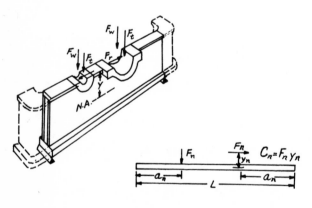

FIGURE 3

where, for the vertical force:

$$I_n = \frac{F_n L^2}{48 E\left(\frac{\Delta}{L}\right)} (3 K_n - 4 K_n^3) \qquad K_n = \frac{a_n}{L}$$

and for the couple:

$$I_n = \frac{C_n L}{16 E\left(\frac{\Delta}{L}\right)} (4 K_n^2 - 1) \qquad K_n = \frac{a_n}{L}$$

Total these values to get the required moment of inertia (I_x) for the side member of the housing.

Forces and couples are positive if they cause the side member to deflect downward under load. Positive forces and couples require positive moments of inertia.

Shear deflection is not investigated here in this discussion; but, in heavily loaded, short sections, this may be a factor and should be considered.

Step 2: Horizontal Stiffness of Housing

If the gears are of helical (but not herringbone) type, there is an end thrust on the shaft (F_e) causing a horizontal bending of the side member.

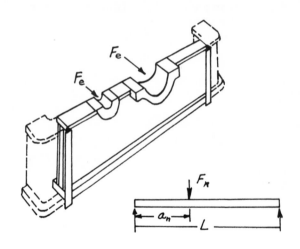

FIGURE 4

where:

$$I_n = \frac{F_n L^2}{48 E\left(\frac{\Delta}{L}\right)} (3 K_n - 4 K_n^3) \qquad K_n = \frac{a_n}{L}$$

The nomograph, Figure 7, can be used to find the individual moments of inertia to resist these side forces.

These values are totaled to give the required moment of inertia (I_y) of the side member about the vertical neutral axis.

Step 3: Torsional Stiffness of Housing

The end thrust of the shaft (F_e), if helical gears are used, acts at the level of the bearing and not at the horizontal neutral axis of the side member. This causes twisting of the side member, and the member must have sufficient torsional resistance for this twisting action.

The torque (T) of each section of the member is the product of this end thrust (F_e) and the distance (y) of the application of the force to the horizontal neutral axis of the member.

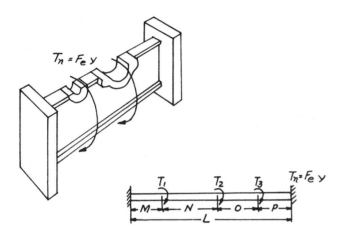

FIGURE 5

where:

$$T_M = \frac{T_1 (N + O + P) + T_2 (O + P) + T_3 (P)}{L}$$

$$T_N = \frac{- T_1 (M) + T_2 (O + P) + T_3 (P)}{L}$$

$$T_O = \frac{- T_1 (M) - T_2 (M + N) + T_3 (P)}{L}$$

$$T_P = \frac{- T_1 (M) - T_2 (M + N) - T_3 (M + N + O)}{L}.$$

Use these equations to find the resultant torques in the various parts of the member and design for the maximum value.

The required torsional resistance of the member is obtained from the following:

$$\theta = \frac{T}{E_s R}$$

or $R = \dfrac{T}{E_s \theta}$

where θ is the allowable unit angular twist, in radians per inch of length; one radian = 57.3 degrees. (Do not confuse with θ used in gear design for helix angle.)

Step 4: Compressive Stiffness of Housing

The section of the housing directly below the bearing must be treated as a column and have sufficient stiffness to carry the weight of the shaft and gears (F_w) as well as the tangential force (F_t). When the side of the housing is made of a single vertical web plate, additional stiffeners or brackets may have to be used directly below the bearing for proper support.

FIGURE 6

The bearing support must have sufficient width to receive the bearing.

4. MOMENT OF INERTIA NOMOGRAPH AND FORMULAS

Use the nomograph, Figure 7, to find the required moments of inertia (I_x) of the side member for each vertical force (P) (caused by the weights of the shaft and gears as well as the tangential force of the gear) and the couple (C) (caused by the radial force of the gear). These values are obtained from Step 1.

Positive forces and moments give positive moments of inertia, and negative values give negative moments of inertia. Total these values to get the required (I_x) for the side member.

Use this nomograph to get similar values of moments of inertia (I_y) resulting from the horizontal end thrust of the helical gears found in Step 2.

For more accurate values, the two formulas of the nomograph have been simplified into the following formulas. For any given value of K where K = a/L, the constant (A) or (B) is found in Table 1. When a force is applied to the member, use the value of A and substitute into the first formula. When a couple is applied to the member, use the value of B and substitute into the second formula.

(1) $\quad I_n = \dfrac{F_n L^2 A}{\left(\dfrac{\Delta}{L}\right)} \quad$ (force P_n)

(2) $\quad I_n = \dfrac{C_n L B}{\left(\dfrac{\Delta}{L}\right)} \quad$ (couple C_n)

FIG. 7   MOMENT OF INERTIA REQUIRED OF SIDE MEMBER OF HOUSING
(For Each Load and Couple)

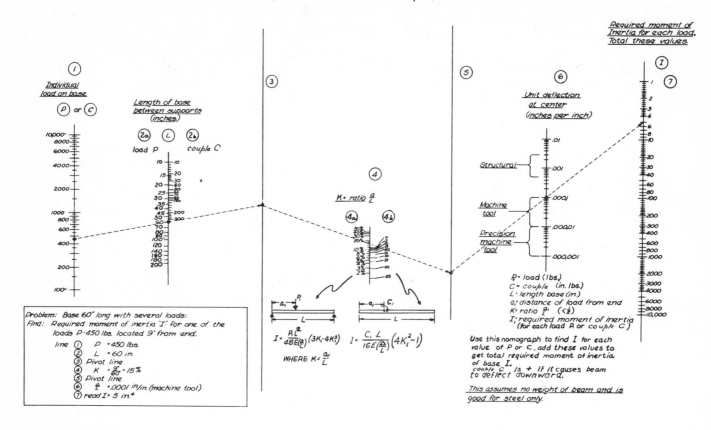

TABLE 1 – CONSTANTS FOR USE IN SIMPLIFIED FORMULAS
(For Finding Moment of Inertia)

K	A	B	K	A	B	K	A	B
0	0	2.083×10^{-9}	.17	3.045×10^{-10}	1.842×10^{-9}	.34	5.002×10^{-10}	1.120×10^{-9}
.01	$.2083 \times 10^{-10}$	2.083	.18	3.588	1.813	.35	6.101	1.063
.02	.4166	2.080	.19	3.768	1.783	.36	6.204	1.003
.03	.6243	2.076	.20	3.944	1.750	.37	6.301	.9425
.04	.8312	2.070	.21	4.118	1.715	.38	6.392	.8900
.05	1.038	2.063	.22	4.268	1.680	.39	6.477	.8158
.06	1.244	2.053	.23	4.453	1.642	.40	6.556	.7500
.07	1.449	2.043	.24	4.616	1.603	.41	6.627	.6825
.08	1.653	2.030	.25	4.774	1.563	.42	6.692	.6133
.09	1.855	2.016	.26	4.928	1.520	.43	6.750	.5425
.10	2.056	2.000	.27	5.079	1.476	.44	6.801	.4700
.11	2.355	1.983	.28	5.224	1.430	.45	6.844	.3958
.12	2.452	1.963	.29	5.364	1.381	.46	6.880	.3221
.13	2.647	1.942	.30	5.500	1.333	.47	6.898	.2425
.14	2.847	1.920	.31	5.631	1.282	.48	6.928	.1633
.15	3.031	1.896	.32	5.756	1.209	.49	6.940	.0825
.16	3.219	1.870	.33	5.876	1.176	.50	7.000	0

Problem 1

Design a welded steel housing for this helical gear reduction unit, Figure 8, driven by a 50-HP motor. Hold to a unit deflection of .00001 in/in. Pressure angle $\phi = 20°$. Helix angle $\theta = 30°$.

Gear   450 RPM counter-clockwise
         24" pitch diameter
         gear wt. 512 lbs
         shaft wt. 114 lbs

Pinion   1800 RPM clockwise
         6" pitch diameter
         pinion wt. 32 lbs
         shaft wt. 52 lbs

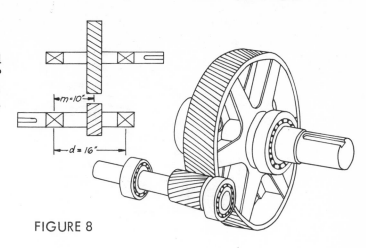

FIGURE 8

	PINION	GEAR	
Vertical reaction of weight	$F_{wB} = \dfrac{a\,W_a + b\,W_b}{d} = \dfrac{(5)(52)+(10)(32)}{16} = \dfrac{36.1\,\#}{\text{(down)}}$	$F_{wB} = \dfrac{a\,W_a + b\,W_b}{d} = \dfrac{(14)(114)+(10)(512)}{16} = \dfrac{420\,\#}{\text{(down)}}$	
Vertical reaction of tangential force	$F_t = \dfrac{126{,}050\,HP}{D\ RPM} = \dfrac{(126{,}050)(50)}{(6)(1800)} = 584\,\#$ $F_{tB} = \dfrac{F_t\,a}{d} = \dfrac{(584)(10)}{(16)} = \dfrac{365\,\#}{\text{(up)}}$	$F_{tB} = $	$\dfrac{365\,\#}{\text{(down)}}$
Horizontal reaction of radial force	$F_{rB} = F_t\,\tan\phi = (365)(.364) = \dfrac{133\,\#}{\text{(to left end)}}$	$F_{rB} = $	$\dfrac{133\,\#}{\text{(to right end)}}$
End thrust of Helical gear	$F_e = F_t\,\tan\theta = (584)(.577) = \dfrac{337\,\#}{\text{(to front)}}$	$F_e = $	$\dfrac{337\,\#}{\text{(to back)}}$
Horizontal reaction of end thrust	$F_{eB} = \dfrac{F_e\,D}{2\,d} = \dfrac{(337)(6)}{(2)(16)} = \dfrac{63.1\,\#}{\text{(to left end)}}$	$F_{eB} = \dfrac{F_e\,D}{2\,d} = \dfrac{(337)(24)}{(2)(16)} = \dfrac{253\,\#}{\text{(to left end)}}$	

The loads and forces on the back side of the housing would be found in a similar manner. In this particular example the front side of the housing is stressed the greatest and will determine the design. The various loads and forces can be diagrammed as in Figure 9 and then totaled.

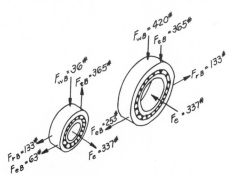
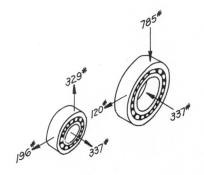

FIGURE 9

<u>Step 1</u>: Vertical Stiffness of Housing

Use nomograph.

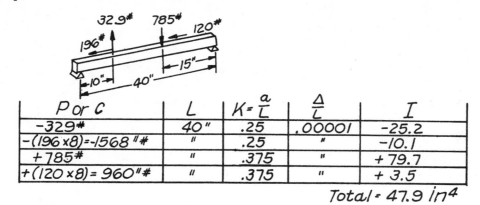

P or C	L	$K = \dfrac{a}{L}$	$\dfrac{\Delta}{L}$	I
−329#	40"	.25	.00001	−25.2
−(196 × 8) = −1568"#	"	.25	"	−10.1
+785#	"	.375	"	+79.7
+(120 × 8) = 960"#	"	.375	"	+ 3.5

Total = 47.9 in⁴

<u>Step 2</u>: Horizontal Stiffness of Housing

Use nomograph.

The worst condition would be to have end thrust on one side member from just one shaft, the thrust from the second shaft being taken by the other side member. In this case the required moment of inertia would be $I_y = 34.2$ in.⁴ .

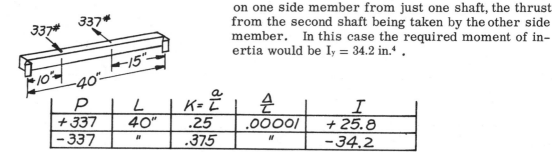

P	L	$K = \dfrac{a}{L}$	$\dfrac{\Delta}{L}$	I
+ 337	40"	.25	.00001	+ 25.8
− 337	"	.375	"	− 34.2

Total   8.4 in⁴

<u>Step 3</u>: Torsional Stiffness of Housing

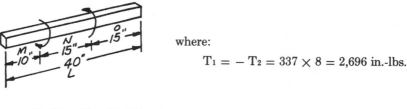

where:

$T_1 = -T_2 = 337 \times 8 = 2{,}696$ in.-lbs.

$$\therefore \quad T_M = \frac{T_1(N+O) + T_2(O)}{L} = \frac{(2696)(30) - (2696)(15)}{40} = +1010 \text{ in.-lbs}$$

$$T_N = \frac{-T_1(M) + T_2(O)}{L} = \frac{-(2696)(10) - (2696)(15)}{40} = -1685 \text{ in.-lbs}$$

$$T_O = \frac{-T_1(M) - T_2(M+N)}{L} = \frac{-(2696)(10) + (2696)(25)}{40} = +1010 \text{ in.-lbs}$$

Maximum twisting action, T = 1685 in.-lbs. The required torsional resistance (R) of this side member will be --

$$R = \frac{T}{E_s \theta} = \frac{1685}{(12 \times 10^6)(.0000002)} = 70.2 \text{ in.}^4$$

where:

θ = allowable unit angular twist, radians per inch in

Let θ = .0000002 radians/linear inch (.000011°/in.)

The cross-section of this side member must have these properties:

$I_x = 48$ in.⁴

$I_y = 34$ in.⁴

R = 70.2 in.⁴

The following section, Figure 10, will meet all of these requirements:

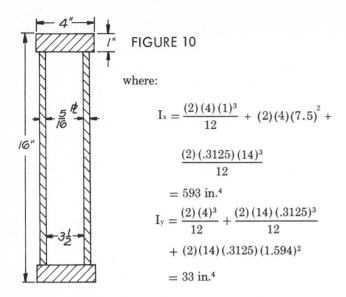

FIGURE 10

where:

$$I_x = \frac{(2)(4)(1)^3}{12} + (2)(4)(7.5)^2 +$$

$$\frac{(2)(.3125)(14)^3}{12}$$

$$= 593 \text{ in.}^4$$

$$I_y = \frac{(2)(4)^3}{12} + \frac{(2)(14)(.3125)^3}{12}$$

$$+ (2)(14)(.3125)(1.594)^2$$

$$= 33 \text{ in.}^4$$

and, since the formula for torsional resistance is--

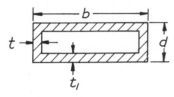

$$R = \frac{2 t t_1 (b - t)^2 (d - t_1)^2}{b t + d t_1 - t^2 - t_1^2}$$

$$= \frac{(2)(1)(\frac{5}{16})(16 - 1)^2(3.5 - \frac{5}{16})^2}{(16)(1) + (3.5)(\frac{5}{16}) - (1)^2 - (\frac{5}{16})^2}$$

$$= 89 \text{ in.}^4$$

Step 4: Check for Compressive Stiffness of Housing

$$A = \frac{P}{\left(\frac{\Delta}{L}\right) E}$$

$$= \frac{785}{(.00001)(30,000,000)}$$

$$= 2.6 \text{ sq. in.}$$

Since the bearing is supported by two $\frac{5}{16}$" plates, the required length of section below the bearing would be--

$$\frac{2.6}{(2)(\frac{5}{16})} = 4\frac{3}{16}"$$

In other words, a section of the side member only $4\frac{3}{16}$" long would support this bearing load within the allowable deflection.

5. AIDS FOR BETTER DESIGN OF WELDED STEEL GEAR HOUSINGS

A gear housing must provide the following:

1. Rigid support for the gear train

2. A container for the lubricating oil

3. Proper cooling of the oil

Ample space around fast turning gears should be provided so as to result in minimum power loss through oil churning. In certain cases the ability

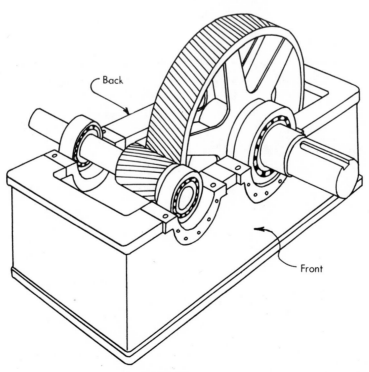

FIGURE 11

of the housing to carry away the heat may determine the horsepower capacity of the unit. Fins can be welded to the outside of the housing under severe heat conditions to dissipate some of the heat into the surrounding air.

Design the housing so that the gear assembly is easily accessible, also so that as much of this may be assembled as a unit outside of the housing and then installed into the housing, preferably as a single completed unit.

Design the housing with proper accessibility for welding. Form housing sides by bending corners and eliminating the corner welds; this improves appearance and reduces welding cost. A slanting bottom to the housing will permit oil to be completely drained.

Avoid close tolerances where they are not absolutely necessary. Much money can be wasted in trying to hold dimensions that are not required. Use a fewer number of pieces to decrease assembly and welding time.

Do not use a premium grade of steel unless necessary. Weld a section of high tensile steel, for example, in the housing where required and make the rest of the housing out of mild steel.

If a section has to be cut out, arrange this so that the cut-out section can be used for some other piece (rectangular pieces for pads, stiffeners, etc.; round pieces for gear blanks, reinforcements around holes, etc.).

In making the flange sections of the housing, consider whether a large thick plate should be flame cut to form this or should be made by cutting long flat bar stock and welding together.

Bearing supports may be flame cut from heavy plate, or be steel forgings or steel castings welded into the side plates of the housing.

Be sure the proper size and amount of welding is shown. Excessive weld size is costly. For a fillet weld having full plate strength, its leg size should be about ¾ of the thickness of the thinner plate. This assumes that the weld extends the full length of the seam and is on both sides of the plate. In most cases full-strength fillet welds are not necessary and in a design based on rigidity, for example housings, fillet welds of 1/3 to 1/2 full strength would be more than sufficient. Stiffeners and diaphragms require very little welding and are often over-welded. For butt welding of thick plates, select proper joint design for minimum welding cost because this has a great effect upon cost.

FIGURE 12

FIGURE 13

Motors and Generators

1. SCOPE OF WELDED STEEL CONSTRUCTION

Welded steel construction is extensively used in electrical motors and generators for size and weight reduction, fabricating economy, and functional appearance. This method produces members of required strength and rigidity.

In a typical motor or generator, spacer or tie bars are welded directly to the stator. A steel sheet is wrapped around this assembly to form a protective shell. This shell may be welded to the tie bars and either left open at the bottom or closed completely with a longitudinal seam weld. In some cases the shell does not cover the full length of the tie bars; and flat bars, previously rolled and welded into circular rings, are welded to each end. The outer edges of the two rings, or of the shell, are machined concentric with the stator inner diameter so as to hold the two end bells that function as brackets for support of the rotor. The end rings are frequently flanged for more rigid support of the end bells.

The longitudinal bars (four or more) support the stator from the shell and/or end rings. In medium and large rotating electrical apparatus, the shell and tie bars sometimes constitute an integral frame made up of channels and flat plates welded together.

Fig. 1 Most medium to large motors and generator housings are built up by welding. The basic force is a result of torque from the rotor.

Feet or legs are welded to the shell, to the end rings, or directly to the stator. Or, the motor or generator housing is fabricated with straight vertical side walls, carried down and flanged to be bolted or welded to a base plate.

Fig. 2 Tie rods and outer shell often are integral parts of motor frame and must support end bearings against end thrust.

2. BASIC DESIGN REQUIREMENTS

It is difficult to determine the actual service forces on the frame of a motor or generator. Usually portions of the frame are designed to withstand the forces resulting from the weights which must be supported and the forces due to normal operation, such as the torque transmitted, etc.

It is possible, however, to overload the motor far in excess of normal operation. For example, placing too many V belts and operating them too tightly on an over-hung shaft can greatly increase the forces over what is normally allowed on the end bracket supporting the bearing. Improper mounting of a motor under an extreme vibrating condition (such as a vibrating screen, or crusher) could break off the supporting feet of the motor, even though they are overdesigned for normal operating conditions.

In general these basic requirements must be designed into the frame and enclosure:

1. Support for the stator and its field coils.

2. Support for the end bearings which support the motor. This must hold the rotor concentric with the stator and be capable of withstanding any possible end thrust.

3. Some means of mounting or holding down the motor or generator. This may be on the end of the frame, but more commonly through feet or legs along the bottom of the frame.

4. The frame must be enclosed to some extent, usually with a thin sheet wrapped around the frame. In some cases it is totally enclosed.

The torque (T) from the rotor exerts a resisting torque on the stator field coils and laminations, and must be transferred through the supporting stator bars into the frame and out through the feet.

This force on any particular part of the frame ($F = \dfrac{T}{r\,n}$) will diminish as the radius (r) and the number of parts (n) increases.

Forces (F_R) and (F_L) on bearing, and force (F_F) on feet of frame result from belt tensions (P) applied to pulley on the end of the shaft.

The use of welded steel construction in motors and generators seldom produces any distinct design problems.

The common practice of providing louvers in the shell around the motor or generator frame may demand special considerations. The importance of this factor is dependent on the gage of material used in the shell, the size and shape of cut-outs, the

magnitude of forces resulting from operation of the rotating apparatus, and relative function of the shell as part of the motor frame.

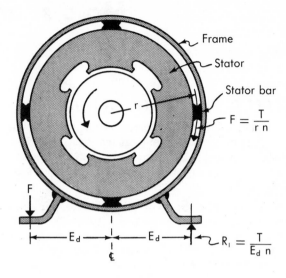

FIGURE 3

3. END BELL DESIGN

Various types of end bells are represented by the sketches in Figure 5. End bells must hold the rotor shaft rigidly and accurately in relation to the stator inner diameter. In this respect they are brackets for purposes of design analysis.

The most important consideration is that of axial end thrust (F_e), which may be in either direction parallel to the rotor shaft and which produces a

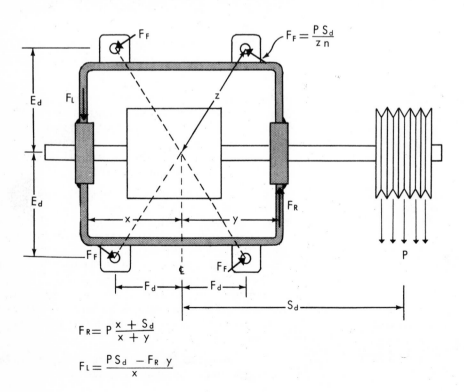

FIGURE 4

$$F_R = P\,\frac{x + S_d}{x + y}$$

$$F_L = \frac{P\,S_d - F_R\,y}{x}$$

bending stress that is maximum in the disc at the hub joint. If the motor or generator is designed for a specific application, the maximum possible end thrust may be easy to determine. If the unit is for more general use, some value must be assumed for this end thrust.

End thrust may be caused by numerous factors such as the weight of the motor if vertically mounted, vibration caused by multi-groove sheaves on an overhung shaft, misaligned V-belts, or the action of shaft-mounted speed reducers.

Most end brackets can be considered as circular flat plates fixed and loaded at the hub. Table 1 presents the formulas for determining radial tensile stress (σ_r) and axial deflection (Δ_e) due to end thrust (F_e). The outer edge of the end bracket is considered to be "fixed" if it is continuously welded to a heavy flange, or if it is relatively thick and bolted to the frame. The outer edge is considered to be simply "supported" if there is no flange, or if the disc is relatively thin.

In Table 1 natural or Naperian logarithms are used, and:

r_o = outer radius of disc (or radius of bolt circle)

r_i = inner radius of disc (at joint with hub)

For ease in computation, the simplified formulas of Figure 6 may be used to solve for radial tensile

Standard commercial dished head   Stamped out of light-gage steel

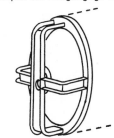

Flat plate flame-cut to shape   Open frame fabricated from rolled sections (channels)

FIGURE 5

stress and axial deflection. Values of K for substitution in these formulas are read quickly from the curves shown. The left vertical axis is used in reading the value of K_1 for the radial tensile stress formula, and the right vertical axis is used in reading the value of K_2 for the deflection formula.

TABLE 1 -- END THRUST ON END BRACKET
Considered as Circular Flat Plate, Fixed and Loaded at Hub

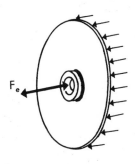

Outer edge fixed

Max at hub

$$\sigma_r = \frac{3 F_e}{2 \pi t^2} \left[1 - \frac{2 r_o^2}{(r_o^2 - r_i^2)} \log_e \frac{r_o}{r_i} \right]$$

$$\Delta_e = \frac{273 F_e}{400 \pi E t^3} \left[r_o^2 - r_i^2 - \frac{4 r_o^2 r_i^2}{(r_o^2 - r_i^2)} \left(\log_e \frac{r_o}{r_i} \right)^2 \right]$$

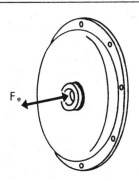

Outer edge just supported

Max at hub

$$\sigma_r = \frac{3 F_e}{2 \pi t^2} \left[\frac{7 (r_o^2 - r_i^2) + 26 r_o^2 \log_e \frac{r_o}{r_i}}{13 r_o^2 + 7 r_i^2} \right]$$

$$\Delta_e = \frac{273 F_e}{400 \pi E t^3} \left[\frac{33 r_o^4 - 7 r_i^4 - 26 r_o^2 r_i^2 - 80 r_o^2 r_i^2 \log_e \frac{r_o}{r_i} - 52 r_o^2 r_i^2 \log_e \left(\frac{r_o}{r_i} \right)^2}{13 r_o^2 + 7 r_i^2} \right]$$

For simplicity use the simplified formulas and curves on Figure 6.

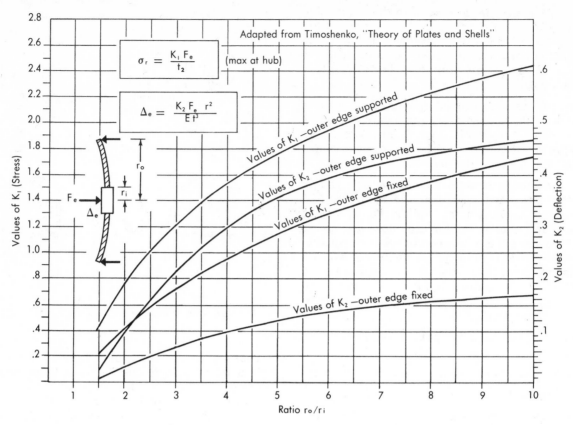

$$\sigma_r = \frac{K_1 F_e}{t_2} \quad \text{(max at hub)}$$

$$\Delta_e = \frac{K_2 F_e r^2}{E t^3}$$

Adapted from Timoshenko, "Theory of Plates and Shells"

Values of K_1 —outer edge supported

Values of K_2 —outer edge supported

Values of K_1 —outer edge fixed

Values of K_2 —outer edge fixed

Ratio r_o/r_i

Values of K_1 (Stress)

Values of K_2 (Deflection)

Fig. 6 Radial tensile stress and axial deflection.

4. DESIGN OF FEET

The approach to analysis of a proposed foot design is best presented by taking an actual problem, Figure 7. The objective is to determine if bending stress and deflection will be within allowable limits.

In using the formula for torque, the service factor is applied as a multiplier to the nominal horsepower. Thus, HP in the formula equals 200% of the motor's 100 horsepower, or 200.

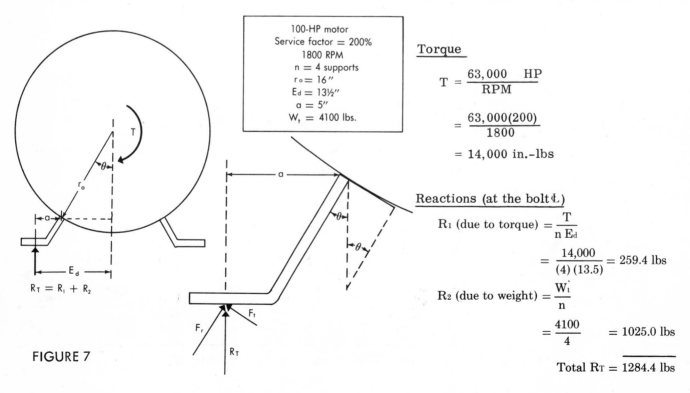

100-HP motor
Service factor = 200%
1800 RPM
n = 4 supports
r_o = 16″
E_d = 13½″
a = 5″
W_t = 4100 lbs.

FIGURE 7

$R_T = R_1 + R_2$

Torque

$$T = \frac{63,000}{RPM} \quad HP$$

$$= \frac{63,000(200)}{1800}$$

$$= 14,000 \text{ in.-lbs}$$

Reactions (at the bolt ₵)

$$R_1 \text{ (due to torque)} = \frac{T}{n E_d}$$

$$= \frac{14,000}{(4)(13.5)} = 259.4 \text{ lbs}$$

$$R_2 \text{ (due to weight)} = \frac{W_t}{n}$$

$$= \frac{4100}{4} = 1025.0 \text{ lbs}$$

$$\text{Total } R_T = 1284.4 \text{ lbs}$$

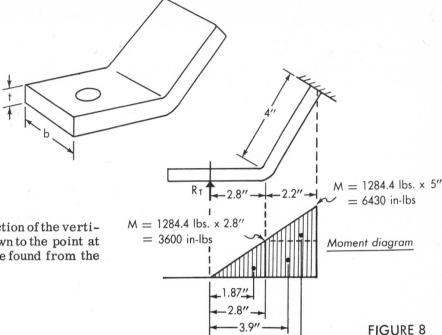

FIGURE 8

The angle θ, formed by intersection of the vertical centerline and a radial line drawn to the point at which the foot joins the shell, can be found from the formula:

$$\text{Sin}\,\theta = \frac{E_d - a}{r}$$

$$= \frac{13.5 - 5}{16}$$

$$= .531$$

$$\therefore \theta = 32.1°$$

Having found this angle, its cosine can be found from tables of natural functions, and the force components of the reaction (R_T) are--

$$F_r = R_T \cos\theta$$

$$= (1284.4)(.845)$$

$$= 1087 \text{ lbs}$$

$$F_t = R_T \sin\theta$$

$$= (1284.4)(.531)$$

$$= 682 \text{ lbs}$$

Although the designer might wish to have these values for tangential and radial forces, they are not used as such in this example. The reaction force (R_T) is all that is needed.

Checking Tentative Foot Section

Try a 1" × 4" bar (b = 4" and t = 1") and determine the maximum bending moment (M), which is the reaction (R_T) times the horizontal distance to the point of support. See Figure 8.

In order to find the bending stress in the foot, first determine the moment of inertia and the section modulus:

$$I = \frac{b\,t^3}{12}$$

$$= \frac{(4)(1)^3}{12}$$

$$= .333 \text{ in.}^4$$

$$S = \frac{I}{c}$$

and since <u>c</u> here = t/2 —

$$S = \frac{.333}{.5}$$

$$= .667 \text{ in.}^3$$

Bending stress in foot

$$\sigma = \frac{M}{S}$$

$$= \frac{6430 \text{ in.-lbs}}{.667 \text{ in.}^3}$$

$$= 9650 \text{ psi} \qquad \text{OK}$$

Then check the vertical deflection of the leg due to the bending moment, by means of the "Area-Moment" method (see Sect. 2.9). The maximum deflection of the beam (leg) equals the algebraic sum of the moments of the several areas under the moment diagram slope taken about the point of deflection (at R_T).

Vertical deflection

$$\Delta_v = \frac{1}{2}\left(\frac{3600''\#}{E\,I}\right)(2.8'')(1.87'') +$$

$$\left(\frac{3600''\#}{E\,I}\right)(4'')(3.9'') +$$

$$\frac{1}{2}\left(\frac{6430''\# - 3600''\#}{E\,I}\right)(4'')(4.27'')$$

$$= \frac{89,690}{E\,I} = \frac{89,690}{(30 \times 10^6)(.333)}$$

$$= \underline{.0090''} \qquad \text{OK}$$

Checking Alternative Design

Although the following design offers poor accessibility for welding, uses more weld metal, and with a double bend may be more costly to form, it is occasionally used in order to provide additional clearance under the motor or generator.

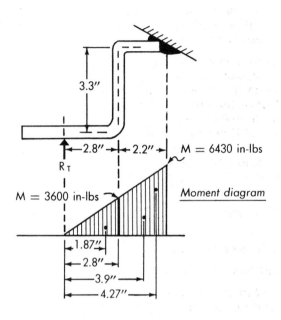

FIGURE 9

Vertical deflection

$$\Delta_v = \frac{1}{2}\left(\frac{3600''\#}{E\,I}\right)(2.8'')(1.87'') +$$

$$\left(\frac{3600''\#}{E\,I}\right)(3.3'')(2.8'') +$$

$$\left(\frac{3600''\#}{E\,I}\right)(2.2'')(3.9'') +$$

$$\frac{1}{2}\left(\frac{6430''\# - 3600''\#}{E\,I}\right)(2.2'')(4.27'')$$

$$= \frac{86,800}{E\,I} = \frac{86,800}{(30 \times 10^6)(.333)}$$

$$= \underline{.0087''} \quad OK$$

Various other types of feet or legs are shown in Figure 10.

Size of Connecting Weld

In most cases only the bending load is of any significance in determining the leg size (ω) of the fillet weld joining the foot to the motor frame. The foot for which stress and deflection were first determined can serve as an example. See Figure 11.

The allowable unit force on the weld is found from tables in Section 6.3 on Weld Size to be—

$$f = 9600\,\omega \text{ lbs/linear inch}$$

and the total allowable force is —

$$F = 9600\,\omega\,b$$

The resisting moment of the weld (M_w) is force times distance:

$$M_w = 9600\,\omega\,b\left(t + \frac{\omega}{2}\right)$$

Since M_w must be set equal to the externally applied bending moment (M), multiplying out and solving for fillet weld leg size (ω) —

$$9600\,b\,t\,\omega + 4800\,b\,\omega^2 = M$$

$$\omega^2 + \frac{9600\,b\,t\,\omega}{4800\,b} - \frac{M}{4800\,b} = 0$$

$$\omega^2 + 2\,t\,\omega - \frac{M}{4800\,b} = 0$$

and:

$$\omega = \frac{-2\,t + \sqrt{4\,t^2 + \dfrac{4\,M}{4800\,b}}}{2} \quad \middle| \quad \text{Only the positive root is of interest}$$

$$= \frac{-2\,(1'') + \sqrt{4\,(1'')^2 + \dfrac{4\,(6430''\#)}{4800\,(4'')}}}{2} = \frac{-2 + \sqrt{4 + 1.34}}{2}$$

$$= .155'' \text{ or } \underline{\text{use } \tfrac{3}{16}''}$$

If, in addition, the radial force of $F_r = 1087$ lbs is to be considered, this acts on the top weld in the same direction as the force (F) from the bending moment but on the bottom weld it acts in the opposite direction. Hence, the additional required weld size for F_r may be added to that required for F.

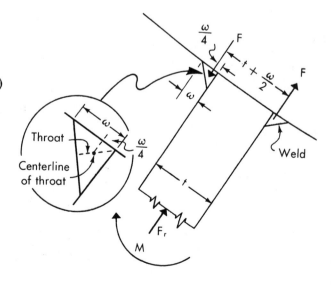

FIGURE 11

Fig. 10 Some types of welded feet for motors and generators.

Additional force on the weld is--

$$f = \frac{F_r}{L}$$

$$= \frac{1087 \text{ lbs}}{2\,(4'')}$$

$$= 136 \text{ lbs/in.}$$

and:

$$\omega = \frac{136}{9600}$$

$$= .014''$$

Adding the size of weld leg required for F_r to that required for F —

.155" + .014" = .169" <u>or still use ³⁄₁₆"</u> ◣

The radial force (F_r) will be always less than the reaction (R_T) and is unlikely ever to be of sufficient value to have a significant effect on the required weld size.

5. EFFECT OF LOUVERS CUT INTO SHELL

Louvers are sometimes needed around motor and generator frames for air to escape around the fan, or as access holes through which to bolt the end of the frame to an engine or other support.

In large rotating apparatus, and in some smaller units, the enclosure or shell in which these cut-outs are provided serves structurally as the frame supporting both stator and rotor. This discussion is centered on this class of apparatus in which, for practical purposes, the enclosure or shell can be considered to be the frame.

In such units, cut-outs weaken the frame to some extent in regard to bending and torsional loads, depending on where they are located.

In the following example, Figure 12, a hole cut into the side of the frame in a region of high vertical shear (a) would weaken the frame's shear carrying capacity, but have little effect on its bending moment

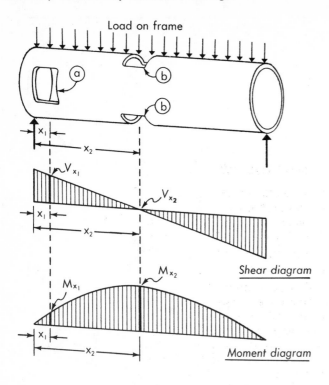

FIGURE 12

carrying capacity. A hole cut in the top or bottom portions of the frame in a region of high moment (b) would weaken its moment carrying capacity but have little effect on its shear carrying capacity.

A series of holes cut around the frame, Figure 13, will weaken the torsional strength and stiffness of the frame.

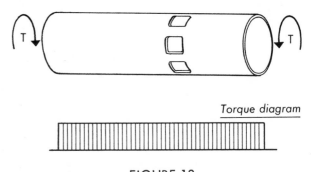

FIGURE 13

Combined Motive Units

Frequently two power units are attached to one another, and the forces developed within the one are shared by the other. Figure 14 shows such an arrangement.

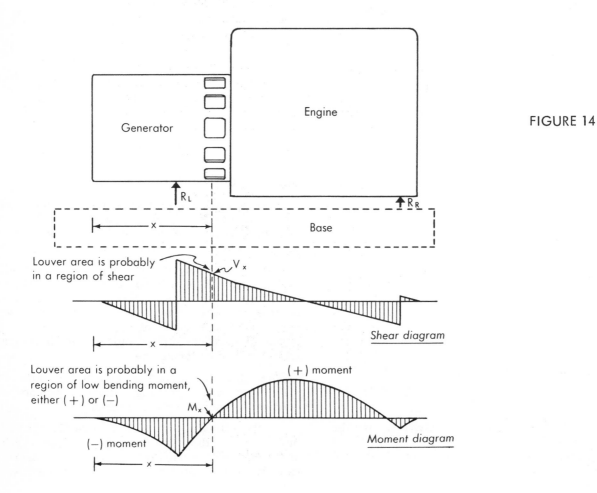

FIGURE 14

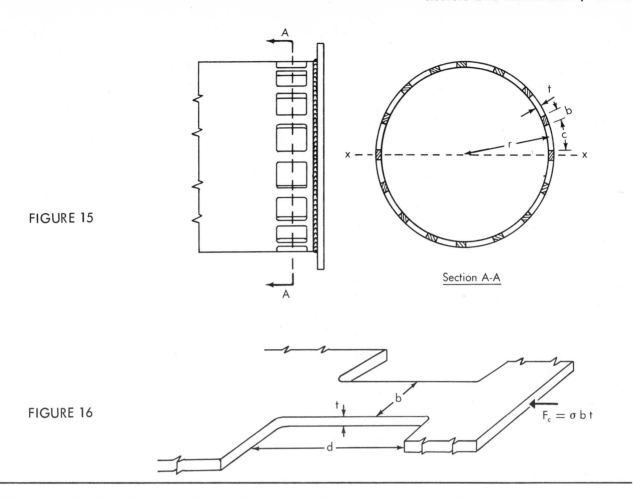

FIGURE 15

Section A-A

FIGURE 16

$F_c = \sigma b t$

This is a statically determinant beam: the moment distribution does not depend on the relative moments of inertia of the frame and engine. The shear diagram and moment diagram can be constructed if the load distribution of the frame and engine is known.

Bending of Frame

The effect of cutting louvers around the frame can be further evaluated by considering a narrow annular section (A-A) taken from the frame, Figure 15.

Since the frame's thickness (t) is small relative to its diameter, its section may be treated as a line. Hence, formulas for properties of thin sections apply:

Properties of whole ring

(without considering effect of cut-outs)

$$I = t\,\pi\,r^3 \quad\dots\dots\dots\dots\dots\dots\dots\dots (1)$$

$$S = t\,\pi\,r^2 \quad\dots\dots\dots\dots\dots\dots\dots\dots (2)$$

It can be assumed that the moment of inertia (I) and the section modulus (S) of cut-out section (A-A) are proportional to properties of the net cross-section.

Properties of net section

$$I_n = I\left(\frac{b}{b+c}\right) \quad\dots\dots\dots\dots\dots\dots (3)$$

$$S_n = S\left(\frac{b}{b+c}\right) \quad\dots\dots\dots\dots\dots\dots (4)$$

From this, the bending stress in the top and bottom elements may be found:

$$\sigma = \frac{M_x}{S_n} \quad\dots\dots\dots\dots\dots\dots\dots\dots (5)$$

Horizontal Compressive Force

The critical element in this case would be the one stressed in compression because of the chance of buckling. If the cut-out louvers are in a region of positive moment, the top element would be in compression; in the negative moment region, the bottom element would be in compression. It is necessary that the element in compression have sufficient strength that it will not buckle.

The element or connecting "leg" between two adjacent cut-outs at the position of highest stress can be considered as a column, resisting the horizontal compressive force (F_c) resulting from the

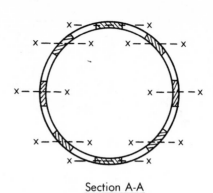

Section A-A

FIGURE 17

bending moment, Figure 16.

$$F_c = \sigma b t \quad \dots \dots \dots \dots \dots \dots \dots \dots (6)$$

It would be well to find the slenderness ratio (L/r) of this element and check its allowable compressive stress to see if the actual compressive stress is within reason.

It will be necessary here to substitute the radius of gyration (r_g) and the axial dimension of the cut-out (d) for the usual properties in finding the slenderness ratio.

Radius of gyration

$$r_g = \sqrt{\frac{I}{A}}$$

$$= \sqrt{\frac{t}{12}}$$

$$\therefore \quad r_g = .289\,t \quad \dots \dots \dots \dots \dots \dots \dots \dots (7)$$

As a guide, this cut-out may be so proportioned that--

$$t \geq \frac{d}{24} \quad \text{or} \quad d \leq 24\,t$$

Then the slenderness ratio $\left(\dfrac{L}{r_g}\right) = \left(\dfrac{d}{.289\,t}\right)$ is held to

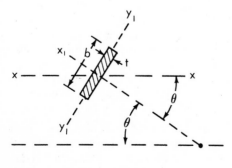

FIGURE 18

a value of 83, thus reducing the allowable compressive stress to about 80% of what would normally be used for tension. This would be a reasonable allowable.

Shear Force

The shear force on elements between cut-out louvers can be found in a similar manner. Consider the annular section (A-A) taken from the frame, Figure 17.

It will be assumed that the ability of an element to resist vertical shear (V_x) is proportional to its stiffness in the vertical direction, or to its individual moment of inertia about axis x-x (I_x). See Figure 18.

The moment of inertia (I_x) about axis x-x for any element, for any given angle (θ) is equal to —

$$I_x = I_{x_1} \cos^2 \theta + I_{y_1} \sin^2 \theta - 2\,I_{x_1 y_1} \sin \theta \cos \theta$$

and since:

$$I_{x_1} = \frac{t\,b^3}{12} \qquad I_{y_1} = \frac{b\,t^3}{12} \qquad I_{x_1 y_1} = 0$$

$$I_x = \frac{t\,b^3}{12} \cos^2 \theta + \frac{b\,t^3}{12} \sin^2 \theta \quad \dots \dots \dots \dots (8)$$

From this, the moment of inertia about axis x-x (I_x) of each of two elements lying in a horizontal plane extending through the axis of the frame is —

(since $\theta = 0°$ or $180°$)

$$I_x = \frac{t\,b^3}{12}$$

The portion of the external vertical shear (V_x) carried by each of these two elements is —

$$V_n = \frac{2\,I_x \,(\text{for } \theta = 0°)}{\text{sum of all the moments of inertia}}\,V_x$$

It can be shown that the sum of the moments of inertia of all the elements is —

$$I_T = \frac{n\,b\,t}{24}\,(b^2 + t^2)$$

where:

    n = number of elements between cut-outs

$$\therefore \boxed{V_n = \frac{4\,b^2}{n\,(b^2 + t^2)}\,V_x} \quad \dotfill (9)$$

This effect of vertical shear force on each of the two elements in the horizontal plane, is illustrated in Figure 19.

Torsional Force

The effect of torque, Figure 20, on individual elements between cut-out louvers, is illustrated in Figure 21.

$$T = \frac{63{,}000 \times HP}{RPM} \quad \text{in.-lbs}$$

Here the circumferential force acting on the element as a result of torque is—

$$\boxed{F_t = \frac{T}{n\,r}} \quad \dotfill (10)$$

Effects of Combined Load

These two forces — V_n from vertical shear, and F_t from torque — will act together on one side of the frame and must be added:

$$\boxed{F = V_n + F_t} \quad \dotfill (11)$$

The effect of this combined load on the bending of this element can be diagrammed as in Figure 22.

Bending moment on element

$$\boxed{M = \frac{F\,d}{2}} \quad \dotfill (12)$$

Bending stress in element

$$\boxed{\sigma = \frac{M}{S}} \quad \dotfill (13)$$

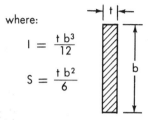

where:

$$I = \frac{t\,b^3}{12}$$

$$S = \frac{t\,b^2}{6}$$

Bending deflection of element

$$\boxed{\Delta_b = \frac{F\,d^3}{12\,E\,I}} \quad \dotfill (14)$$

The effect of this combined load on the shear of this element can be diagrammed as in Figures 23 and 24.

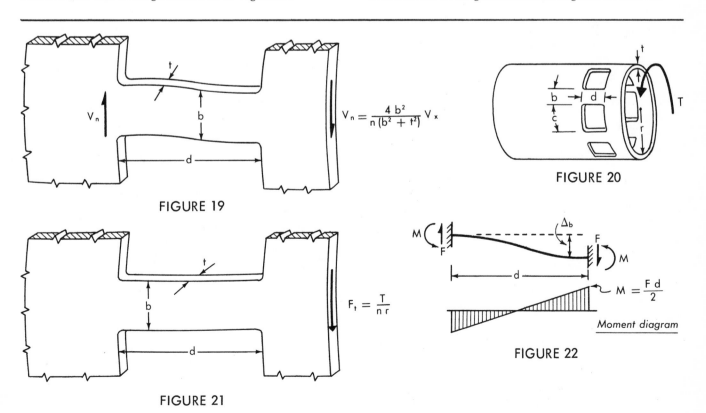

FIGURE 19

$$V_n = \frac{4\,b^2}{n\,(b^2 + t^2)}\,V_x$$

FIGURE 20

FIGURE 21

$$F_t = \frac{T}{n\,r}$$

$$M = \frac{F\,d}{2}$$

Moment diagram

FIGURE 22

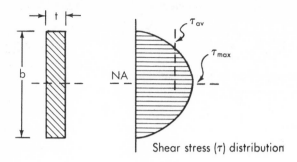

Shear stress (τ) distribution

FIGURE 23

Shear stress in element

$$\tau_{max} = 1.5 \ \tau_{av} = \frac{1.5 \ F}{b \ t} \quad \dots\dots\dots\dots\dots\dots (15)$$

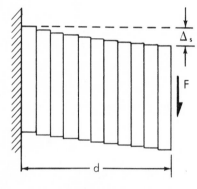

FIGURE 24

Shear deflection of element

$$\Delta_s = \frac{\alpha \ F \ d}{A \ E_s} = \frac{1.5 \ F \ d}{b \ t \ E_s} \quad \dots\dots\dots\dots\dots (16)$$

where:

α = form factor = $\dfrac{\tau_{max}}{\tau_{av}}$ = 1.5

E_s = 12 × 10^6 (modulus of elasticity in shear)

Total deflection of element

$\Delta = \Delta_b + \Delta_s$

This would represent an angular rotation of the frame of —

$$\theta = \frac{\Delta}{r} \text{ radians}$$

6. RESISTANCE TO CONCENTRATED LOAD

In the study of stresses and deflection of cylinders under various types of loads, it is difficult to find an example which exactly fits the particular load condition found in the frame of a motor or generator.

The following, taken from Roark's "Formulas for Stress and Strain", 2nd Edition, p. 260 (see also Timoshenko's "Theory of Plates and Shells", 2nd edition, p. 506) may be used to give an indication of the stress and deformation of the frame acting as a shell under a concentrated force (P).

As shown in Figure 25, the condition considered is a radial load (P) concentrated on a small area of radius (b) and acting at a point remote from the ends of the frame. For example, this might be the force applied to the top of the frame by a lifting lug, or the force applied to the side of the frame through a supporting leg.

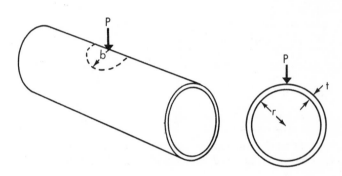

FIGURE 25

Radial deflection

$$\Delta = \frac{.135 \ P \ r^2}{E \ t^3} \quad \dots\dots\dots\dots\dots\dots\dots\dots (17)$$

Circumferential bending stress

$$\sigma_{max} = \frac{P}{t^2} \left[.9685 \ \log_{10}\left(\frac{.215 \ r}{b}\right) + .478 \right] \quad \dots\dots\dots (18)$$

In all cases there is an air gap between the rotor and the stator and this must be held within a certain percentage during the operation. From this an allowable displacement of the side of the frame can be developed for use in the above formula.

How to Design Bearing Supports

1. IMPORTANCE OF STEEL

Welded steel construction provides great flexibility in the design of housings, frames and other machine members that must incorporate bearing supports. In most designs, the shafts are hung within a housing and extend through side walls at each end, Figure 1.

Alignment and parallelism of bearing seat surfaces are usually critical to the performance of the equipment's drive system. The required accuracy can best be obtained and maintained by using steel in the housing and in the bearing supports. Steel's high modulus of elasticity ($E = 30 \times 10^6$ psi) and availability in high-tensile strengths are great assets.

The length of needed bearing support is usually considerably longer than the plate thickness of the side member need be. By using welded steel construction, there is no waste of material in achieving the optimum strength and rigidity where required.

Section 4.8 on Gear Housings provides some basic information on bearing forces. This information will help in determining wall thickness of bearing supports and weld sizes.

The following examples illustrate various ideas for developing designs of bearing supports as used on transmissions, housings and gear boxes.

2. MOUNTING OF BEARING SUPPORT

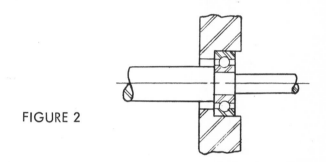

FIGURE 2

The simplest of bearing supports, and the lowest cost, is obtained by mounting the shaft and bearing directly in the housing wall, Figure 2. This can be done where wall thickness is sufficient to provide the necessary bearing area or can be increased slightly without appreciable increase in cost.

For additional bearing support if needed, bosses

Fig. 1 Efficient weldesign offers many advantages in a heavy gear housing of this scale (bottom half shown here).

can be added to the side walls by welding. This type of boss is determined by the designer's requirements for loading, alignment and ease of manufacture.

Simplest in construction and lowest in cost is the addition of a steel collar by fillet welding the collar to the side of the housing, Figure 3. The design, however, has its limitations. Extra time is needed to locate the collar in proper position. In the final boring of the boss a slight irregularity may occur as the boring tool leaves one surface and starts the next. Chips from boring might possibly become wedged in the crevice and tend to force the collar away from the side wall.

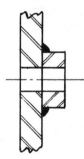

FIGURE 3

An insert can be fillet welded to the side wall to provide a continuous bearing surface, Figure 4. With fillet welds inside and out, the bearing support has greater strength and resistance to bending.

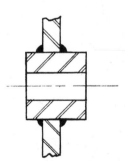

FIGURE 4

The insert can be made in several ways, such as flame-cut from steel plates, or sawed from solid stock or tubing. The hole in the side of the housing is flame-cut or machined. Special care is needed to align the insert in the correct position with the side of the housing.

The problem of aligning the insert perpendicular to the side wall is simplified by using a shoulder or step, Figure 5. For a slight addition in machining costs, changes for misalignment in fabrication are thereby eliminated.

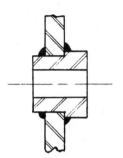

FIGURE 5

3. FLUSH-MOUNTED BEARING SUPPORTS

Designs for bearing supports flush with the wall can be engineered in several different ways, Figure 6.

Since a butt weld is required instead of a fillet weld at the flush surface, either the side wall or the insert must be beveled before welding. Generally, it is simpler to bevel the insert during machining. The side wall can be beveled if necessary by flame-cutting or machining while the opening is being prepared.

4. SPLIT HOUSINGS

Bearing supports necessarily located at the split in a transmission or other housing can be handled efficiently in several different ways, Figure 7.

For small bearings, the split bearing support may be formed from bent plate and fillet welded to the housing. The support can also be made from steel tubings split longitudinally.

For larger heavier bearings, the support can be solid, rectangular stock. The hole is then bored with the remaining half of the housing assembly in place.

Where extremely heavy bearing support is required, the insert could be easily flame-cut to shape from thick steel plates. Intricate sections required for oil seals and lubrication needs can be developed by use of steel castings fillet welded to side walls.

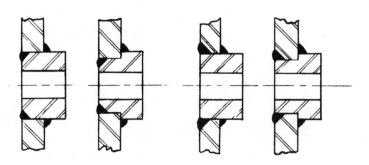

FIGURE 6

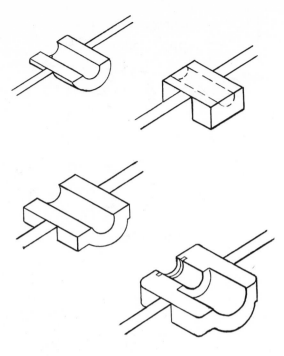

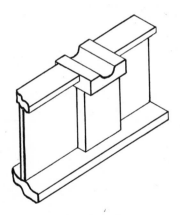

FIGURE 7

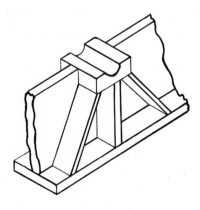

FIGURE 9

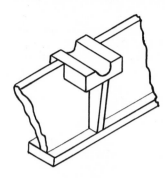

5. HEAVY BEARING LOADS

Stiffeners can be used for heavy loads. Efficient use of stiffeners can save on the thickness and weight of side walls where high compressive and bending loads are involved.

The simplest stiffener is the addition of a web below the insert, Figure 8. The web is fillet welded to both the insert and the side wall of the housing.

FIGURE 8

For heavier loads, additional stiffeners are developed by fabricating a web from steel plate in the form of a channel, Figure 9. Similar results are obtained by merely cutting to required length a standard steel channel available at any steel warehouse.

Figures 10 and 11 show how maximum rigidity can be incorporated by the use of stiffeners where bending loads and thrusts are developed in several directions. In many cases, webs or stiffeners are inserted between bearing supports to tie the supports together.

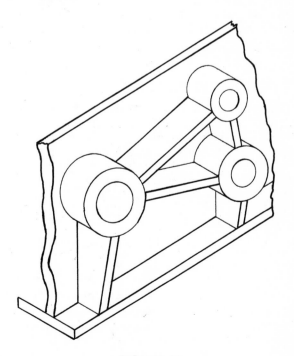

FIGURE 10

FIGURE 11

A typical side frame as used on a printing press is shown in Figure 12. The contour and openings are accurately flame-cut by machine. Bearing supports where needed are machined from barstock or tubing, welded to the side plate and finish-machined in place.

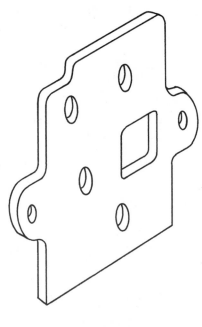

FIGURE 12

6. CLOSELY SPACED BEARINGS

Supports for closely spaced bearings can be designed as a single unit, in order to increase rigidity and improve parallelism of seating surfaces. Figure 13 shows several possibilities.

7. TOP-MOUNTED BEARINGS

Bearing supports must often be mounted to the top panel of a base or other flat surface, in support of a shaft running parallel with the surface. Numerous possibilities exist for achieving the necessary rigidity or strength, while keeping fabrication costs to a minimum. Figure 14 illustrates some of these design ideas.

Fig. 13 Several design ideas for mounting closely-spaced bearings where alignment of seating surfaces is critical.

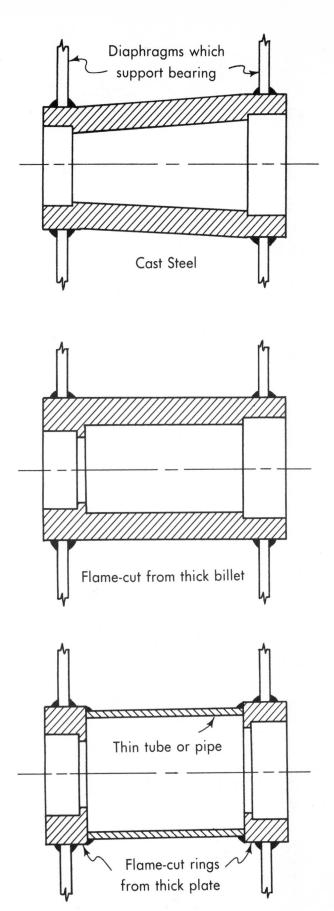

Diaphragms which support bearing

Cast Steel

Flame-cut from thick billet

Thin tube or pipe

Flame-cut rings from thick plate

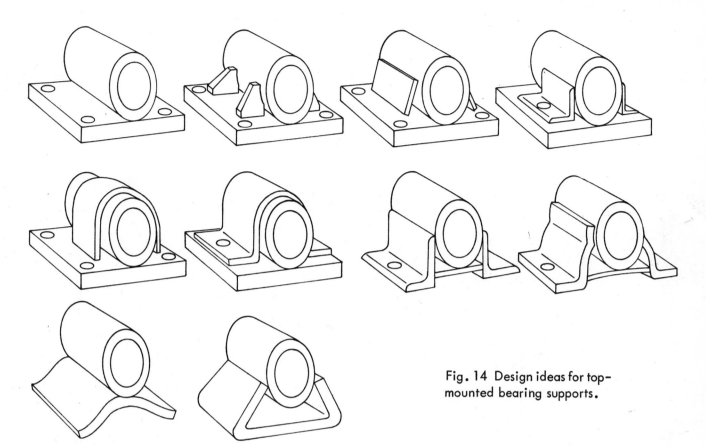

Fig. 14 Design ideas for top-mounted bearing supports.

Converting cast iron "main head" of a forage chopper to steel reduced weight from 289 pounds to 117 pounds, cost 12%. Additional benefit was experienced during final assembly of the chopper because the part was easier to handle.

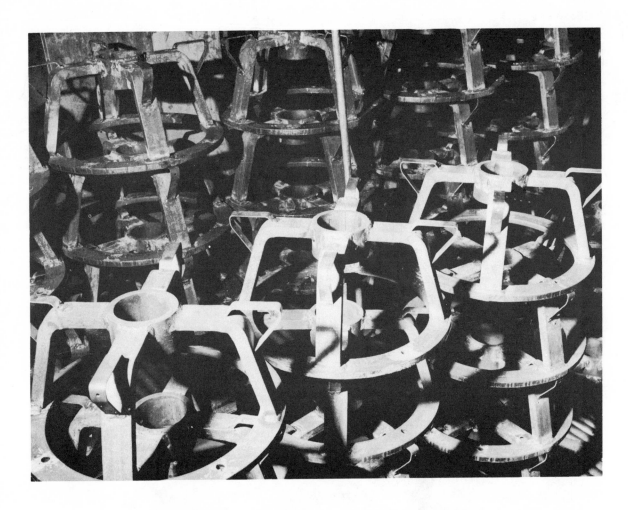

Fabricated bearing brackets for motor generator welders
effectively use standard steel shapes – channel, bar stock,
heavy walled tubing – and arc welding.

How to Design Bosses and Pads

1. ARE THEY NECESSARY ?

Many machine designers indicate bosses and pads on their bases, mostly as a carry-over from casting design. The characteristic rough cast surface requires machining to provide smooth, flat areas where other components are to be joined. In order to reduce the surface area to be machined, bosses or raised sections are provided. See Figure 1.

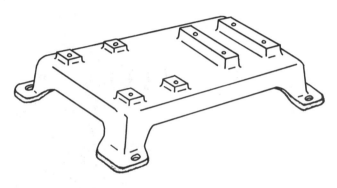

FIGURE 1

In most cases, the inherent smooth surface of steel plate eliminates the necessity of machining weldments. Supported machinery can be bolted directly to them without misalignment or other mounting problems. Figure 2 shows how bolt holes and mounting holes can be integrated into the weldment. Further economy results from prepunching the material prior to forming and welding.

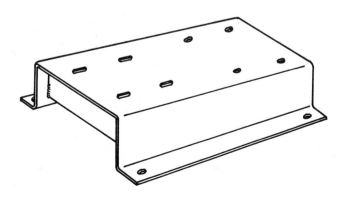

FIGURE 2

Bosses and pads may be advisable on steel weldments to satisfy three needs: (1) to increase the panel thickness to permit cutting enough threads to securely engage attaching bolts; (2) to provide different elevations on which to support components having a common centerline but different heights; and (3) to decrease the area to be machined on limited applications when machined mating surfaces are required.

2. BASIC PROBLEMS

Most pads involve nothing more than welding a plate, either continuously or intermittently, to the face of the weldment. See Figure 3. Thickness and width of plate are the controlling factors for achieving satisfactory results with this mounting technique.

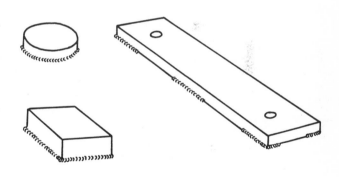

FIGURE 3

Where a larger area is required or the pad does not have sufficient thickness, the fillet welds around the outer edge of the pad may tend to force the center of the pad to pull away slightly from the panel because of angular distortion. See Figure 4.

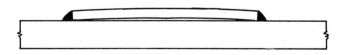

FIGURE 4

This can make it difficult to produce a flat mounting surface after machining, for example:

1. If the thin pad has sprung away from the panel, tool pressure during machining may force the pad back toward the panel. After the cut has been made, the pad may spring outward again maintaining its curved contour.

2. In some cases where holes must be drilled or tapped, the cutting tool conceivably might tend to separate the pad from the panel and force small turnings into the crevice between surfaces.

Plug welding extremely wide and thin pads at various points will hold them tightly against the main panel and correct this problem. See Figure 5.

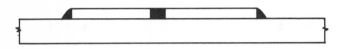

FIGURE 5

3. THICKNESS WHERE NEEDED

For more critical applications, it may be desirable to weld a thicker plate inserted into the supporting panel of the steel weldment. See Figure 6. This will give solid material for subsequent machining, especially for boring or drilling, and will eliminate any danger of the pad lifting away from the panel. Some applications may demand a 100% weld between insert and panel; but in most cases a weld on each side of the panel is sufficient. The vertical forces on the pad usually govern this decision.

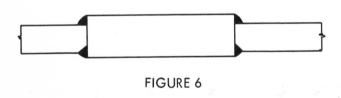

FIGURE 6

The next three sketches show a typical cast section with a machined boss around a relatively large opening, and its equivalent in steel. The cast boss, Figure 7, reduces the amount of machining needed to produce a mating surface adjacent to the opening.

The weldment, Figure 8, satisfies this condition by having the "boss thickness" extend the entire width of the weldment. However, this plate, though somewhat thinner than the corresponding cast section, frequently must have its entire surface machined to provide the same limited-area contact with an attaching unit.

A design alternative, shown in Figure 9, might

be used to advantage. Here the thicker section needed to receive studs or bolts is produced by welding an insert of rectangular cross-section into the thinner plate of the panel. Frequently, scrap material from previous weldments can be efficiently salvaged for this purpose. Here again the welded design achieves increased material efficiency by placing the right amount where it is needed while reducing both weight and necessary machining.

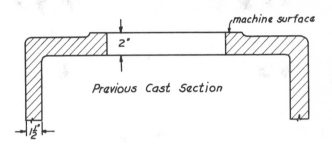

FIGURE 7

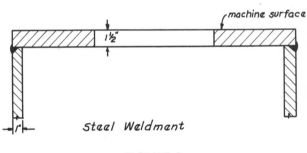

FIGURE 8

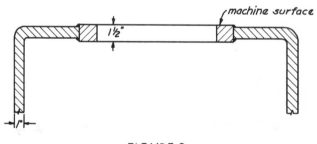

FIGURE 9

Figure 9 illustrates another welded design technique of gaining additional production economy. Since the top and sides of the base are now of the same thickness, they may be formed from one plate and the corner welds along the length of the base are thereby eliminated.

4. MULTIPLE MOUNTING ELEVATIONS

In many machine designs, various units of a drive system are mounted on the same axial centerline-- motor, speed reducer, etc. These units usually vary in height. Pads may be flame-cut from plate, sawed from bar stock, or made of scrap material saved from previous weldments. Higher mounting supports can be constructed from standard rolled shapes such as I sections, T sections, angles, channels, and formed plates. See Figure 10.

to stock and later assembled in a variety of combinations to meet the customer's requirements without delaying shipment.

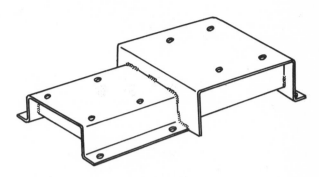

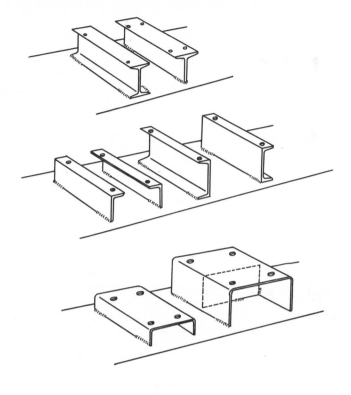

FIGURE 10

FIGURE 11

Two separate weldments have been integrated into a single unit in Figure 11, thereby providing stable support of component members at different levels. This technique may be especially useful in motor-pump bases and similar applications. Where bases have to be tailored to meet varied requirements, units of varying heights can be manufactured

Efficiency and flexibility features of welded design permit economical placement of bosses or pads wherever they are most useful. In Figure 12, a mounting pad is supported on brackets out from the main frame. These supports may be fabricated as a subassembly and then welded in place.

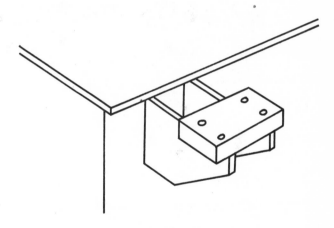

FIGURE 12

Standard structural shapes and formed steel, plus welding, simplified the construction of this oil-pump motor base.

Welded steel construction provided an economical solution to the problem of providing various mounting elevations on this machine base.

How to Design Machine Brackets

1. STEEL PERMITS DESIGN ECONOMY

Brackets and similar components for positioning and supporting other machine members, offer many opportunities for improvement of design economy. For equal strength, steel sections can be 25% the size of cast iron sections. For equal rigidity, sections can generally be 50% the thickness of cast iron sections.

Redesigning on the basis of calculated loads permits more efficient use of material. Product designs can sometimes be made with about ⅕ the original material needed. With welded steel construction, components of the bracket can often be sheared to shape. In other cases, the components can be bent to shape, reducing the amount of welding and thus further reducing manufacturing costs.

Figure 1 shows various types of steel brackets fabricated economically with arc welding. The basic principles of their design are outlined in the text that follows. For purposes of illustration, the discussion uses the simplest type brackets to support motors, transmission devices, and operating members of a machine.

2. DESIGN EVOLUTION

It is natural that when redesigning a casting to welded steel, the designer tends to adhere closely to the shape of the original cast part. Although this may be considered an acceptable first step, the alert designer does not restrict his thinking to preconceived ideas, and looks beyond the first concept to see what can be done by other approaches to the problem.

With steel, virtually any design approach is possible. The steel designer is not restricted by pattern and molding limitations. Extremely thin sections can be used. Materials can be placed where they can carry the greatest load with the least section. Every pound of metal can be put to use effectively.

For example, a simple redesign of the cast bracket (A), Figure 2, for welded steel is shown below (B). Although the design nearly duplicates the configuration of the casting, material is reduced by 40%. This is not an efficient design for welded steel however, requiring four separate pieces, and

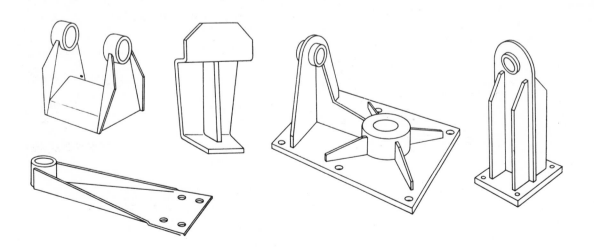

Fig. 1 Typical brackets as found on many machines. These are sheared from relatively thin stock, formed, tack-welded, and then finish welded, utilizing high-speed fillet welds made in the downhand position.

1

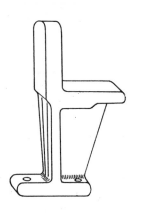
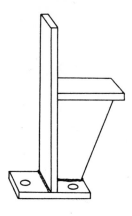
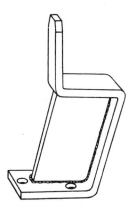

(A) Original Casting

(B) First Redesign
Weight: 40% less
Cost: About the same

(C) Second Redesign
Weight: 40% less
Cost: 50% less

FIGURE 2

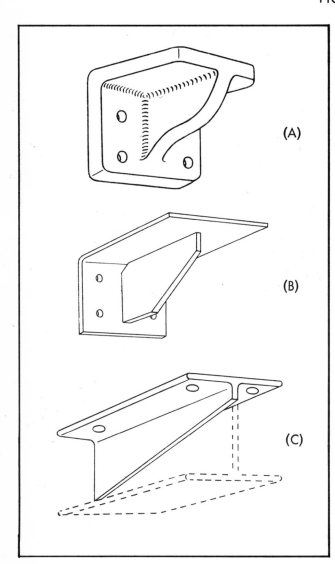

(A)

(B)

(C)

FIGURE 3

fabrication costs reduce the material savings.

A true savings is realized when a completely different approach is taken (C). This design utilizes only two pieces of steel--sheared, bent and welded. It represents a weight reduction of 40% and cost savings of about 50%.

Similarly, several different approaches can be taken in redesigning the cast iron machine bracket shown (A) in Figure 3.

In one redesign (B), identical loads can be carried with steel having half the section of the original casting. The bracket is a plate simply bent to shape, with a stiffening web added by fillet welding.

A bracket (C) serving the same need is cut from a standard "I" beam by flame-cutting the web at 45°, giving two similar brackets for one length of "I" beam.

The long bracket, Figure 4, required relatively heavy sections as a casting (A) to maintain necessary rigidity. Material thickness can be reduced about 50% when redesigned (B) to duplicate the shape of the original casting.

However, a more efficient redesign (C) uses even lighter material bent to shape and two stiffeners welded across the bottom to prevent wobbling.

3. BRACING OF HIGH-LOAD BRACKETS

On larger size brackets, Figure 5, box sections or diagonal bracing can be used to attain maximum structural rigidity at minimum weight. Where clearance is needed through the center, the box section (A) is fabricated from two side members, brake-formed to a channel shape. The two channel shapes are then butt welded on opposite sides with fast downhand or automatic submerged-arc welding.

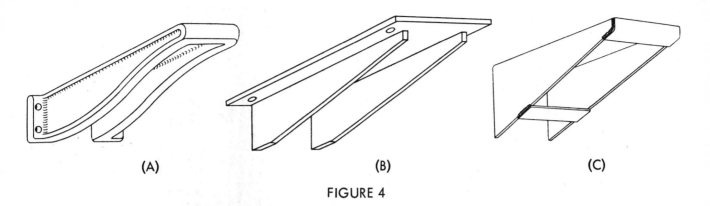

FIGURE 4

With diagonal bracing, side members are brake-formed to channel shape and steel stiffeners welded to the inside as shown in design B, Figure 5.

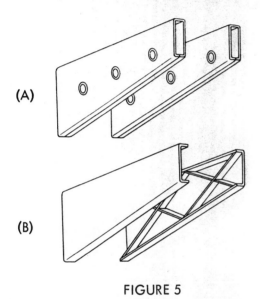

FIGURE 5

Figure 6 shows another way in which a channel member can be utilized to fabricate a machine bracket. Sawed or flame-cut from standard structural shapes, the channel is fillet welded to the top and side of the machine bracket.

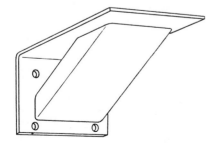

FIGURE 6

Where desirable, corner reinforcement of simple machine brackets can be accomplished as in Figure 7. Design A is for brackets supporting a post on an industrial truck. Design B is for brackets for internal support.

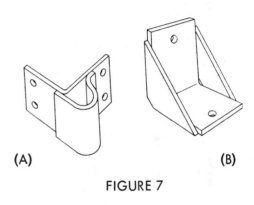

FIGURE 7

Where removable brackets subject to high loading are involved, the design idea shown in Figure 8 can be utilized. A seat clip (B) is welded to the side frame of the machine, immediately beneath the bracket position. The bracket is then allowed to rest on the clip, removing the high vertical shear load from the bolts.

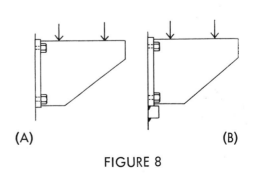

FIGURE 8

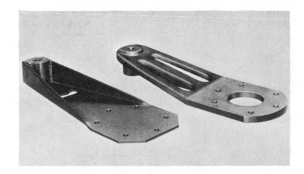

Very substantial savings can often be made by designing relatively simple members for welding rather than some slower, costlier process. Brackets, as shown above, are good examples of conversion possibilities that can pay off for the designer.

How To Design Flywheels

1. IMPORTANCE OF STEEL

It is important that flywheels be built of a sound, dependable, high strength material. Rolled steel answers these requirements. Because of the low tensile strength of cast irons, cast flywheels must be restricted in speed to keep the rim from flying to pieces.

In order to store the desired amount of energy in the rim while keeping rim stresses low, the cast iron flywheel must--

a. have a large rim radius (r_m),

b. be massive, and

c. turn at a rather low RPM

Steel, on the other hand, is not limited by low tensile strength and casting defects. Because of its higher strength and uniformity of material, a welded steel flywheel can safely operate at higher speeds with substantial reduction in weight and cost.

For a given required value of rim energy (E_k),

the maximum rim radius (r_m) must be reduced as the speed of revolution increases. For flywheels with the same rim sectional area and of same material, rim weight varies as the cube of the rim radius.

When designing for low manufacturing cost, it is desirable to make the flywheel as small as possible and run at higher rotating speeds. A welded steel flywheel, therefore, is preferable since the steel wheel can be run safely at higher speeds and stores more energy per pound of metal.

A comparison of gray iron and welded steel flywheels (Fig. 1) shows the relative sizes and speeds of flywheels for developing the same 100,000 ft-lbs of energy.

In many machines several shafts are used, each turning at different speeds. For lowest weight and cost of the flywheel, it is important to place the flywheel on the highest speed shaft possible for the amount of energy which must be stored in the rim. For increased rim energy (E_k), it may be necessary to place the flywheel on the slower turning shafts; this will allow the rim radius to be increased.

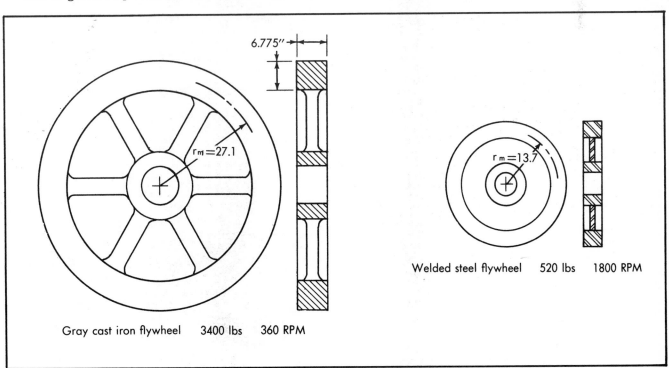

Gray cast iron flywheel   3400 lbs   360 RPM

Welded steel flywheel   520 lbs   1800 RPM

FIGURE 1

2. REQUIRED RIM ENERGY

E_k is usually obtained from an analysis of the energy fluctuations per cycle. For example, the work done by a punch is the average force of shearing multiplied by the thickness of the plate being sheared, and is measured as the area under the force-displacement diagram.

In most cases this area can be represented by 20% to 80% of the product of the maximum shearing force and the thickness of the plate. This maximum shearing force is the ultimate shearing strength of the metal multiplied by the area of the sheared edge. If the ultimate shear strength (τ_u) is not known, it may be taken as ¾ of the ultimate tensile strength (σ_u).

For example, the energy required to punch a 1"-diameter hole in a ½"-thick plate, having a shearing strength of 50,000 psi, would be--

$$E_k = \tfrac{1}{2}\, t\, F$$

where the force

$$F = \tau \pi\, \text{dia}\, t$$

$$\therefore E_k = \tfrac{1}{2}\,(\tfrac{1}{2}")\,(50{,}000 \text{ psi})\, 3.1416\,(1")\,(\tfrac{1}{2}")$$

$$= 19{,}242 \text{ in.-lbs}$$

$$= 1604 \text{ ft-lbs}$$

DEFINITIONS OF SYMBOLS USED IN FLYWHEEL DESIGN

σ = stress (tensile or bending), psi
τ = shear stress in flywheel shaft, psi
ω = leg size of fillet weld, in.

c = distance of neutral axis to outer fiber of section, in.
d = diameter of flywheel drive shaft, in.
n = number of spokes or arms in flywheel
r_m = mean radius of rim, in.
t_r = thickness of rim, in.

A_r = cross-sectional area of rim, in.^{2} = $t_r W_r$ = $K_1{}^2 K_2 r_m{}^2$
A_s = cross-sectional area of spoke, in.^{2}

C = coefficient of speed fluctuation = $\dfrac{RPM_1 - RPM_2}{RPM_m}$

E_k = energy stored in rim, ft-lbs
ΔE_k = energy given up by flywheel, ft-lbs = $E_{k1} - E_{k2}$
F_r = force on rim, lbs
F_s = force on spoke, lbs
K = ratio of minimum to maximum load, fatigue cycle
(See Sect. 3.2, Fatigue Loading, and see Formula 17, this section)

K_1 = ratio of rim thickness to mean rim radius = $\dfrac{t_r}{r_m}$
(See Table 1)

K_2 = ratio of rim width to rim thickness = $\dfrac{W_r}{t_r}$
(See Table 2)

L = length of spoke, in.
(often assumed = r_m for simplified computation)
M_r = bending moment in rim at spoke, in.-lbs
RPM = speed of flywheel rotation, rev per min
RPM_1 = initial speed of flywheel rotation
RPM_2 = final speed after energy is given up
RPM_m = mean speed = $\dfrac{RPM_1 + RPM_2}{2}$
S = section modulus of spoke, in.^{3}
T = torque, in.-lbs
W_r = width of rim, in.
W_t = weight of flywheel, lbs.
Y = $1 + \dfrac{6.57}{n^2 K_1}$

The proposed flywheel's kinetic energy is obtained from the following:

$$E_k = \tfrac{1}{2}\, m\, V^2 = \tfrac{1}{2}\, m \left(2\, \pi\, r_m\, \frac{RPM}{60}\right)^2 \text{ ft-lbs}$$

Since:

$$F = m\, a$$

$$W_t = m\, g$$

where:

m = mass, and is the quantity of matter

W_t = weight, and equals the force of gravity (g) acting on this mass (m)

British Gravitational Units —

W_t = pounds

$g = 32.2 \text{ ft/sec}^2$

hence:

$$m = W_t/g \quad \text{and}$$

$$E_k = \tfrac{1}{2}\left(\frac{W_t}{32.2}\right)\left(2\,\pi\,\frac{r_m}{12}\,\frac{RPM}{60}\right)^2$$

$$\text{or}\quad \boxed{E_k = \frac{W_t\, r_m{}^2\, RPM^2}{845{,}500} \text{ ft-lbs}}$$

Energy given up by the flywheel, or the change in energy, is —

$$\Delta E_k = E_{k1} - E_{k2}$$

$$\boxed{\Delta E_k = \frac{W_t\, r_m{}^2}{845{,}500}\,(RPM_1{}^2 - RPM_2)^2}$$

It can also be shown that —

$$\boxed{RPM_2 = RPM_1\left(\frac{2 - C}{2 + C}\right)}$$

3. CALCULATING STRESSES IN FLYWHEELS

In designing flywheels, centrifugal force is the prime consideration. The stresses are statically indeterminate.

On one extreme, if the spokes offer no restraining action (as in Fig. 2), the rim acts simply as a revolving ring with just an axial tensile force resulting from the centrifugal force of the rim. In this ideal case, there is no inward radial force applied to the rim by the spokes.

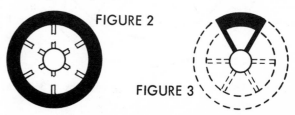

FIGURE 2

FIGURE 3

On the other extreme, if the spokes are absolutely rigid and do not stretch (see Fig. 3), the portion of the rim between the supporting spokes will act as a

TABLE 1 – RATIO OF THICKNESS TO RADIUS OF RIM

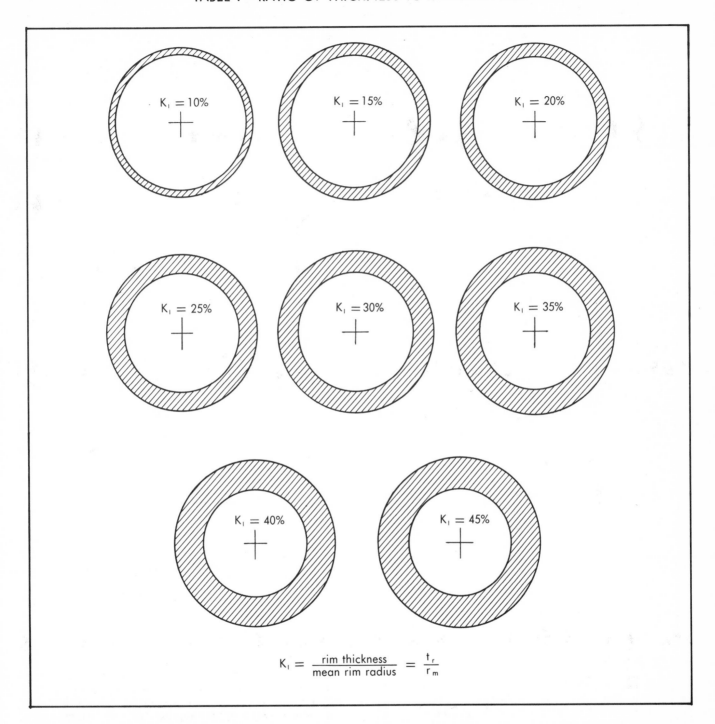

$$K_1 = \frac{\text{rim thickness}}{\text{mean rim radius}} = \frac{t_r}{r_m}$$

uniformly loaded beam with fixed ends; the loading is due to the centrifugal force acting on the rim.

Formulas 1, 2 and 3 are based on these extreme conditions and thus represent maximum values. Since the actual conditions will be a compromise between these two extremes, the actual values will be somewhat less.

Rim and Tensile Stress

The rim of a rotating wheel tends to expand as speed increases; hence it causes axial tensile stresses in the rim. Formula 1 assumes no restraining action of the spokes and gives the <u>maximum</u> value. The actual value would be less, decreasing with greater spoke restraint, area of spoke (A_s) and number of spokes (n).

$$\sigma_t = \frac{r_m^2 \, RPM_1^2}{124,400} \qquad \dots \dots (1)$$

TABLE 2 – RATIO OF WIDTH TO THICKNESS OF RIM

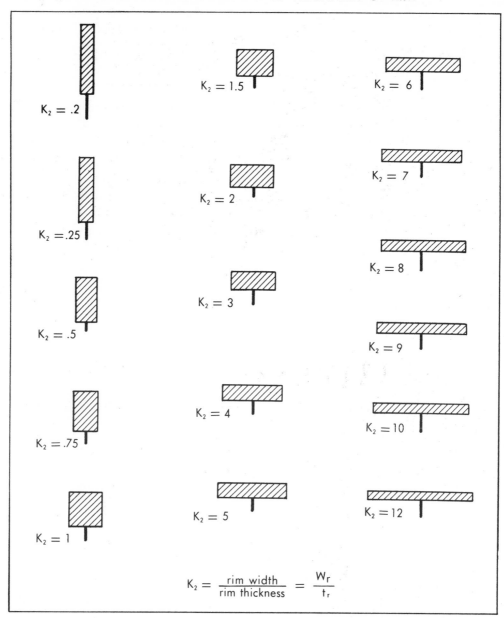

$$K_2 = \frac{\text{rim width}}{\text{rim thickness}} = \frac{W_r}{t_r}$$

Spoke Tensile Stress

The above Formula 1 gives the maximum tensile stress in the rim if unrestrained. Assuming now that the expanding rim pulls the spokes out along with it, both undergo the same amount of strain (ε), and therefore both have the same tensile stress (σ_t). Actually this condition does not quite exist since any restraining action of the spokes will reduce the expansion of the rim and therefore reduce this rim stress. Nevertheless Formula 2 represents a <u>maximum</u> axial tensile stress in the spokes; hence,

$$\sigma_t = \frac{r_m^2\,\text{RPM}_1^2}{124,400} \quad \dots\dots\dots\dots\dots\dots (2)$$

Rim Bending Stress

The rim segment between adjacent restraining spokes acts as a curved beam fixed at both ends. Uniform loading of the segment by centrifugal force causes a bending stress in the rim. Formula 3 gives the <u>maximum</u> value of this stress; the actual would be <u>less with</u> greater rim thickness (t_r) and number of spokes or arms (n). A <u>solid disc</u> would be considered to have an infinite number of spokes ($n = \infty$) and the resulting bending stress in the rim would be zero.

$$\sigma_b = \frac{r_m^3\,\text{RPM}_1^2}{6300\,n^2\,t_r} = \frac{r_m^2\,\text{RPM}_1^2}{6300\,n^2\,K_1} \quad \dots\dots\dots\dots (3)$$

K_1 is the ratio of rim thickness (t_r) to mean rim radius (r_m). See Table 1, which shows the general effect of changing this ratio.

Resultant Rim Stress

Most machine design texts assume the spokes to stretch about 75% of the amount required if the rim were free to expand under centrifugal force. This means the total tensile and bending stress in the rim would equal about ¾ of the rim tensile stress (Formula 1) and ¼ of the rim bending stress (Formula 3).

$$\sigma_T = \frac{3}{4}\left(\frac{r_m^2\, RPM_1^2}{124,400}\right) + \frac{1}{4}\left(\frac{r_m^2\, RPM_1^2}{6300\, n^2\, K_1}\right)$$

$$\boxed{\sigma_T = \frac{r_m^2\, RPM_1^2}{165,800}\left(1 + \frac{6.57}{n^2\, K_1}\right)} \quad \dots \dots \dots \dots (4)$$

Spoke Strength

A sudden change in speed causes the flywheel to absorb or deliver power. The result is a torque which causes bending stresses in the spokes. Therefore, the spokes are usually designed to about ¾ of the required torque strength of the driving shaft. Here for simplicity, we assume that length of spoke = r_m and thus L has dropped out of the formula.

$$\boxed{\sigma_b = \frac{\tau\, d^3}{6.8\, n\, S}} \quad \dots \dots \dots \dots \dots \dots \dots (5)$$

Where the flywheel also serves as a pulley, the tangential force on the rim creates bending stresses in the spokes. On thick-rim flywheels, all of the spokes are assumed to carry the tangential load. On thin-rim flywheels, half of the spokes are assumed to carry this load.

(max at hub)

$$\boxed{\sigma_b = \frac{F\, L}{n\, S}} \quad \dots \dots \dots \dots \dots \dots \dots (6)$$

The tensile stresses in the spoke (2) should be added to the bending stresses in the spoke (5) or (6), and the resultant (σ_T) should not exceed the allowable stresses for repeated and impact loads.

Based on shaft strength:

$$\boxed{\sigma_T = \frac{r_m^2\, RPM_1^2}{124,400} + \frac{\tau\, d^3}{6.8\, n\, S}} \quad \dots \dots \dots (7a)$$

required section modulus of spoke is —

$$S = \frac{124,400\, \tau\, d^3}{6.8\, n\, (124,400\, \sigma_T - r_m^2\, RPM_1^2)}$$

$$\text{or} \quad \boxed{S = \frac{\tau\, d^3}{6.8\, n\, \sigma_T\left(1 - \frac{1.33}{Y}\right)}} \quad \dots \dots \dots (7b)$$

The value of Y, once computed, usually can be used repeatedly to simplify the flywheel calculations.

Based on tangential force on flywheel rim:

$$\boxed{\sigma_T = \frac{r_m^2\, RPM_1^2}{124,400} + \frac{F\, L}{n\, S}} \quad \dots \dots \dots \dots \dots (8a)$$

required section modulus of spoke is —

$$S = \frac{124,400\, F\, L}{n\, (124,400\, \sigma_T - r_m^2\, RPM_1^2)}$$

$$\text{or} \quad \boxed{S = \frac{F\, L}{n\, \sigma_T\left(1 - \frac{1.33}{Y}\right)}} \quad \dots \dots \dots \dots \dots (8b)$$

Rim Energy

The cross-sectional area of the rim, based on the energy (E_k) which must be stored in the rim, is found from the following:

$$\boxed{A_r = t_r\, W_r = K_1^2\, K_2\, r_m^2} \quad \dots \dots \dots \dots \dots (9a)$$

$$\boxed{A_r = \frac{\Delta E_k\, 476,000}{r_m^3\, (RPM_1^2 - RPM_2^2)} = \frac{\Delta E_k\, 238,000}{C\, r_m^3\, RPM_m^2}} \quad \dots (9b)$$

K_1 is the ratio of rim thickness (t_r) to rim mean radius (r_m). K_2 is the ratio of rim width (W_r) to rim thickness (t_r). Table 2 shows the general effect of changing this ratio. C is the coefficient of speed fluctuation, and = $(RPM_1 - RPM_2)/RPM_m$.

Rotating Disc

The maximum stress in a rotating disc is the tangential stress, and is maximum at the inner radius:

$$\boxed{\sigma_t = \frac{RPM_1^2\, (3.3\, r_2^2 + .7\, r_1^2)}{497,500}} \quad \dots \dots \dots \dots (10)$$

which is the max. tangential stress at $r = r_1$

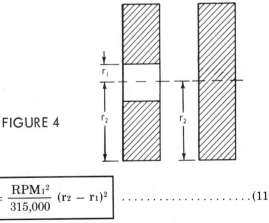

FIGURE 4

$$\boxed{\sigma_r = \frac{RPM_1^2}{315,000}\, (r_2 - r_1)^2} \quad \dots \dots \dots \dots \dots (11)$$

which is the max. radial stress at $r = \sqrt{r_2\, r_1}$

For solid disc: $r_1 = 0$ and max σ_r = max σ_t

4. RIM DIMENSIONS

In the design of a flywheel, the dimensions are usually assumed. Then the various stresses are checked, using Formulas 1 through 11. It is possible to shorten the process by combining Formulas 4 (resultant rim stress) and 9 (required rim area for stored energy). Thus:

$$Y = 1 + \frac{6.57}{n^2 K_1} \quad \dots \dots (12)$$

$$r_m = \frac{407.2 \sqrt{\sigma_T}}{RPM \sqrt{Y}} \quad \dots \dots (13)$$

$$K_2 = \frac{\Delta E_k (2 + C)^2 Y}{2.79 C K_1^2 r_m^3 \sigma_r} \quad \dots \dots (14)$$

Here, the procedure is to select a reasonable rim radius (r_m) and then solve for rim profile (K_2). An alternative is to select a desirable rim profile and then solve for rim radius.

If a solid disc is used instead of spokes, then $n = \infty$, and using Formula 1--

$$r_m = \frac{352.7 \sqrt{\sigma_T}}{RPM} \quad \dots \dots (15)$$

$$K_2 = \frac{\Delta E_k (2 + C)^2}{2.09 C K_1^2 r_m^3 \sigma_T} \quad \dots \dots (16)$$

Required dimensions of the rim cross-section are thus —

$$t_r = K_1 r_m$$
$$W_r = K_2 t_r \quad \text{and}$$
$$A_r = t_r W_r$$

Combined Action of Rim and Spokes

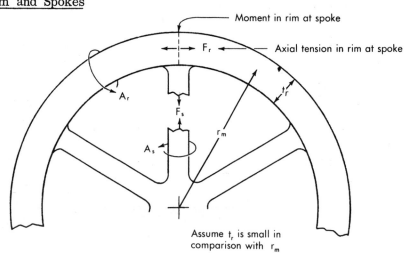

Moment in rim at spoke

Axial tension in rim at spoke

Assume t_r is small in comparison with r_m

FIGURE 5

TABLE 3

Number of Spokes	Axial tensile force in spoke F_s	Axial tensile force in rim at spoke F_r	Bending moment in rim at spoke M_r
4	$\dfrac{A_r \sigma_t}{.1094\left(\dfrac{r}{t_r}\right)^2 + .965 + 1.5 \dfrac{A_r}{A_s}}$	$A_r \sigma - .5000\, F_s$	$.1366\, F_s\, r_m$
6	$\dfrac{A_r \sigma_t}{.03042\left(\dfrac{r}{t_r}\right)^2 + 1.436 + 1.5 \dfrac{A_r}{A_s}}$	$A_r \sigma - .8660\, F_s$	$.0889\, F_s\, r_m$
8	$\dfrac{A_r \sigma_t}{.01368\left(\dfrac{r}{t_r}\right)^2 + 1.911 + 1.5 \dfrac{A_r}{A_s}}$	$A_r \sigma - 1.207\, F_s$	$.0661\, F_s\, r_m$
10	$\dfrac{A_r \sigma_t}{.0054\left(\dfrac{r}{t_r}\right)^2 + 2.388 + 1.5 \dfrac{A_r}{A_s}}$	$A_r \sigma - 1.539\, F_s$	$.0526\, F_s\, r_m$

The stresses from these forces (F_r and M_r) should be added together to give maximum stress in rim. The axial tensile stress from this force (F_s) should be added to the bending stress previously found to give the maximum stress in the spoke.

5. TIMOSHENKO'S FORMULAS

The designer should be cautioned against using Formula 4, resultant rim stress, in trying to arrive at too close a value for stress, because of the uncertain degree of rigidity at the intersection of the spoke and the rim. Timoshenko has made a more detailed study of this condition basing his work upon the strain energy method of analysis. See Figure 5.

According to the factor expressed by Formula 1, the axial tensile stress in the rim caused by the rim expanding under the action of centrifugal force (if unrestrained by spokes) would be--

$$\sigma_t = \frac{r^2 \, RPM_1^2}{124,400}$$

Any restraining action of the spokes against this expansion would change these conditions.

In Strength of Materials, Part II, Timoshenko has analyzed the stresses in the spoke and rim of a rotating wheel and the formulas of Table 3 are derived from his work.

6. ALLOWABLE FATIGUE FORCE ON WELD

The allowable fatigue force on a fillet weld depends to a great extent upon the value of the fatigue cycle, or ratio of the minimum force to maximum force during the changing load.

$$K = \frac{F_{min}}{F_{max}}$$

Since the tensile stress in the spoke and likewise the tensile force is directly proportional to the square of the speed (RPM) of the flywheel, it is seen that--

Speed Fluctuation

$$C = \frac{RPM_1 - RPM_2}{RPM_m} \text{ where } RPM_m = \frac{RPM_1 + RPM_2}{2}$$

$$\therefore \quad C = \frac{2\,(RPM_1 - RPM_2)}{RPM_1 + RPM_2}$$

and $C(RPM_1) + C(RPM_2) = 2\,(RPM_1) - 2\,(RPM_2)$

or $RPM_2 = RPM_1 \left(\dfrac{2 - C}{2 + C} \right)$

The stress being directly proportional to the square of the flywheel speed —

$\sigma_1 \, \alpha \, (RPM_1)^2$

$\sigma_2 \, \alpha \, (RPM_2)^2$

so $K = \dfrac{\sigma_1}{\sigma_2} = \left(\dfrac{RPM_1}{RPM_2} \right)^2 = \left[\dfrac{RPM_2 \left(\dfrac{2 - C}{2 + C} \right)}{RPM_2} \right]^2 = \left(\dfrac{2 - C}{2 + C} \right)^2$

$$\boxed{K = \left(\frac{2 - C}{2 + C} \right)^2} \quad \dots\dots\dots\dots\dots\dots (17)$$

Fatigue Force

The allowable fatigue force on a fillet weld at 2,000,000 cycles may be found from the following--

$$\boxed{f = \frac{5090 \, \omega}{1 - \dfrac{K}{2}}} \quad \dots\dots\dots\dots\dots\dots\dots (18)$$

Solving for size of fillet weld to use in joining flywheel rim to spokes on the basis of stress, may provide a size within the allowable fatigue limit but yet insufficient for a good weld.

In order to avoid too fast a rate of cooling when welding thick plates, the AWS Specifications for Welded Highway and Railway Bridges list the minimum size of fillet weld to be made for a given thickness of plate, Table 4. The listed minimum weld size presumably will provide sufficient welding heat input into the plate to give the desired slow rate of cooling. An additional note provides that the minimum size of fillet weld does not have to be less than the thickness of the thinner plate.

TABLE 4 - MINIMUM WELD SIZES
For Thick Plates

Thickness of thicker plate joined	Minimum leg size (ω) of fillet weld
to ½″ incl.	3⁄16″
over ½″ to ¾″	¼″
over ¾″ to 1½″	5⁄16″
over 1½″ to 2¼″	⅜″
over 2¼″ to 6″	½″
over 6″	⅝″

This is not foolproof. For example, a plate thicker than 6″ would require a minimum weld size of ⅝″; yet in actual practice this would be made in several passes, each pass equivalent to about a 5⁄16″ fillet and giving a heat input approximately that of a 5⁄16″ weld. This probably would not be sufficient unless the plates were preheated.

Since the first pass of the joint is the most critical, it is recommended that this be made with the low-hydrogen electrode, with a rather slow travel speed, so as to provide as much heat input as possible and thereby provide a good strong first pass.

Problem 1

To design a welded steel flywheel for the following conditions:

ΔE_k = 100,000 ft-lbs, the energy to be given up by flywheel = $E_{k1} - E_{k2}$

C = 0.2 speed fluctuation for rock crusher

RPM_1 = 1800

σ_T = 5000 psi allowable combined tensile and bending stress

τ = 5000 psi assumed shear stress in shaft

d = 4" diameter of flywheel shaft

Six spokes are to be used, and the rim thickness (t_r) is to be 30% of the mean rim radius (r_m); hence —

n = 6

K_1 = .30

Step 1: DETERMINE DIMENSIONS OF RIM

$$(12) \quad Y = 1 + \frac{6.57}{n^2 K_1}$$

$$= 1 + \frac{6.57}{(6)^2 (.30)}$$

$$= 1.608$$

$$(13) \quad r_m = \frac{407.2 \sqrt{\sigma_T}}{RPM \sqrt{Y}}$$

$$= \frac{407.2 \sqrt{5000}}{1800 \sqrt{1.608}}$$

$$= \underline{12.62"}$$

$$(14) \quad K_2 = \frac{\Delta E_k (2 + C)^2 Y}{2.79 \, C \, K_1^2 \, r_m^3 \, \sigma_T}$$

$$= \frac{(100,000)(2 + .2)^2 (1.608)}{(2.79)(.2)(.30)^2 (12.62)^3 (5000)}$$

$$= 1.54$$

The dimensions of the rim are thus —

t_r = $K_1 r_m$

= (.3) (12.62)

= 3.786 " or use 3¾"

W_r = $K_2 t_r$

= (1.54) (3.786)

= 5.83" or use 5⅞"

A_r = $t_r W_r$

= (3.75) (5.875)

= 22.03 in.²

Step 2: DETERMINE DIMENSIONS OF SPOKE

Based on strength of shaft:

$$(7a) \quad S = \frac{\tau \, d^3}{6.8 \, n \, \sigma_T \left(1 - \frac{1.33}{Y}\right)}$$

$$= \frac{(5000)(4)^3}{6.8 (6)(5000)\left(1 - \frac{1.33}{1.608}\right)}$$

$$= 9.07 \text{ in.}^3$$

Hence, use 2" x 5¼" spoke, which checks out:

$$S = \frac{(2)(5.25)^2}{6}$$

$$= 9.2 \text{ in.}^3 \quad OK$$

and A_s = (2)(5.25)

= 10.5 in.²

These dimensions produce a flywheel design as shown in Figure 6.

FIGURE 6

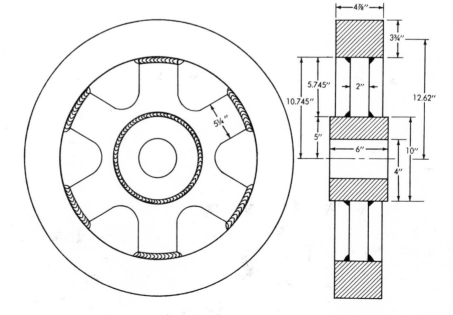

Step 3: CHECK THIS DESIGN

Axial tensile stress in unrestrained rim

(1) $\sigma_t = \dfrac{r_m^2\, RPM_1^2}{124{,}400}$

$= \dfrac{(12.62)^2\,(1800)^2}{124{,}400}$

$= 4{,}140 \text{ psi}$

According to Timoshenko's formulas:
Axial tensile force in spoke (F_s)

$F_s = \dfrac{A_r\, \sigma_t}{.0304\left(\dfrac{r_m}{t_r}\right)^2 + 1.436 + 1.5\dfrac{A_r}{A_s}}$

$= \dfrac{(18.28)\,(4140)}{.0304\left(\dfrac{12.62}{3.75}\right)^2 + 1.436 + 1.5\left(\dfrac{22.03}{10.5}\right)}$

$= 18{,}500 \text{ lbs}$

and check the spoke's tensile stress —

$\sigma_t = \dfrac{F_s}{A_r}$

$= \dfrac{18{,}500}{10.5}$

$= \underline{1{,}760 \text{ psi}}$ OK

Axial tensile force in rim (F_r)

$F_r = A_r\, \sigma_t - .8660\, F_s$

$= (22.03)\,(4140) - .8660\,(18{,}500)$

$= 75{,}100 \text{ lbs}$

and check the rim's tensile stress —

$\sigma_t = \dfrac{F_r}{A_r}$

$= \dfrac{75{,}100}{22.03}$

$= 3410 \text{ psi}$

Bending moment in rim at spoke (M_r)

$M_r = .0889\, F_s\, r_m$

$= .0889\,(18{,}500)\,(12.62)$

$= 20{,}800 \text{ in.-lbs}$

and check bending stress in rim —

$\sigma_b = \dfrac{M_r}{S_r}$ $\bigg|$ where $S_r = \dfrac{(4.875)(3.75)^2}{6}$

$= \dfrac{20{,}800}{11.42}$ $= 11.42 \text{ in.}^3$

$= 1820 \text{ psi}$

Total tensile and bending stress in rim

$\sigma_T = 3410 + 1820$

$= \underline{5230 \text{ psi}}$ OK

Step 4: DETERMINE FILLET WELD SIZE AROUND
SPOKE AT HUB

The moment (M) on the spoke and the connecting weld equals the torque (T) applied to the hub of the flywheel, assuming for simplicity that the length of the spoke $= r_m$.

The torque on the flywheel hub is obtained from the shear stress in the flywheel shaft:

$\tau = \dfrac{T\,c}{J}$ or $T = \dfrac{\tau\, J}{c}$ $\bigg|$ where $J = \dfrac{\pi\, d^4}{32}$ and $c = \dfrac{d}{2}$

$\therefore\ \ T = \dfrac{\tau\, \pi\, d^3}{16}$

$= \dfrac{(5000)\,\pi\,(4)^3}{16}$

$= 62{,}830 \text{ in.-lbs}$

There are six spokes and connecting welds; hence the moment on each weld is--

$M = \dfrac{T}{n}$

$= \dfrac{62{,}830}{6}$

$= 10{,}470 \text{ in.-lbs}$

The maximum tensile force in the spokes would be the stress found in Formula 2 multiplied by the spoke area (A_s), or--

$F_s = \sigma A_s = \dfrac{r_m^2\, RPM_1^2}{124{,}400}\, A_s$

$= \dfrac{(12.62)^2\,(1800)^2}{124{,}400}\,(10.5)$

$= 43{,}500 \text{ lbs}$

Properties of the welded connection, treated as a line:

$S_w = bd + \dfrac{d^2}{3}$

$= (2)\,(5.25) + \dfrac{(5.25)^2}{3}$

$= 19.7 \text{ in.}^2$

$A_w = 2\,(b + d)$

$= 2\,(2 + 5.25)$

$= 14.5 \text{"}$

Forces on the weld may then be found:

Bending

$f_b = \dfrac{M}{S_w}$

$= \dfrac{10{,}470}{19.7}$

$= 530 \text{ lbs/linear in.}$

TABLE 5 - FABRICATING FLYWHEELS AND THICK-RIM PULLEYS

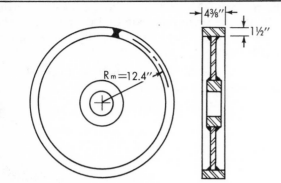

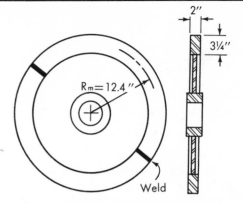

Keeping the rim thickness to 1½" permits rolling to shape.

In this design, keeping rim width to 2" allows flame burning of half sections, butt welded together to eliminate rolling.

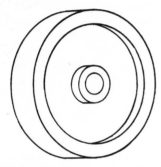

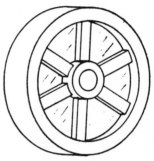

The simplest flywheel is a rim attached to a solid disc web.

For greater web stiffness, formed channel sections may be welded to the web.

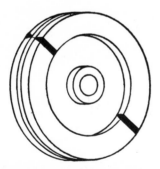

To save rolling, the rim may be flame burned from heavy plate. It is possible to cut the rim in two sections and nest the sections so there is little scrap.

Sometimes rolled sections such as I beams are used for the spokes.

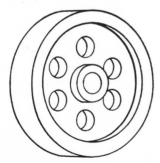

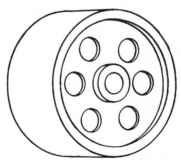

Holes may be cut in the web to reduce the weight if the material can be used for hubs or bosses, or if the scrap value is more than the cost of cutting.

If the flywheel is to serve as a pulley it must have a wide face. Two webs can be used for greater stiffness.

Tension

$$f_t = \frac{F_s}{A_w}$$

$$= \frac{43,500}{14.5}$$

$$= 3000 \text{ lbs/linear in.}$$

Total force on weld

$$f_r = f_b + f_t$$

$$= 530 + 3000$$

$$= 3530 \text{ lbs/linear in.}$$

The fluctuation of flywheel speed (RPM) will vary the force in the spoke and connecting weld. This produces a fatigue type of load and will reduce the allowable strength of the weld.

Fatigue cycle

$$(17) \quad K = \left(\frac{2 - C}{2 + C}\right)^2$$

$$= \left(\frac{2 - .2}{2 + .2}\right)^2 = \left(\frac{1.8}{2.2}\right)^2$$

$$= .67$$

Allowable force on fillet weld

$$(18) \quad f = \frac{5090 \, \omega}{1 - \dfrac{K}{2}}$$

$$= \frac{5090 \, (1)}{1 - \dfrac{(.67)}{2}}$$

$$= 7660 \text{ lbs/linear in.}$$

Required leg size of fillet weld

$$\omega = \frac{f_r}{f}$$

$$= \frac{3530}{7660}$$

$$= \underline{.461" \text{ or use } \tfrac{1}{2}"} \; \triangle$$

7. FABRICATING HINTS

Table 5 shows some proven ideas that can be considered in holding material and fabricating costs to a minimum, or in meeting special service requirements.

Welded steel flywheel (right) for engine-driven welding generator saved 35% in manufacturing cost over cast iron counterpart (left), with no sacrifice of inertia properties.

This 50" steel flywheel has been tack-welded and will be mounted in motorized positioner for final welding. The result will be a low-cost, safe and efficient flywheel.

Arc welding slashed costs in fabricating the components of this large gear and sheave assembly. Photo at left shows sheave spider and gear spider near completion. Photo below shows the final assembly after machining.

How to Design
Steel Pulleys and Sheaves

1. DESIGNING FOR STRESS

Pulleys are subjected to a combination of stresses resulting from the centrifugal force and the tension in the belts acting on the pulley. Maximum strength and rigidity can be achieved with minimum weight by using welded steel fabrication.

By recognizing the various stresses in the operation of the pulley and designing for these stresses, steel may be used to the best advantage. This means a better, more dependable pulley at less cost.

There are several types of forces which are applied to a pulley when in service and these must be considered:

1. The tensile forces in the belt result in a uniform inward radial pressure against the face of the pulley rim.

2. The tensile forces in the belt, if applied off-center to the pulley, will set up some bending stresses in the disc, resulting in some deformation.

3. Stresses may result from the centrifugal force acting on pulley parts.

4. The welds joining the hub, rim, and disc must be capable of transmitting the power from the belt.

2. FORCES ON PULLEY RIM FROM BELT

It can be shown that the tensile force in the belt causes an inward radial force (R) having the value of:

$$R = \frac{F}{r} \text{ lbs/in. of circumference}$$

When this is divided by the width of the belt (W_b), it results in a uniform inward radial pressure of:

$$\boxed{w_b = \frac{F}{r\,W_b} \text{ psi}} \dots\dots\dots\dots\dots\dots\dots\dots\dots\dots\dots\dots(1)$$

Definitions of Symbols Used in Pulley Design

Δ = deflection, in.
ω = leg size of fillet weld, in.
σ = stress, in.
ρ = density of belt material
α = (1) $180 - \theta$
    (2) factor governed by r_h/r, in determining Δ of disc
β = factor governed by r_h/r, in determining σ of disc
θ = included angle formed by arc of belt contact with pulley rim, given in radians in formula
ϕ = angular deflection, disc to hub

b = width of V-belt at outer surface
c = distance of neutral axis to outer fiber of section
f = coefficient of friction, belt to pulley
n = number of spokes or arms supporting pulley rim
r = (1) radius of pulley rim
    (2) radius to center of fillet weld throat
    (3) radius to disc outer edge
r_h = radius of hub OD
r_i = radius of disc inner edge = r_h
r_m = mean radius of pulley rim
t_d = thickness of pulley disc
t_r = thickness of pulley rim
w = uniform radial force, lbs/linear inch of rim width (w_b)
w_b = uniform radial force, inward on pulley rim, lbs/in.
w_c = uniform radial force, outward on pulley rim, resulting from rim's centrifugal force, lbs/in.

F = belt tensile force causing inward radial pressure against pulley rim
F_1 = maximum belt tensile force (tight)
F_2 = minor belt tensile force (slack)
F_c = centrifugal force acting on the belt
F_i = initial belt tension
F_t = net belt tension needed to transfer torque load
N = number of belts on pulley
T = torque transmitted by pulley, in.-lbs
V = belt speed, fpm
W_b = width of belt, or of that portion of pulley rim contacted by belt
W_d = span between discs supporting pulley rim
W_r = full width of pulley rim

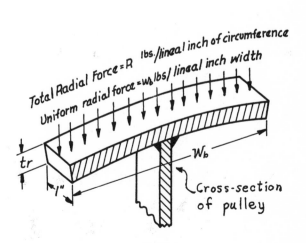

FIGURE 1

Here a narrow cross-section of the rim is considered as a beam, using only the width of the belt (W_b), which equals the width of the pulley rim in contact with the belt and subjected to the resulting radial pressure (w_b).

There is also a centrifugal force acting on the rim resulting in a uniform outward radial pressure of:

$$w_c = \frac{t_r r \, RPM^2}{124,400} \, psi \quad \dots \dots \dots \dots \dots \dots (2)$$
$$\text{(For steel)}$$

The centrifugal force offsets the belt force to some extent and w_c may be deducted from w_b to obtain the net radial pressure (w) on the rim. In some pulleys, the centrifugal force is of sufficient magnitude relative to belt force, that w_c on the portion of the pulley rim circumference not in contact with the belt is greater than the net radial pressure on the rim under the belt. In such an instance, w_c should be substituted for w in the following formulas when applicable.

Since a running belt is tight in one direction (F_1) and slack in the other direction (F_2), most machine design texts show the following formula for belts:

$$\frac{F_1 - F_c}{F_2 - F_c} = e^{f\theta}$$

where:

$e = 2.718$

$f = $ coefficient of friction, belt to pulley

$\theta = $ included angle formed by arc of belt contact with pulley rim, radians

$F_c = $ tension on the belt due to centrifugal force, as determined by later Formula 8

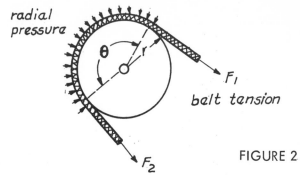

radial pressure

belt tension

FIGURE 2

Since:

$$F_t = F_1 - F_2 = \frac{63,030 \times HP}{r \times RPM} \quad \dots \dots \dots \dots (3)$$

it can be shown that the following expression is true:

$$F = \frac{63,030 \times HP}{r \times RPM} \left[\frac{e^{f\theta}}{e^{f\theta} - 1} \right] + F_c$$
$$F_1 = F_i + F_t + F_c$$

This shows that the maximum belt tension (F_1) is made up of three forces: that caused by the initial belt tension (F_i); that caused by the transmission of power (F_t), taking into account the coefficient of friction (f) and the angle of belt contact (θ); and that due to the centrifugal force acting on the belt (F_c).

The centrifugal force acting on the belt results in an outward radial pull; therefore, this portion of the belt tension (F_c) will not contribute to the inward radial pressure on the pulley rim and will be deducted.

The force (F) in the belt contributing to the inward radial pressure against the pulley rim is thus—

$$F = F_1 - F_c \quad \dots \dots \dots \dots \dots \dots \dots \dots \dots \dots (4)$$

VALUES OF $\dfrac{e^{f\theta}}{e^{f\theta} - 1}$

COEFFICIENT OF FRICTION (f)

TABLE 1

Arc of Belt Contact θ	.25	.30	.35	.40	.45	.50	.55	.60
120°	2.45	2.15	1.93	1.76	1.64	1.54	1.46	1.40
130°	2.32	2.03	1.82	1.68	1.56	1.47	1.40	1.34
140°	2.19	1.93	1.74	1.61	1.50	1.42	1.35	1.30
150°	2.09	1.84	1.67	1.54	1.45	1.37	1.31	1.26
160°	1.99	1.76	1.61	1.49	1.40	1.33	1.27	1.23
170°	1.91	1.70	1.55	1.44	1.36	1.29	1.24	1.20
180°	1.84	1.64	1.50	1.40	1.32	1.26	1.22	1.18
190°	1.78	1.59	1.46	1.36	1.29	1.24	1.19	1.16
200°	1.72	1.54	1.42	1.32	1.26	1.21	1.17	1.14
210°	1.67	1.50	1.38	1.30	1.24	1.19	1.15	1.12
220°	1.62	1.46	1.35	1.27	1.22	1.17	1.14	1.11
230°	1.58	1.43	1.33	1.25	1.20	1.16	1.12	1.10
240°	1.54	1.40	1.30	1.23	1.18	1.14	1.11	1.09

or:

$$F = \frac{63,030 \times HP}{r \times RPM} \left[\frac{e^{f\theta}}{e^{f\theta} - 1} \right] \quad \dots\dots\dots\dots (5)$$

Since:

$$w_b = \frac{F}{r\,W_b}$$

this becomes —

$$w_b = \frac{63,030 \times HP}{r^2\,W_b\,RPM} \left[\frac{e^{f\theta}}{e^{f\theta} - 1} \right] \quad \dots\dots\dots\dots (6)$$

See Table 1 for values of $\left[\dfrac{e^{f\theta}}{e^{f\theta} - 1} \right]$

This force (F) or pressure (w_b) is the minimum value for these conditions. They will be greater if the initial belt tension (F_i) is increased.

This can be handled by increasing the required (minimum) initial belt tension (F_i) by a factor $(1 + k)$ where k is the increase expressed as a decimal; this factor in the bracket would then become—

$$\left[\frac{e^{f\theta} + k}{e^{f\theta} - k} \right]$$

or, to use Table 1 or Nomograph 1 (Fig. 4), simply multiply the result by $(1 + k)$.

V-Belts

V-belts may be considered, simply by using the proper equivalent coefficient of friction for the belt (f_e) Because of the tapered groove, friction is greatly increased according to the following:

$$f_e = \frac{f}{\sin \beta} \quad \dots\dots\dots\dots\dots\dots\dots (7)$$

One machine design text suggests the equivalent coefficients of friction for V-belts shown in Table 2.

FIGURE 3

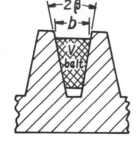

TABLE 2

groove angle	2β	30°	32°	34°	36°	38°
equivalent coefficient of friction	f_e	.50	.47	.45	.42	.40

In most cases the maximum allowable working tensile force for the belt may be found in manufacturer's literature and this value (F_1) may be used directly in the design of the rim. Since $F = F_1 - F_c$ it will be necessary to calculate the additional tensile force in the belt due to centrifugal force (F_c) and, if large, to deduct this from the manufacturer's value of F_1.

$$F_c = \frac{W_b\,t_b\,\rho\,r^2\,RPM^2}{35,200} \text{ lbs} \quad \dots\dots\dots\dots (8a)$$

ρ = density of belt material

In the case of V-belts, the maximum permissible working load per belt is given as:

$$F_1 = 145\,b^2 \text{ lbs}$$

b = belt width at outer surface

The tensile force in the belt due to centrifugal force (F_c) will be —

$$F_c = \frac{b^2\,r^2\,RPM^2}{1,800,000} \text{ lbs} \quad \dots\dots\dots\dots (8b)$$

Since the net force (F) in the belt $= F_1 - F_c$:

$$F_T = N\,b^2 \left[145 - \left(\frac{r\,RPM}{1342} \right)^2 \right] \text{ lbs} \quad \dots\dots\dots (9)$$

For V-belts (total)

N = number of belts

Summary: Forces on Pulley

1. If the maximum allowable working tension in the flat belt or V-belt (F_1) can be found in manufacturer's literature, and the effect of centrifugal force of the belt (F_c) is calculated by means of Formula 8, the net tensile force of the belt acting on the rim of the pulley (F) is the difference between these two, see Formula 4, and the uniform inward radial force (w_b) is found from Formula 1.

2. The net force of the belt acting on the rim of the pulley (F) can also be found in the case of V-belts by Formula 9. The uniform inward radial force (w_b) is found from Formula 1.

3. The uniform inward radial force (w_b) caused by a flat belt or V-belts may be found directly by Formula 6 if sufficient information is known.

The above three methods will allow the uniform inward radial force (w_b) acting on the pulley rim to be found. There is an opposite uniform radial force acting outward (w_c) due to the centrifugal force of the rim itself. In the portion of the arc of the pulley where the belt is not in contact, only w_c acts. For that portion of the pulley where the belt does make contact, the difference between w_b and w_c must be used.

When the pulley is at rest there is no outward radial centrifugal force (w_c), just the inward radial belt pressure (w_b) due to the initial tension in the belt.

For slower turning pulleys of high horsepower, w_b becomes very large and w_c becomes very small. As the speed of the pulley increases (assuming constant horsepower), w_b decreases and w_c increases greatly.

Table 1 may be used to find values of:

$$\left[\frac{e^{f\theta}}{e^{f\theta} - 1} \right]$$

or Nomograph 1 (Fig. 4) may be used.

Nomograph 2 (Fig. 5) may be used to find the net belt tension (F) for flat belts or V-belts.

3. BENDING OF RIM CROSS-SECTION

If a cross-section of the rim were examined, it would be seen that this section, when isolated from the rest of the rim, would act as a beam under the action of the uniform radial pressure (w_b).

The following Table 3 gives the maximum bending stress as well as the over-all displacement or deformation for three types of rim support.

A single disc is used in (a). Two discs at each outer edge of the rim are shown in (b). Two discs are used in (c) but each is set in 22% of the width; this results in much lower stress and deflection so that a thinner rim may be used.

FIG. 4 – FRICTION FACTOR, FLAT BELTS (Nomograph 1)

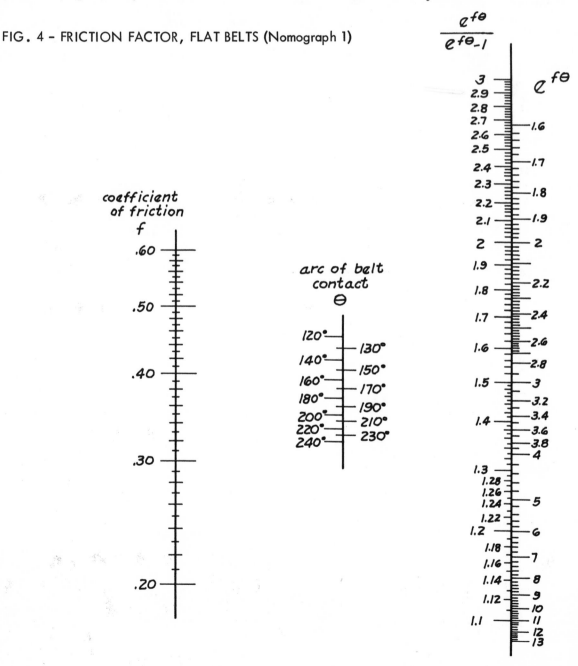

TABLE 3

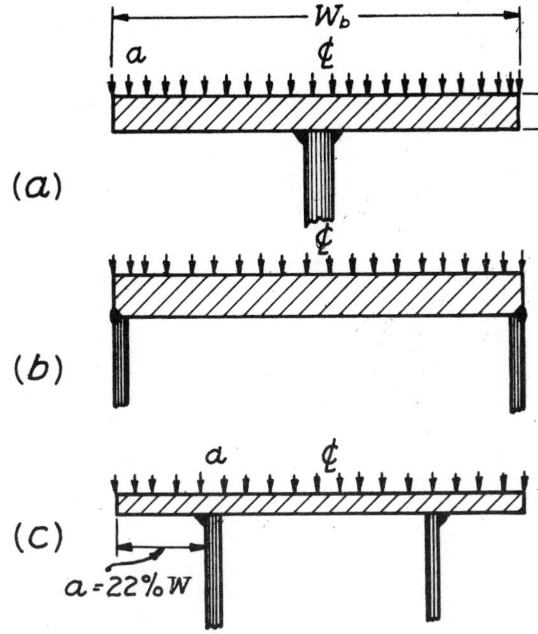

$$\sigma_{\text{¢}} = \frac{.75\, w\, W_b^2}{t_r^2} \quad (10_a)$$

$$\Delta_a = \frac{31.25 \times 10^{-10}\, w\, W_b^4}{t_r^3} \quad (11_a)$$

(a)

$$\sigma_{\text{¢}} = \frac{.75\, w\, W_b^2}{t_r^2} \quad (10_b)$$

$$\Delta_{\text{¢}} = \frac{52.08 \times 10^{-10}\, w\, W_b^4}{t_r^3} \quad (11_b)$$

(b)

$$\sigma_a = \frac{.1452\, w\, W_b^2}{t_r^2} \quad (10_c)$$

$$\Delta_{\text{overall}} = \frac{1.37 \times 10^{-10}\, w\, W_b^4}{t_r^3} \quad (11_c)$$

(c)

$$a = 22\% \, W$$

FIG. 5 - NET BELT TENSION (Nomograph 2)

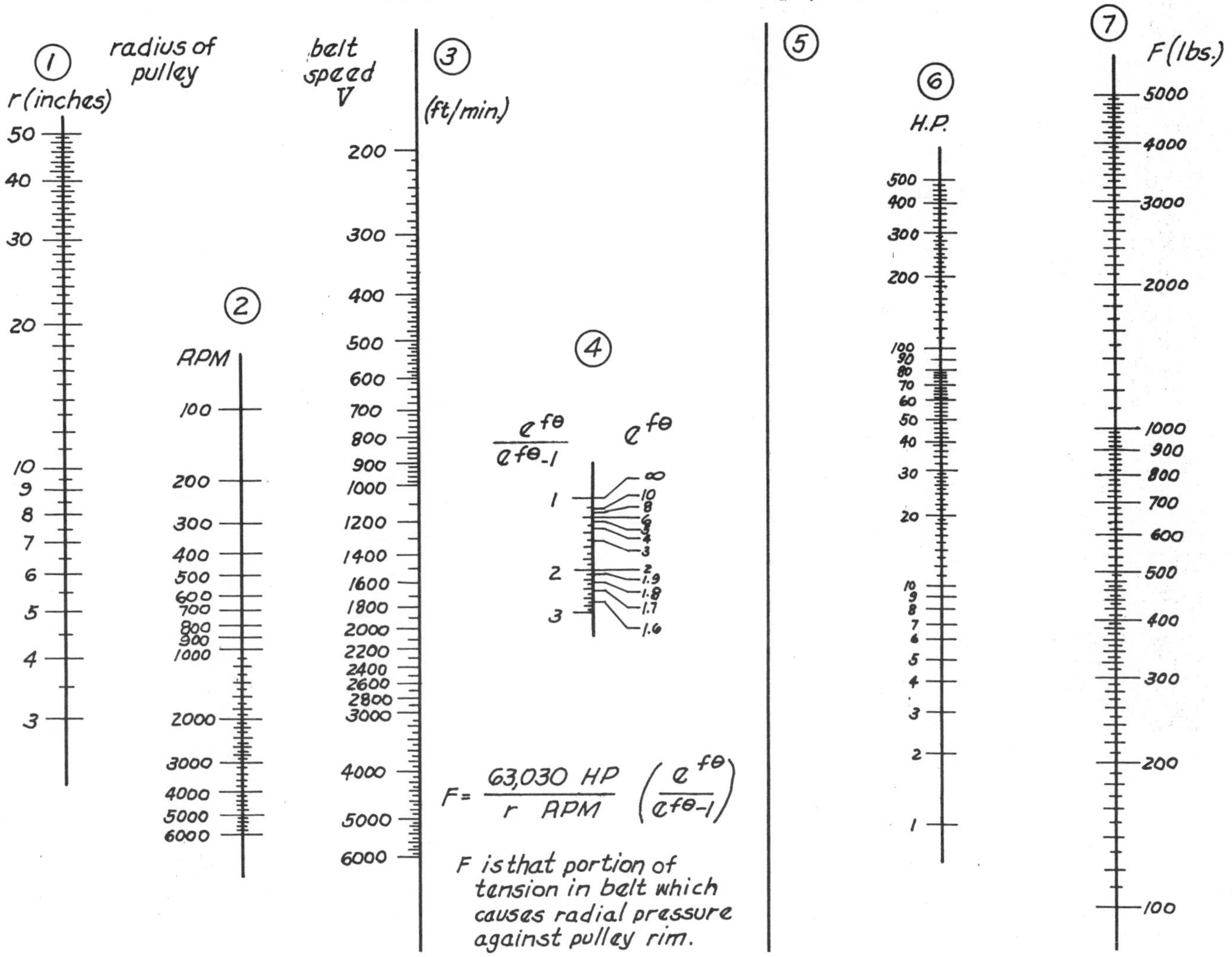

$$F = \frac{63,030\ HP}{r\ RPM}\left(\frac{e^{f\theta}}{e^{f\theta}-1}\right)$$

F is that portion of tension in belt which causes radial pressure against pulley rim.

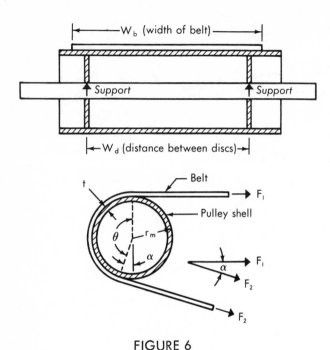

FIGURE 6

If two discs are properly spaced (c), the rim bending stress will be reduced down to 19% and the over-all deflection down to 2.6% as compared to (b) where the two discs are placed at the edges of the rim.

Large Pulleys

Large pulleys that carry wide belts under considerable tension, may require a more precise method of calculating bending stress. See Figure 6.

Treat the whole pulley as a simply supported beam, uniformly loaded. Belt width (W_b) will usually be either

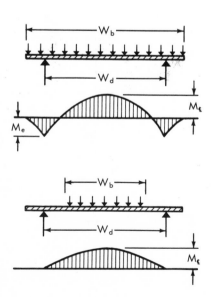

FIGURE 7

greater ($>$) or lesser ($<$) than the distance between supporting discs (W_d). See Figure 7.

The maximum bending moment (M_{max}) is controlled by this relationship between belt width and span between discs. The following formulas apply:

when $W_b < 1.708\ W_d$

$$M_{max} = M_t = \frac{F}{8}(2\ W_d - W_b) \quad \dots \dots (12a)$$

when $W_b = 1.708\ W_d$

$$M_{max} = M_t = M_e = .03675\ F\ W_d \quad \dots \dots (12b)$$

when $W_b > 1.708\ W_d$

$$M_{max} = M_e = \frac{F}{8}\left(W_b - 2\ W_d + \frac{W_d^2}{W_b}\right) \quad \dots \dots (12c)$$

Here, the tension of the slack belt (F_2) may be of greater importance in determining the net force (F). Centrifugal force (F_c) on the belt, which is a factor in the case of smaller, faster-moving belts, is seldom of consequence here. Refer to Figure 8.

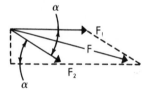

FIGURE 8

where:

when $\alpha = 180° - \theta$

$$F = \sqrt{(F_1 + F_2 \cos \alpha)^2 + (F_2 \sin \alpha)^2} \quad \dots \dots (13a)$$

when $\theta = 180°$

$$F = F_1 + F_2 \quad \dots \dots (13b)$$

Since the bending stress in the pulley shell (rim) is —

$$\sigma = \frac{M\ c}{I} \qquad \text{where: } c = r_m$$
$$I = t\ \pi\ r_m^3$$

it can be more conveniently stated as —

$$\sigma = \frac{M_{max}}{t\ \pi\ r_m^2} \quad \dots \dots (14)$$

4. BENDING OF RIM SEGMENT BETWEEN SPOKES

If spokes or arms are used to support the pulley rim, the portion of the rim between the spokes will be uniformly loaded as a beam by the radial pressure (w_b). See Figure 9.

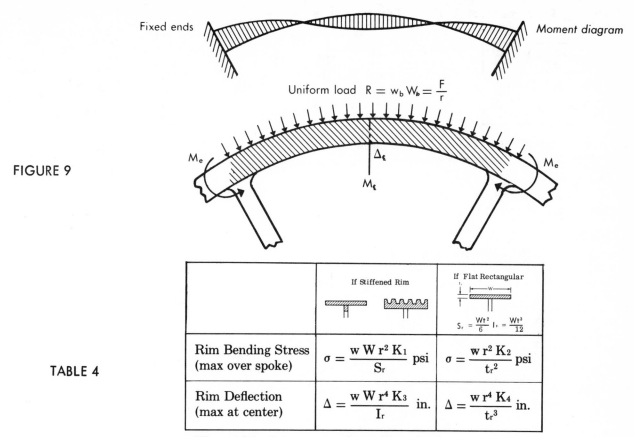

Fixed ends

Moment diagram

Uniform load $R = w_b W_b = \dfrac{F}{r}$

M_e Δ_ℓ M_e

M_ℓ

FIGURE 9

TABLE 4

	If Stiffened Rim	If Flat Rectangular $S_r = \dfrac{Wt^2}{6}$ $I_r = \dfrac{Wt^3}{12}$
Rim Bending Stress (max over spoke)	$\sigma = \dfrac{w\,W\,r^2\,K_1}{S_r}$ psi	$\sigma = \dfrac{w\,r^2\,K_2}{t_r^2}$ psi
Rim Deflection (max at center)	$\Delta = \dfrac{w\,W\,r^4\,K_3}{I_r}$ in.	$\Delta = \dfrac{w\,r^4\,K_4}{t_r^3}$ in.

W = width of rim supporting uniform load

The maximum bending moment will occur over the spoke or support. The following formulas are used to determine both the bending stress in the rim as well as the deflection of the rim. The maximum bending stress occurs in the rim over the spokes. The maximum deflection is at midspan.

The formulas of Table 4 apply to a rim of flat rectangular cross-section, or to one stiffened by the presence of belt grooves or a continuous rib connecting spokes to the rim. If the rim is not stiffened, the mean radius of the rim can be used as the value of rim radius (r). If the rim is stiffened, the radius to the center of gravity of the rim should be used as the value of rim radius (r).

Table 5 will supply the values of the four constants (K) for a given number of pulley spokes or arms.

TABLE 5

Number of Spokes	Rim Bending Stress K_1	K_2	Rim Deflection K_3	K_4
4	.1667	1.000	3.47×10^{-10}	4.17×10^{-9}
6	.0833	.500	$.868 \times 10^{-10}$	1.04×10^{-9}
8	.0488	.293	$.298 \times 10^{-10}$	$.357 \times 10^{-9}$

5. THICKNESS OF PULLEY DISC

Assume that the disc of the pulley should be thick enough to withstand a bending moment caused by the application of the belt tensions F_1 and F_2 at a point, say 10% off the centerline of the pulley rim (see Fig. 10a). Then consider this moment (M) to be applied to the pulley disc when the outer edge is supported (see Fig. 10b).

Under these considerations, the following two formulas may be derived, based upon Roark's

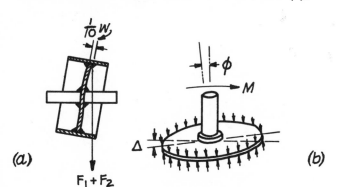

(a)   (b)

FIGURE 10

"Formulas for Stress and Strain" II Edition, pages 189, 210.

$$\Delta = \frac{(F_1 + F_2)\, r\, W}{10\,\alpha\, E\, t_d^3} \quad \dots\dots\dots\dots\dots\dots (15)$$

$$\sigma = \frac{\beta\,(F_1 + F_2)\, W}{10\, r\, t_d^2} \quad \dots\dots\dots\dots\dots\dots (16)$$

Nomograph 3 (Fig. 11) may be used to find these values for deflection and stress.

Table 6 of values for α and β are from the same work by Roark but were modified by Professor A. R. Holowenko of Purdue University.

Check for End Thrust

When using flat discs to support the pulley rim, a limited amount of end thrust (F_c) should be assumed. End thrust, tending to cause a radial

TABLE 6

(assume edges simply supported)

$\dfrac{r_h}{r}$	α	β
.10	.713	9.478
.15	.944	6.255
.20	1.219	4.623
.25	1.557	3.627
.30	1.989	2.948
.35	2.557	2.500
.40	3.323	2.063
.45	4.390	1.751
.50	5.928	1.489
.55	8.226	1.265
.60	11.852	1.068
.65	17.875	.892
.70	28.047	.731
.75	50.209	.585
.80	99.073	.449

FIG. 11 – PULLEY DISC DEFLECTION AND STRESS (Nomograph 3)

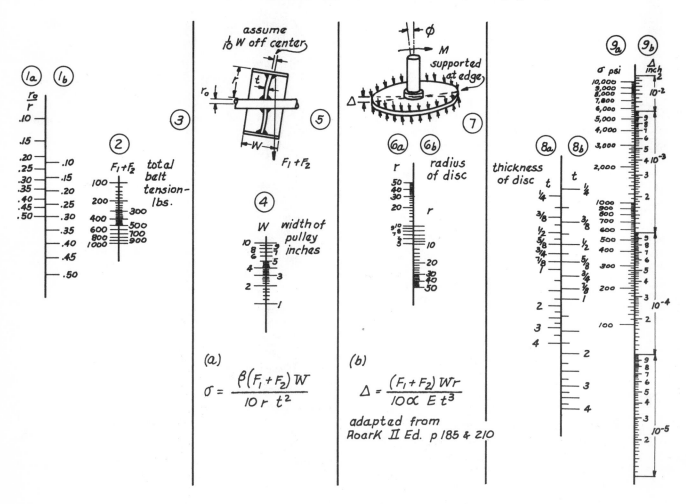

(a)
$$\sigma = \frac{\beta\left(F_1 + F_2\right) W}{10\, r\, t^2}$$

(b)
$$\Delta = \frac{(F_1 + F_2)\, W r}{10\,\alpha\, E\, t^3}$$

adapted from
Roark II Ed. p 185 & 210

TABLE 7

	3/16"	1/4"	5/16"	3/8"	7/16"	1/2"	9/16"	5/8"	3/4"	7/8"	1"
TABLE OF ALLOWABLE TORQUE TRANSMITTED BY ONE WELD (INCH-POUNDS) Leg Size of Fillet Weld, Inches											
1"	11,950	15,950	20,550	25,100	29,700	34,800	39,900	45,150	56,500	68,500	81,600
1-1/4"	18,450	24,800	31,400	38,300	45,400	52,800	60,500	68,000	84,300	101,000	119,500
1-1/2"	26,230	35,400	44,900	54,400	64,200	74,400	84,700	95,300	117,200	140,300	165,000
1-3/4"	35,600	47,900	60,500	73,200	86,500	99,700	113,300	127,400	150,000	186,200	218,000
2"	46,300	62,300	78,500	95,000	111,800	129,200	146,500	164,200	200,700	238,500	278,000
2-1/4"	58,500	78,500	99,000	119,700	140,400	162,000	184,000	206,000	250,300	298,000	345,000
2-1/2"	72,050	96,720	121,720	147,090	172,930	198,830	225,520	252,100	306,870	362,070	421,600

tensile stress (σ_r) that is maximum at the inner edge of the disc (at juncture of the hub), may result from angular misalignment of the pulleys, misalignment of the belt, or other abnormal service conditions.

The graph shown as Figure 3 in Section 5.4 on Gears, with related formulas and text, can be used as a guide in checking the proposed design for disc resistance to end thrust.

6. AMOUNT OF WELD REQUIRED

The two main welds on a pulley are those joining the disc to the hub and the disc to the rim. Because the length of each of these circumferential welds as well as its torque arm depends on its radius, the weld at the hub becomes the most critical due to its smaller radius (r_h).

The formula for the torque transmitted safely by the weld at the hub, based on the exact method, is—

$$T = \pi \, 9600 \left[\left(r_h + \frac{\omega}{2} \right)^3 - \frac{r_h^4}{r_h + \frac{\omega}{2}} \right] \quad \dots\dots\dots (17)$$

For convenience, the allowable torque transmitted by the weld at the hub may be found from Table 7. Both the above Formula 17 and Table 7 provide values for one weld only.

For larger pulley diameters, where the radius to the center of the fillet weld throat is large in comparison to the weld's leg size (ω), the following formula is used:

$$T = 2 \pi \, 9600 \, \omega \, r^2 \quad \dots\dots\dots\dots\dots\dots (18)$$

For simplicity on very large-diameter pulleys, the radius (r) to the center of the weld throat is assumed to be equal to the radius of one of the members being joined. See Figure 12. On such pulleys the hub-to-disc and the rim-to-disc welds should be figured separately.

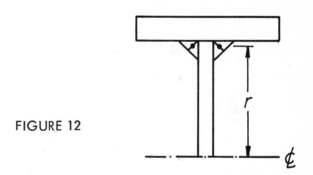

FIGURE 12

Problem 1

To design a flat-faced welded steel pulley to meet the following service conditions:

Horsepower transmitted by belt = 20 HP × service factor of 1.35 = 27 HP

Pulley radius (r) = 12"

Pulley hub radius (r_h) = 2.5"

Belt contact (θ) = 180° = π radians

Coefficient of friction (f) = 0.50

Width of belt (W_b) = 7"

Width of pulley rim (W_r) = 8"

Speed of pulley = 600 RPM

Belt density (ρ) = .035 lbs/cu in.

Belt thickness (t_b) = .282"

Allowable bending stress in rim (σ) = 5000 psi

For simplicity, assume a single value for pulley radius; most pulley rims are thin shells. In designing, the actual pulley radius is not finalized until after other calculations are made in which a certain radius must be assumed.

<u>Step 1:</u> DETERMINE REQUIRED RIM THICKNESS

The net tensile force of the belt causing radial pressure (w_b) against the pulley rim is--

$$(5) \quad F = \frac{63,030 \times HP}{r \, RPM} \left[\frac{e^{f\theta}}{e^{f\theta} - 1} \right] \quad \left| \begin{array}{l} \text{From Table 2 --} \\ \frac{e^{f\theta}}{e^{f\theta} - 1} = 1.26 \end{array} \right.$$

$$= \frac{63,030 \, (27) \, (1.26)}{(12) \, (600)}$$

$$= 298 \text{ lbs}$$

The resulting radial unit pressure inward against the pulley rim is--

$$(1) \quad w_b = \frac{F}{r \, W_b}$$

$$= \frac{298}{(12) \, (7)}$$

$$= 3.55 \text{ psi}$$

The section of the rim not under belt contact is subject to centrifugal force only:

$$(2) \quad w_c = \frac{t_r \, r \, RPM^2}{124,400}$$

Assume the pulley rim can be adequately supported by a single disc. From Table 3, the maximum bending stress in the rim is found to be--

$$(10a) \quad \sigma = \frac{.75 \, w \, W_b^2}{t_r^2}$$

in which the outward radial pressure resulting from centrifugal force (w_c) is substituted for $\underline{w}$:

$$\sigma = \frac{.75 \, W_b^2}{t_r^2} \frac{t_r \, r \, RPM^2}{124,400}$$

or

$$t_r = \frac{.75 \, r \, RPM^2 \, W_b^2}{\sigma \, 124,400}$$

$$= \frac{.75 \, (12) \, (600)^2 \, (7)^2}{(5000) \, (124,400)}$$

$$= .255'' \text{ or use } \frac{1}{4}'' \text{ rim thickness}$$

Therefore --

$$(2) \quad w_c = \frac{t_r \, r \, RPM^2}{124,400}$$

$$= \frac{(\frac{1}{4}) \, (12) \, (600)^2}{124,400}$$

$$= 8.68 \text{ psi, radially outward}$$

Since w_b = 3.55 psi, greater pressure w_c governs and the ¼" rim thickness is   OK.

<u>Step 2:</u> DETERMINE REQUIRED DISC THICKNESS

It is necessary to know the tensile forces in both the tight and slack belt (F_1) and (F_2). To do this, the tensile force due to centrifugal force (F_c) must be found.

$$(8a) \quad F_c = \frac{W_b \, t_b \, \rho \, r^2 \, RPM^2}{35,200}$$

$$= \frac{(7) \, (.282) \, (.035) \, (12)^2 \, (600)^2}{35,200}$$

$$= 101.5 \text{ lbs}$$

Since --

$$(4) \quad F = F_1 - F_c$$

$$F_1 = F + F_c$$

$$= 298 + 101.5$$

$$= 400 \text{ lbs (in tight belt)}$$

and since --

$$(3) \quad F_1 - F_2 = \frac{63,030 \, HP}{r \, RPM}$$

$$F_2 = F_1 - \frac{63,030 \, HP}{r \, RPM}$$

$$= 400 - \frac{63,030 \, (27)}{(12) \, (600)} = 400 - 236$$

$$= 164 \text{ lbs}$$

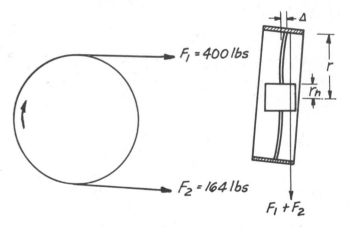

FIGURE 13

Here the ratio --

$$\frac{r_h}{r} = \frac{2.5}{12} = .208$$

and, from Table 6, corresponding values are obtained:

$$\alpha = 1.2, \text{ and } \beta = 4.6$$

Since the deflection of the disc due to belt forces, Figure 13, is--

$$(15) \quad \Delta = \frac{(F_1 + F_2) \, W_b \, r}{10 \, \alpha \, E \, t_d^3}$$

or

$$t_d^3 = \frac{(F_1 + F_2) \, W_b \, r}{10 \, \alpha \, E \, \Delta}$$

and assuming Δ should be held to a maximum of .01" —

$$t_d{}^3 = \frac{(400 + 164)(7)(12)}{10(1.2)(3 \times 10^7)(.01)}$$

$$= .01316$$

∴ $t_d = .236"$ or use ¼" disc thickness

Check the stress in this disc —

(16) $$\sigma = \frac{\beta(F_1 + F_2)W_b}{10\,r\,t_d{}^2}$$

$$= \frac{(4.6)(400 + 164)(7)}{10(12)(\tfrac{1}{4})^2}$$

$$= 2420 \text{ psi}\quad \text{OK, being within the allowable limits}$$

Step 3:   CHECK WELD SIZE AROUND HUB

The torque carried by the pulley and trans-

mitted by the welds joining the disc to the hub is--

$$T = \frac{63,030 \times HP}{RPM}$$

$$= \frac{63,030(27)}{600}$$

$$= 2840 \text{ in.-lbs for two welds, or}$$

$$T = 1420 \text{ in.-lbs for just one weld}$$

Assume a ³⁄₁₆" fillet weld to be used.

The maximum allowable torque carried by one weld, as obtained from Table 6 for $r_h = 2.5"$ and $\omega = $ ³⁄₁₆", is--

$$T = 72,050 \text{ in.-lbs}$$

which far exceeds the calculated torque, and thus the assumed ³⁄₁₆" fillet weld is OK.

Problem 2

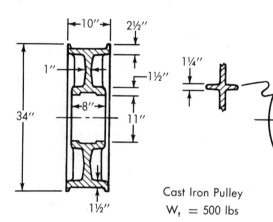

FIGURE 14

Cast Iron Pulley
$W_t = 500$ lbs

To redesign a cast iron multi-groove sheave, Figure 14, for fabrication from rolled steel. The sheave serves an idler function, being free to rotate freely by means of a bearing on the shaft, and it can be assumed that the sheave transmits no torque.

The old sheave was cast as one piece, having a minimum web thickness of 1" and ribbed to form six spokes. The rim has a thickness of 1.5" at the bottom of the grooves.

In designing for welded steel fabrication, the hub thickness might be decreased. A tubular section of necessary inside diameter and wall thickness could be cut with a power hack-saw to the proper length.

Step 1:   DETERMINE REQUIRED RIM THICKNESS

Because of the rather large width of the rim (10"), two webs or discs, about ⅜" thick, can be used to join the rim to the hub. See Figure 15. This will greatly reduce the bending stresses and deflection of the rim, thus allowing some reduction in rim thickness additional to that permitted merely

by the greater rigidity of steel.

By using two webs, the two outside portions of the rim will be loaded as a cantilever beam, while the portion inside of the web support will be a beam with partially fixed or restrained supports. The cantilever portion of the rim (a) will have its maximum bending moment over the web support, while the inside portion of the rim (W_d) will have its maximum bending moment at its center. It can be shown that the least bending moment will result if the spacing of the webs is such that the overhang of the rim is approximately equal to 22% of the rim width under the belt (W_b).

Since the radius and width of the rim must remain the same, the only dimension which may be decreased in order to take advantage of the stiffness of steel is the rim thickness. Since steel has about twice the modulus of elasticity of cast iron, the steel sheave would require just 50% of the moment of inertia of a similar section of cast iron for equal rigidity. Since the moment of inertia of a rectangular section of the rim varies as the cube of the thickness, the required thickness

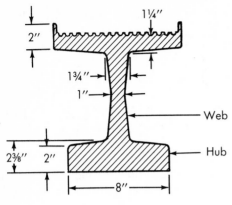

Cast Iron Section

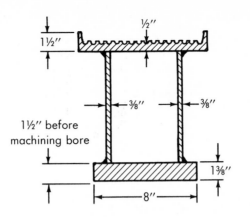

FIGURE 15

Welded Steel Section

of the steel rim would be the cube root of 50% of the cast iron thickness or--

$$t_s{}^3 = 50\% \; t_c{}^3$$

$$t_s = t_c \sqrt[3]{.50\%} \text{ or}$$

$$\boxed{t_s = .79\% \; t_c} \quad \dots \dots \dots \dots \dots (19)$$

This is assuming that the same type of beam is considered in both cases.

The cast iron rim is 1.25" thick at the bottom of the grooves. Since 79% of this is 1", the steel rim would be 1" thick at the bottom of the grooves, assuming the same type of beam, in other words both the old and new designs using just one web.

However, there is an additional advantage in the steel design because two webs are to be used instead of just one. Going from the single-web design, in which 50% of the rim cantilevers out to each side of the web, to the two-web design with only 22% of the rim cantilevering out, there is an appreciable factor.

Considering the cast iron rim as a beam supported at midpoint, Figure 16a--

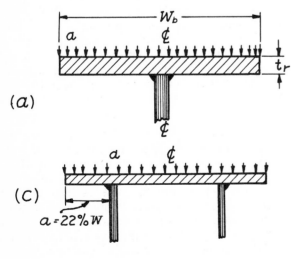

(a)

(c)

a = 22% W

FIGURE 16

the thickness of its rim can be stated as a function of the rim's strength--

$$(10a) \quad \sigma = \frac{.75 \; w \; W_b{}^2}{t_r{}^2}$$

$$\text{or} \quad t_r = .866 \sqrt{\frac{w \; W_b{}^2}{\sigma}}$$

or it can be stated as a function of the rim's stiffness —

$$(11a) \quad \Delta = \frac{31.25 \times 10^{-10} \; w \; W_b{}^4}{t_r{}^3}$$

$$\text{or} \quad t_r = 1.46 \times 10^{-3} \sqrt[3]{\frac{w \; W_b{}^4}{\Delta}}$$

Considering the proposed steel rim as a beam supported at two points, Figure 16c, the thickness of its rim can be stated as a function of the rim's strength--

$$(10a) \quad \sigma = \frac{.1452 \; w \; W_b{}^2}{t_r{}^2}$$

$$\text{or} \quad t_r = .381 \sqrt{\frac{w \; W_b{}^2}{\sigma}}$$

or it can be stated as a function of the rim's stiffness —

$$(11c) \quad \Delta = \frac{1.37 \times 10^{-10} \; w \; W_b{}^4}{t_r{}^3}$$

$$\text{or} \quad t_r = .516 \times 10^{-3} \sqrt{\frac{w \; W_b{}^4}{\Delta}}$$

Therefore, the required thickness of the steel rim —

Based on equivalent strength

$$t_s = t_c \frac{.381}{.866} \sqrt{\frac{\sigma_c}{\sigma_s}}$$

$$= t_c \frac{.381}{.866} \sqrt{\frac{1}{4}} \quad \text{if } \sigma_s = 4 \; \sigma_c$$

$$\text{or} \quad \boxed{t_s = 22\% \; t_c}$$

$$t_s = .22 \, (1.25)$$

$$= .275"$$

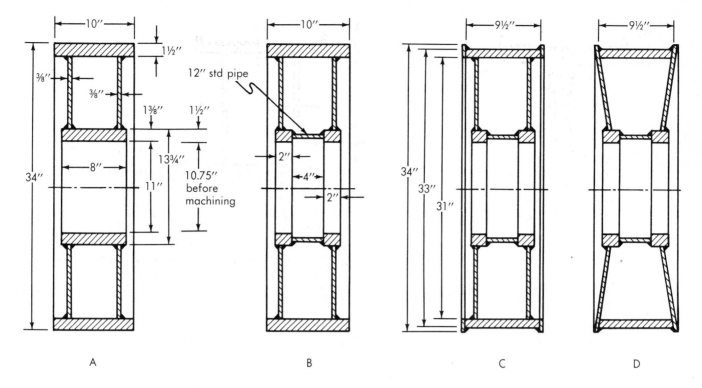

A   B   C   D

FIGURE 17

Based on equivalent stiffness

$$t_s = t_c \frac{.516}{1.46} \sqrt[3]{\frac{E_c}{E_s}}$$

$$= t_c \frac{.516}{1.46} \sqrt[3]{\frac{1}{2}} \quad \text{if } E_s = 2\,E_c$$

or $\boxed{t_s = 28\% \; t_c}$

$t_s = .28\,(1.25)$

$= .350$ or use ⅜" rim thickness below grooves

Step 2: COMPLETE THE SHEAVE DESIGN

The disc thickness can be determined as in previous problem, and also the required fillet weld size.

Further economies can be made in the design as evidenced by the design evolution sketched in Figure 17.

The first welded steel design is shown at A. The hub is made by cutting off 8" of thick-wall tubing, which has a thickness of 1.5" and an ID of 10.75". This allows ⅛" for machining to the required 11" bore size.

The second welded steel design, shown at B, avoids the use of thick-wall tubing. Here, the hub is formed by rolling two rings out of 1.5" × 2" bar stock and butt welding the ends together. These are then spaced with a 4" length of standard 12" pipe. This hub gives proper support to the bearings, reduces weight, and eliminates the purchase of more costly tubing.

Designs A and B called for considerable machining from a 1.5" thick rim blank in order to provide the flanges for guiding the belt when slack. To avoid this, design C calls for a rim blank with just enough stock to allow machining of the grooves plus $t_r = $ ⅜" for required rigidity. Rolled rings are welded to the ends of the rim to provide the flanges. Design B has an initial weight of 630 lbs, while design C's weight is only 460 lbs.

The alternative design at D can be considered, since combining the flange and web disc will save some machining and welding. However, the beam characteristics of the rim are thereby changed and the required rim thickness should be refigured by using Formulas 10b and 11b.

Fabricators of pulleys, rolls and gears usually use automatic submerged-arc welding to quickly join the web to the rim and to the hub. These welds are very seldom stress-relieved.

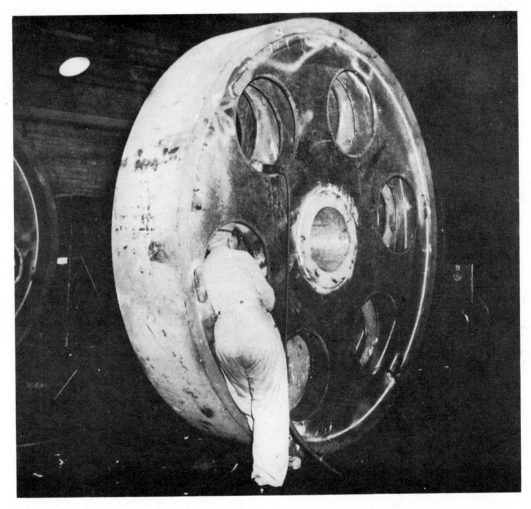

Complete gear blank for marine drive is fabricated economically by modern high speed arc welding.

How to Design Steel Rolls

1. DESIGN FREEDOM

Many large rolls are employed by Industry for calendering, screening, pulverizing, conveyorizing, spooling, filament winding, laminating, printing, and other purposes. Such rolls are economically fabricated from steel with the aid of modern high speed arc-welding processes.

The Figure 1 design for a roll reflects design thinking from a period before welding was used extensively. The two discs are pressed onto the shaft, and the outer shell of the roll is pressed over this. The inner shaft probably takes much of the bending load instead of transferring it through the discs to the outer drum.

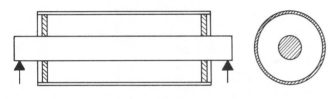

FIGURE 1

In a welded roll, all of the parts act together. Since a shaft would contribute very little of the moment of inertia of the entire roll for bending, or the polar moment of inertia for twisting, it generally is omitted. Short lengths on each end serve as support at the bearings. See Figure 2.

FIGURE 2

A shaft extending the full length of the roll might help in assembling the roll, since it affords a straight section on which to assemble the discs and outer shell. However, this greatly increases the weight and cost of shafting required; therefore, the roll is seldom fabricated in this manner.

For normal bearing loads, a single disc is used on each end of the roll. This disc may be considered as a circular plate, uniformly supported around its edge and subjected to a bending moment by the shaft, and the resulting bending stresses found.

The bearing force multiplied by the distance at which it is applied from the centerline of the disc, is the bending moment.

The nomograph "Stress in Trunnion Disc", Figure 4, will quickly give the required thickness of disc for a given radial tensile stress. For heavier bearing loads, this thickness will increase. Remember: the rotating disc reverses its stress every half-revolution so that the allowable fatigue strength in tension for a complete reversal must be considered.

The nomograph "Angular Tilt of Trunnion Disc", Figure 5, quickly gives the amount of angular deflection resulting from the bending moment on the shaft. The thickness of the shaft can be adjusted to keep this tilt within the maximum allowable for the specific application.

Sometimes a hole is cut into the disc, and the shaft stub extends through and is welded on both sides as in Figure 3 (a). Usually the shaft stub is simply butted against the disc and a single heavy fillet weld joins the two (b). This method saves cutting the disc and does not require a longer shaft stub. Fillet welds may be used; but for heavier bearing loads, it may be necessary to bevel the hole in the disc (c), or bevel the end of the shaft (d) in order to get more of a groove weld.

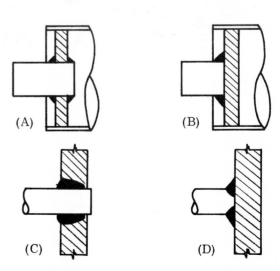

(A) (B) (C) (D)

FIGURE 3

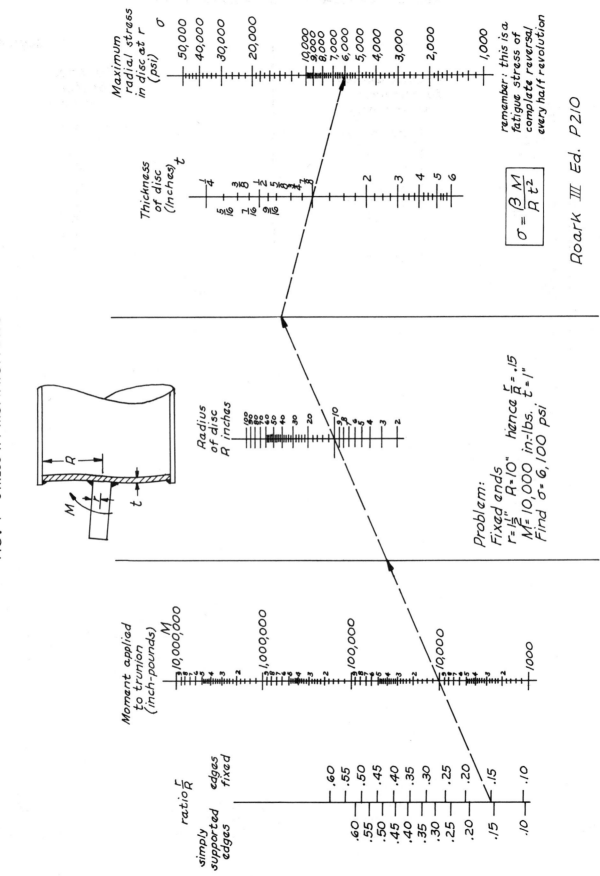

FIG. 4 – STRESS IN TRUNNION DISC

FIG. 5 – ANGULAR TILT OF TRUNNION DISC

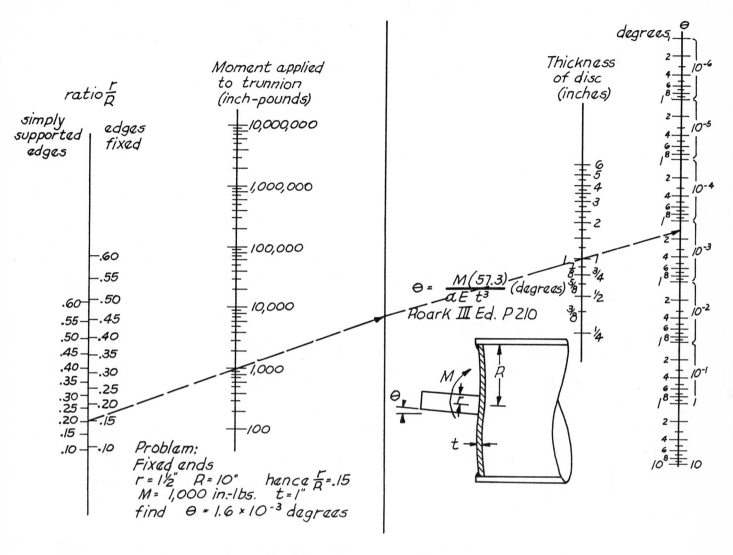

ratio $\frac{r}{R}$

simply supported edges | edges fixed

Moment applied to trunnion (inch-pounds)

Thickness of disc (inches)

degrees, θ

$$\theta = \frac{M(57.3)}{\alpha E t^3} \text{ (degrees)}$$

Roark III Ed. P 210

Problem:
Fixed ends
r = 1½" R = 10"   hence $\frac{r}{R}$ = .15
M = 1,000 in.-lbs.   t = 1"
find θ = 1.6 × 10⁻³ degrees

Usually the disc and the shaft stub are welded together as a subassembly. This allows a weld to be placed on both sides of this disc if the shaft extends through the disc.

2. STIFFENING OF ROLL

For additional strength and stiffness when needed, brackets may be welded on the disc, radiating outward from the shaft stub. See Figure 6.

For heavier loads, which would require excessively thick discs, two thinner discs may be used, spaced a given distance apart, Figure 7.

Usually the inner disc and shaft stub are welded together as a subassembly, Figure 8 (a). This unit is then welded into the roll (b). The outer disc is then slipped over and welded in place (c).

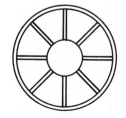

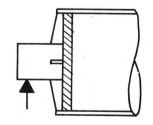

FIGURE 6

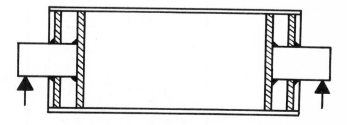

FIGURE 7

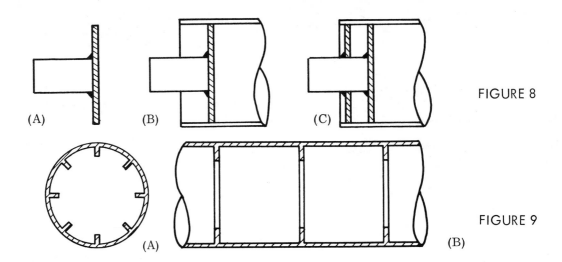

FIGURE 8

(A)   (B)   (C)

FIGURE 9

(A)   (B)

3. INTERNAL STIFFENING OF SHELLS

When cast rolls required stiffening of the shell, it was easier to use longitudinal ribs, Figure 9 (a), rather than transverse rings (b). When additional stiffening is required in a welded steel roll to maintain a perfect circle with a lighter outer shell, internal rings (b) intermittently welded to the inside of the shell are recommended. These will give constant stiffening of the shell as it is rotated. The rings can be inserted near the centerline of the roll, working outward towards both ends as these are welded in.

4. WELDING OF SHAFT STUB TO DISC AND DISC TO SHELL

The welding at the shaft is more critical because the small radius increases the force from the load (bending force from the bearing load, and twisting force if any torque is transmitted) and also decreases the length of the weld. The resulting force per linear inch varies inversely as the square of the radius.

This explains why for critical loads, single fillet welds may be used on the disc at the outer shell whereas groove welds or double fillets may be required at the hub, Figure 10.

The simplest method to determine weld size is:

1. Treat the weld as a line and use standard bending and torsion formulas to find the resulting unit forces on the weld. See Table 1.

2. Vectorially add these forces which occur at the same part of the welded joint, to find the resultant force on the weld.

TABLE 1 - FORCES ON SHAFT-TO-DISC WELD

Load Condition	Design Formula for force on weld lbs/inch of weld	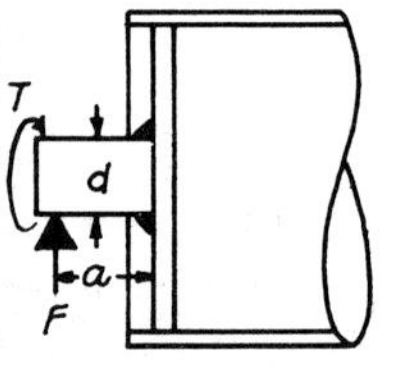 single disc property of weld	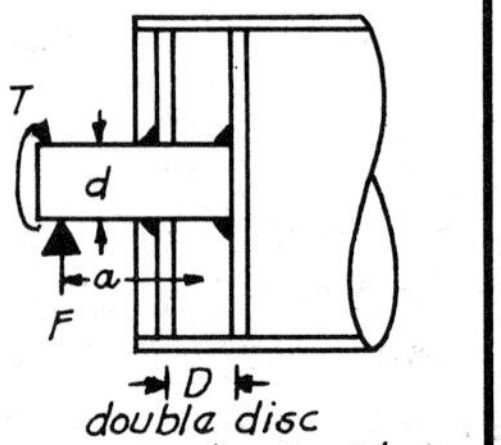 double disc property of weld
bending	$f_b = \dfrac{M}{S_w} = \dfrac{Fa}{S_w}$	$S_w = \dfrac{\pi d^2}{4}$	$S_w = \dfrac{\pi d^2}{2} + \pi D^2$ assume loose fit and weld carries whole load
twisting $T = \dfrac{63,000\,HP}{RPM}$	$f_t = T\left(\dfrac{C}{J_w}\right)$	$\dfrac{J_w}{C} = \dfrac{\pi d^2}{2}$	$\dfrac{J_w}{C} = \pi d^2$
vertical shear	$f_v = \dfrac{F}{A_w}$	$A_w = \pi d$	$A_w = 2\pi d$

3. Weld size is then found by dividing this resultant value by the allowable force for the particular type of weld.

Remember, every time the roll rotates half a revolution, the bending forces on the weld completely reverse. This becomes a fatigue situation in which K = -1; that is, the minimum force is equal to a negative value of the maximum force, or a complete reversal of force. Consult the table of "Allowable Fatigue Values for Welds" in Section 3.2 on Fatigue.

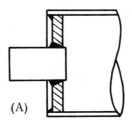 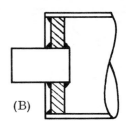

(A) (B)

FIGURE 10

Problem 1

To determine the fillet weld size to use in joining hub to disc, given a bearing load on the trunnion of 6300 lbs and transmitted torque = 150 HP at 100 RPM. Figure 11 shows pertinent dimensions.

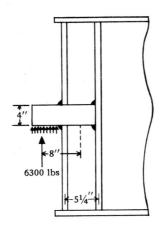

FIGURE 11

The torque transmitted through the weld is--

$$T = \frac{63,030 \times HP}{RPM}$$

$$= \frac{63,030(150)}{100}$$

$$= 94,500 \text{ in.-lbs}$$

Step 1: DETERMINE PROPERTIES OF THE WELD

Treating the weld as a line, find its properties according to the formulas given in Table 1. See Figure 12 for definitions of "d" and "D".

Polar section modulus

$$\frac{J_w}{c} = \pi d^2$$

$$= \pi (4)^2$$

$$= 50.3 \text{ in.}^2$$

Section modulus

$$S_w = \frac{\pi d^2}{2} + \pi D^2$$

$$= \pi \left[\frac{(4)^2}{2} + (5\tfrac{1}{4})^2 \right]$$

$$= 111.7 \text{ in.}^2$$

Area of weld

$$A_w = 2 \pi d$$

$$= 2 \pi (4)$$

$$= 25.2''$$

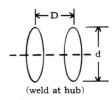

(weld at hub)

FIGURE 12

Step 2: DETERMINE PRINCIPAL FORCES ON WELD

Using the formulas in Table 1, find the principal forces on welds:

Bending

$$f_b = \frac{M}{S_w}$$

$$= \frac{(6300)(8)}{(111.7)}$$

$$= 451 \text{ lbs/in.}$$

Twisting

$$f_t = \frac{T c}{J_w}$$

$$= \frac{(94,500)}{(50.3)}$$

$$= 1880 \text{ lbs/in.}$$

Vertical shear

$$f_v = \frac{V}{A_w}$$

$$= \frac{(6300)}{(25.2)}$$

$$= 250 \text{ lbs/in.}$$

<u>Step 3</u>: FIND RESULTANT FORCE ON WELD

Diagram the three component forces, as shown in Figure 13.

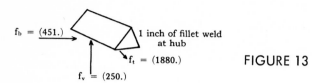

$f_b = (451.)$ 1 inch of fillet weld at hub

$f_t = (1880.)$

$f_v = (250.)$

FIGURE 13

The actual resultant force on the weld is then—

$$f_R = \sqrt{f_b^2 + f_t^2 + f_v^2}$$

$$= \sqrt{(451)^2 + (1880)^2 + (250)^2}$$

$$= 1950 \text{ lbs/in. (still treating the weld as a line)}$$

Since this is fatigue loading, assume that N = 2,000,000 cycles and use the corresponding formula from the Table of "Allowable Fatigue Strength of Weld Metal", Sect. 3.2. Assume in this case a com-plete reversal of load, hence $K = \dfrac{min}{max} = -1$ and the allowable force would be—

$$f_a = \frac{5090\,\omega}{1 - \dfrac{k}{2}}$$

$$= \frac{5090\,\omega}{1 + \frac{1}{2}}$$

$$= 3390 \text{ lbs/in. (allowable)}$$

<u>Step 4</u>: DETERMINE LEG SIZE OF WELD

The leg size of the fillet welds joining hub to discs of the roll should be—

$$\boxed{\omega = \frac{f_R}{f_a}}$$

$$\omega = \frac{1950}{3370}$$

$$= .58'' \text{ or use } \frac{5}{8}''$$

Problem 2

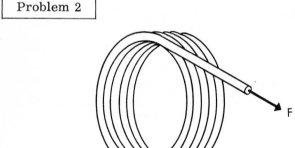

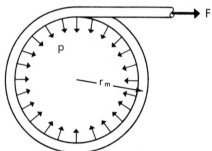

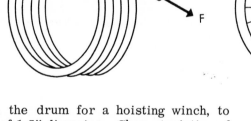

FIGURE 14

To design the drum for a hoisting winch, to handle cable of 1.5" diameter. Characteristics of the cable call for it to be wound at a 9.75" mean radius of turn. Net tensile force in the cable is 9,000 lbs.

Background on Drum Construction

Welded steel construction of the drum has the advantage of stronger and more rigid material. A thinner shell may be used, thus reducing the inertia of the rotating drum which would help when the load must be accelerated or decelerated.

Because the steel may be placed exactly where it is needed, it is possible with good fabricating methods to obtain a better balanced drum.

Under heavy loads, it is well to groove the drum so that the cable will fit as closely as possible and retain its round shape without squashing out into an oval shape.

A larger diameter drum will increase the life of the wire cable as well as its usable strength, but there is a practical limit to this size, because of weight and cost limitations of the winch.

The cable manufacturer can supply recommended drum diameters for a given cable diameter. It has been suggested that the drum diameter should be at least 500 times the diameter of the outside wires of the cable.

In this example the outer radius of the shell will be 9.0".

<u>Step 1</u>: DETERMINE RADIAL FORCE AGAINST DRUM

In this analysis, the turns of cable are treated as a shell. The tensile force in the cable (F), being = $\sigma\,b\,t$, creates a uniform inward radial force (p) against the drum about which it is wound. See Figure 14.

This is similar to the tensile stress (σ) in a thin-wall container shell due to internal pressure (p). The analogy is sketched in Figure 15.

It is known that in an analogous cylindrical shell, the stress is--

$$\sigma = \frac{p \, r_m}{t} \qquad \text{but } F = \sigma \, b \, t \qquad \boxed{A_{cable} = b \, t}$$

$$\therefore \quad F = \frac{p \, r_m}{t} \, b \, t$$

$$= p \, r_m \, b$$

$$\text{and} \quad \boxed{p = \frac{F}{r_m \, b}}$$

where:

σ = tensile (or compressive) stress, psi

p = uniform internal (or external) radial pressure, psi

r_m = mean radius of turns of cable on drum, in.

b = width of drum per turn of cable = dia. of cable

t = thickness of comparative shell of same cross-sectional area as cable (per width "b"), in. = $(\pi/4)b$

F = tensile force in cable, lbs

In this particular problem, the uniform external radial pressure acting inward against the surface of the drum is--

1st layer of cable

$$p_1 = \frac{F}{r_m \, b}$$

$$= \frac{9000}{(9.75)(1.5)}$$

$$= 615 \text{ psi}$$

2nd layer of cable

$$p_2 = \frac{F}{r_m \, b}$$

$$= \frac{9000}{(11.05)(1.5)}$$

$$= 544 \text{ psi}$$

3rd layer of cable

$$p_3 = \frac{F}{r_m \, b}$$

$$= \frac{9000}{(12.35)(1.5)}$$

$$= 486 \text{ psi}$$

Although each succeeding layer of cable should add to the pressure against the drum, the outside

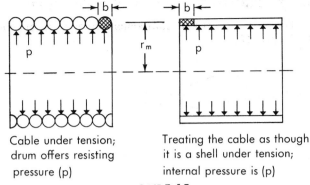

Cable under tension; drum offers resisting pressure (p)

Treating the cable as though it is a shell under tension; internal pressure is (p)

FIGURE 15

layers will tend to force the preceding layers into a smaller diameter, reducing their tension; in like manner, their pressure against the drum will be reduced. For this reason only the effect of outer two layers will be considered.

$$p = p_2 + p_3$$

$$= 544 + 486$$

$$= 1030 \text{ psi}$$

Step 2: DETERMINE THICKNESS OF DRUM

The drum is considered as a shell or tube subjected to external pressure (p). If this tube is relatively short, the ends will give added support against buckling and the indicated critical buckling pressure (p_{cr}) will be much higher. The more conservative method would be to treat this as a long tube, with no allowance for the stiffening effect of the ends. According to "Strength of Materials," Part 2, Timoshenko, p. 602, and to "Formulas for Stress and Strain, 2nd Edition, Roark, p. 306, the following formula is used:

$$p_{cr} = \frac{E \, t^3}{4 \, (1 - \nu^2) \, r^3}$$

For steel this becomes —

$$\boxed{p_{cr} = 8.24 \times 10^6 \left(\frac{t}{r} \right)^3}$$

This is the critical external pressure on shell at which buckling might occur. From this, required shell thickness would be--

$$\boxed{t = .00495 \, r \sqrt[3]{p_1}}$$

Resulting stress in the shell under this pressure must not exceed yield strength of the steel.

The minimum shell thickness (t) needed for a critical buckling pressure (p_{cr}) of 2½ times the working pressure (1030 psi), will be found:

$$p_{cr} = 2\tfrac{1}{2} \, (1030)$$

$$= 2580 \text{ psi}$$

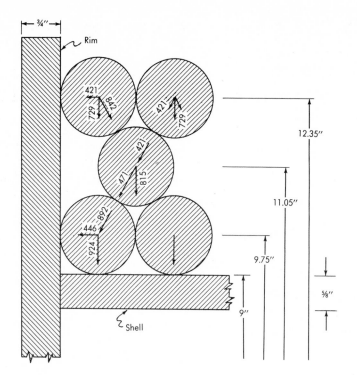

FIGURE 16

Using the above formula, with this pressure, the minimum drum thickness is found to be--

$$t = .00495 (9) \sqrt[3]{2580}$$

$$= .612\text{"} \text{ or use } \tfrac{5}{8}\text{" thick plate}$$

This thickness would bring the mean rim radius down to 8.6875". Substituting this value for the 9" radius in the formula and reworking, gives a drum thickness (t) of .59", which still requires the ⅝" plate.

Step 3: DETERMINE THICKNESS OF RIM

The end disc of the drum can be extended to serve as a rim or flange to keep the cable from spreading out. See Figure 16. This rim must withstand the horizontal components of the inward force from the cables. Assume a plate thickness for the disc, in this case ¾".

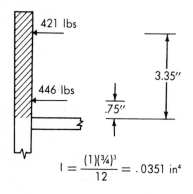

FIGURE 17

The inward radial force is--

$$R = \frac{F}{r} \text{ lbs/in. of circumference}$$

$$\therefore R_1 = \frac{9000}{9.75}$$

$$= 924 \text{ lbs/in.}$$

$$R_2 = \frac{9000}{11.05}$$

$$= 815 \text{ lbs/in.}$$

$$R_3 = \frac{9000}{12.35}$$

$$= 729 \text{ lbs/in.}$$

Consider a 1" wide radial strip of rim as a cantilever beam supported at the drum shell, Figure 17, where horizontal force components found by vectoral analysis indicated above are taken as loads on the beam.

Here, the bending moment due to these horizontal force components is--

$$M = (421)(3.35) + (446)(.75)$$

$$= 1744 \text{ in.-lbs}$$

and $\sigma = \dfrac{Mc}{I}$

$$= \frac{(1744)(.375)}{(.0351)}$$

$$= 18,640 \text{ psi} \quad OK$$

where:

$$I = \frac{(1)(.75)^3}{12}$$

$$= .0351 \text{ in.}^4$$

This would indicate the ¾" thickness of the end disc to be thick enough so as not to require additional stiffening at the rim. If this thickness were reduced to ½", the resulting stress would increase to 42,700 psi which would be excessive and stiffeners would be required. This is illustrated in later Figure 20, designs B and C.

Step 4: CHECK THICKNESS OF END DISC

Assume the cable to be pulled 20° off of center, and the resulting end thrust to be taken by just one end disc. See Figure 18.

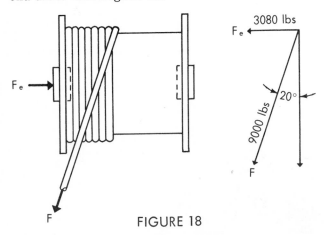

FIGURE 18

Consider the disc as a circular flat plate, the inner edge being fixed and supported, with a uniform load applied around the outer edge. The radial tensile stress (σ_r) at the inside edge (= hub OD) is found by the following formula, adapted from "Formulas for Stress and Strain," Roark, 2nd Edition, p. 195, case 22:

$$\sigma_r = .4774 \frac{F_e}{t^2} \left[\frac{26\, r^2 \log_e \frac{r}{r_1} + 7\,(r^2 - r_1{}^2)}{13\, r^2 + 7\, r_1{}^2} \right]$$

(For Steel)

In this case —

$r = 8.6875"$

$r_1 = 4"$

$t = ¾"$

$F_e = 3080$ lbs

$\log_e \dfrac{r}{r_1} = \log_e \dfrac{8.6875}{4}$

$\qquad = .7747$

FIGURE 19

and $\sigma_r = .4774 \dfrac{(3080)}{(¾)^2}$

$$\times \left[\frac{26\,(8.6875)^2\,(.7747) + 7\,(8.6875^2 - 4^2)}{13\,(8.6875)^2 + 7\,(4)^2} \right]$$

$= \underline{4,630}$ psi   OK

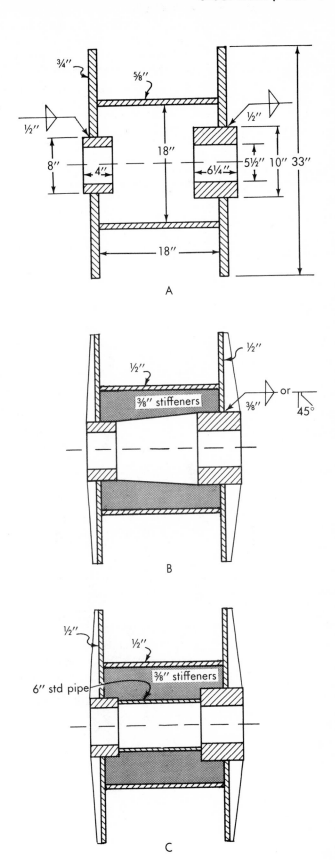

FIGURE 20

This indicates the resulting radial tensile stress at the inner edge, at the hub, to be 4630 psi, which is reasonably low, and additional ribs or stiffening should not be required. For discs of ½" thickness, this stress increases to 10,400 psi; and, if both discs are assumed to be effective in resisting this end thrust, the stress would be 5200 psi.

Step 5: DETERMINE WELD SIZE

The procedure discussed earlier in this Section may be used, or an approximate method used.

In general, for full strength welds, a leg size of about ¾ of the thickness of the thinner plate should be used; this should outpull the plate.

For rigidity designs, where full strength welds are not required, for attaching stiffeners for ex-

ample, usually about ½ to ⅓ of the usual weld is required. This reduction in the amount of fillet welds may be either leg size, length or both.

Step 6: COMPLETE THE DESIGN

Design A in Figure 20 uses a ⅝" thick shell and ¾" thick end discs. Because of this, no additional stiffening should be required. Each bearing hub is flame-cut from thick plate.

Design B uses a ½" thick shell and ½" thick end discs. Because of this reduction in thickness, ⅜" thick stiffeners are added inside of the shell, just between the two discs.

Design C makes use of a length of 6" diameter standard pipe for additional stiffness between the two bearing hubs.

Cable winding drum presents unique opportunity for savings through good design analysis of stresses and the proper use of welded steel.

How to Design Large Steel Gears

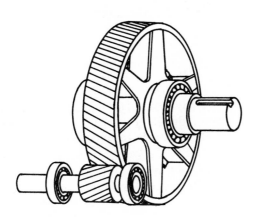

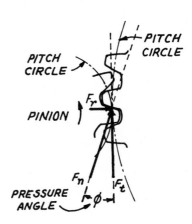

FIGURE 1

1. BASIC REQUIREMENTS

Gears must have the necessary strength and rigidity to withstand a complex network of stresses resulting from the various forces applied to the teeth. Steel weldments will meet these requirements, and offer the designer greater design flexibility and significant economies in weight and cost over one-piece castings or forgings.

The rim may be made of an alloy steel and heat treated to a given gear tooth hardness for optimum strength and wear life, while a lower cost steel will provide the strength and rigidity needed in the arms. Dissimilar metals are easily welded, allowing the designer to efficiently use the steel that most economically develops the performance desired in each portion of the gear.

The force transmitted by a gear appears as a pressure (F_n) between the contacting teeth surfaces directed along the line of action normal to the tooth profile, Figure 1. This pressure generates several new forces on the tooth, all of which act on the components of the gear and influence its final design. The various forces acting within the gear structure are the following:

1. Tangential force (F_t) on the gear rim from the torque.

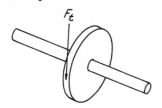

$$F_t = \frac{126,050 \times HP}{D \times RPM}$$

$$F_t = \frac{33,000 \times HP}{V}$$

2. Radial force (F_r) on the gear rim as a function of the tangential force and pressure angle of the gear teeth.

$$F_r = F_t \tan \phi$$

3. End thrust (F_e) on the rim of helical gears parallel to the gear axis.

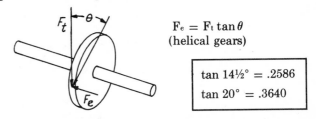

$$F_e = F_t \tan \theta$$
(helical gears)

$\tan 14\frac{1}{2}° = .2586$
$\tan 20° = .3640$

4. Centrifugal force (F_c) on the rim and arms of large diameter, high speed gears.

Since these forces must be transferred by the gear's hub, arms or disc, and rim, the designer's objective is to design these components to accomplish the transfer of forces without failing, while achieving maximum material and manufacturing economy.

2. THE HUB

The gear hub must be thick enough to be keyed to the shaft and to provide a sufficiently rigid support for the gear arms.

1

The length of the hub must prevent any significant wobble of the gear on the shaft as the result of surface deformation and fretting corrosion caused by excessive unit pressures at the hubshaft interface. Usually, this hub length is 1.25 to 2 times the shaft diameter and is equal to or greater than the width of the rim face.

3. THE ARMS

Gear arms are subjected to complex loading. They must be strong and rigid enough to transmit the torque between the rim and the hub, to withstand any axial tension resulting from centrifugal forces, and to resist any side bending due to end thrust if a helical gear.

The torque (T) produces a bending moment (M) on the arms. When designing for this moment, the total torque is usually assumed to be uniformly divided among all the arms (n_a). Each arm is then treated as a cantilever beam fixed and supported at the hub, and loaded at the pitch circle. Torque is not used directly, but tangential force (F_t).

The bending stress in the arm can be calculated as follows:

$$M = \frac{F_t}{n_a} L$$

DEFINITIONS OF SYMBOLS

Δ = deflection, in.
ω = leg size of fillet weld, in.
σ = stress, psi
θ = helix angle if helical gear, degrees
ϕ = pressure angle, degrees

c = distance of neutral axis to outer fiber of section, in.
e = moment arm, in.
n_a = number of gear arms
r = (1) radius of center of gravity of rim below root circle, in.
(2) radius of center of fillet weld throat, in.
r_h = radius of hub, in.
t_r = thickness of rim below teeth, in.

D = pitch diameter of gear, in.
E = material's modulus of elasticity, psi
F_e = end thrust, lbs
F_n = actual pressure normal to tooth face, lbs

F_r = radial force on tooth, lbs
F_t = tangential force on tooth, lbs
HP = horsepower transmitted
I = moment of inertia, in.^{4}
L = length of member, in.
M = bending moment, in.-lbs
M_r = maximum bending moment due to radial force, in.-lbs
M_t = maximum bending moment due to tangential force, in.-lbs
N = number of gear teeth
P = diametral pitch, in.
RPM = revolutions per minute of gear
S = section modulus, in.^{3}
T = torque transmitted by gear, in.-lbs
V = pitch line velocity, fpm
W = width of rim, in.

---

and, since:

$$M = \sigma \frac{I}{c} = \sigma S$$

$$\therefore \quad \sigma = \frac{F_t L}{n_a S}$$

where all properties (M, I, c, S, L) apply to the arm or its cross-section.

4. THE RIM

The gear rim and its support must be rigid enough to minimize deflection caused by the radial force (F_r) and the tangential force (F_t) acting at the tooth surface. Deflection of the rim from either force induces non-uniform tooth loading, which--if severe -- leads to excessive wear and even to tooth breakage.

The minimum thickness of the rim below the root circle usually equals the thickness of the tooth at the pitch circle. A formula for calculating this value, suggested by the Nuttall Works of Westinghouse Electric Corporation, is--

$$t_r = \frac{1}{P} \sqrt[3]{\frac{N}{2 n_a}}$$

5. BENDING OF RIM BETWEEN ARMS

In one approach to designing the net rim section, analysis is made of the bending moment and of the deflection of the rim resulting from the radial force and the tangential force acting respectively at the tooth surface.

The rim segment analyzed is considered to be an isolated curved beam with fixed ends, and is that portion of the rim intersected by the centerlines of two adjacent arms. The arc length along this rim segment's center of gravity is used to locate the points at which tangential force (F_t) and radial force (F_r) cause maximum stress and deflection values. This arc length is represented in diagrams in the lower part of Figure 2.

Analyzing these forces separately shows that the radial force (F_r) develops maximum moment at the end of the rim segment when the force is applied at the position indicated. This point is approx. ⅓ of the arc length in from the end.

The maximum moment caused by the tangential force (F_t) occurs when this force is applied at the end of the rim segment.

Maximum deflection of the rim below the point of tooth contact and resulting from the radial force (F_r) occurs when the radial force is applied at midspan.

The radial deflection of the rim resulting from the tangential force (F_t), at the point where this force is applied, reaches a maximum value when the force is applied near mid-span.

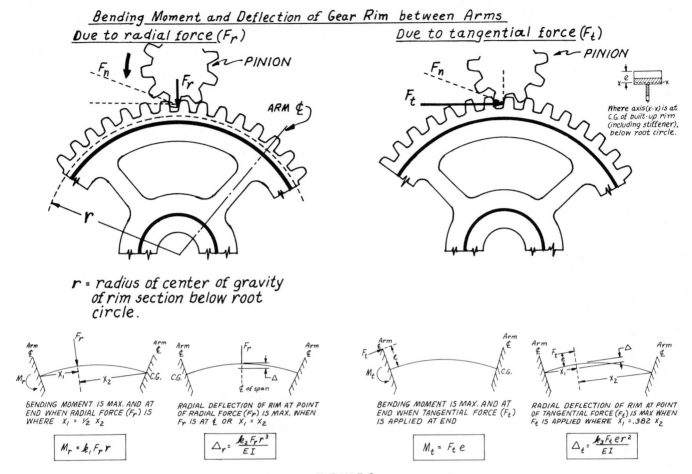

FIGURE 2

The points at which the radial force (F_r) and tangential force (F_t) produce maximum bending moment (M) respectively in the rim, are rather close to each other. Therefore, their moments can be added together to simplify the analysis. This approach is conservative.

This applies also to the location of the radial force and the tangential force for maximum deflection (Δ) of the rim section.

The combined expressions are--

$$M_{max} = k_1 F_r r + F_t e$$

$$\Delta_{max} = \frac{r^2}{E I} (k_2 F_r r + k_3 F_t e)$$

Moment Arm (e)

The moment arm (e) for the tangential force (F_t) is the distance from the point on the tooth where this force is applied, to the center of gravity (x–x) of the stiffened rim cross-section below the root circle. For simplicity, F_t can be assumed to be applied at the tooth crest where the distance (e) is the greatest. See the sketch of tooth section inserted in upper right of Figure 2.

It is also assumed that the tangential force is carried by just one tooth, which again is on the conservative side.

Values of Constant (k)

The influence of the gear arms on properties of the rim segment between arms is represented in the formulas by the constants k_1, k_2 and k_3. Values obtained from Table 1, according to the number of gear arms (n_a), should be substituted into the formulas.

TABLE 1			
CONSTANTS FOR GEAR RIM FORMULAS			
Number of arms n_a	k_1	k_2	k_3
4	.199	.0148	.0149
5	.170	.0095	.0112
6	.144	.0052	.0084
8	.113	.0023	.0051
10	.092	.0012	.0035

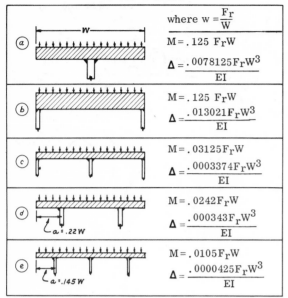

TABLE 2

FORMULAS FOR GEAR RIMS SUPPORTED
BY SOLID DISCS

	where $w = \dfrac{F_r}{W}$
(a)	$M = .125\, F_r W$ $\Delta = \dfrac{.0078125 F_r W^3}{EI}$
(b)	$M = .125\, F_r W$ $\Delta = \dfrac{.013021 F_r W^3}{EI}$
(c)	$M = .03125\, F_r W$ $\Delta = \dfrac{.0003374 F_r W^3}{EI}$
(d)	$M = .0242 F_r W$ $\Delta = \dfrac{.000343 F_r W^3}{EI}$ $a = .22\,W$
(e)	$M = .0105 F_r W$ $\Delta = \dfrac{.0000425 F_r W^3}{EI}$ $a = .145\,W$

6. BENDING OF RIM SUPPORTED BY SOLID DISC

In determining the deflection in a gear rim supported by one or more solid discs, a cross-section of the rim is considered to be an isolated beam under the action of the radial force (F_r) acting across the rim width (W).

Table 2 gives formulas for the maximum bending moment as well as the over-all displacement or deformation (from highest to lowest point) with five types of rim support. These formulas assume a uniform load over the full width of the rim face.

A single, centered disc is used in (a). Two discs at each outer edge of the rim are shown in (b). Three discs are shown in (c), one at centerline and the other two at the outer edges of the rim. Two discs are shown in (d), but each is set in from the edge 22% of the rim width; this results in much lower bending moment and deflection. Three discs are used in (e), with one at centerline and the outer discs set in 14.5% of the rim width; this further reduces the bending moment and deflection.

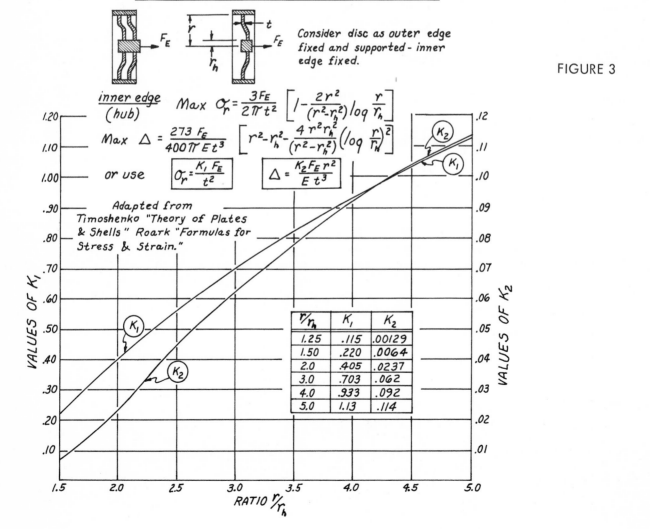

Consider End Thrust on Disc of Gear

Consider disc as outer edge fixed and supported- inner edge fixed.

FIGURE 3

inner edge (hub)

$\text{Max } \sigma_r = \dfrac{3 F_E}{2 \pi t^2}\left[1 - \dfrac{2r^2}{(r^2 - r_h^2)} \log \dfrac{r}{r_h}\right]$

$\text{Max } \Delta = \dfrac{273 F_E}{400 \pi E t^3}\left[r^2 - r_h^2 - \dfrac{4 r^2 r_h^2}{(r^2 - r_h^2)}\left(\log \dfrac{r}{r_h}\right)^2\right]$

or use $\boxed{\sigma_r = \dfrac{K_1 F_E}{t^2}}$ $\boxed{\Delta = \dfrac{K_2 F_E r^2}{E t^3}}$

Adapted from Timoshenko "Theory of Plates & Shells" Roark "Formulas for Stress & Strain."

r/r_h	K_1	K_2
1.25	.115	.00129
1.50	.220	.0064
2.0	.405	.0237
3.0	.703	.062
4.0	.933	.092
5.0	1.13	.114

VALUES OF K_1

VALUES OF K_2

RATIO $\dfrac{r}{r_h}$

The relative rim thicknesses required to resist the same force with the same stiffness are represented diagrammatically.

Moment of Inertia

The greatest problem in this analysis is to accurately determine the arc length of the rim segment which is to withstand this radial force (F_r), Figure 4. This depends on relative sizes of the two meshing gears, on the tooth geometry, etc.

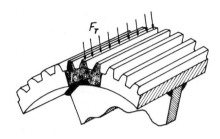

FIGURE 4

A conservative approach is to consider this arc length to be equal to the diametral pitch, on the basis of one tooth resisting the full bending moment resulting from the radial force.

Since this decision influences the value of the cross-section's actual moment of inertia, good engineering judgment is needed in deciding to what extent this conservative approach might be modified.

7. BENDING OF GEAR DISC DUE TO END THRUST

If the gear being designed is a helical gear, the end thrust is--

$$F_e = F_t \tan \theta$$

On other types of gears, it is well to assume a certain end thrust and to design the disc to withstand this force. For example, use 10% of the tangential force.

The formulas and curves on the graph, Figure 3, can be used to determine the maximum stress in the disc at the hub, as well as the deflection. Here the disc is considered as having its outer (rim) edge fixed and supported, and its inner (hub) edge fixed.

The end thrust (F_e) is assumed to be equally distributed between the discs, if more than one is provided.

8. AMOUNT OF WELD REQUIRED

The two main welds on a gear are those joining the disc to the hub, and the disc to the rim. Because the length of each of these circumferential welds as well as its torque arm depends on its radius, the weld at the hub becomes the most critical because of its smaller radius (r_h).

The formula for the torque transmitted safely by the weld at the hub, based upon an exact method, is--

$$T = \pi \, 9600 \left[\left(r_h + \frac{\omega}{2} \right)^3 - \frac{r_h^4}{r_h + \frac{\omega}{2}} \right]$$

For convenience, the allowable torque transmitted by the weld at the hub may be found from Table 3. Both the formula and Table 3 provide values for one weld only.

For larger gear diameters where the radius (r) to the center of the fillet weld throat is large in comparison to the weld's leg size (ω), Figure 5, the following formula is used:

$$T = 2 \pi \, 9600 \, \omega \, r^2$$

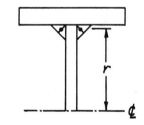

FIGURE 5

For simplicity on very large-diameter gears, the radius (r) to the center of the weld throat is assumed to be equal to the radius of one of the members being joined.

TABLE 3
TABLE OF ALLOWABLE TORQUE TRANSMITTED BY ONE WELD (INCH POUNDS)
Leg Size of Fillet Weld, Inches
RADIUS OF HUB INCHES	3/16"	1/4"	5/16"	3/8"	7/16"	1/2"	9/16"	5/8"	3/4"	7/8"	1"
1"	11,950	15,950	20,550	25,100	29,700	34,800	39,900	45,150	56,500	68,500	81,600
1-1/4"	18,450	24,800	31,400	38,300	45,400	52,800	60,500	68,000	84,300	101,000	119,500
1-1/2"	26,230	35,400	44,900	54,400	64,200	74,400	84,700	95,300	117,200	140,300	165,000
1-3/4"	35,600	47,900	60,500	73,200	86,500	99,700	113,300	127,400	150,000	186,200	218,000
2"	46,300	62,300	78,500	95,000	111,800	129,200	146,500	164,200	200,700	238,500	278,000
2-1/4"	58,500	78,500	99,000	119,700	140,400	162,000	184,000	206,000	250,300	298,000	345,000
2-1/2"	72,050	96,720	121,720	147,090	172,930	198,830	225,520	252,100	306,870	362,070	421,600

Problem 1

Check this proposed design of a gear for stresses and deflection:

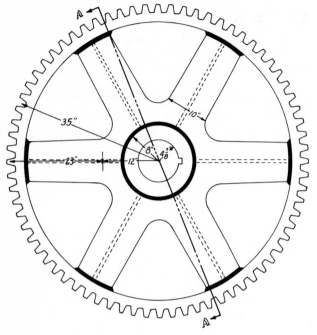

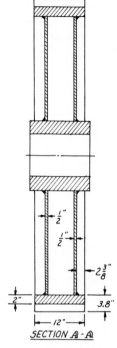

where:

number of teeth (N) = 70

diametral pitch (P) = 1"

pressure angle (ϕ) = 20°

number of arms (n_a) = 6

horsepower (HP) = 1000

pitch circle radius = 35"

overload factor = 1.25

FIGURE 6

SECTION A-A

For simplicity and conservative design, assume the radius of rim section's center of gravity to be equal to the pitch circle radius, r = 35".

Step 1: Determine Forces on Gear

Tangential force

$$F_t = \frac{126{,}000 \times HP}{D \times RPM}$$

$$= \frac{126{,}000 \, (1000 \times 1.25)}{(70)(100)}$$

$$= 22{,}350 \text{ lbs}$$

Radial force

$$F_r = F_t \tan \phi$$

$$= (22{,}350)(.3640)$$

$$= 8{,}140 \text{ lbs}$$

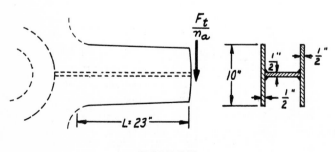

FIGURE 7

Step 2: Determine Stress in Gear Arm

Treat the arm as a cantilever beam, supported and fixed at the hub end, Figure 7.

Here:

$$S = \frac{t \, d^2}{6} = \frac{(1)(10)^2}{6}$$

$$= 16.6 \text{ in.}^3$$

where the web along the neutral axis is neglected because it is ineffective.

Bending moment on the arm

$$M = \frac{F_t}{n_a} L = \sigma S$$

Bending stress in the arm

$$\sigma = \frac{F_t \, L}{n_a \, S}$$

$$= \frac{(22{,}350)(23)}{(6)(16.6)}$$

$$= 5{,}165 \text{ psi}$$

which is well within the yield strength of steel.

Step 3: Determine Bending Stress in Rim Segment

Between Arms

Minimum thickness of gear rim below the root

circle, or whole tooth depth, must be--

$$t = \frac{1}{P} \sqrt[3]{\frac{N}{2 n_a}}$$

$$= \frac{1}{1} \sqrt[3]{\frac{70}{2 \times 6}}$$

$$= 1.8" \text{ or use } \underline{2"}$$

Rim cross-section's moment of inertia

$$I = \frac{12"(2")^3}{12} = 8.0 \text{ in.}^4$$

$$\therefore \quad S = \frac{I}{c} = \frac{8.0}{1} = 8.0 \text{ in.}^3$$

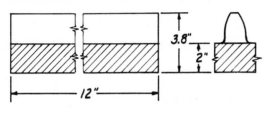

FIGURE 8

Since the proposed tooth profile provides a tooth depth of 1.8", the moment arm is--

$$e = .8"$$

From Table 1, the constants for $n_a = 6$ are found to be —

$$k_1 = .144 \qquad k_2 = .0052 \qquad k_3 = .0084$$

Maximum bending moment on the gear rim between arms

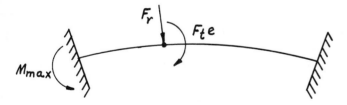

FIGURE 9

$$M_{max} = k_1 F_r r + F_t e$$

$$= (.144)(8140)(35) + (22,350)(2.8)$$

$$= 103,600 \text{ in.-lbs}$$

Bending stress in the rim

$$\sigma = \frac{M}{S} = \frac{103,600}{8.0}$$

$$= \underline{13,000 \text{ psi}}$$

which is a reasonable value.

Step 4: Determine Deflection of Rim Segment Between Arms

The maximum deflection of the gear rim between arms is--

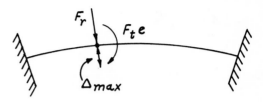

FIGURE 10

$$\Delta \max = \frac{r^2}{E I} (k_2 F_r r + k_3 F_t e)$$

$$= \frac{(35)^2}{(30 \times 10^6)(8)} [1481.48 + 525.67]$$

$$= .0102"$$

This deflection would be excessive, resulting in excessive wear.

The gear design can be altered so as to better support the rim, making it stiffer and lowering its bending stress. One way to do this is to make the arm spider a continuous disc so as to achieve the effect of a built-up rim, Figure 11.

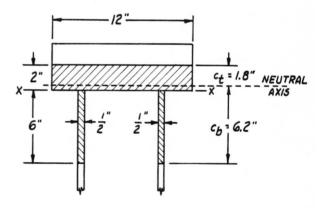

FIGURE 11

Moment of inertia of built-up rim

The moment of inertia of this built-up rim's cross-section is obtained by the moment-of-elements method, treating the 2 disc elements as 1:

	A	d	M=Ad	I=Md	I_g
12" × 2"	24.0	+1.0	+24.0	+24.0	8.0
1" × 6"	6.0	-3.0	-18.0	+54.0	18.0
Total	30.0		+6.0	+104.0	

where d = distance from element's center of gravity to reference axis x-x.

Thus, the moment of inertia about the entire rim section's neutral axis is--

$$I_{NA} = I_x - \frac{M^2}{A}$$

$$= 104.0 - \frac{(+6)^2}{30}$$

$$= 102.8 \text{ in.}^4$$

Distance of NA from x-x $= \frac{M}{A} = \frac{+6}{30}$

$$d = +.20''$$

Section modulus of built-up rim

The section modulus of the built-up rim's cross-section above and below this neutral axis is--

$$S_{top} = \frac{I}{c_t} = \frac{102.8}{1.8}$$

$$= 57.2 \text{ in.}^3$$

$$S_{bottom} = \frac{I}{c_b} = \frac{102.8}{6.2}$$

$$= 16.6 \text{ in.}^3$$

Bending stress in built-up rim

Bending stress in the rim, between arms, is obtained by substituting the lower section modulus (S) into the original equation--

$$\sigma = \frac{M}{S} = \frac{103,600}{16.6}$$

$$= 6,240 \text{ psi}$$

which is <u>less than half</u> the original figure.

Deflection of segment of built-up rim

Rim deflection, between arms, is obtained by substituting its moment of inertia (I) into the original equation:

$$\Delta = \frac{r^2}{E I} (k_2 F_r r + k_3 F_t e)$$

$$= \frac{(35)^2 (2007)}{(30 \times 10^6)(102.8)}$$

$$= .0008'' \quad \text{OK}$$

In this case, a deflection of .0008'' is tolerable. Therefore, the design sequence is continued on the basis of using disc(s) rather than gear arms.

Step 5: Determine the Bending Stress and Deflection of the Rim's Cross-Section

Check the bending moment on the rim's cross-section on the basis of the rim being supported by two discs set in at .22 W (see Table 2):

$$M_{max} = .0241 F_r W$$

$$= (.0241)(8140)(12)$$

$$= 2,355 \text{ in.-lbs}$$

Assume just one tooth to resist this moment, Figure 12.

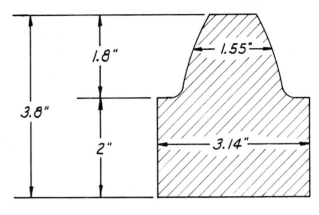

FIGURE 12

Then:

$$I = 9.7 \text{ in.}^4 \text{ approx.}$$

$$S = 4.4 \text{ in.}^3 \text{ approx.}$$

Bending stress

$$\sigma = \frac{M}{S}$$

$$= \frac{2,355}{4.4}$$

$$= 535 \text{ psi} \quad \text{OK}$$

Bending deflection

The over-all deflection of the rim cross-section, between the highest point to the lowest point on the rim, is obtained from the Table 2 formula for a rim supported by two discs set in at .22 W. See Figure 13.

$$\Delta = \frac{.000343 \, F_r \, W^3}{E \, I}$$

$$= \frac{.000343 \,(8140)\,(12)^3}{(30 \times 10^6)(9.7)}$$

$$= .0000165'' \quad \text{OK}$$

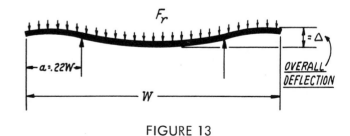

FIGURE 13

Step 6: Determine the Stress and Deflection of Disc

To check bending stress and deflection of each

disc due to end thrust, assume this force (F_e) to be about 10% of the tangential force (F_t), or--

$$F_e = .10 \, (22,350)$$
$$= 2,235$$

which is distributed between two discs:

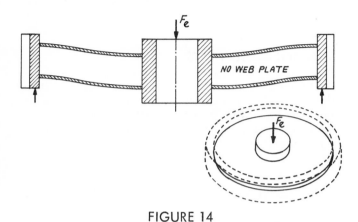

FIGURE 14

The ratio of the radius of the disc's outer edge (r) to the radius of the disc's inner edge (r_h) is--

$$\frac{r}{r_h} = \frac{32}{8} = 4.0$$

From the graph, Figure 3, this ratio provides the constants--

$$K_1 = .933 \qquad K_2 = .092$$

Maximum bending stress (radial) at the hub

$$\sigma_r = \frac{K_1 \, F_e}{t^2}$$
$$= \frac{(.933)(1120 \text{ lbs on one disc})}{(.5)^2}$$
$$= 4,180 \text{ psi}$$

Maximum deflection of the disc

$$\Delta = \frac{K_2 \, F_e \, r^2}{E \, t^3}$$
$$= \frac{(.092)(1120 \text{ lbs})(35)^2}{(30 \times 10^6)(.5)^3}$$
$$= .030'' \qquad \underline{\text{This is excessive.}}$$

Some stiffeners or webs should be placed between the two discs perpendicular to them.

Stiffening of discs

Web plates, ½" × 6¼", can be placed in between the two discs to effect an I-beam section for the arms, Figure 15. This will give the gear sufficient rigidity in line with the shaft for end thrust forces.

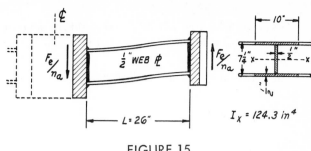

FIGURE 15

Consider each arm as a simple beam fixed on each end, and loaded with--

$$\frac{F_e}{n_a} = \frac{2235 \text{ lbs}}{6}$$
$$= 373 \text{ lbs}$$

Bending moment

Maximum bending moment at ends of the arm, resulting from end thrust, is then--

$$M = \frac{F \, L}{2}$$
$$= \frac{(373)(26)}{2}$$
$$= 4,850 \text{ in.-lbs} \qquad \text{OK}$$

Bending stress

$$\sigma = \frac{M \, c}{I}$$
$$= \frac{(4,850)(3.625)}{124.3}$$
$$= 140 \text{ psi} \qquad \text{OK}$$

Deflection of arm

Maximum deflection of the arm, resulting from end thrust, is--

$$\Delta = \frac{F \, L^3}{12 \, E \, I}$$
$$= \frac{(373)(26)^3}{12 \, (30 \times 10^6)(124.3)}$$
$$= .000147'' \qquad \text{OK}$$

Step 7: Determine the Effect of Centrifugal Force

$$\sigma = \frac{r^2 \, RPM^2}{124,400} = \frac{(35)^2 \, (100)^2}{124,400}$$
$$= \underline{98.5 \text{ psi}}$$

which indicates that centrifugal force is no problem at this speed.

Step 8: Determine Weld Size

Assume there are two ⅜" fillet welds around the hub. Just one weld on the outside of each disc joining it to the hub.

The allowable torque transferred by each weld is--

$$T_w = 2 \pi 9600 \, \omega \, r^2$$

where:

ω = leg size of fillet weld

r = radius to center of weld throat

For two welds, the allowable torque would be--

$$T_w = 2 \times 2 \pi 9600 \, (.375)(8)^2$$
$$= 2,895,000 \text{ in.-lbs}$$

Since the actual torque to be transferred is only--

$$T = \frac{63,030 \times HP}{RPM} = \frac{63,030 (1250)}{100}$$
$$= 790,000 \text{ in.-lbs}$$

Conclusion: Two ⅜" fillet welds around the hub, on the outside of each disc joining it to the hub, are adequate.

9. FABRICATING HINTS

Welded steel gears allow extreme flexibility in their manufacture as well as in design. There are many ways in which to reduce the material and fabricating costs. Figure 17 illustrates just a few of these techniques.

FIG. 16 - FINALIZED GEAR DESIGN

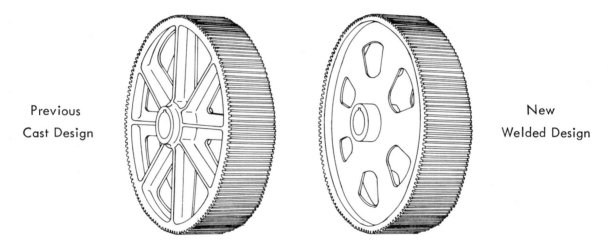

Previous Cast Design

New Welded Design

Large steel gears that are fabricated with the help of modern arc welding meet the severest requirements at lowest cost of manufacture.

FIG. 17 - IDEAS FOR ECONOMICAL GEAR FABRICATION

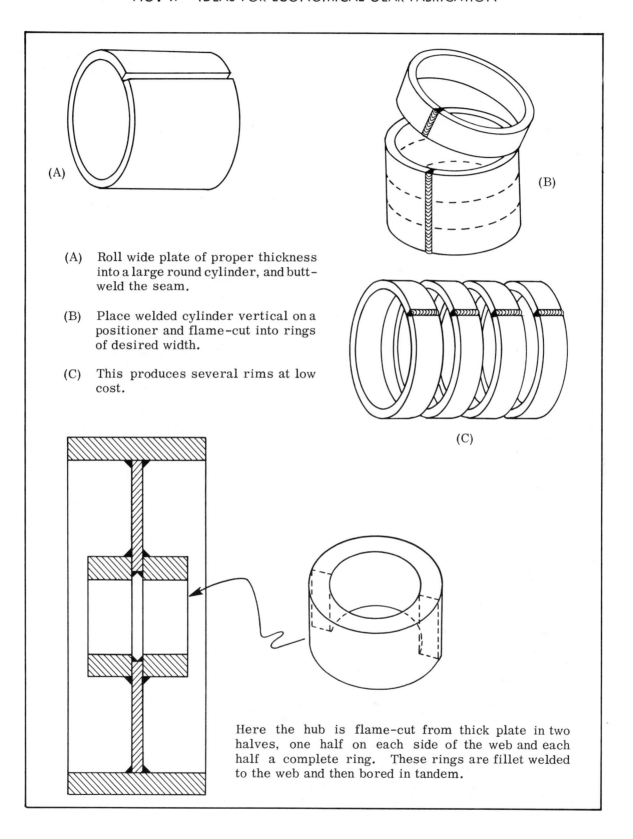

(A)

(B)

(A) Roll wide plate of proper thickness into a large round cylinder, and butt-weld the seam.

(B) Place welded cylinder vertical on a positioner and flame-cut into rings of desired width.

(C) This produces several rims at low cost.

(C)

Here the hub is flame-cut from thick plate in two halves, one half on each side of the web and each half a complete ring. These rings are fillet welded to the web and then bored in tandem.

With arc-welded construction, gear housings as well as gears can be made economically. Efficient bearing supports permits lighter-gage plate, saving weight and cost of material. Gear alignment is assured for many years of service, with good bearing and gear life as associated benefits.

Weldability of Steel

1. THE SHIELDED ARC WELDING PROCESS

In order to evaluate the weldability of steels, a limited knowledge of the basic arc welding process is advisable.

Welding consists of joining two pieces of metal by establishing a metallurgical bond between them. Many different welding processes may be used to produce bonding through the application of pressure and/or through fusion. Arc welding is a fusion process. The bond between the metals is produced by reducing to a molten state the surfaces to be joined and then allowing the metal to solidify. When the molten metal solidifies, union is completed.

In the arc welding process, the intense heat required to reduce the metal to a liquid state is produced by an electric arc. The arc is formed between the work to be welded and a metal wire or rod called the electrode. The arc, which produces a temperature of about 6500°F at the tip of the electrode, is formed by bringing the electrode close to the metal to be joined. The tremendous heat at the tip of the electrode melts filler metal and base metal, thus liquifying them in a common pool called a crater.* As the areas solidify, the metals are joined into one solid homogeneous piece. By moving the electrode along the seam or joint to be welded, the surfaces to be joined are welded together along their entire length.

The electric arc is the most widely used source of energy for the intense heat required for fusion

*For some applications, filler metal is deposited by a consumable welding electrode; for others, a "nonconsumable" electrode supplies the heat and a separate welding rod the filler metal.

welding. The arc is an electrical discharge or spark sustained in a gap in the electrical circuit. The resistance of the air or gas in the gap to the passage of the current, transforms the electrical energy into heat at extremely high temperatures. Electrical power consists of amperes and voltage. The amount of energy available is the product of the amperes and the voltage flowing through the circuit and is measured in watts and kilowatts. The energy used is affected by such variables as the constituents in electrode coatings, the type of current (AC or DC), the direction of current flow, and many others.

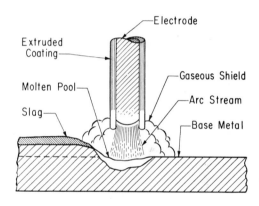

FIGURE 2

In all modern arc welding processes, the arc is shielded to control the complex arc phenomenon and to improve the physical properties of the weld deposit. This shielding is accomplished through various techniques: a chemical coating on the electrode wire, inert gases, granular flux compounds, and metallic salts placed in the core of the electrode. Arc shielding varies with the type of arc welding process used. In all cases, however, the shielding is intended: 1) to protect the molten metal from the air, either with gas, vapor or slag; 2) to add alloying and fluxing ingredients; and 3) to control the melting of the rod for more effective use of the arc energy.

The arc welding process requires a continuous supply of electric current sufficient in amperage and voltage to maintain an arc. This current may be either alternating (AC) or direct (DC), but it must be provided through a source which can be controlled to satisfy the variables of the welding process: amperage and voltage.

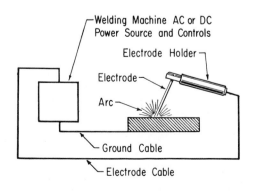

FIGURE 1

2. WELDABILITY OF STEEL

Most steels can be commercially arc welded. Weldability of a steel refers only to the relative ease of producing a satisfactory joint. A steel is said to be ideally weldable if the required weld joint can be made without difficulty or excessive cost.

Some steels are more suited to high-speed welding than others. Analysis of the electrode core wire is accurately controlled to produce good welds, but since the plate metal becomes part of the weld, control of the plate analysis is also important. When higher currents are used to get higher welding speeds, more of the plate metal mixes with the weld. If possible, select an easily welded steel that doesn't require expensive electrodes or complicated welding procedures. Table 1 gives a range of carbon steel analyses for maximum welding speed.

TABLE 1 - PREFERRED ANALYSIS
Of Carbon Steel for Good Weldability

Element		Normal Range, %	Steel Exceeding Any One of the Following Percentages Will Probably Require Extra Care
Carbon	C	.06 - .20	.35
Manganese	Mn	.35 - .80	1.40
Silicon	Si	.10 max	.30
Sulphur	S	.035 max	.050
Phosphorus	P	.030 max	.040

The commonly used mild steels fall within the preferred analysis listed. Sulphur content of these steels is usually below 0.035%, although the specification limits permit as much as 0.050% These steels all have a tensile strength approximating 67,000 psi with 32% elongation in 2". For steels outside this analysis, welding procedures can be modified.

It must be recognized that continued progress is being made in metallurgical control of steel, as well as in the development of welding processes, electrodes and fluxes. This tends to broaden the range of "weldability" with respect to steel analysis. High-strength alloy steels and most of the stainless steels also can be welded routinely by standard procedures. Their use, however, invariably reduces welding speed and increases cost in comparison with "preferred analysis" steels. The design group would do well to standardize on as limited a number of steels as is practical.

3. WELDING OF THICK SECTIONS

Plates and sections as produced in the steel mill undergo a rather slow cooling after being rolled while red hot. Because of their greater mass, thick sections cool more slowly than thin.

For a given carbon and alloy content, slower cooling from the critical temperature results in a lower strength, but higher ductility. Higher carbon or alloy content increases this strength.

For plate thicknesses in most common use, the mill has no difficulty in meeting the minimum yield strength required. However, for very thick sections, because of their slower cooling, the carbon or alloy content will probably have to be increased in order to maintain this yield strength.

TABLE 2 - SUGGESTED PREHEAT & INTERPASS TEMPERATURES (°F)

When Using Low-Hydrogen Electrodes or Submerged-Arc Process

Steel	Plate Thickness				
	¼"	½"	1"	2"	4"
1020	-	-	-	-	150
1025	-	-	-	-	200
1030	-	-	-	100	200
1035	-	-	-	200	300
1040	-	-	200	300	300
1045	100	200	300	350	350
1050	200	300	350	400	400
1060	300	400	400	450	500
1070	400	450	500	500	550
1080	450	500	550	550	600

Above table for general guidance. Preferably use Lincoln Preheat Calculator for any given analysis of steel.

A weld will cool faster on a thick plate than on a thin plate. The thicker plate, as already mentioned, may have a higher carbon or alloy content. Both of these factors will work together to produce a weld of higher strength but lower ductility. More control must be used in welding thick plate. Preheating may be required, on extreme thicknesses, to decrease the rate of cooling of the weld.

TABLE 3 - SUGGESTED PREHEAT & INTERPASS TEMPERATURES (°F)

When Using Non-Low-Hydrogen Electrodes

Steel	Plate Thickness		
	¼"	½"	1"
1020	-	-	100
1025	-	-	150
1030	-	-	250

For general guidance. Use Lincoln Preheat Calculator for any given analysis of steel.

Joint Design

1. FACTORS AFFECTING PROCEDURES

For every welding job there is one procedure which will complete the joint at the lowest possible cost. The accomplishment of this task requires a knowledge of the factors affecting the type of weld to be performed.

The main factors to be considered are:

1. Type of joint to be made, included angle, root opening, and land (root face).

2. Type and size of electrode.

3. Type of current, polarity and amount (amperes).

4. Arc length (arc voltage).

5. Arc speed.

6. Position of welds (flat, horizontal, vertical, and overhead).

A large number of the above-mentioned factors can be determined by actually welding a sample joint. Such items as the type and size of electrode, polarity, current, arc characteristics, and shop techniques are best determined by the fabricator. The engineer must realize that these problems are present and should include them in his consideration of the joint designs.

Figure 1 indicates that the root opening (R) is the separation between the members to be joined.

A root opening is used for electrode accessibility to the base or root of the joint. The smaller the angle of the bevel, the larger the root opening must be to get good fusion at the root.

If the root opening is too small, root fusion is more difficult to obtain and smaller electrodes must be used, thus slowing down the welding process.

If the root opening is too large, weld quality does not suffer but more weld metal is required; this increases weld cost and will tend to increase distortion.

Figure 2 indicates how the root opening must be increased as the bevel's included angle is decreased. Backup strips are used on larger root openings. All three preparations are acceptable; all are conducive to good welding procedure and good weld quality. Selection, therefore, is usually based on cost.

Root opening and joint preparation will directly affect weld cost (pounds of metal required), and choice should be made with this in mind. Joint preparation includes the work required on plate edges prior to welding and includes beveling, providing a land, etc.

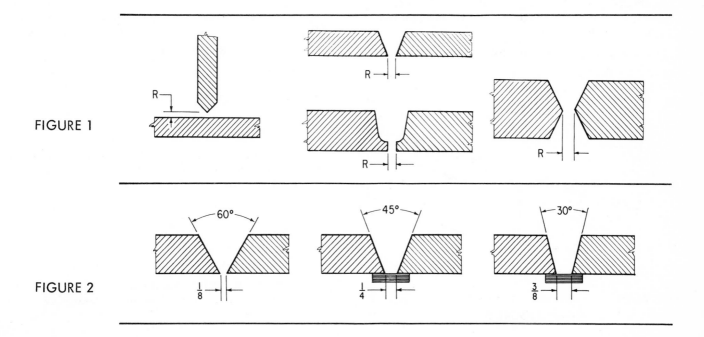

FIGURE 1

FIGURE 2

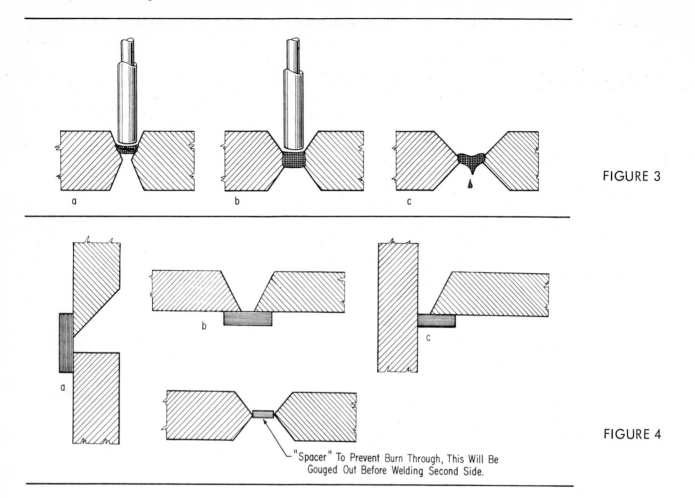

FIGURE 3

"Spacer" To Prevent Burn Through, This Will Be
Gouged Out Before Welding Second Side.

FIGURE 4

In Figure 3a if bevel and/or gap is too small, the weld will bridge the gap leaving slag at the root. Excessive back gouging is then required.

Figure 3b shows how proper joint preparation and procedure will produce good root fusion and will minimize back gouging.

In Figure 3c a large root opening will result in burn-through. Spacer strip may be used, in which case the joint must be back gouged.

Backup strips are commonly used when all welding must be done from one side, or when the root opening is excessive. Backup strips, shown in Figure 4a, b and c, are generally left in place and become an integral part of the joint.

Spacer strips may be used especially in the case of double-vee joints to prevent burn-through. The spacer, Figure 4d, to prevent burn-through, will be gouged out before welding the second side.

<u>Backup Strips</u>

Backup strip material should conform to the base metal. Feather edges of the plate are recommended when using a backup strip.

Short intermittent tack welds should be used to hold the backup strip in place, and these should preferably be staggered to reduce any initial restraint of the joint. They should not be directly opposite one another, Figure 5.

The backup strip should be in intimate contact with both plate edges to avoid trapped slag at the root, Figure 6.

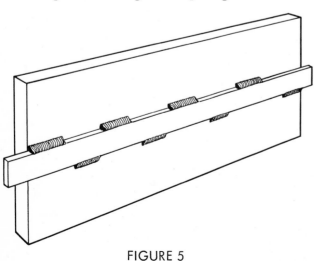

FIGURE 5

Weld Reinforcement

On a butt joint, a nominal weld reinforcement (approximately 1/16" above flush) is all that is necessary, Figure 7, left. Additional buildup, Figure 7, right, serves no useful purpose, and will increase the weld cost.

Care should be taken to keep both the width and the height of the reinforcement to a minimum.

2. EDGE PREPARATION

The main purpose of a land, Figure 8, is to provide an additional thickness of metal, as opposed to a feather edge, in order to minimize any burn-through tendency. A feather edge preparation is more prone to burn-through than a joint with a land, especially if the gap gets a little too large, Figure 9.

A land is not as easily obtained as a feather edge. A feather edge is generally a matter of one cut with a torch, while a land will usually require two cuts or possibly a torch cut plus machining.

A land usually requires back gouging if a 100% weld is required. A land is not recommended when welding into a backup strip, Figure 10, since a gas pocket would be formed.

Plate edges are beveled to permit accessibility to all parts of the joint and insure good fusion throughout the entire weld cross-section. Accessibility can be gained by compromising between maximum bevel and minimum root opening, Figure 11.

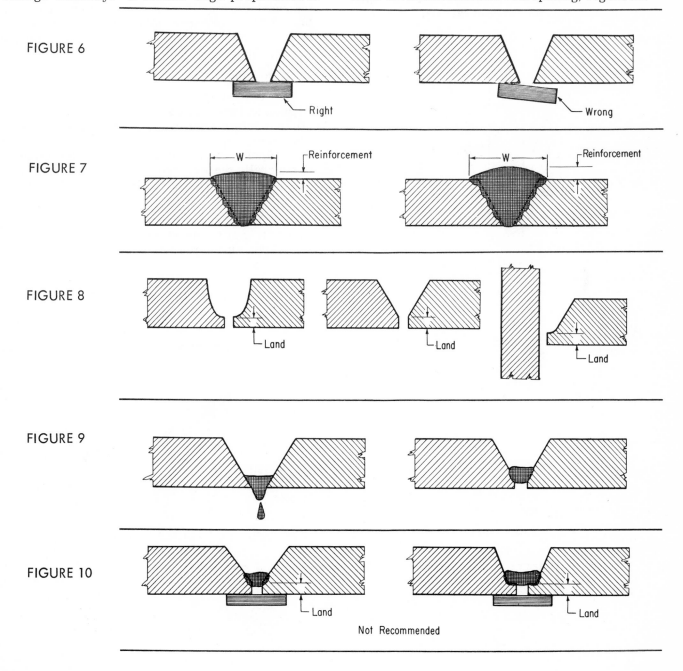

FIGURE 6

Right

Wrong

FIGURE 7

W — Reinforcement

W — Reinforcement

FIGURE 8

Land

Land

Land

FIGURE 9

FIGURE 10

Land

Land

Not Recommended

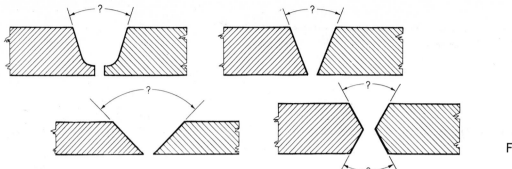

FIGURE 11

Degree of bevel may be dictated by the importance of maintaining proper electrode angle in confined quarters, Figure 12. For the joint illustrated, the minimum recommended bevel is 45°.

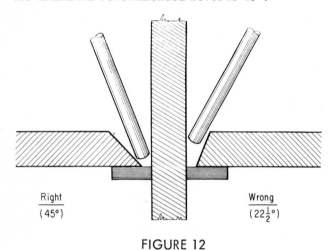

Right
(45°)

Wrong
(22½°)

FIGURE 12

U and J versus Vee Preparations

J and U preparations are excellent to work with but economically they have little to offer because preparation requires machining as opposed to simple torch cutting. Also a J or U groove requires a land, Figure 13, and thus back gouging.

Back Gouging

To consistently obtain complete fusion when welding a plate, back gouging is required on virtually all joints except single "vees" with feather edge. This may be done by any convenient means: grinding, chipping, or arc-air gouging. The latter method is generally the most economical and leaves an ideal contour for subsequent beads.

Without back gouging, penetration is incomplete, Figure 14. Proper back chipping should be deep enough to expose sound weld metal, and the contour should permit the electrode complete accessibility, Figure 15.

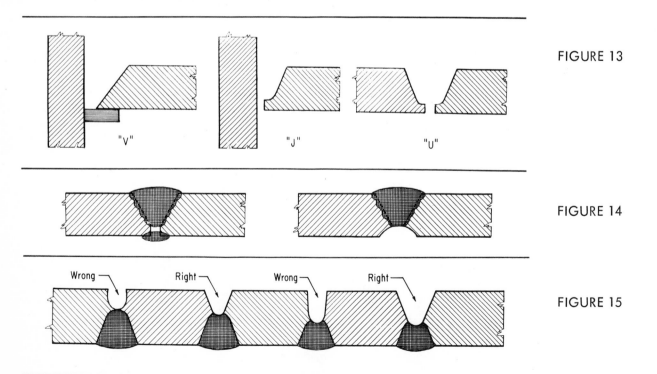

FIGURE 13

"V"   "J"   "U"

FIGURE 14

Wrong   Right   Wrong   Right

FIGURE 15

FIGURE 16 – PREQUALIFIED AWS JOINTS (MANUAL WELDING)
Full-Strength Groove Welds

	SINGLE (Welded From Both Sides Without Backing Strip)	SINGLE (Welded From One Side Using Backing Strip)	DOUBLE (Welded From Both Sides)
SQUARE BUTT	220-B' , 220-BA'	220-A	
VEE	220-C' , 220-CA'	220-E , 220-EA	220-F' , 220-G'
BEVEL	220-D¹,² , 220-DA' , 220-DB'	220-H² , 220-HA	220-J¹,² , 220-JA'
J	220-N¹,² , 220-NB' , 220-NA'		220-P¹,² , 220-PA
U	220-L' , 220-LA'		220-M'

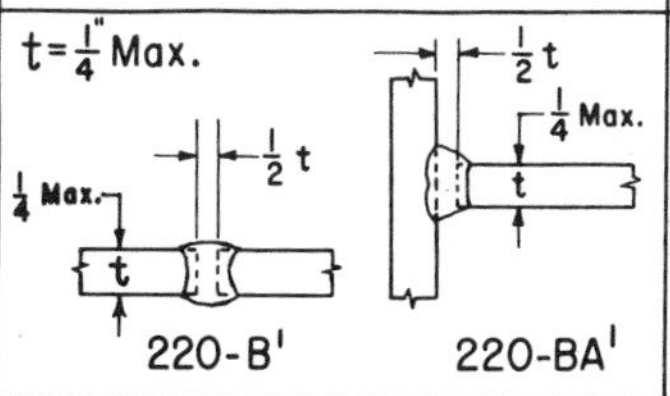

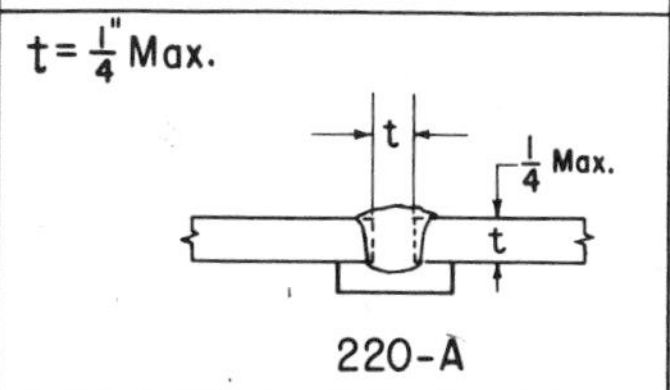

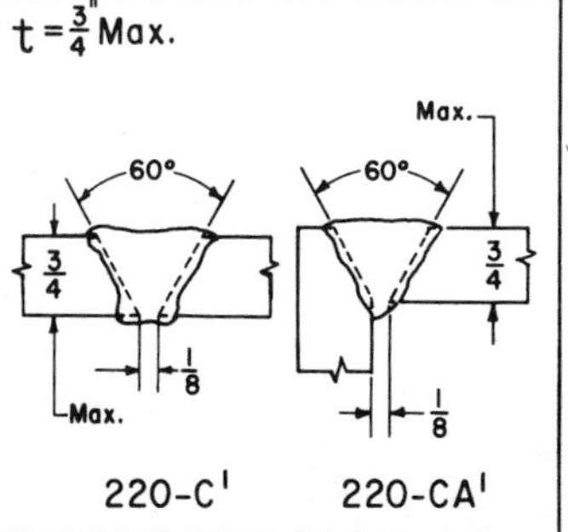

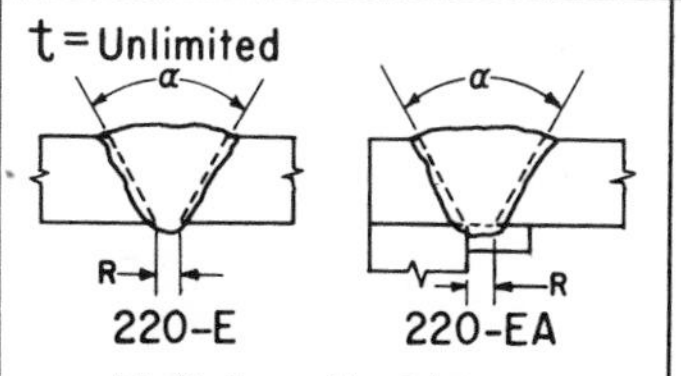

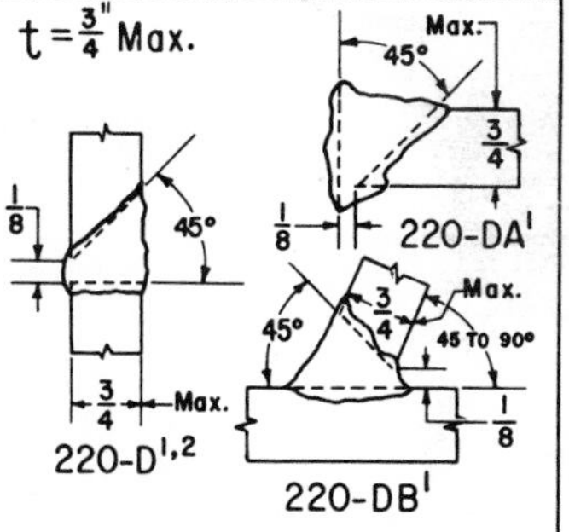

Limitations For Joints (220-E, 220-EA):

α	R	Permitted Welding Positions
45°	1/4	All Positions
30°	3/8	Flat and Overhead Only
20°	1/2	Flat and Overhead Only

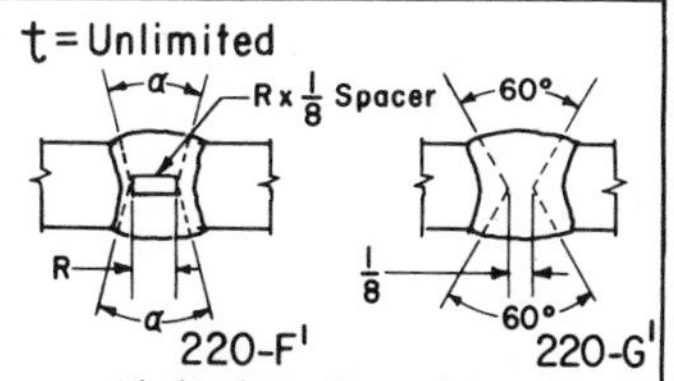

Limitations For Joints (220-F', 220-G'):

α	R	Permitted Welding Positions
45°	1/4	All Positions
30°	3/8	Flat and Overhead Only
20°	1/2	Flat and Overhead Only

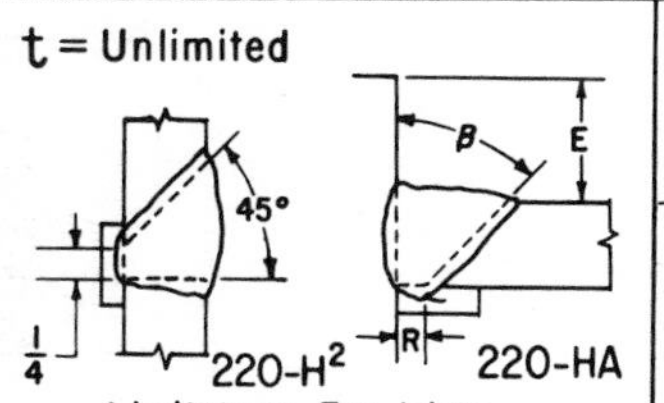

Limitations For Joints (220-H²):

β	R	Permitted Welding Positions	E
45°	1/4	All positions	Unlimited
30°	3/8	Flat and Overhead Only	Not Over 3

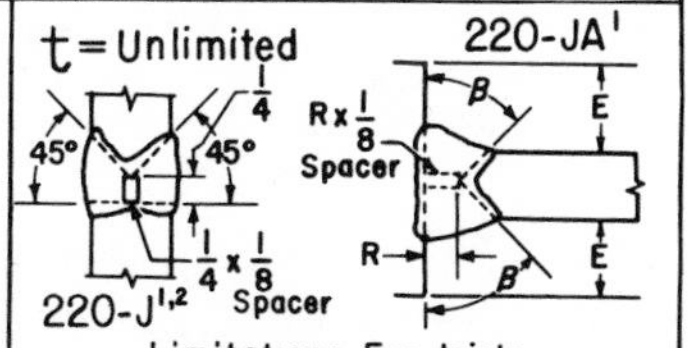

Limitations For Joints (220-J):

β	R	Permitted Welding Positions	E
		No Spacer	
45°	1/8	All Positions	Unlimited
		With Spacer	
45°	1/4	All Positions	Unlimited
30°	3/8	Flat and Overhead Only	Not Over 3

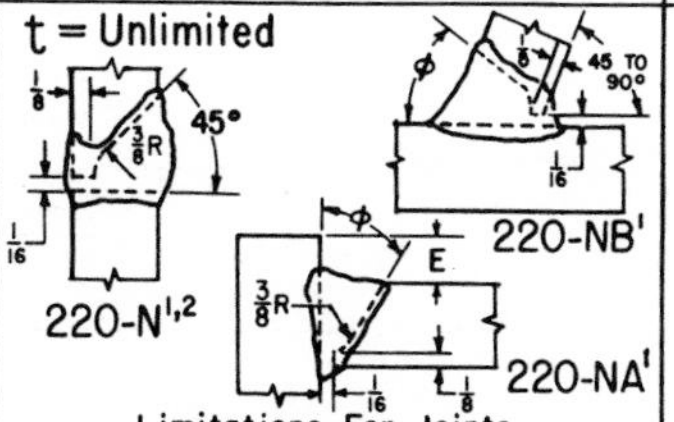

Limitations For Joints (220-NA):

φ	Permitted Welding Positions	E (220-NA)
45°	All Positions	Unlimited
30°	Flat and Overhead Only	Not Over 3

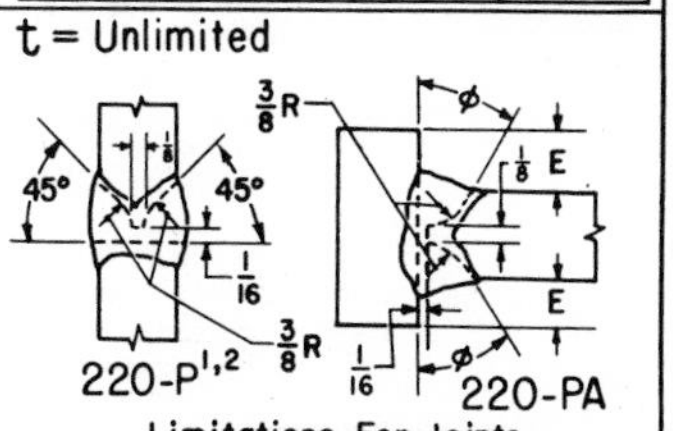

Limitations For Joints (220-PA):

φ	Permitted Welding Positions	E (220-PA)
45°	All Positions	Unlimited
30°	Flat and Overhead Only	Not Over 3

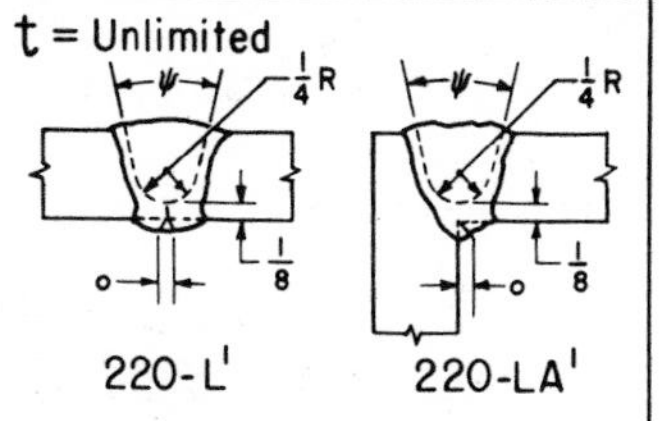

Limitations For Joints (220-L', 220-LA'):

ψ	Permitted Welding Positions
45°	All Positions
20°	Flat and Overhead Only

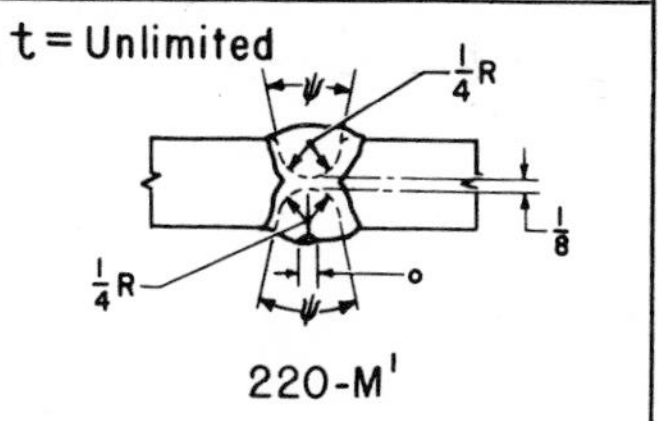

Limitations For Joints (220-M'):

ψ	Permitted Welding Positions
45°	All Positions
20°	Flat and Overhead Only

1. Gouge root before welding second side (Par 505 j)
2. For horizontal joints only (Par 220 b)

FIGURE 17 - PREQUALIFIED AWS JOINTS (SUBMERGED-ARC AUTOMATIC WELDING)
Full-Strength Groove Welds

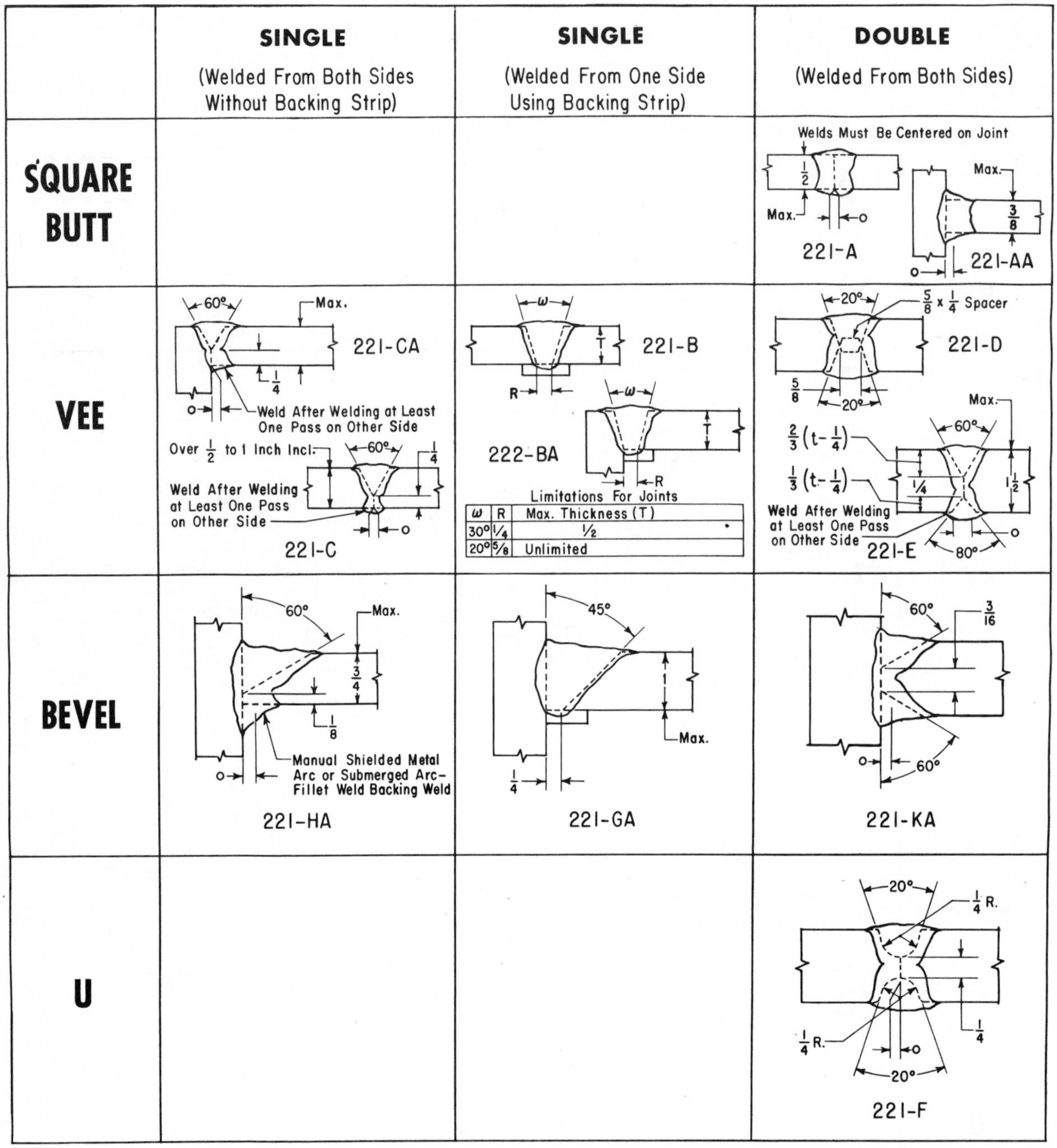

	SINGLE (Welded From Both Sides Without Backing Strip)	**SINGLE** (Welded From One Side Using Backing Strip)	**DOUBLE** (Welded From Both Sides)
SQUARE BUTT			221-A 221-AA
VEE	221-CA 221-C	221-B 222-BA	221-D 221-E
BEVEL	221-HA	221-GA	221-KA
U			221-F

3. TYPES OF JOINTS

The type of joint to be made depends on the design condition and may be one of the following: groove, fillet, plug or T joint. These joints may be made using various edge preparations, such as: square butt, Vee, bevel, J, or U. Certain of these joints have been prequalified by the American Welding Society (AWS) and are illustrated in two charts, Figure 16 for manual welding and in Figure 17 for submerged-arc automatic welding.

The choice between two or more types of joint is not always dictated solely by the design function. The choice often directly affects the cost of welding. For example, Figure 18 illustrates this influence. The choice is to be made between 45° fillet welds or some type of T groove joints.

(a) For full-strength welds, the leg of the fillet weld must be about 75% of the plate thickness.

(b) Full strength may also be obtained by double beveling the edge of the plate 45° and spacing the plate so the root opening is ⅛" to allow for complete penetration. The amount of weld metal compared to the conventional fillet weld varies from 75% for a 1" plate to 56% for a 4" plate. For plates up to about 1½" thickness, the extra cost of beveling the plate and the probable need to use lower welding current in the 45° groove tend to offset the lower cost of weld metal for this type of joint. But for heavier plate the reduction in weld metal is great enough to overcome any extra preparation cost.

(c) Full strength may also be obtained by beveling the edge of the plate 60° so as to place some of the weld within the plate; a 60° fillet is then placed on the outside. The minimum depth of bevel and the additional leg of fillet are both equal to 29% of the plate thickness. For all plate thicknesses, the amount of weld metal is approximately half that of the conventional fillet. This joint has the additional advantage that almost high welding current may be used as in the making of the fillet weld.

All of this is shown in the graph, Figure 18. The cross-over point in this chart between the conventional fillet welds and the 45° full penetrated T groove joint is about 1½" plate. The 60° bevel, partly penetrated joint, with 60° fillets appears to be the lowest in cost above 1" in thicknesses. The relative position of these curves will vary according to the welding and cutting costs used.

It would be a good idea for each company to make a similar cost study of the welding in their

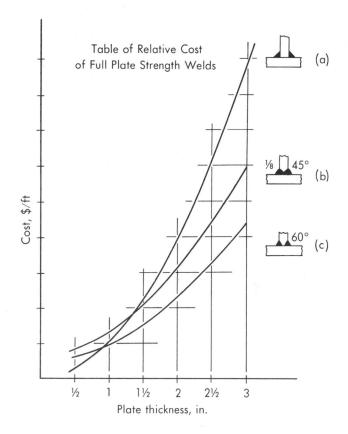

FIGURE 18

shop for guidance of their engineers in quickly selecting the most economical weld. Naturally the various costs (labor, welding, cutting, handling, assembly, etc.) will vary with each company.

4. WELDING SYMBOLS

The symbols in the chart, Figure 19, denoting the type of weld to be applied to a particular weldment have been standardized and adopted by the American Welding Society. Like any systematic plan of symbols, these welding notations quickly indicate to the designer, draftsman, production supervisor, and weldor alike, the exact welding details established for each joint or connection to satisfy all conditions of material strength and service required. Adapting this system of symbols to your engineering department will assure that the correct welding instructions are transmitted to all concerned and prevent misinterpretation of instructions, and resulting production cost increases.

FIGURE 19

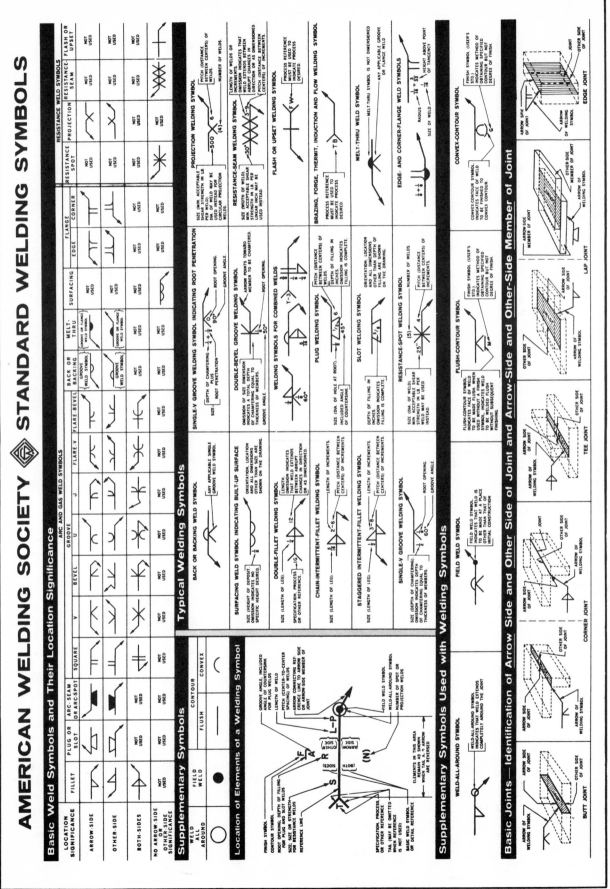

AMERICAN WELDING SOCIETY ⬦ STANDARD WELDING SYMBOLS

(COURTESY AMERICAN WELDING SOCIETY)

Although at first it may appear that many different symbols are involved, the system of symbols is broken down into basic elements or fundamentals. Any combination of these elements can then be built up to conform to any set of conditions governing a welded joint.

The system must be adapted to each particular organization. Basically, around 80% of all welded machinery structure connections are made by fillet welds, 15% are groove welds and 5% require special welds. In pressure vessel welding, approximately 90% of all connections are groove welds.

Therefore, it is wise in the initial stages to limit the use of symbols to just fillet welds and simple groove welds and to detail **any** special welds on the drawings. After the shop and draftsmen get used to these simple symbols, then they can branch into the ones that are more rarely used. Figure 20 shows the practical application of these symbols to various typical joints.

FIGURE 20 – TYPICAL APPLICATIONS OF AWS DRAFTING SYMBOLS FOR WELDS

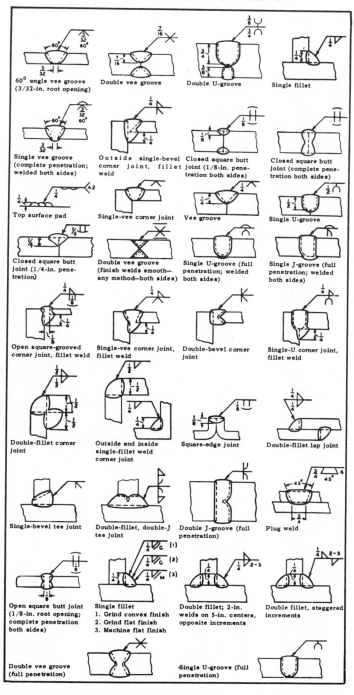

Clean arc-welded design from top to bottom in this automatic dial-type assembly machine permitted the builder to start production of the chassis before many of the machine's design details had been finalized.

Determining Weld Size

1. IMPORTANCE OF WELD SIZE

Overwelding is one of the major factors of welding cost. Specifying the correct size of weld is the first step in obtaining low-cost welding. This demands a simple method to figure the proper amount of weld to provide adequate strength for all types of connections.

In strength connections, groove welds must be made all the way through the plate, i.e., 100% penetration. Since a groove weld, properly made, has equal or better strength than the plate, there is no need for calculating the stress in the weld or attempting to determine its size. However, the size of a groove weld may be needed for estimating or other reasons. When welding alloy steels, it is necessary to match the weld-metal strength to plate strength but this is primarily a matter of proper electrode selection and of welding technique.

With fillet welds, it is possible to have too small a weld or too large a weld; therefore, it is necessary to be able to determine the proper weld size.

2. RULE OF THUMB FOR FILLET WELD SIZE

In order to develop the full strength of a plate by means of fillet welds, it is necessary that the leg size of the fillet be ¾ of the plate thickness:

$$\omega = \tfrac{3}{4} t \quad \dotfill (1)$$

this assumes:

   a) fillet weld on both sides of plate,

   b) fillet weld for full length of plate, and

   c) t = thickness of the thinner plate, if the two being joined are of different gage.

For mild steel, this welded joint will out-pull the plate under any type and direction of loading.

When the member is designed to maintain a certain amount of stiffness or rigidity, the stresses are usually of a rather low value. The weld as such does not contribute noticeably to the stiffness of the built-up section. The weld size is still dependent on the forces which must be transferred although they are low.

In many rigidity designs, it is difficult to compute these forces and it is sometimes assumed that

the stresses in the adjacent plate are lower than ⅓ to ½ of the allowable. This means, as a rule of thumb, that a rigidity design would require a fillet weld leg size ⅓ to ½ of that required for a strength design, or in other words,

$$\omega = \tfrac{1}{4} t \text{ to } \tfrac{3}{8} t \quad \dotfill (2)$$

assuming, as before, both sides welded full length, and based on the thinner plate. This range in leg size (¼ t to ⅜ t) usually results in well proportioned fillet welds.

If for some reason the weld is only made on one side of the plate, weld size should be doubled.

TABLE 1 – RULE-OF-THUMB FILLET WELD SIZES

PLATE THICKNESS (t)	STRENGTH DESIGN	RIGIDITY DESIGN	
	FULL STRENGTH WELD ($\omega = 3/4\ t$)	50% OF FULL STRENGTH WELD ($\omega = 3/8\ t$)	33% OF FULL STRENGTH WELD ($\omega = 1/4\ t$)
1/4	3/16	3/16*	3/16*
5/16	1/4	3/16*	3/16*
3/8	5/16	3/16*	3/16*
7/16	3/8	3/16	3/16*
1/2	3/8	3/16	3/16*
9/16	7/16	1/4	1/4 *
5/8	1/2	1/4	1/4 *
3/4	9/16	5/16	1/4 *
7/8	5/8	3/8	5/16*
1	3/4	3/8	5/16*
1 1/8	7/8	7/16	5/16
1 1/4	1	1/2	5/16
1 3/8	1	1/2	3/8
1 1/2	1 1/8	9/16	3/8
1 5/8	1 1/4	5/8	7/16
1 3/4	1 3/8	3/4	7/16
2	1 1/2	3/4	1/2
2 1/8	1 5/8	7/8	9/16
2 1/4	1 3/4	7/8	9/16
2 3/8	1 3/4	1	5/8
2 1/2	1 7/8	1	5/8
2 5/8	2	1	3/4
2 3/4	2	1	3/4
3	2 1/4	1 1/8	3/4

*These values have been adjusted to comply with AWS-recommended minimums

TABLE 2 – MINIMUM WELD SIZES FOR THICK PLATES (AWS)

THICKNESS OF THICKER PLATE JOINED t	MINIMUM LEG SIZE OF FILLET WELD ω
to 1/2" incl.	3/16"
over 1/2" thru 3/4"	1/4"
over 3/4" thru 1 1/2"	5/16"
over 1 1/2" thru 2 1/4"	3/8"
over 2 1/4" thru 6"	1/2"
over 6"	5/8"

Minimum leg size need not exceed thickness of the thinner plate.

Table 1 gives the leg size of fillet welds for various plate thicknesses, based on formulas #1 and #2. Values have been adjusted where necessary to comply with AWS-recommended minimums for thick plates (Table 2).

For rigidity designs, the fillet weld may be reduced by using intermittent welds.

Thick Plates

The American Welding Society recognizes that thick plates offer greater restraint, and produce a faster cooling rate for the welds. As a result they recommend the minimum fillet weld sizes in Table 2 for various plate thicknesses, based on the thicker plate.

This table is predicated on the theory that the required minimum weld size will provide sufficient welding heat input into the plate to give the desired slow rate of cooling.

This is not a complete answer to this problem; for example, a plate thicker than 6" would require a minimum weld size of ⅝", yet in actual practice this would be made in several passes. Each pass would be equivalent to about a ⁵⁄₁₆" fillet, and have the heat input of approximately a ⁵⁄₁₆" weld which may not be sufficient unless the plates are preheated.

A partial solution to this problem would be the following: Since the first pass of the joint is the most critical, it should be made with low-hydrogen electrodes and a rather slow travel speed. Resulting superior weld physicals, weld contour, and maximum heat input provide a good strong root bead.

3. TYPES OF WELDS

a. Primary welds transmit the entire load at the particular point where they are located. If the weld fails, the member fails. The weld must have the same property as the member at this point. In brief, the weld becomes the member at this point.

b. Secondary welds simply hold the parts together, thus forming the member. In most cases, the forces on these welds are low.

c. Parallel welds have forces applied parallel to their axis. In the case of fillet welds, the throat is stressed only in shear. For an equal-legged fillet, the maximum shear stress occurs on the 45° throat.

d. Transverse welds have forces applied transversely or at right angles to their axis. In the case of fillet welds, the throat is stressed in both shear and normal (in tension or compression). For an equal-legged fillet weld, the maximum shear stress occurs on the 67½° throat, and the maximum normal stress occurs on the 22½° throat.

4. SIMPLE TENSILE, COMPRESSIVE OR SHEAR LOADS ON WELDS

For a simple tensile, compressive or shear load, the given load is divided by the length of the weld to arrive at the applied unit force, lbs per linear inch of weld. From this force, the proper leg size of fillet weld or throat of groove weld may be found.

5. BENDING OR TWISTING LOADS ON WELDS

The problem here is to determine the properties of the welded connection in order to check the stress in the weld without first knowing its leg size. Some design texts suggest assuming a certain weld-leg size and then calculating the stress in the weld to see if it is overstressed or understressed. If the result is too far off, then the weld-leg size is readjusted.

TABLE 3 - DETERMINING FORCE ON WELD

Type of Loading		standard design formula stress lbs/in^2	treating the weld as a line force lbs/in
PRIMARY WELDS transmit entire load at this point			
	tension or compression	$\sigma = \dfrac{P}{A}$	$f = \dfrac{P}{A_w}$
	vertical shear	$\sigma = \dfrac{V}{A}$	$f = \dfrac{V}{A_w}$
	bending	$\sigma = \dfrac{M}{S}$	$f = \dfrac{M}{S_w}$
	twisting	$\sigma = \dfrac{TC}{J}$	$f = \dfrac{TC}{J_w}$
SECONDARY WELDS hold section together - low stress			
	horizontal shear	$\tau = \dfrac{VAy}{It}$	$f = \dfrac{VAy}{In}$
	torsional horizontal shear	$\tau = \dfrac{TC}{J}$	$f = \dfrac{TCt}{J}$

This has the following disadvantages:

1. Some decision must be made as to what throat section is going to be used to determine the property of the weld. Usually some objection can be raised to any throat section chosen.

2. The resulting stresses must be combined and, for several types of loading, this can be rather complicated.

In contrast, the following is a simple method to determine the correct amount of welding required for adequate strength. This is a method in which the weld is treated as a line, having no area, but a definite length and outline. This method has the following advantages:

1. It is not necessary to consider throat areas because only a line is considered.

2. Properties of the welded connection are easily found from a table without knowing weld-leg size.

3. Forces are considered on a unit length of weld instead of stresses, thus eliminating the knotty problem of combining stresses.

4. It is true that the stress distribution within a fillet weld is complex, due to eccentricity of the applied force, shape of the fillet, notch effect of the root, etc.; however, these same conditions exist in the actual fillet welds tested and have been recorded as a unit force per unit length of weld.

6. DETERMINING FORCE ON WELD

Visualize the welded connection as a single line, having the same outline as the connection, but no cross-sectional area. Notice, Figure 1, that the area (A_w) of the welded connection now becomes just the length of the weld.

Instead of trying to determine the stress on the weld (this cannot be done unless the weld size is known), the problem becomes a much simpler one

TABLE 4 - PROPERTIES OF WELD TREATED AS LINE

Outline of Welded Joint (b=width, d=depth)	Bending (about horizontal axis x-x)	Twisting
vertical line, depth d	$S_w = \frac{d^2}{6}$ in.^{2}	$J_w = \frac{d^3}{12}$ in.^{3}
horizontal line, width b	$S_w = \frac{d^2}{3}$	$J_w = \frac{d(3b^2+d^2)}{6}$
two horizontal lines, width b, depth d	$S_w = bd$	$J_w = \frac{b^3+3bd^2}{6}$
L-shape	$S_w = \frac{4bd+d^2}{6} = \frac{d^2(4b+d)}{6(2b+d)}$ top / bottom	$J_w = \frac{(b+d)^4 - 6b^2d^2}{12(b+d)}$
channel open top	$S_w = bd + \frac{d^2}{6}$	$J_w = \frac{(2b+d)^3}{12} - \frac{b^2(b+d)^2}{(2b+d)}$
U-shape	$S_w = \frac{2bd+d^2}{3} = \frac{d^2(2b+d)}{3(b+d)}$ top / bottom	$J_w = \frac{(b+2d)^3}{12} - \frac{d^2(b+d)^2}{(b+2d)}$
box	$S_w = bd + \frac{d^2}{3}$	$J_w = \frac{(b+d)^3}{6}$
H / double vertical	$S_w = \frac{2bd+d^2}{3} = \frac{d^2(2b+d)}{3(b+d)}$ top / bottom	$J_w = \frac{(b+2d)^3}{12} - \frac{d^2(b+d)^2}{(b+2d)}$
T-shape	$S_w = \frac{4bd+d^2}{3} = \frac{4bd^2+d^3}{6b+3d}$ top / bottom	$J_w = \frac{d^3(4b+d)}{6(b+d)} + \frac{b^3}{6}$
I-shape	$S_w = bd + \frac{d^2}{3}$	$J_w = \frac{b^3+3bd^2+d^3}{6}$
double-I	$S_w = 2bd + \frac{d^2}{3}$	$J_w = \frac{2b^3+6bd^2+d^3}{6}$
circle	$S_w = \frac{\pi d^2}{4}$	$J_w = \frac{\pi d^3}{4}$
two circles	$S_w = \frac{\pi d^2}{2} + \pi D^2$	

of determining the force on the weld.

By inserting the property of the welded connection treated as a line into the standard design formula used for that particular type of load (see Table 3), the force on the weld may be found in terms of lbs per linear inch of weld.

Example: Bending

Standard design formula (bending stress)	Same formula used for weld (treating weld as a line)
$\sigma = \dfrac{M}{S} = \dfrac{lbs}{in.^2}$ stress	$f = \dfrac{M}{S_w} = \dfrac{lbs}{in.}$ force

Normally the use of these standard design formulas results in a unit stress, psi; however, when the weld is treated as a line, these formulas result in a force on the weld, lbs per linear inch.

For secondary welds, the weld is not treated as a line, but standard design formulas are used to find the force on the weld, lbs per linear inch.

In problems involving bending or twisting loads Table 4 is used to determine properties of the weld

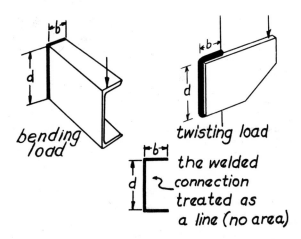

Fig. 1 Treating weld as a line.

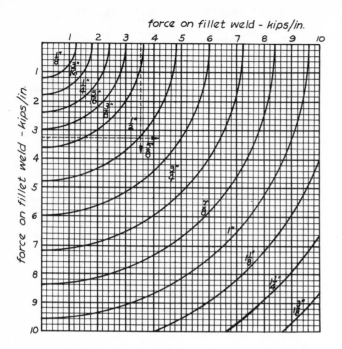

force on fillet weld - kips/in.

force on fillet weld - kips/in.

Fig. 2 Fillet weld leg size for combined forces.

treated as a line. It contains the section modulus (S_w), for bending, and polar moment of inertia (J_w), for twisting, of some 13 typical welded connections with the weld treated as a line.

For any given connection, two dimensions are needed, width (b) and depth (d).

Section modulus (S_w) is used for welds subject to bending loads, and polar moment of inertia (J_w) for twisting loads.

Section moduli (S_w) from these formulas are for maximum force at the top as well as the bottom

portions of the welded connections. For the unsymmetrical connections shown in this table, maximum bending force is at the bottom.

If there is more than one force applied to the weld, these are found and combined. All forces which are combined (vectorially added) must occur at the same position in the welded joint.

Determining Weld Size by Using Allowables

Weld size is obtained by dividing the resulting force on the weld found above, by the allowable strength of the particular type of weld used (fillet or groove), obtained from Table 5 (steady loads) or Table 6 (fatigue loads).

For a joint which has only a transverse load applied to the weld (either fillet or groove weld), the allowable transverse load may be used from the table. If part of the load is applied parallel (even if there are transverse loads in addition), the allowable parallel load which is lower must be used.

If there are two forces at right angles to each other, the resultant is equal to the square root of the sum of the squares of these two forces.

$$f_r = \sqrt{f_1^2 + f_2^2} \quad \dots\dots\dots\dots\dots\dots(3)$$

If there are three forces, each at right angles to each other, the resultant is equal to the square root of the sum of the squares of the three forces.

$$f_r = \sqrt{f_1^2 + f_2^2 + f_3^2} \quad \dots\dots\dots\dots(4)$$

The chart in Figure 2 can be used for E60 welds to combine two forces and indicate the proper fillet-weld leg size.

Fillet Weld (For 1" weld leg)	Groove weld (for 1" weld thickness)	Partial Penetration Groove weld* (For 1" weld thickness)
Parallel Load		
E60 or SAW – 1 9600 (AWS)	$\tau = .40\ \sigma_y$ of base metal (shear) (AWS)	E60 or SAW – 1 13,600 (AISC)
E70 or SAW – 2 11,200 (AWS)		E70 or SAW – 2 15,800 (AISC)
Transverse Load		
E60 or SAW – 1 11,200	$\sigma = .60\ \sigma_y$ of base metal (tension) (AWS)	E60 or SAW – 1 13,600 (AISC)
E70 or SAW – 2 13,100		E70 or SAW – 2 15,800 (AISC)

TABLE 5 - ALLOWABLE STEADY LOADS (lbs/linear in. of weld)

*For bevel joint, deduct first 1/4" for effective throat.

(The E60 designation applies to all welding electrodes capable of producing weld metal having a tensile strength of 60,000 psi. Most welding of machinery is done with electrodes in this group.)

One important advantage to this method, in addition to its simplicity, is that no new formulas must be used, nothing new must be learned. Assume an engineer has just designed a beam. For strength he has used the standard formula $\sigma = M/S$. Substituting the load on the beam (M) and the property of the beam (S) into this formula, he has found the bending stress (σ). Now, he substitutes the property of the weld, treating it as a line (S_w), obtained from Table 4, into the same formula. Using the same load (M), $f = M/S_w$; he thus finds the force on the weld (f) per linear inch. The weld size is then found by dividing the force on the weld by the allowable force.

Applying System to Any Welded Connection

1. Find the position on the welded connection where the combination of forces will be maximum. There may be more than one which should be considered.

2. Find the value of each of the forces on the welded connection at this point. (a) Use Table 3 for the standard design formula to find the force on the weld. (b) Use Table 4 to find the property of the weld treated as a line.

3. Combine (vectorially) all of the forces on the weld at this point.

4. Determine the required weld size by dividing this resultant value by the allowable force in Tables 5 or 6.

TABLE 6 – ALLOWABLE FATIGUE STRESS
for A7, A373 And A36 Steels And their Welds

	2,000,000 cycles	600,000 cycles	100,000 cycles	But Not to Exceed
Base Metal In Tension Connected By Fillet Welds But not to exceed ➡	① $\sigma = \dfrac{7500}{1 - 2/3\,K}$ psi P_t	③ $\sigma = \dfrac{10,500}{1 - 2/3\,K}$ psi P_t	⑤ $\sigma = \dfrac{15,000}{1-2/3\,K}$ psi P_t	$\dfrac{2\,P_c}{3\,K}$ psi
Base Metal Compression Connected By Fillet Welds	② $\sigma = \dfrac{7500}{1 - 2/3\,K}$ psi	④ $\sigma = \dfrac{10,500}{1 - 2/3\,K}$ psi	⑥ $\sigma = \dfrac{15,000}{1 - 2/3\,K}$ psi	P_c psi $\dfrac{P_c}{1 - \dfrac{K}{2}}$ psi
Butt Weld In Tension	⑦ $\sigma = \dfrac{16,000}{1 - \dfrac{8}{10}\,K}$ psi	⑪ $\sigma = \dfrac{17,000}{1 - \dfrac{7}{10}\,K}$ psi	⑮ $\sigma = \dfrac{18,000}{1 - \dfrac{K}{2}}$ psi	P_t psi
Butt Weld Compression	⑧ $\sigma = \dfrac{18,000}{1 - K}$ psi	⑫ $\sigma = \dfrac{18,000}{1 - .8K}$ psi	⑯ $\sigma = \dfrac{18,000}{1 - \dfrac{K}{2}}$ psi	P_c psi
Butt Weld In Shear	⑨ $\tau = \dfrac{9,000}{1 - \dfrac{K}{2}}$ psi	⑬ $\tau = \dfrac{10,000}{1 - \dfrac{K}{2}}$ psi	⑰ $\tau = \dfrac{13,000}{1 - \dfrac{K}{2}}$ psi	13,000 psi
Fillet Welds ω = Leg Size	⑩ $f = \dfrac{5100\,\omega}{1 - \dfrac{K}{2}}$ lb/in.	⑭ $f = \dfrac{7100\,\omega}{1 - \dfrac{K}{2}}$ lb/in.	⑱ $f = \dfrac{8800\,\omega}{1 - \dfrac{K}{2}}$ lb/in.	8800 ω lb/in.

Adapted from AWS Bridge Specifications.   K = min/max

P_c = Allowable unit compressive stress for member.

P_t = Allowable unit tensile stress for member.

Problem 1

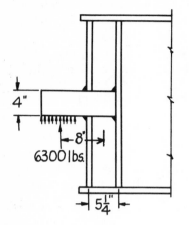

FIGURE 3

Determine size of required fillet weld for hub shown in Figure 3. The bearing load is 6300 lbs. Torque transmitted is 150 HP at 100 RPM, or:

$$T = \frac{63{,}030 \times HP}{RPM}$$

$$= \frac{63{,}030 \times (150)}{(100)}$$

$$= 94{,}500 \text{ in.-lbs}$$

Step 1: FIND PROPERTIES OF WELD, TREATING IT AS A LINE (use Table 4).

$$J_w = 2\,\frac{\pi d^3}{2}$$

$$= 2\,\frac{\pi (4)^3}{2}$$

$$= 100.5 \text{ in.}^3$$

$$S_w = \frac{\pi d^2}{2} + \pi D^2$$

$$= \pi\left[\frac{(4)^2}{2} + (5.25)^2\right]$$

$$= 111.7 \text{ in.}^2$$

$$A_w = 2\,\pi\,d$$

$$= 2\,\pi\,(4)$$

$$= 25.2"$$

Step 2: FIND THE VARIOUS FORCES ON WELD, INSERTING PROPERTIES OF WELD FOUND A-BOVE (use Table 3).

Bending

$$f_b = \frac{M}{S_w}$$

$$= \frac{(6300)(8)}{(111.7)}$$

$$= 451 \text{ lbs/in.}$$

Twisting

$$f_t = \frac{T c}{J_w}$$

$$= \frac{(94{,}500)(2)}{(100.5)}$$

$$= 1880 \text{ lbs/in.}$$

Vertical shear

$$f_v = \frac{V}{A_w}$$

$$= \frac{(6300)}{(25.2)}$$

$$= 250 \text{ lbs/in.}$$

Step 3: DETERMINE ACTUAL RESULTANT FORCE AND ALLOWABLE FORCE ON THE WELD.

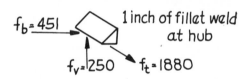

$$f_r = \sqrt{f_b^2 + f_t^2 + f_v^2}$$

$$= \sqrt{(451)^2 + (1880)^2 + (250)^2}$$

$$= 1950 \text{ lbs/in.} \quad \text{(actual resultant force)}$$

Since this is fatigue loading, assume service life of N = 2,000,000 cycles and use Table 6 formula. In this case, assume a complete reversal of load; hence K = min/max = –1 and:

$$f = \frac{5090}{1 - \dfrac{K}{2}}$$

$$= \frac{5090}{1 + \frac{1}{2}}$$

$$= 3370 \text{ lbs/in.} \quad \text{(allowable force)}$$

Step 4: NOW REQUIRED LEG SIZE OF FILLET WELD AROUND HUB CAN BE FOUND.

$$\omega = \frac{\text{actual force}}{\text{allowable force}}$$

$$= \frac{(1950)}{(3370)}$$

$$= .58" \text{ or use } \frac{5}{8}"$$

Problem 2

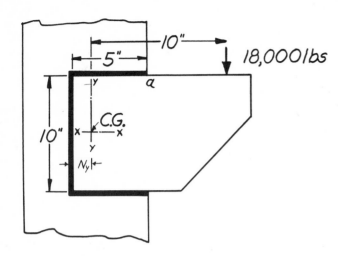

FIGURE 4

Determine the size of required fillet weld for the bracket shown in Figure 4, to carry a load of 18,000 lbs.

Step 1: FIND PROPERTIES OF WELD, TREATING IT AS A LINE (use Table 4).

$$N_y = \frac{b^2}{2\,b + d}$$

$$= \frac{(5)^2}{2\,(5 + 10)}$$

$$= 1.25''$$

$$J_w = \frac{(2\,b + d)^3}{12} - \frac{b^2\,(b + d)^2}{(2\,b + d)}$$

$$= \frac{(2 \times 5 + 10)^3}{12} - \frac{(5)^2\,(5 + 10)^2}{(2 \times 5 + 10)}$$

$$= 385.9 \text{ in.}^3$$

$$A_w = 20''$$

Step 2: FIND THE VARIOUS FORCES ON WELD, INSERTING PROPERTIES OF WELD FOUND A-BOVE (see Table 3).

Point a is where combined forces are maximum. Twisting force is broken into horizontal and vertical components by proper value of c (see sketch).

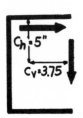

Twisting (horizontal component)

$$f_{t_h} = \frac{T\,c_h}{J_w}$$

$$= \frac{(180,000)\,(5)}{(385.9)}$$

$$= 2340 \text{ lbs/in.}$$

Twisting (vertical component)

$$f_{t_v} = \frac{T\,c_v}{J_w}$$

$$= \frac{(180,000)\,(3.75)}{(385.9)}$$

$$= 1750 \text{ lbs/in.}$$

Vertical shear

$$f_{s_v} = \frac{P}{A_w}$$

$$= \frac{(18,000)}{(20)}$$

$$= 900 \text{ lbs/in.}$$

Step 3: DETERMINE ACTUAL RESULTANT FORCE ON WELD.

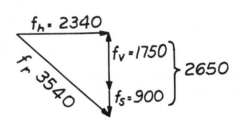

$$f_r = \sqrt{f_{t_h}{}^2 + (f_{t_v} + f_{s_v})^2}$$

$$= \sqrt{(2340)^2 + (2650)^2}$$

$$= 3540 \text{ lbs/in.}$$

Step 4: NOW FIND REQUIRED LEG SIZE OF FILLET WELD CONNECTING THE BRACKET.

$$\omega = \frac{\text{actual force}}{\text{allowable force}}$$

$$= \frac{3540}{9600}$$

$$= .368'' \text{ or use } \tfrac{3}{8}'' \triangle$$

7. HORIZONTAL SHEAR FORCES

Any weld joining the flange of a beam to its web is stressed in horizontal shear (Fig. 5). Normally a designer is accustomed to specifying a certain size fillet weld for a given plate thickness (leg size about 3/4 of the plate thickness) in order for the weld to have full plate strength. However, this particular joint between the flange and web is one exception to this rule. In order to prevent web buckling, a lower allowable shear stress is usually used; this results in a thicker web. The welds are in an area next to the flange where there is no buckling problem and, therefore, no reduction in allowable load is used. From a design standpoint, these welds may be very small, their actual size sometimes determined by the minimum allowed because of the thickness of the flange plate, in order to assure the proper slow cooling rate of the weld on the heavier plate.

General Rules

Outside of simply holding the flanges and web of a beam together, or to transmit any unusually high force between the flange and web at right angles to the member (for example, bearing supports, lifting lugs, etc.), the real purpose of the weld between the flange and web is to transmit the horizontal shear forces, and the size of the weld is determined by the value of these shear forces.

It will help in the analysis of a beam if it is recognized that the shear diagram is also a picture of the amount and location of the welding required between the flange and web.

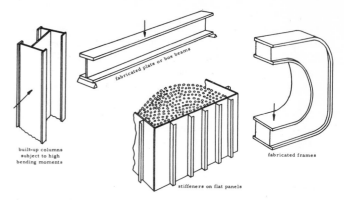

Fig. 5 These flange-to-web welds are stressed in horizontal shear and the forces on them can be determined.

A study of Figure 6 will show that 1) loads applied transversely to members cause bending moments; 2) bending moments varying along the length of the beam cause horizontal shear forces; and 3) horizontal shear forces require welds to transmit these forces between the flange and web of the beam.

Notice: 1) Shear forces occur only when the bending moment varies along the length. 2) It is quite possible for portions of a beam to have little or no shear--notice the middle portions of beams 1 and 2--this is because the bending moment is constant within this area. 3) If there should be a difference in shear along the length of the beam, the shear forces are usually greatest at the ends of the beam (see beam 3). This is why stiffeners are

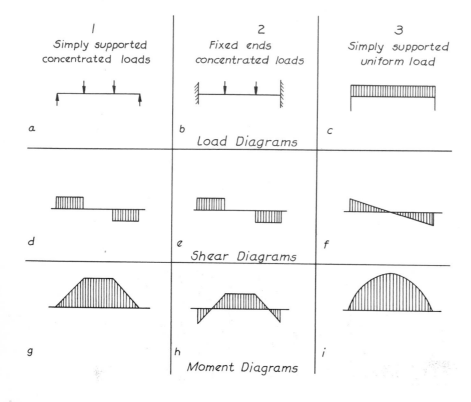

Fig. 6 Shear diagram pictures the amount and location of welding required to transmit horizontal shear forces between flange and web.

sometimes welded continuously at their ends for a distance even though they are welded intermittently the rest of their length. 4) Fixed ends will shift the moment diagram so that the maximum moment is less. What is taken off at the middle of the beam is added to the ends. Even though this does happen, the shear diagram remains unchanged, so that the amount of welding between flange and web will be the same regardless of end conditions of the beam.

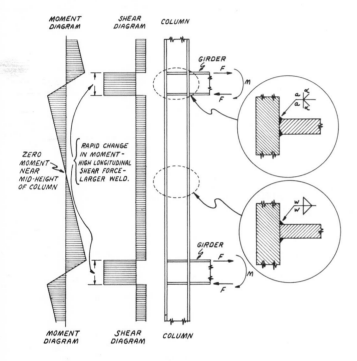

MOMENT DIAGRAM   SHEAR DIAGRAM   COLUMN

Fig. 7 Shear diagram of frame indicates where the amount of welding is critical.

To apply these rules, consider the welded frame in Figure 7. The moment diagram for this loaded frame is shown on the left-hand side. The bending moment is gradually changing throughout the vertical portion of the frame. The shear diagram shows that this results in a small amount of shear in the frame. Using the horizontal shear formula (f =

Vay/In), this would require a small amount of welding between the flange and web. Intermittent welding would probably be sufficient. However, at the point where the crane bending moment is applied, the moment diagram shows a very fast rate of change. Since the shear value is equal to the rate of change in the bending moment, it is very high and more welding is required at this region.

Use continuous welding where loads or moments are applied to a member, even though intermittent welding may be used throughout the rest of the fabricated frame.

Finding Weld Size

The horizontal shear forces acting on the weld joining a flange to web, Figures 8 and 9, may be found from the following formula:

$$f = \frac{V a y}{I n} \quad\quad\quad\quad\quad\quad\quad (5)$$

where:

f = force on weld, lbs/lin in.

V = total shear on section at a given position along beam, lbs

a = area of flange held by weld, sq in.

y = distance between the center of gravity of flange area and the neutral axis of whole section, in.

I = moment of inertia of whole section, in.[4]

n = number of welds joining flange to web

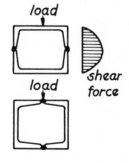

Fig. 8 Locate weld at point of minimum stress. Horizontal shear force is maximum along neutral axis. Welds in top example must carry maximum shear force; there is no shear on welds in bottom example.

Fig. 9 Examples of welds in horizontal shear.

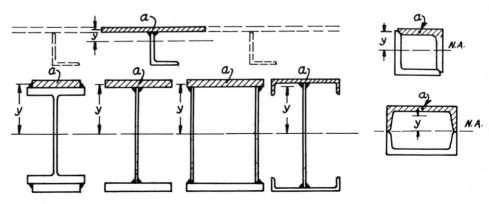

Nomograph to Calculate Weld Size

The nomograph in Figure 10 may be used to find the required weld size where two welds are used, one on each side of the web.

If a continuous fillet weld is to be used, read the weld size on the right-hand side to the next larger fraction of an inch.

If intermittent fillet welds are to be used, read the weld size as a decimal and divide this by the actual size used. When expressed as a percentage, this will give the length of weld to be used per unit length. For convenience, Table 7 has various intermittent weld lengths and distances between centers for given percentages of continuous welds.

$$\% = \frac{\text{calculated leg size (continuous)}}{\text{actual leg size used (intermittent)}}$$

TABLE 7 - INTERMITTENT WELDS
Length and Spacing

Continuous weld, %	Length of intermittent welds and distance between centers, in.		
75	..	3–4	..
66	..	..	4–6
60	..	3–5	..
57	..	..	4–7
50	2–4	3–6	4–8
44	..	..	4–9
43	..	3–7	..
40	2–5	..	4–10
37	..	3–8	..
33	2–6	3–9	4–12
30	..	3–10	..
25	2–8	3–12	..
20	2–10	..	..
16	2–12	..	..

Figure 10 - REQUIRED LEG SIZE OF CONTINUOUS WELD
For Joining Flange to Web of Fabricated Beam

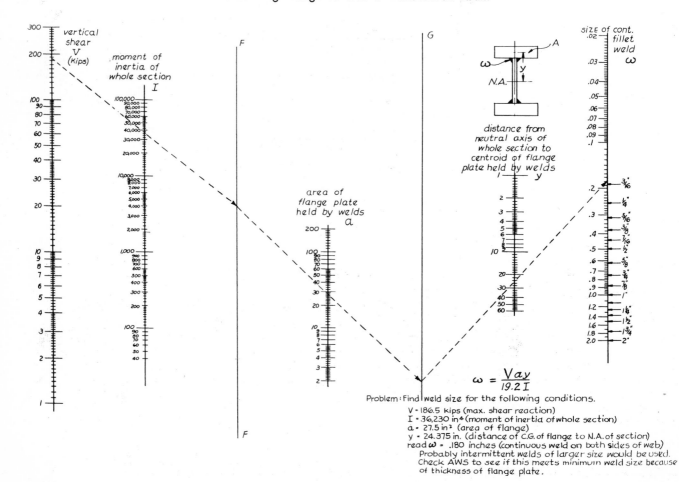

$$\omega = \frac{Vay}{19.2\,I}$$

Problem: Find weld size for the following conditions.

V = 186.5 kips (max. shear reaction)
I = 36,230 in.⁴ (moment of inertia of whole section)
a = 27.5 in.² (area of flange)
y = 24.375 in. (distance of C.G. of flange to N.A. of section)
read ω = .180 inches (continuous weld on both sides of web)
Probably intermittent welds of larger size would be used.
Check AWS to see if this meets minimum weld size because of thickness of flange plate.

Figure 11 – REQUIRED LEG SIZE OF INTERMITTENT WELD
For Joining Flange to Web of Fabricated Beam

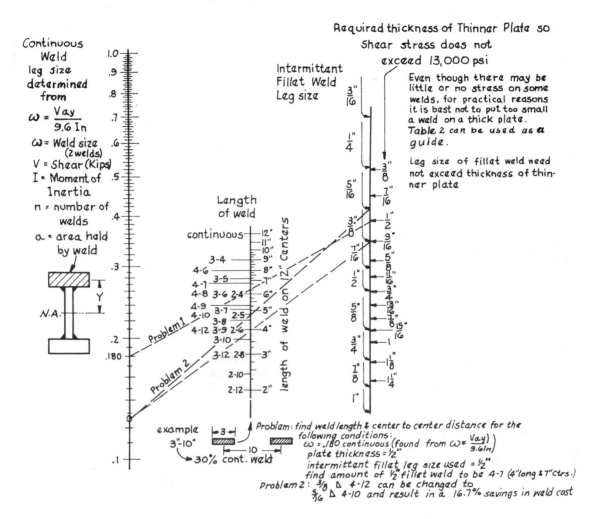

Nomograph to Calculate Intermittent Weld Size

The nomograph in Figure 11 will be helpful in deciding the spacing of intermittent welds after the required continuous weld size has been determined.

The left-hand axis is the required continuous fillet weld size determined from the formula:

$$\omega = \frac{V a y}{2 \times 9600 \times I} \quad \dots\dots\dots\dots\dots\dots\dots (6)$$

or from nomograph, Figure 10.

The right-hand axis is the size of intermittent fillet weld used. It is important that the leg size of weld used in determining weld spacing is not so large that it will overstress the plate. Sometimes the allowable shear stress in the web of the plate girder is held to 13,000 psi. Therefore, in this case, the maximum leg size of fillet weld used for design should not exceed ⅔ web thickness. Be sure that the actual weld-leg size chosen on this right-hand axis does not indicate a plate thickness greater than the web of the girder. If so, then move upward along this axis to the actual web thickness and use this value to determine proper weld spacing.

The middle axis is the resulting weld spacing expressed as a length of intermittent weld and distance between centers. Also on this axis is the required length of intermittent weld for 12" centers.

To use this nomograph, draw a line between the left axis (calculated fillet weld-leg size if continuous) and the right axis (actual intermittent weld-leg size used or the thickness of web), taking into account the information in Table 7. The proper weld spacing is read on the middle axis.

Problem 3

For the fabricated plate girder in Figure 12, determine the proper amount of fillet welds to join flanges to the web.

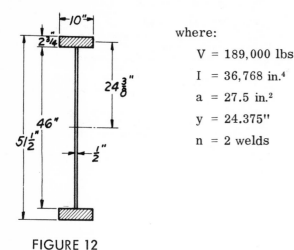

FIGURE 12

where:

$$V = 189,000 \text{ lbs}$$
$$I = 36,768 \text{ in.}^4$$
$$a = 27.5 \text{ in.}^2$$
$$y = 24.375''$$
$$n = 2 \text{ welds}$$

Horizontal shear force on weld

$$f_h = \frac{V a y}{I n}$$

$$= \frac{(189,000)(27.5)(24.375)}{(36,768)(2)}$$

$$= 1720 \text{ lbs/in.}$$

Required leg size of weld

$$\omega = \frac{\text{actual force}}{\text{allowable force}}$$

$$= \frac{1720}{9600}$$

$$= .180''$$

This would be the minimum leg size of a continuous fillet weld; however, ½" fillet welds are recommended because of the thick 2¾" flange plate (see table inserted in the nomograph, Fig. 11). In this particular case, the leg size of the fillet weld need not exceed the web thickness (thinner plate). Because of the greater strength of the ½" fillet, intermittent welds may be used but must not stress the web above 13,000 psi. Therefore, the length of weld must be increased to spread the load over a greater length of web. For this reason the size of intermittent fillet weld used in design calculations or for determination of length must not exceed ⅔ of the web thickness, or here:

⅔ of ½" (web) = .333"

The percentage of continuous weld length needed for this intermittent weld will be--

$$\% = \frac{\text{continuous leg size}}{\text{intermittent leg size}}$$

$$= \frac{(.180'')}{(.333'')}$$

$$= 54\%$$

Hence, use

1/2" △ 4"———7"   (see Table 7)

This may also be worked out on the nomograph, Figure 11. It undoubtedly would be faster to use ½" continuous fillet welds and make them with the submerged-arc automatic process.

Problem 4

A fillet weld is required, using

3/8" △ 4"———12"

that is, intermittent welds having leg size of ⅜" and length of 4", set on 12" centers. A ⅜" fillet weld usually requires 2 passes, unless the work is positioned. A 2-pass weld requires more inspection to maintain size and weld quality. The shop would like to change this to a ⁵⁄₁₆" weld. This single-pass weld is easier to make and there is little chance of it being undersize.

Using the nomograph, Figure 11, a line is drawn from the weld size of ⅜" on the right axis through 4"———12" on the middle axis, to the left axis. This point on the left axis becomes a pivot point, from which a line is drawn to weld size of ⁵⁄₁₆" on the right axis, the answer of 4"———10" (length of weld, then distance between centers) being read on the middle axis where the line crosses it.

In other words, ⅜" intermittent fillet welds, 4" long on 12" centers, may be replaced with ⁵⁄₁₆" welds, 4" long on 10" centers, providing same strength. This change would permit welding in one pass instead of two passes, with a saving of approx. 16⅔% in welding time and cost.

8. HOW TO MEASURE SIZE OF FILLET WELDS

The size of a fillet weld is difficult to measure without proper gages. Fillet shapes are concave, convex, or flat. They may have equal or unequal legs. However, the true fillet size is measured by finding the leg-length of the largest isosceles right triangle (a triangle with a 90° corner and legs of equal length) which can be inscribed within the weld cross-section, with the legs in line with the original surface of the metal.

The gages shown in Figure 13 give quick, easy measurement of fillet size. Two gage types are available: one for a convex fillet, another for a concave fillet. Figures 14 to 18 explain their use.

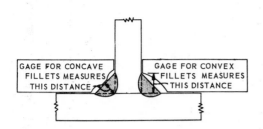

Fig. 13 Two types of fillet weld gages. Convex fillets may be measured with gage of type shown on the right; in this case it measures the leg size. Concave fillets are measured with a gage like the one on the left; in this case it measures the weld throat.

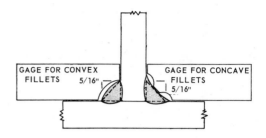

Fig. 14 With equal legged 45° fillets, either type gage (concave or convex) may be used. Both will indicate the same size fillet.

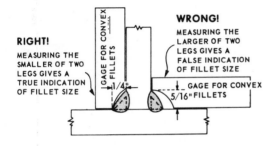

Fig. 15 Measuring convex fillets. Notice that the largest isosceles right triangle which can be inscribed within the cross-section of the fillet is determined by the shorter leg's dimension.

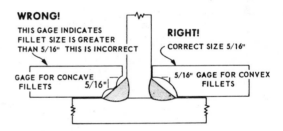

Fig. 16 It may not be readily apparent whether the above fillet is flat, slightly concave, or convex. But by checking the fillet with both types of gages, it would be apparent that the vertical leg is smaller than the bottom leg and that this is the true fillet size. The concave gage would give the impression that the fillet is larger than 5/16" and this would be incorrect.

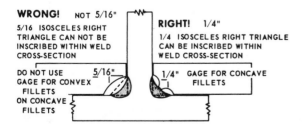

Fig. 17 Right and wrong method of gaging a concave fillet.

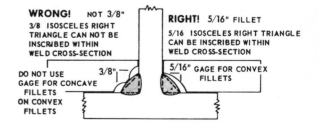

Fig. 18 Right and wrong method of gaging a convex fillet.

Problem 5

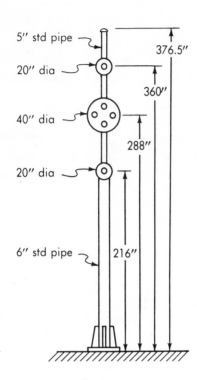

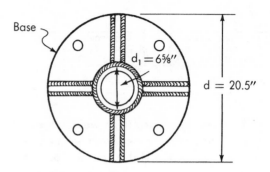

FIGURE 19

Determine the leg size of fillet weld for the base of a signal tower, Figure 19, assuming wind pressure of 30 lbs/sq ft or pressure of p = .208 psi.

Step 1: FIND PROPERTIES OF WELD, TREAT-ING IT AS A LINE.

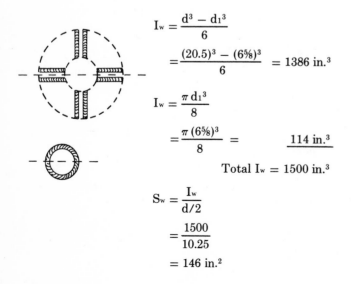

$$I_w = \frac{d^3 - d_1{}^3}{6}$$

$$= \frac{(20.5)^3 - (6\tfrac{5}{8})^3}{6} = 1386 \text{ in.}^3$$

$$I_w = \frac{\pi \, d_1{}^3}{8}$$

$$= \frac{\pi \, (6\tfrac{5}{8})^3}{8} = \underline{\qquad 114 \text{ in.}^3}$$

Total $I_w = 1500$ in.^{3}

$$S_w = \frac{I_w}{d/2}$$

$$= \frac{1500}{10.25}$$

$$= 146 \text{ in.}^2$$

Step 2: FIND THE FORCE INVOLVED.

Moment acting on tower due to wind pressure:

$$M = (.208)\left(\frac{\pi \, 20^2}{4}\right)(360) + (.208)\left(\frac{\pi \, 40^2}{4}\right)(288)$$

$$+ (.208)\left(\frac{\pi \, 20^2}{4}\right)(216) + (.208)(556)(160.5)(296.3)$$

$$+ (.208)(6\tfrac{5}{8})(216)(108)$$

$$= 200,000 \text{ in.-lbs}$$

Bending stress in pipe (column)

$$\sigma = \frac{M \, c}{I}$$

$$= \frac{(200,000)(3.3125")}{(28.14 \text{ in.}^4)}$$

$$= 23,600 \text{ psi}$$

Step 3: FIND FORCE ON FILLET WELD AT COLUMN BASE.

$$f = \frac{M}{S_w}$$

$$= \frac{200,000 \text{ in.-lbs}}{146 \text{ in.}^2}$$

$$= 1370 \text{ lbs/linear in.}$$

Step 4: NOW FIND REQUIRED LEG SIZE OF FILLET WELD AT BASE.

$$\omega = \frac{\text{actual force}}{\text{allowable force}}$$

$$= \frac{1370}{9600}$$

$= .143"$ but use $\tfrac{5}{16}"$ ◺ all around, the minimum fillet weld size for 1" base plate

Problem 6

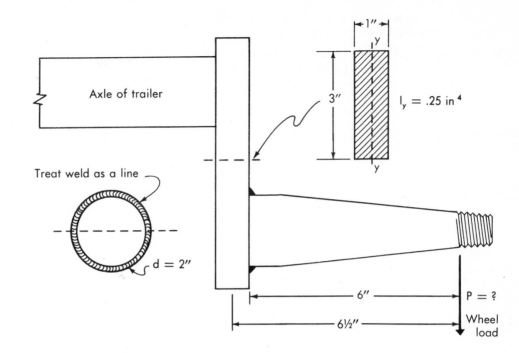

FIGURE 20

Determine size of fillet weld on wheel spindle, Figure 20, to have equivalent strength of member. Load P is unknown.

Step 1:   FIND PROPERTIES OF WELD, TREATING IT AS A LINE.

$$S_w = \frac{\pi\, d^2}{4}$$

$$= \frac{\pi\, 2^2}{4}$$

$$= \pi \text{ in.}^2$$

$$A_w = \pi\, d$$

$$= 2\,\pi \text{ in.}$$

Step 2:   FIND THE FORCES INVOLVED.

In the 1" × 3" bar, stressed to an allowable of 20,000 psi, the bending moment is--

$$M = \frac{\sigma\, I}{c}$$

$$= \frac{(20{,}000 \text{ psi})(.25 \text{ in.}^4)}{(\frac{1}{2}")}$$

$$= 10{,}000 \text{ in.-lbs}$$

and:

$$P = \frac{M}{d}$$

$$= \frac{10{,}000 \text{ in.-lbs}}{6\,1/2"}$$

$$= 1540 \text{ lbs}$$

Bending force on weld

$$f_b = \frac{M}{S_w}$$

$$= \frac{(1540)(6)}{\pi}$$

$$= 2940 \text{ lbs/in.}$$

Vertical shear on the weld

$$f_v = \frac{V}{A_w} = \frac{P}{A_w}$$

$$= \frac{1540}{2\,\pi}$$

$$= 245 \text{ lbs/in.}$$

Step 3:   FIND ACTUAL RESULTANT FORCE ON WELD.

$$f_r = \sqrt{f_b{}^2 + f_v{}^2}$$

$$= \sqrt{2940^2 + 245^2}$$

$$= 2950 \text{ lbs/in.}$$

Step 4:   NOW FIND LEG SIZE FOR FILLET WELD.

$$\omega = \frac{\text{actual force}}{\text{allowable force}}$$

$$= \frac{2950}{9600}$$

$$= .308" \text{ or use } \frac{5}{16}" \; \triangle$$

Problem 7

Determine the required size of connecting weld on lifting element of fork truck, Figure 21.

The maximum capacity is assumed to be applied at the outer end of the fork. This whole unit tends to pivot about the lower corner where it bears up against the lower crossbar. The resulting horizontal force (F_h) at the upper end of the fork is taken by the top crossbar. The crossbar is welded to the vertical member of the lifting element.

Here:

$$F_h (15") = P (30")$$
$$F_h = 2\,P = 2\,(3000)$$
$$= 6000 \text{ lbs}$$

In this case, the horizontal force (F_h) is applied at the tip of the bar at some eccentricity (e) to the weld's center of gravity, Figure 22. This subjects the connecting weld to some bending forces as well as to uniformly distributed transverse forces and vertical forces.

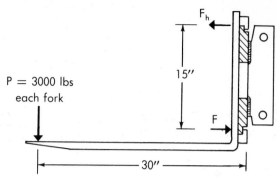

FIGURE 21

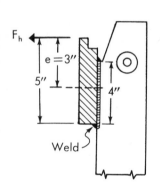 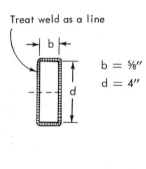

FIGURE 22

Step 1:   FIND THE REQUIRED PROPERTY OF WELD, TREATING IT AS A LINE.

$$S_w = b\,d + \frac{d^2}{3}$$
$$= (\text{⅝})\,(4) + \frac{(4)^2}{3}$$
$$= 7.83 \text{ in.}^2$$

Step 2:   FIND THE VARIOUS FORCES ON WELD.

Bending force

$$f_b = \frac{M}{S_w}$$
$$= \frac{(6000)(3)}{(7.83)}$$
$$= 2300 \text{ lbs/in.}$$

Transverse force

$$f_t = \frac{F_h}{A}$$
$$= \frac{(6000)}{(8)}$$
$$= 750 \text{ lbs/in.}$$

Vertical force

$$f_v = \frac{P}{A}$$
$$= \frac{(3000)}{(8)}$$
$$= 375 \text{ lbs/in.}$$

Step 3:   FIND ACTUAL RESULTANT FORCE ON WELD, AND THE ALLOWABLE FORCE.

$$f_r = \sqrt{(f_b + f_t)^2 + f_v^2}$$
$$= \sqrt{(2300 + 750)^2 + 375^2}$$
$$= 3070 \text{ lbs/in.}$$

Assuming a fatigue cycle of K = (min stress)/(max stress) = 0 and required life of N = 2,000,000 cycles, the allowable force on the weld is--

$$f = \frac{5090\,\omega}{1 - K/2} \qquad \text{(from Table 6)}$$
$$= 5090\,\omega \text{ lbs/in.}$$

Step 4:   NOW FIND LEG SIZE OF FILLET WELD.

$$\omega = \frac{\text{actual force}}{\text{allowable force}}$$
$$= \frac{3070}{5090}$$
$$= .603" \text{ or use } \text{⅝}" \;\triangle$$

If it can be assumed that this load of P = 3000 lbs is distributed equally between the two forks, this leg size of fillet would be reduced to half, or

$$\omega = \text{⁵⁄₁₆}" \;\triangle$$

If it can be assumed that the actual number of fatigue cycles is only N = about 600,000 cycles (representing an average lift every 2 minutes, per 8-hr day, for 10 yrs), the allowable load would be--

$$f = \frac{7070\,\omega}{1 - K/2}$$

$$= 7070\,\omega$$

and the required leg size of the fillet weld would be

$$\omega = \frac{3070}{7070}$$

$$= .435''\text{ or } \underline{\text{use } \frac{7}{16}''}\ \triangle$$

And if it again can be assumed that the load is distributed equally between the two forks, this leg size of fillet would be reduced to half, or

$$\omega = \frac{7}{32}''\text{ or } \underline{\text{use } \frac{1}{4}''}\ \triangle$$

Problem 8

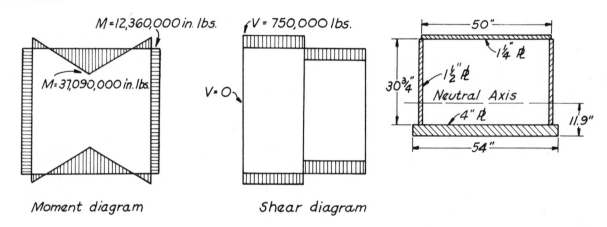

Moment diagram   Shear diagram

FIGURE 23

Determine the required size of welds to join the 4" flange plate to the 1½" web plates on a large welded press frame (Fig. 23), which must withstand a 750-ton (1,500,000 lbs) vertical load.

Although the horizontal portions of this frame have a changing bending moment (M) and this causes a shear reaction (V) of 750,000 lbs, the vertical portions have a constant bending moment and therefore no shear reaction. This means that the main requirement for welds occurs only in the horizontal portion; the welds on the vertical portion only have to hold the sections together.

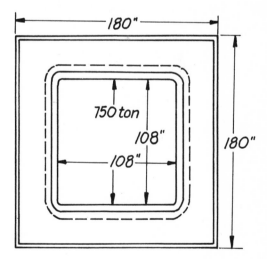

Step 1:   FIND PROPERTIES OF FRAME'S CROSS-SECTION.

$$I = 67,800 \text{ in.}^4$$

$$a = (4'')(54'')$$

$$= 216 \text{ in.}^2$$

$$y = 11.9'' - 2''$$

$$= 9.9''$$

$$V = 750,000 \text{ lbs}$$

$$n = \text{number of welds}$$

$$= 2$$

Step 2:   FIND THE VARIOUS FORCES ON WELD.

Horizontal shear

$$f_s = \frac{V a y}{I n}$$

$$= \frac{(750,000)(216)(9.9)}{(67,800)(2)}$$

$$= 11,800 \text{ lbs/in.}$$

Compression (assume 750-ton load spread out over 60" of frame - 2 webs)

$$f_c = \frac{P}{L}$$

$$= \frac{\frac{1}{2}(1,500,000)}{60}$$

$$= 12,500 \text{ lbs/in.}$$

Step 3: DETERMINE ACTUAL RESULTANT FORCE ON WELD.

$$f_r = \sqrt{f_s{}^2 + f_c{}^2}$$

$$= \sqrt{(11,800)^2 + (12,500)^2}$$

$$= 17,200 \text{ lbs/in.}$$

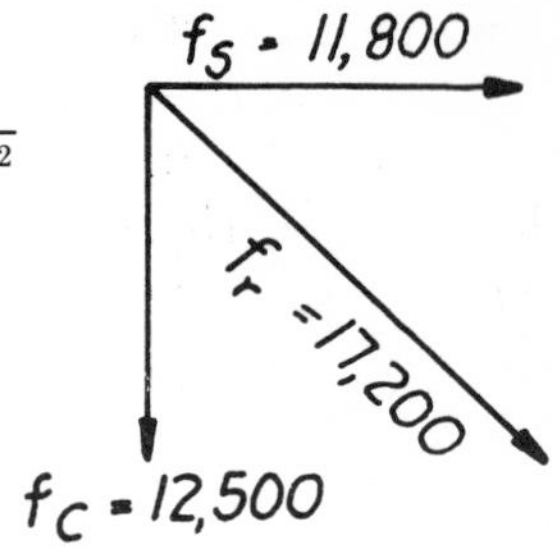

$f_s = 11,800$

$f_r = 17,200$

$f_c = 12,500$

Step 4:   DETERMINE SIZE OF WELD.

The decision as to whether a fillet weld or some type of groove T-weld will be used depends mostly on cost. See the following illustration.

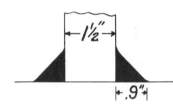

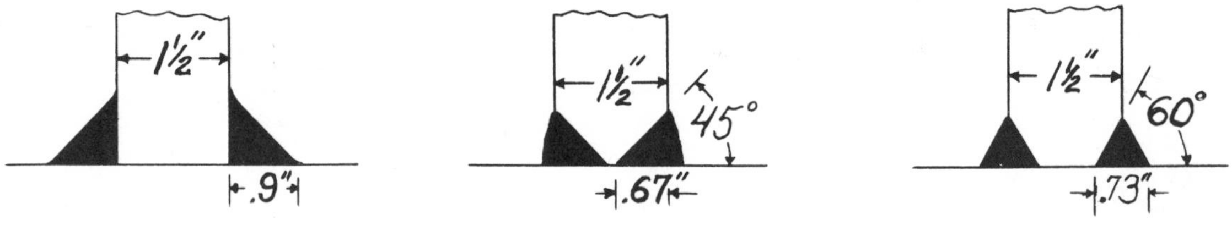

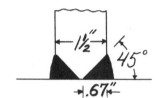

(a) 45° fillet welds
Force on each weld is
  ½ × 17,200 = 8600 lbs/in.
Allowable load on this weld is
  9600 lbs/in.
  (for a leg size of 1")
leg size is: $\omega = \frac{8600}{9600} = .9"$
or 1" leg size.

(b) 45° bevel T groove joint
Force on joint is 17,200 lbs/in.
Allowable load on this joint is
  13,000 lbs/in.
  (for a throat of 1")
minimum throat is $t = \frac{17,200}{13,000} =$
  1.33" throat
If full penetration of the 1½" plate is desired, this will be more than adequate.

(c) 60° bevel, 60° fillet partially penetrated joint
Force on each weld is
  ½ × 17,200 = 8600 lbs/in.
Allowable load on this weld is
  11,780 lbs/in.
leg size is: $\omega = \frac{8600}{11780} =$

  .73" leg size.

FIGURE 24

Estimating Welding Cost

1. COST FACTORS

There are several methods which may be used to study welding cost, and these depend on the need for such a study. For example, is it needed to estimate a new job for bidding? Or, is it needed to compare one procedure against another? Or, is the chief need one of determining the amount of electrode to order?

A good method of cost estimating should give the final cost quickly; yet indicate what portion of the operation is more expensive, i.e. where the welding dollar is really being spent.

The final cost includes at least these items: a) labor and overhead for plate preparation, assembling, welding, cleaning, and sometimes stress-relieving; b) electrode, flux, and gas; and c) electric power.

Table 1 includes a number of useful formulas for determining various cost components.

Unfortunately there is no one all-inclusive formula by which all types of welding jobs may be studied. The simplest type of cost estimation is a job that requires a long, single-pass fillet or groove weld. Next comes the long, multi-pass weld, where a different procedure may be used for each pass. In both examples, it is sufficient to assume a reasonable operating factor due to the downtime between electrodes consumed and to apply this to the actual arc time. This downtime is affected by the weldor, as well as the job. A more complicated weld may require a handling time factor. This handling time is affected more by the job, than by the welding.

Three items which are difficult to tie down, yet greatly affect the cost of a weld, are these:

1. The amount of filler weld metal required; this varies with size of weld, size of root opening or fit up, amount of reinforcement, included angle of groove, etc.

2. The operating factor used, i.e. the ratio of actual arc time to the over-all welding time.

3. The amount of handling and cleaning time.

This section includes various tables and nomographs which are helpful in making true cost estimates. No estimating system, however, is satisfactory without the estimator applying his good judgment and perception.

2. COST OF WELD METAL

The cost of welding is directly affected by the amount of weld metal required. Very few people realize the great increase in weld metal and cost that results from a slight increase in weld size.

The cross-sectional area of a weld generally varies as the square of the weld size. For example, making a 5/16" leg size fillet weld when a 1/4" weld is desired, increases the leg by 25% but the area is increased by 56%. The amount of reinforcement is difficult to specify and control; yet the range of its variance can substantially affect the amount of weld metal required. A slight increase in root opening increases the amount of weld metal for the entire thickness and length of the weld. The resulting percentage increase in weld metal is usually surprising.

Computing Weld Weight

Designers or associated personnel frequently have to compute the weight of weld metal required on a particular job, as a matter of either cost estimating or determining the amount of material to be ordered for a particular job. Sometimes these computations must be based on the size and configuration of the joint. The normal procedure to follow in such a case is to compute the cross-sectional area of the joint in square inches and then convert this into pounds per linear foot by multiplying by the factor 3.4. To simplify these computations, Table 2 (weight in lbs/linear ft) has been developed; its use is illustrated in Problem 1.

Tables 3, 4, and 5 provide precalculated weights for specific joints and read directly in lbs per foot of joint.

For estimating the weight of manual electrode required, roughly add another 50% to this amount of weld metal.

In order to arrive at the labor cost per foot of joint, it is necessary to know the speed at which the joint can be welded. This may be found in prepared data on standard welding procedures, both for manual welding as well as the submerged-arc process. For special joints for which no information is available, the deposition rate (lbs/hr) may be determined from tables and charts for given welding currents. The joint speed is then found by dividing this deposition rate by the amount of weld metal required (lbs/linear ft.).

TABLE 1 – USEFUL WELDING COST FORMULAS

SPEED	TIME	JOINT SPEED
$\dfrac{ft}{hr} = 5\,\dfrac{in}{min}$	$\dfrac{min}{ft} = \dfrac{60}{ft/hr} = \dfrac{12}{in/min}$	$S = \dfrac{1}{\dfrac{1}{S_1} + \dfrac{1}{S_2} + \dfrac{1}{S_3}}$

JOINT SPEED	ROD MELTED PER FOOT	ROD MELTED PER HOUR
$\dfrac{ft}{hr} = \dfrac{60\,D}{J}$	$\dfrac{lb\ rod\ melted}{ft\ weld} = \dfrac{1200\,M}{N\,L_m\,S}$	$\dfrac{lb\ rod\ melted}{hr} = \dfrac{6000\,M\,(OF)}{N\,L_m}$

ROD MILEAGE	ROD CONSUMED PER FOOT	ROD CONSUMED PER HOUR
$\dfrac{in\ of\ weld}{one\ rod} = L_w = \dfrac{L_m\,S}{M}$	$\dfrac{lb\ rod\ consumed}{ft\ weld} = \dfrac{1200\,M}{N\,L_m\,S\,E_3}$	$\dfrac{lb\ rod\ consumed}{hr} = \dfrac{6000\,M\,(OF)}{N\,L_m\,E_3}$

APPROXIMATE MELT OFF RATE

$$= \frac{E(arc\ volts)\ I(welding\ current)}{1000} = \frac{lb\ rod\ melted}{hr}$$

APPROXIMATE COST OF SUBMERGED ARC AUTOMATIC WELD

$$= \frac{¢}{ft} = \frac{.0065\ I\ (F+W) + 20\ L}{S}$$

WELD COST

	per foot of each pass	per 1b of deposit
LABOR OVERHEAD	$\dfrac{¢}{ft} = \dfrac{20\,L}{S\,(OF)}$	$\dfrac{¢}{1b} = \dfrac{5\,L}{3\,D\,(OF)}$
MANUAL ELECTRODE	$\dfrac{¢}{ft} = \dfrac{1200\,M\,W}{N\,L_m\,S\,E_3}$	$\dfrac{¢}{1b} = \dfrac{W}{E_2}$
AUTOMATIC WIRE & FLUX	$\dfrac{¢}{ft} = \dfrac{12\,m\,(W+RF)}{S\,E_3} = \dfrac{J\,(W+RF)}{E_2}$	$\dfrac{¢}{1b} = \dfrac{W+RF}{E_2}$
GAS	$\dfrac{¢}{ft} = \dfrac{20\,G}{S}$	$\dfrac{¢}{1b} = \dfrac{5\,G}{3\,D}$

L = labor + overhead ($/hr)
W = wire or rod cost (¢lb)
F = flux cost (¢/lb)
G = gas cost ($/hr)
R = ratio of flux to wire
D = (lb weld deposited/min)
M = (in rod melted/min) = L_m/T
C = (lb rod consumed/min) with stub
m = (lb rod melted/min) no stub

N = number rods/100 lbs
I = welding current (amperes)
S = (in weld/min) = L_w/T
T = time to melt one rod (min)
L_m = (in rod melted/rod)
L_w = (in weld/rod)
J = (lb weld/ft of joint)
OF = operating factor

W_r = weight one rod with stub (lbs) = $100/N$
W_s = weight of one stub (lbs)
E_1 = deposition efficiency $\dfrac{lb\ weld\ deposited}{lb\ rod\ melted} = \dfrac{D}{m}$
E_2 = overall deposition efficiency $\dfrac{lb\ weld\ deposited}{lb\ rod\ consumed} = \dfrac{D}{C} = E_1 E_3$
E_3 = melting efficiency $\dfrac{lb\ rod\ melted}{lb\ rod\ consumed} = \dfrac{m}{C} = \dfrac{W_r - W_s}{W_r}$

TABLE 2 - WEIGHT OF WELD METAL
(Pounds Per Foot of Joint)
Based on Joint Design

FILLET WELDS — flat / convex / concave

Values below are for leg size 10% oversize, consistent with normal shop practices.

"d" or "r" Dimension	BUTT WELDS "t" Dimension 1/16"	1/8"	3/16"	1/4"	3/8"	1/2"	"r"	Included Angle 14°	20°	60°	45° (1/2 of 90°)	70°	FILLET flat	convex	concave
1/16"	.027	.053	.080	.106	.159	.212	.021	.0065	.0094	.031	.027	.037			
1/8"	.040	.080	.119	.159	.239	.318	.083	.0147	.021	.069	.060	.084	.032	.039	.037
3/16"	.053	.106	.159	.212	.318	.425	.188	.026	.037	.123	.106	.149	.072	.087	.083
1/4"	.066	.133	.199	.265	.390	.531	.334	.041	.059	.192	.166	.232	.129	.155	.147
5/16"	.080	.159	.239	.318	.478	.637	.531	.059	.084	.276	.239	.334	.201	.242	.230
3/8"	.091	.186	.279	.371	.557	.743	.750	.080	.115	.376	.326	.456	.289	.349	.331
7/16"	.106	.212	.318	.425	.637	.849	1.02	.104	.150	.491	.425	.595	.394	.475	.451
1/2"	.119	.239	.358	.478	.716	.955	1.33	.132	.190	.621	.538	.753	.514	.620	.589
9/16"	.133	.265	.398	.531	.796	1.06		.163	.234	.766	.664	.930	.651	.785	.745
5/8"	.146	.292	.438	.584	.876	1.17		.197	.283	.927	.804	1.13	.804	.970	.920
11/16"	.159	.318	.478	.637	.955	1.27		.234	.337	1.11	.956	1.34			
3/4"	.172	.345	.517	.690	1.04	1.38		.275	.396	1.30	1.12	1.57	1.16	1.40	1.32
13/16"	.186	.371	.557	.743	1.11	1.49		.319	.459	1.50	1.30	1.82			
7/8"	.199	.398	.597	.796	1.19	1.59		.367	.527	1.73	1.50	2.07	1.58	1.90	1.80
15/16"	.212	.425	.627	.849	1.25	1.70		.417	.599	1.96	1.70	2.38			
1"	.226	.451	.677	.902	1.35	1.80		.471	.676	2.22	1.92	2.68	2.06	2.48	2.36
1-1/16"	.239	.478	.716	.955	1.43	1.91		.528	.758	2.48	2.15	3.02			
1-1/8"	.252	.504	.756	1.01	1.51	2.02		.588	.845	2.77	2.40	3.36	2.60	3.14	2.98
1-3/16"	.265	.531	.796	1.06	1.59	2.12		.651	.936	3.07	2.66	3.72			
1-1/4"	.279	.557	.836	1.11	1.67	2.23		.718	1.03	3.38	2.93	4.10	3.21	3.88	3.68
1-5/16"	.292	.584	.876	1.17	1.75	2.34		.789	1.13	3.71	3.21	4.50			
1-3/8"	.305	.610	.915	1.22	1.83	2.44		.836	1.24	4.05	3.51	4.91	3.89	4.69	4.45
1-7/16"	.318	.637	.955	1.27	1.91	2.55		.938	1.35	4.42	3.82	5.36			
1-1/2"	.332	.664	.995	1.33	1.99	2.65		1.02	1.46	4.79	4.15	5.81	4.62	5.58	5.30
1-9/16"	.345	.690	1.04	1.38	2.07	2.76		1.10	1.58	5.18	4.49	6.29			
1-5/8"	.358	.716	1.07	1.43	2.15	2.87		1.19	1.71	5.59	4.84	6.80	5.43	6.55	6.22
1-11/16"	.371	.743	1.11	1.49	2.23	2.97		1.28	1.84	6.01	5.20	7.29			
1-3/4"	.385	.769	1.15	1.54	2.31	3.08		1.37	1.97	6.45	5.58	7.81	6.29	7.59	7.21
1-13/16"	.398	.796	1.19	1.59	2.39	3.18		1.47	2.10	6.90	5.97	8.36			
1-7/8"	.411	.822	1.23	1.65	2.47	3.29		1.56	2.25	7.36	6.38	8.94	7.23	8.72	8.28
1-15/16"	.425	.836	1.25	1.67	2.51	3.34		1.62	2.33	7.60	6.59	9.23			
2"	.425	.849	1.27	1.70	2.55	3.40		1.67	2.40	7.85	6.80	9.52	8.23	9.93	9.43

TABLE 3 – WEIGHT OF WELD METAL (lbs/ft of Joint)

Plate thickness	30° reinforcement	20° reinforcement	30° reinforcement	20° reinforcement	30° reinforcement	20° reinforcement	30° reinforcement	20° reinforcement	30° reinforcement
5/8	.456	.364	.544	.452	2.53	1.96	1.33	1.11	.427
3/4	.811	.649	.735	.626	3.02	2.40	1.71	1.43	.616
7/8	1.26	1.01	1.01	.830	3.54	2.86	2.14	1.79	.901
1	1.82	1.46	1.33	1.06	4.07	3.34	2.61	2.19	1.09
1 1/8	2.48	1.99	1.62	1.30	4.63	3.84	3.13	2.64	1.39
1 1/4	3.24	2.60	1.93	1.56	5.19	4.35	3.70	3.12	1.71
1 3/8	4.11	3.28	2.26	1.83	5.80	4.89	4.30	3.63	2.07
1 1/2	5.07	4.06	2.62	2.13	6.41	5.45	4.96	4.19	2.46
1 5/8	6.14	4.91	3.01	2.45	7.06	6.02	5.66	4.78	2.89
1 3/4	7.30	5.84	3.41	2.79	7.72	6.62	6.40	5.41	3.35
2	9.94	7.94	4.29	3.52	9.11	7.85	8.03	6.79	4.38
2 1/8	11.4	9.12	4.75	3.91	9.85	8.51	8.91	7.54	4.94
2 1/4	13.0	10.4	5.25	4.32	10.6	9.18	9.83	8.32	5.54
2 3/8	14.7	11.7	5.77	4.75	11.4	9.87	10.8	9.14	6.18
2 1/2	16.4	13.1	6.31	5.20	12.2	10.6	11.8	10.0	6.85
2 5/8	18.3	14.7	6.88	5.67	13.0	11.4	12.9	10.9	7.55
2 3/4	20.3	16.2	7.46	6.16	13.8	12.1	14.0	11.8	8.28
3	24.6	19.6	8.71	7.20	15.5	13.6	16.3	13.8	9.85

TABLE 4 – WEIGHT OF WELD METAL (lbs/ft of Joint)

Plate thickness							
5/8	.854	.501	1.45	1.39	1.52	1.09	1.15
3/4	1.15	.805	1.95	1.79	1.89	1.45	1.49
7/8	1.48	1.18	2.50	2.22	2.29	1.99	1.85
1	1.86	1.63	3.13	2.70	2.72	2.30	2.23
1 1/8	2.28	2.14	3.83	3.22	3.17	2.79	2.63
1 1/4	2.74	2.73	4.59	3.76	3.55	3.31	3.06
1 3/8	3.24	3.39	5.42	4.26	4.15	3.88	3.52
1 1/2	3.78	4.12	6.31	4.99	4.67	4.49	3.99
1 5/8	4.36	4.92	7.28	5.56	5.22	5.14	4.49
1 3/4	4.99	5.80	8.32	6.36	5.80	5.83	5.02
2	6.35	7.76	10.6	7.90	7.02	7.33	6.14
2 1/8	7.10	8.85	11.8	8.73	7.67	8.05	6.74
2 1/4	7.88	9.99	12.1	9.58	8.33	9.00	7.35
2 3/8	8.73	11.3	14.5	10.5	9.04	9.91	8.00
2 1/2	9.60	12.5	15.9	11.4	9.66	10.9	8.66
2 5/8	10.5	13.9	17.5	12.4	10.5	11.8	9.35
2 3/4	11.5	15.3	19.0	13.4	11.3	12.8	10.1
3	13.5	18.4	22.4	15.6	12.9	15.0	11.6

TABLE 5 - WEIGHT OF WELD METAL
(lbs/ft of Joint)
Reinforcement: 10% W, Width of Joint

Plate thickness ↓	60°	20°	20°	0°	20°	0°
1	1.81	2.24	1.82		1.54	
1 1/8	2.17	2.61	2.17		1.89	
1 1/4	2.61	2.99	2.52		2.27	
1 3/8	3.09	3.37	2.88		2.65	
1 1/2	3.57	3.76	3.27		3.07	
1 5/8	4.12	4.18	3.65		3.50	
1 3/4	4.67	4.59	4.05		3.94	
2	5.93	5.44	4.87		4.91	
2 1/8	6.58	5.88	5.28		5.40	
2 1/4	7.32	6.34	5.72		5.94	
2 3/8	8.05	6.80	6.16		6.50	
2 1/2	8.87	7.28	6.63		7.06	
2 5/8	9.67	7.76	7.10		7.65	
2 3/4	10.5	8.26	7.57		8.25	
3	12.4	9.27	8.55		9.54	
3 1/8	13.3	9.80	8.90		10.2	10.2
3 1/4	14.5	10.3	9.40		10.8	10.8
3 1/2	16.5	11.2	10.6		12.3	12.1
3 3/4	18.8	12.5	11.6		13.8	13.3
4	21.2	13.7	12.9		15.4	14.7
4 1/2	26.4	16.2	15.2		18.9	17.2
5	32.3	18.8	17.8		22.6	19.8
5 1/2	38.7	21.6	20.5	20.4	26.7	22.3
6	45.7	24.6	23.4	23.0	31.0	25.0
6 1/2	53.3	27.8	26.4	25.4	35.6	27.0
7	61.4	30.4	29.6	28.1	40.5	30.1
7 1/2	70.0	34.3	32.9	30.6	46.0	32.8
8	79.5	37.9	36.4	33.3	51.7	35.3
9	99.9	45.5	43.9	38.4	63.9	40.4
10	122.6	53.8	52.0	43.5	77.4	45.6

FIGURE 1 - WEIGHT OF WELD METAL
(lbs/ft of Joint)
Based on Procedures, Using Submerged-Arc Process

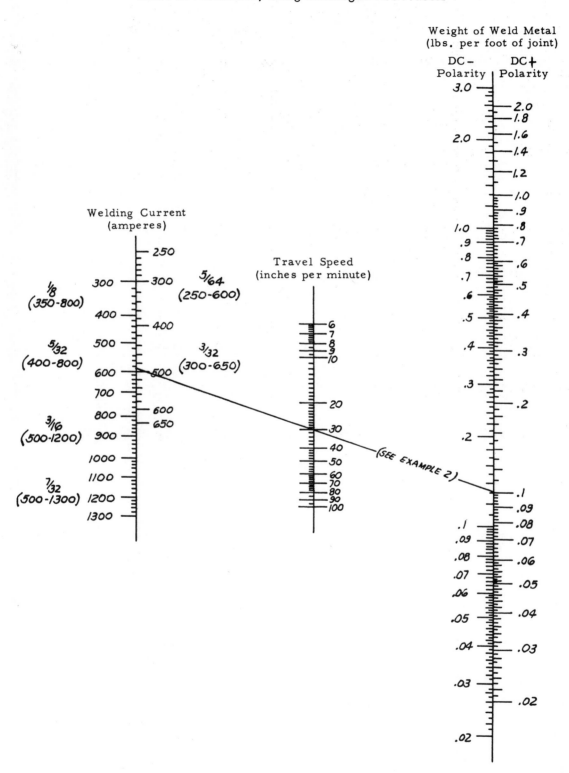

Computing the Weight of Weld Metal Based on Joint Design

With Table 2, computations based on joint design are easy. Essentially, it is a matter of dividing the cross-section of the area to be filled with weld metal, into standard geometric areas. The contributions of the individual areas can be found in the chart. Totaling these, gives the pounds of weld metal per foot required by the joint. For example, consider the following joint design (Fig. 2):

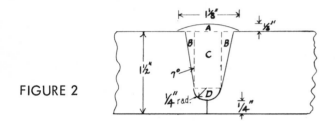

FIGURE 2

This joint can be broken into component areas A, B, C and D. Referring to Table 2, the contribution of each of these component areas to the total weight of weld metal required by the joint is simply picked off the chart as follows (Fig. 3):

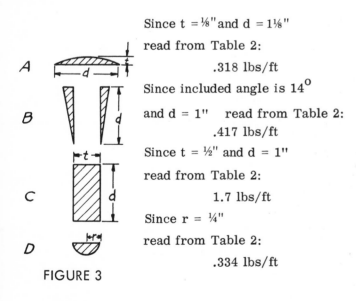

Since $t = \frac{1}{8}$" and $d = 1\frac{1}{8}$"

read from Table 2:

.318 lbs/ft

Since included angle is 14°

and $d = 1$"   read from Table 2:

.417 lbs/ft

Since $t = \frac{1}{2}$" and $d = 1$"

read from Table 2:

1.7 lbs/ft

Since $r = \frac{1}{4}$"

read from Table 2:

.334 lbs/ft

FIGURE 3

Adding these, the total weight becomes 2.77 lbs of weld metal per foot of joint.

Problem 2

Computing the Weight of Weld Metal Based on Welding Procedures

When the welding procedures for a particular job

are known, it is a simple matter to determine the weight of weld metal that will be deposited per foot of joint through the use of the nomograph for submerged arc welding Figure 1. Simply line up a straight-edge through the point on the left scale that represents the welding current being used and the point on the middle scale that represents the travel speed being used. Where the straight-edge intersects the right scale, read the amount of weld metal per foot of joint.

There is one note of caution. Be sure to use the proper side of the Welding Current scale, depending on the size of electrode used, and the correct side of the Weight of Weld Metal scale, depending on the polarity used.

As an example, the line drawn on the nomograph represents the procedure which uses 590 amps on $\frac{1}{8}$" electrode at a travel speed of 30 in./min. The resultant weight of weld metal is .10 lbs per foot of joint if DC positive polarity is used, or .13 lbs if DC negative polarity is used.

Problem 3

Adjusting Procedures to Provide the Required Amount of Weld Metal

For some types of joints, there are no established welding procedures. When such is the case, the normal method is to find an established procedure for a similar joint and alter it slightly to accommodate the desired joint. The nomograph for submerged-arc welding, Figure 1, can eliminate a lot of hit-and-miss approaches to the selection of the proper procedure.

For example, consider the following submerged-arc automatic joint (Fig. 4):

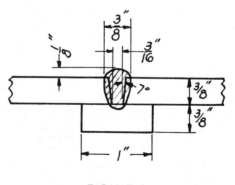

FIGURE 4

There are no established procedures for this joint. Probably the closest is that for the following joint (Fig. 5):

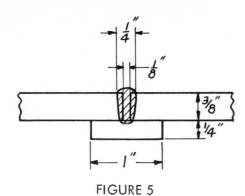

FIGURE 5

Power: DC+

Amperes: 670

Volts: 29

Electrode Size: ⁵⁄₃₂"

Travel Speed: 16"/min

In adjusting this procedure to the new joint, it is reasonable to assume that the 670 amps would be about right and, therefore, the simplest thing to do would be to slow down the welding speed enough to provide the amount of fill required. To do this, first determine the amount of weld metal required to fill the new joint in the manner outlined in Problem 1. In this case, it is determined to be .404 lbs/ft of joint.

Then, use the nomograph to determine the proper speed setting as follows.

Locate 670 amps on the left-hand side of the welding scale (for ⁵⁄₃₂" electrode) and .404 lbs/ft on the DC+ polarity side of the weld metal scale. Draw a straight line between them. This intersects the travel speed line at 9"/min, which is an estimate of the speed which should be used to provide adequate fill in the joint. With this much of the procedure fixed, it is a simple matter to adjust the voltage to provide the desired bead shape.

* * * * * * * * * *

3. OPERATING FACTOR

The selection of a proper operating factor (OF) is difficult, and yet affects the final cost more than any other single item. Even though some difficulty is encountered in obtaining this value, it is necessary to establish an approximately true value rather than to simply ignore it or assume it to be 100%. Consider the following:

METHOD A	METHOD B
¼" electrode A @ 20¢/lb	¼" electrode B @ 14¢/lb
uses ¼ # rod/ft of weld	uses ¼ # rod/ft of weld
speed is 18 in./min	speed is 16 in./min
labor & overhead, $6.00/hr	labor & overhead, $6.00/hr
Total cost of welding using <u>100%</u> operating factor:	Total cost of welding using <u>100%</u> operating factor:
11.7 ¢/ft	10.9 ¢/ft

This indicates that, with 100% operating factor, electrode B would have the least cost, and would save 6.6%.

Total cost of welding using <u>30%</u> operating factor	Total cost of welding using <u>30%</u> operating factor
27.2 ¢/ft	28.4 ¢/ft

This indicates that, with 30% operating factor, electrode A would have the least cost and would save 4.1%.

In other words, the operating factor does affect the welding cost sufficiently to be considered.

Since one might question the practice of assuming the same operating factor for various electrodes and procedures, consider the following example.

A welding engineer is interested in replacing his present E-6012 electrode on a certain job with the iron powder E-6024 electrode. The following is his cost study:

E-6012 ELECTRODE	E-6024 ELECTRODE
$\frac{5}{16}$" leg fillet . 30# rod/ft	$\frac{5}{16}$" leg fillet . 30# rod/ft
$\frac{5}{16}$" E-6012 rod @ 375 amps AC	$\frac{5}{16}$" E-6024 rod @ 375 amps AC
melt-off rate M = $7\frac{3}{4}$ in./min	melt-off rate M = 10.2 in./min
speed S = 9 in./min	speed S = 13 in./min
length rod melted L_m = 16"	length rod melted L_m = 16"
time T = 2.06 min/rod	time T = 1.57 min/rod

Assume a 50% operating factor (OF)
and $6.00/hr labor and overhead (L)

labor cost	labor cost
$\frac{20L}{S\,(OF)} = \frac{(20)(6)}{(9)(50\%)} = 26.7$ ¢/ft	$\frac{20\,L}{S\,(OF)} = \frac{(20)(6)}{(13)(50\%)} = 18.5$ ¢/ft

or a saving in labor of 30.7% by using the iron powder
electrode E-6024.

But this analysis reveals the following: The arc time for the E-6012 electrode per rod is 2.06 minutes; using a 50% operating factor, this represents a downtime of 2.06 minutes per rod. This downtime between electrodes includes time to lift up the helmet, clean the slag off the weld, insert a new electrode into the holder, etc. On the same basis the arc time for the E-6024 electrode would be 1.57 minutes per rod; and using the same operating factor of 50%, this means a downtime of only 1.57 minutes per rod.

It might appear at first that simply substituting the E-6024 electrode into the holder would decrease the downtime; i.e. the operator can lift up his helmet faster, knock off the slag faster, pick up and insert the next electrode faster, etc. Of course this is not true.

A more accurate method would be to use a fixed downtime, adjusting the operating factor accordingly. Re-examine this cost study, using an average downtime between electrodes of 2.06 minutes:

E-6012 ELECTRODE	E-6024 ELECTRODE
operating factor = 50%	operating factor = $\frac{1.57}{(1.57) + (2.06)}$ = 43.5%
labor cost	labor cost
$\frac{20\,L}{S\,(OF)} = \frac{(20)(6)}{(9)(50\%)} = 26.7$ ¢/ft	$\frac{20\,L}{S\,(OF)} = \frac{(20)(6)}{(13)(43.5\%)} = 21.2$ ¢/ft

or a saving in labor cost of 21% by using the E-6024 electrode.

Assume E = $\frac{\text{lbs rod melted}}{\text{lbs rod consumed}}$ = 90%

rod cost	rod cost
$\frac{1200\,M\,W}{N\,L_m\,S\,E_3} = \frac{(1200)(7\,3/4)(14.9)}{(219)(16)(9)(90\%)}$ = 4.9 ¢/ft	$\frac{1200\,M\,W}{N\,L_m\,S\,E_3} = \frac{(1200)(10.2)(16.9)}{(218)(16)(13)(90\%)}$ = 5.1 ¢/ft
Total 26.7 + 4.9 = 31.6 ¢/ft	Total 21.2 + 5.1 = 26.3 ¢/ft

or a total saving in labor and rod cost of 16.8% by using
the E-6024 electrode.

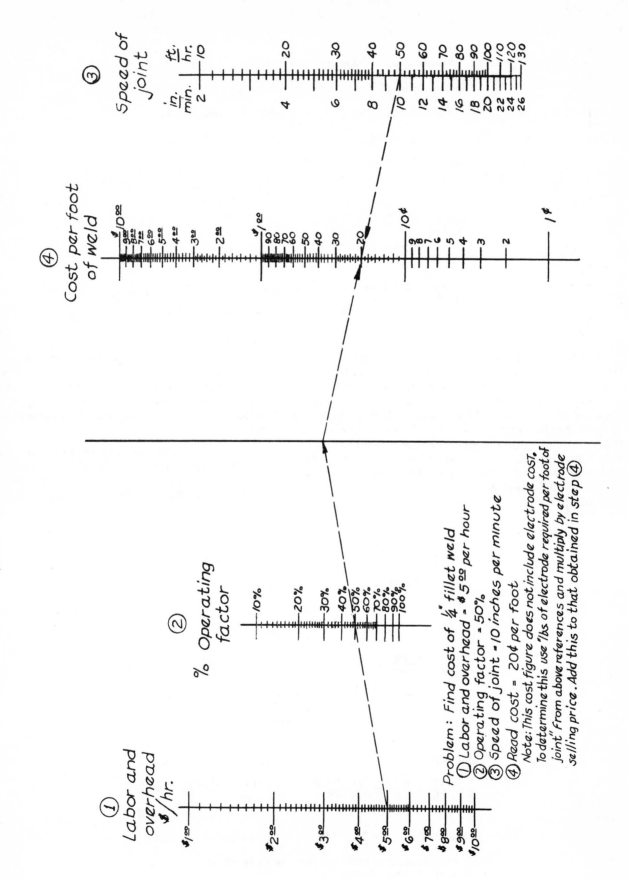

FIGURE 6 – WELDING COST ESTIMATOR
(Does Not Include Cost of Filler Metal)

Notice that the decreased arc time with the E-6024 results in a slightly lower operating factor, 43.5% instead of 50%, although the joint does cost less.

One might further suggest using a downtime per electrode and a handling time per foot of weld. These figures, if available, would give a more true picture of the welding cost, but it would mean making a time study of the job, which we are trying to avoid.

The nomograph, Figure 6, may be used to quickly read the labor and overhead cost per foot of weld.

4. COST PER HOUR

As a matter of interest, consider the cost per hour for these two procedures:

E-6012 ELECTRODE	E-6024 ELECTRODE
rod consumed per hr	rod consumed per hr
$\dfrac{6000 \, M \,(OF)}{N \, L_m \, E_3} = \dfrac{(6000)(7 \, 3/4)(50\%)}{(219)(16)(90\%)}$ $= 7.37 \text{ lbs/hr}$	$\dfrac{6000 \, M \,(OF)}{N \, L_m \, E_3} = \dfrac{(6000)(10.2)(43.5\%)}{(218(16)(90\%)}$ $= 8.49 \text{ lbs/hr}$
rod cost	rod cost
7.37 x 14.9 ¢/lb = $1.10/hr	8.49 x 16.9 ¢/lb = $1.44/hr
labor cost = 6.00	labor cost = 6.00
Total = $7.10/hr	Total = $7.44/hr

It can be expected then that the cost per hour for making the same size weld will increase slightly with faster procedures. Obviously the increase equals the difference in cost of electrode consumed. Of course the number of units turned out per hour is greater, so the unit cost is less.

5. ESTIMATING ACTUAL WELDING TIME

After the length and size of the various welds have been determined, there are three ways to estimate the actual welding time:

1. Convert these values into weight of weld metal per linear foot, and total for the entire job. Determine the deposition rate from the given welding current, and from this find the arc time. This method is especially useful when there is no standard welding data for the particular joint.

2. If standard welding data is available in tables, giving the arc travel speeds for various types and sizes of welds, in terms of inches per minute, apply this to the total lengths of each type and size of weld on the job.

3. Time the actual weld or job.

Most welding procedures are based on good welding conditions. These assume a weldable steel, clean smooth edge preparation, proper fit-up, proper position of plates for welding, sufficient accessibility so the welding operator can easily observe the weld and place the electrode in the proper position, and welds sufficiently long so the length of crater is not a factor in determining weld strength. Under these standard conditions, the weld should have acceptable appearance. Failure to provide these conditions requires a substantial reduction in welding current and immediately increases cost.

It is impossible to put a qualitative value on these factors, therefore the designer or engineer must learn to anticipate such problems and, by observation or consulting with shop personnel or other engineers who have actual welding experience, modify his estimate accordingly.

| Problem 4 |

Estimate the welding cost on the drum shown in Figure 7.

In this cost estimate, treat the submerged-arc automatic welding by finding the total pounds of weld metal required for all of the joints (9.74 lbs) and then applying the deposition rate for the particular welding current (700 amperes = .34 lbs/min).

To cover the handling time needed to put the parts into a positioner for the various positions of automatic welding, apply an operating factor of 33% to the arc time.

Treat the manual welding by totaling each of the different weld sizes and applying a speed of welding to these. These travel speeds normally are taken from standard welding procedures, but in this case assume the welding current to be reduced about a third because of short welds, welding around the edges of plates, and general inaccessibility. Therefore for estimating, use ⅔ of the arc speed from the standards. For example, if the standard for the ⁵⁄₁₆" fillet weld is 9 in./min, use a figure of 6 in./min. Since the assembly time is figured separately, use an operating factor of 50% for the manual welding.

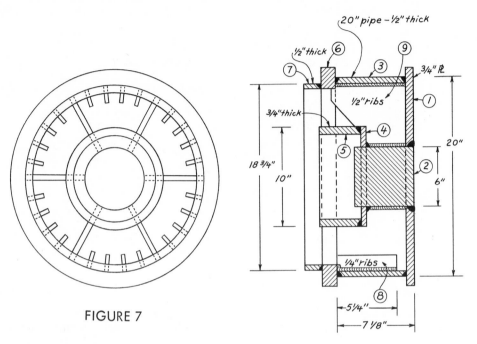

FIGURE 7

The cost study of this drum, assuming joint details that provide the following weld metal values, using Table 2:

Submerged-Arc Automatic Welding

① to ②	21" of 3/4" butt	1.67#		9.74# of weld metal		
③ to ①	63" of 1/2" butt			@ 700 Amps (.34#/min)		
③ to ⑥	63" of 1/2" butt	7.65#		or 29 min, and		
⑦ to ⑥	59" of 1/2" butt			@ 33% OF	90.0 min	
④ to ⑤	31" of 1/2" butt					
④ to ②	21" of 3/8" fillet	.42#				

Manual Welding

⑧	252"	of	3/16"	fillet	@	8"/min = 31.5 min	75.5 min	
⑨	264"	of	5/16"	fillet	@	6"/min = 44.0 min	@ 50% OF 151.0 min	

Assembly   90.0 min

Total   331   min

Cost at $2.00/hr labor & 200% OH $ 33.10

Control of Shrinkage and Distortion

1. WELDING FACTORS THAT CAUSE MOVEMENT

In making a weld, the heating and cooling cycle always causes shrinkage in both base metal and weld metal, and shrinkage forces tend to cause a degree of distortion. Designers and engineers must anticipate and provide control of this shrinkage to achieve the full economies of arc-welded steel construction. Suggested solutions for correction or elimination are based on both theoretical analysis and the practical experience of fabricating shops.

The enormous temperature differential in the arc area, creates a non-uniform distribution of heat in the part. As the temperature increases, such properties as yield strength decrease, the modulus of elasticity decreases, the coefficient of thermal expansion increases, the thermal conductivity decreases, and the specific heat increases. See Figure 1. To anticipate the movement of material from a straightforward analysis of heat is difficult.

Restraint from external clamping, internal restraint due to mass, and the stiffness of the steel plate itself also must be considered. All these factors have a definite influence on the degree of movement.

Finally it is necessary to consider the factor of time as it affects the rapidly changing conditions. The period of time during which a specific condition is in effect controls the importance of that condition.

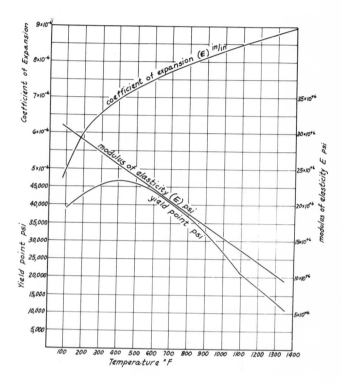

Fig. 1 Properties of a metal change at elevated temperatures, complicating the analysis of weld shrinkage. Graph is for mild steel.

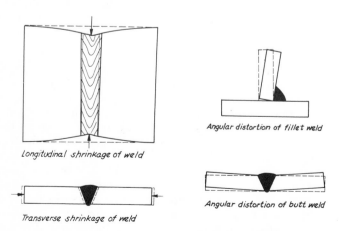

Longitudinal shrinkage of weld

Transverse shrinkage of weld

Angular distortion of fillet weld

Angular distortion of butt weld

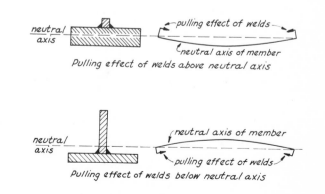

neutral axis — pulling effect of welds — neutral axis of member

Pulling effect of welds above neutral axis

neutral axis — neutral axis of member — pulling effect of welds

Pulling effect of welds below neutral axis

Fig. 2 An imbalance of forces resulting from shrinkage of weld deposit tends to cause angular distortion or bowing.

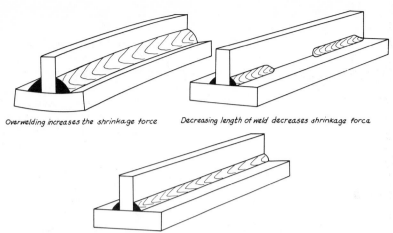

Overwelding increases the shrinkage force

Decreasing length of weld decreases shrinkage force

Decreasing leg size of weld decreases shrinkage force

Fig. 3 Excessive distortion is frequently caused by overwelding.

These variable conditions are further influenced by the welding process itself. Different welding procedures, type and size of electrode, welding current, speed of travel, joint design, preheating and cooling rates--all these bear significantly on the problem.

It is obvious that distortion cannot be analyzed by viewing each one of these factors separately. A solution based on correcting the combined effect is the only practicable approach.

Distortion of members occurring after welding has been completed is discussed in Sect. 3.4, Dimensional Stability.

2. EVIDENCES AND CAUSE OF DISTORTION

When distortion occurs, it appears as a shortening of the weld area. This generally can be cataloged as longitudinal shrinkage and transverse shrinkage, Figure 2. Further, if transverse shrinkage is not uniform throughout the thickness of the

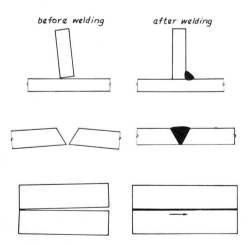

before welding   after welding

Fig. 4 Parts are often preset so that weld shrinkage will pull them back into correct alignment.

weld, angular distortion will result. When longitudinal shrinkage acts in a direction that is not along the neutral axis of the member, the result is bowing or cambering (also shown in Fig. 2).

Distortion results when a condition of non-uniform expansion and contraction is created. Distortion can be anticipated by evaluating the following factors:

1. The weld along with some adjacent metal contracts on cooling, producing a shrinkage force, F.

2. The shrinkage force acts about the neutral axis of a member. The distance between the center of gravity of the weld area and this neutral axis represents the moment arm, d.

3. The moment of inertia of the section, I, resists this contraction. The I of a section also resists straightening, should it be necessary.

3. THE INFLUENCE OF OVERWELDING

Overwelding increases the shrinkage force, F, and the tendency to distort. Anything that reduces the amount of welding such as decreasing the leg size, reducing the weld length, or using intermittent welding techniques, will minimize this condition. See Figure 3.

Overwelding can be caused inadvertently by a chain of events. The designer may specify the next larger weld size because of a lack of confidence in welding. When the part reaches the shop floor, the shop foreman, wishing to play it safe, marks the piece up for the next weld size. The weldor, having just been criticized for making undersize welds, makes real sure that these welds are still larger. The result--a ¼" fillet has become a ½" weld. These men usually do not realize that weld metal increases as the square of the leg size. The apparently harmless ¼" increase in the leg size has increased the amount of weld metal deposited, the weld shrinkage and the weld cost by 4 times.

4. CONTROL OF WELD SHRINKAGE

One technique used to control weld shrinkage involves prebending the member or presetting the joint before welding. In this way the net effect of weld shrinkage pulls the member or connection back into proper alignment (Fig. 4).

Whenever possible, welding should be balanced around the neutral axis of the member. This makes the moment arm, d, equal to zero. Even though a shrinkage force, F, does exist, the shrinkage moment (d × F) becomes zero (Fig. 5).

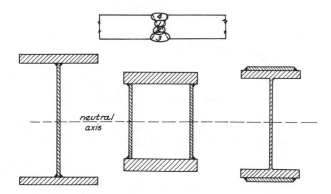

Fig. 5 Balancing welds or weld beads about the neutral axis of the member, reduces angular distortion to zero.

Frequently the neutral axis of the member is below the center of gravity of the welds as shown in Figure 6. By making the welds with the submerged-arc automatic welding process, the deep penetration characteristic of this process further lowers the center of gravity of the weld deposit and reduces the moment arm, thereby reducing the shrinkage moment.

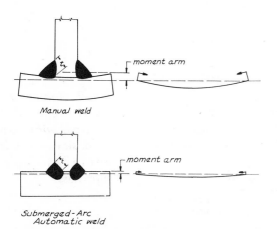

Manual weld

Submerged-Arc Automatic weld

Fig. 6 Deep-penetration welding processes and procedures places the weld closer to the neutral axis, reducing moment arm and net effect of shrinkage forces.

Adjacent Base Metal

Shrinkage of weld metal alone is not sufficient to account for the amount of shrinkage sometimes actually encountered. The heat of welding causes the metal just adjacent to the weld deposit to expand. However, this metal is restrained by the relatively cooler sections of the remainder of the plate. Almost all the volume expansion must take place in thickness. On cooling, this heated section undergoes volume contraction, building up shrinkage stresses in the longitudinal and transverse direction, and this adjacent base metal tends to shrink along with the weld metal.

Effect of High Welding Speeds

The volume of this adjacent base metal which contributes to the distortion can be controlled by welding procedures. Higher welding speeds through the use of powdered-iron-type manual electrodes, semi-automatic and fully automatic submerged-arc welding equipment, or vapor-shielded automatic welding equipment reduces the amount of adjacent material affected by the heat of the arc and progressively decreases distortion.

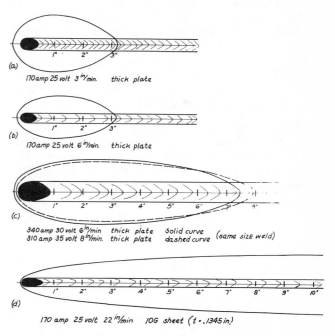

(a) 170 amp 25 volt 3 in/min.   thick plate

(b) 170 amp 25 volt 6 in/min.   thick plate

(c) 340 amp 30 volt 6 in/min.   thick plate   Solid curve
310 amp 35 volt 8 in/min.   thick plate   dashed curve (same size weld)

(d) 170 amp 25 volt 22 in/min   10G sheet (t = .1345 in.)

Fig. 7 Variance of welding technique. In each case, surface isotherm of 300°F is shown surrounding welding source.

The effect of welding current and arc speed on adjacent base metal is illustrated in Figure 7. Approximately the same weld size was produced with procedures (a) and (c). The important difference lies in the fact that the higher-speed welding technique produced a slightly narrower isotherm, measuring outward from the edge of the molten pool. The width of this isotherm of 300°F can be used to indicate the amount of adjacent metal shrinkage along with the weld, and therefore distortion; this helps to explain why in general faster welding speeds result in less distortion. This slight difference is also evident in a comparison of the quantity of welding heat applied to the plate.

For (a),

$$\frac{E\,I\,60}{V} = \frac{(25\text{ v})(170\text{ amp})(60)}{3''/\text{min}}$$

$$= 85,000 \text{ Joules/linear in. of weld}$$

For (c),

$$\frac{E\,I\,60}{V} = \frac{(35\text{ v})(310\text{ amp})(60)}{8''/\text{min}}$$

$$= 81,000 \text{ Joules/linear in. of weld}$$

Another condition can be observed by using conditions (a) and (b) of Figure 7. Two butt joints were made, one in the vertical position and the other in the horizontal position, using a multiple-pass groove weld. The same welding current (170 amps) was used in both joints. The vertical joint used a vertical-up weaving procedure, 3 passes at a speed of 3"/min., procedure (a). The horizontal joint used a series of 6 stringer passes at a speed of 6"/min., procedure (b). The faster welding of (b), 6"/min., produces a narrower isotherm. However, it required 6 passes rather than 3 of procedure (a), and the net result is an over-all cumulative shrinkage effect greater than that for (a).

This helps to explain why a given weld made with more passes will have slightly greater transverse shrinkage than one made with fewer passes. The transverse shrinkage can be reduced by using fewer passes. A further reduction can also be achieved by using larger electrodes.

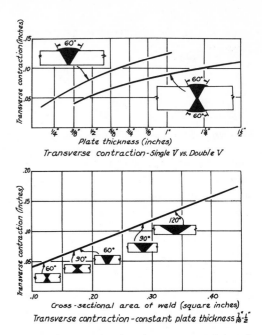

Transverse contraction—Single V vs. Double V

Transverse contraction—constant plate thickness $\frac{1}{8} - \frac{1}{2}$"

Fig. 8 Transverse shrinkage varies directly with amount of weld deposit.

In the weld on sheet metal, Figure 7 (d), it is noticed that a greater portion of the adjacent base metal is affected as compared to the weld itself. This, combined with the fact that the thin sheet metal is less rigid than the thick plate (its rigidity varies as its thickness cubed), helps to explain why sheet metal always presents more of a distortion problem.

5. TRANSVERSE SHRINKAGE

Transverse shrinkage becomes an important factor where the net effect of individual weld shrinkage can be cumulative.

The charts in Figure 8 throw some light on

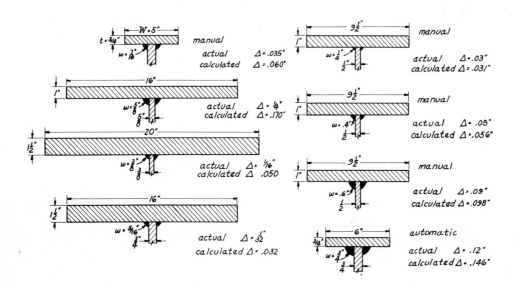

Fig. 9 Warpage varies directly with flange width and weld size, and inversely with plate thickness.

transverse shrinkage. In the lower chart transverse shrinkage, for a given plate thickness, is seen to vary directly with the cross-sectional area of the weld. The large included angles only help to illustrate this relationship and do not represent common practice. The relative effects of single and double V-joints are seen in the upper chart. Both charts assume no unusual restraint of the plates against transverse movement. Calculations show that transverse shrinkage is about 10% of the average width of the cross-section of the weld area.

$$\Delta_{trans} = .10 \frac{A_{weld}}{t}$$

$$= .10 \times \text{aver. width of weld}$$

Where the submerged-arc process is involved, the cross-section of the fused part of the joint is considered rather than simply the area of the weld metal deposited.

6. ANGULAR DISTORTION

The formula for calculating warpage is--

$$\Delta = \frac{0.02 \, W \, \omega^{1.3}}{t^2}$$

Figure 9 gives both the actual and calculated warpage for each of eight different flanges, fillet welded as indicated. The close agreement between the two values verifies the formula used. Only three exceed the American Welding Society allowable (1% of the width of the flange). It should be noted that these were overwelded.

7. BENDING OF LONGITUDINAL MEMBERS

Distortion or bending of longitudinal members results from development of a shrinkage force applied at some distance from the neutral axis of the member. The amount of distortion is directly controlled by the magnitude of the shrinkage moment and the member's resistance to bending as indicated by its moment of inertia.

Assuming no unusual initial stresses, the following formula indicates the amount of distortion or bending that will result from any longitudinal welding on a given member:

$$\Delta = 0.005 \frac{A_w \, d \, L^2}{I}$$

where:

A_w = total cross-sectional area within the fusion line, of all welds, in.²

d = distance between the center of gravity of the weld group and the neutral axis of the member, in.

L = length of the member, assuming welding the full length, in.

I = moment of inertia of the member, in.⁴

Δ = resulting vertical movement, in.

Measurement of actual distortion verifies the formula for theoretical calculation of distortion, Figure 10.

In some instances when equal welds are positioned symmetrically around neutral axis of a member, a certain amount of distortion still occurs even though the magnitudes of the shrinkage moments are equal and opposite. It is believed some plastic flow or upset occurs in the compressive area next to the weld area after the first weld is made. Because of this upset, the initial distortion, from the first weld, is not quite offset by the second weld on the opposite side. Where multiple-pass welding is involved, this condition can be corrected, as illustrated in the groove-weld sequence, Figure 5.

Fig. 10 Actual measured distortion corresponds well with calculated distortion, using the formula given.

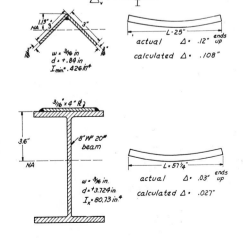

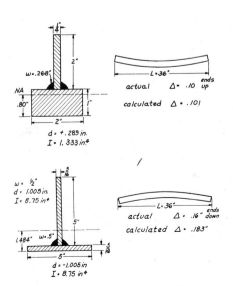

Here Pass 1 is on the top side. Pass 2, deposited on the opposite side, does not quite pull the plates back into flat alignment; therefore Pass 3 is added to the same side. The net result will usually pull the plate slightly beyond the flat position and Pass 4, on the top side, should bring this plate back into flat alignment. Frequently this problem is of no major importance since the sections to be welded are large enough in respect to the size of the weld to prevent the occurrence of this upsetting. As a result, on large sections the second weld on the opposite side is just as effective as the first weld.

In cases where the welds are not symmetrically balanced about the neutral axis of the section, advantage may be taken of this difference in distortion by first completing the joint nearest the neutral axis (it has the shorter moment arm) and then welding the joint on the side farthest from the neutral axis (taking advantage of its greater moment arm). See Figure 11, which illustrates a masonry plate welded to the bottom flange of a rolled beam. On the left, the welds are not symmetrical, so weld (a) was made first. Weld (b) follows since it has a greater moment arm. On the right, the wider masonry plate extends slightly on the left, and allows both welds to be made at the same time (since

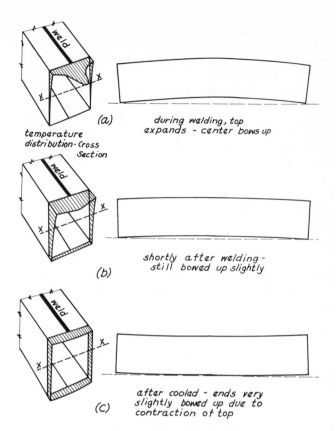

(a)

temperature distribution- Cross Section

during welding, top expands - center bows up

(b)

shortly after welding - still bowed up slightly

(c)

after cooled - ends very slightly bowed up due to contraction of top

Fig. 12 To avoid bowing of long, thin box sections welded up from two channels, the first weld is protected against cooling until the second weld is completed. The two welds are then allowed to cool simultaneously.

they are both in the flat position). The equal moment arms in this situation should result in no sweep of the beam. In both cases the welds will produce some camber but this is usually desirable.

Many long slender members are made by welding together two light-gage formed sections. Waiting until the first weld has cooled before making the second weld on the opposite side, usually results in some final bowing since the second weld may not quite pull the member back, Figure 12. Notice (a) the heating of the top side of the member by the first weld initially causes some expansion and bowing upward. Turning the member over quickly while it is still in this shape and depositing the second weld, increases the shrinking effect of the second weld deposit and the member is usually straight after cooling to room temperature.

The sequence for automatic welding to produce the four fillets on a fabricated plate girder can be varied without major effect on distortion. In most cases this sequence is based on the type of fixture used and the method of moving the girder from one welding position to another (Fig. 13). When a single automatic welder is used, the girder is usually positioned at an angle between $30°$ and $45°$, per-

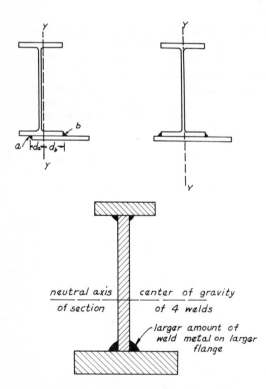

neutral axis of section

center of gravity of 4 welds

larger amount of weld metal on larger flange

Fig. 11 Where welds are not balanced about the neutral axis of the section, distortion can be minimized by welding first the joint nearest the neutral axis and then the joint farthest from the neutral axis. Similarly, weld sizes may be varied to help balance forces.

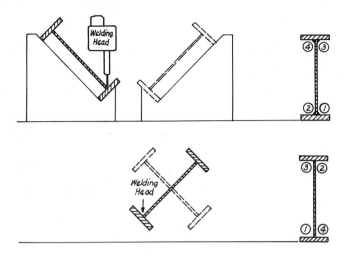

Fig. 13 Proper welding position and sequence for fabrication when girder is supported by inclined fixture (top) or trunnion-type fixture (bottom).

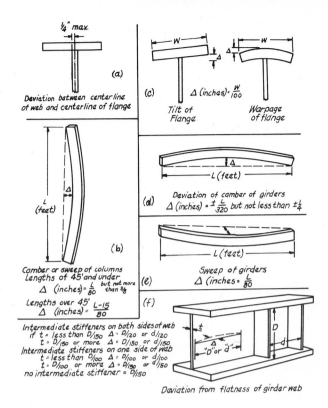

Fig. 14 AWS permissable tolerances for common welded members.

mitting the welds to be deposited in the flat position. This position is desirable since it makes welding easier and slightly faster. It also permits better control of bead shape and the production of larger welds when necessary.

Permissible AWS tolerances for most welded members are illustrated in Figure 14: (a) deviation between centerline of web and centerline of flange; (b) camber or sweep of columns; (c) at left, tilt of flange, and at right, warpage of flange; (d) deviation of camber of girders; (e) sweep of girders; (f) deviation from flatness of girder web.

8. PROPER ALIGNMENT OF PLATES

Various methods have been used for pulling plate edges into alignment and maintaining this alignment during welding. The most widely used technique (Fig. 15) calls for welding small clips to the edge of one plate. Driving a steel wedge between each clip and the second plate brings both edges into

alignment. Welding the clips on one side only, simplifies removal.

In the top part of Figure 16, pressure is applied by steel wedges whereas, in the bottom part of this figure, pressure is applied by tightening the strongbacks with bolts previously welded to the plate.

9. PEENING AND FLAME SHRINKING

Peening is used occasionally to control distortion. Since the weld area contracts, peening, if properly applied, tends to expand it. However, this expansion occurs only near the surface.

Fig. 15 Small clip angles and wedges can be used to economically maintain alignment of plates during welding. If clips are welded on one side only, they can later be knocked off with a hammer.

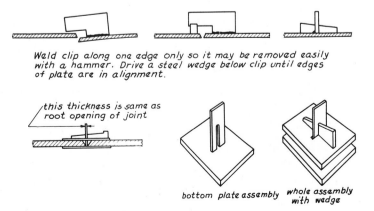

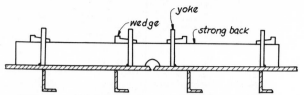

Plates forced into alignment and held there by means of strong backs. The pressure being applied by means of a wedge driven in between a yoke and the strong back.

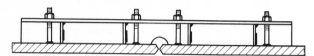

For heavier plates, this pressure may be applied by means of bolts temporarily welded to the plate. The strongback is then pulled tightly against the plate.

Fig. 16 Large plates can be aligned against strongbacks, the plates being pulled up by means of yoke and wedge combination; or, bolts are welded to the plates and run through the strongbacks to facilitate alignment.

Upsetting or expansion of the weld metal by peening is most effective at higher temperatures where the yield strength of the metal is rather low. Unfortunately, most of the distortion occurs later at the lower temperatures after the yield strength has been restored to its higher value. For this reason, peening does not accomplish the desired results. An additional disadvantage of peening is that it work-hardens the surface of the metal and uses up some of the available ductility.

Flame shrinking or flame straightening is another method of correcting distortion, through localized heating with a torch. The heat causes the metal in this area to expand, and this expansion is restrained in all directions by the surrounding cooler metal. As a result, this area of the metal expands abnormally through its thickness and upon cooling tends to become shorter in all directions. The section so treated will become shorter and stressed in tension with each successive application of heat.

The bending of a member by welding and its straightening by flame shrinking is analogous to the case of a stool which will tilt to one side when the legs on one side are shortened but will again become erect when the opposite legs are also shortened the same amount.

10. SUMMARY AND CHECK LIST

Transverse distortion

1. Depends on restraint.

2. Is equal to about 10% of the average width of the weld area.

3. Increases with the weld area for the same plate thickness.

4. Increases with the root opening and the included angle.

5. Is directly proportional to the welding heat input per inch, that is, Joules per inch.

Angular distortion can be reduced by:

1. Use of a double bevel, V, J, or U for butt joints.

2. Alternating welds from side to side.

3. Beveling the web of a T-joint; this will reduce the moment arm of the weld and reduce the angular movement.

4. Use of the smallest leg size for fillet welds, since the distortion varies approximately with the 1.3 power of the leg size of such a weld.

5. Use of thicker flanges; distortion varies approximately inversely with the square of the flange thickness.

Bending of long members by longitudinal welds can be partially controlled by:

1. Balancing welds about the neutral axis of the member.

a. Making welds of the same size at the same distance on the opposite side of the neutral axis of the member.

b. For welds of different sizes--if at different distances from the neutral axis of the member-- making the welds that are farther away smaller.

2. If the welding is not symmetrical, this result is achieved by:

a. Prebending the member.

b. Supporting the member in the middle and letting the ends sag, and for the opposite effect, by supporting the member at the ends and letting the middle sag.

c. Breaking the member into sub-assemblies so that each part is welded about its own neutral axis.

Deflection is directly proportional to the shrinkage moment of the welds (weld area times its distance from the neutral axis of the member) and inversely proportional to the moment of inertia of the member. Although a high moment of inertia for the member is desired to resist bending, it also makes the member more difficult to straighten, once it has become distorted. Flame shrinking may be applied to the longer side if welding has bent the member.

Assembly procedures that help control distortion:

1. Clamp the member in position and hold during welding.

2. Preset the joint to offset expected contraction.

3. Prebend the member to offset expected distortion.

4. Before welding, clamp two similar members back to back with some prebending.

5. If stress-relieving is required, weld two similar members back to back and keep fastened until after stress relief.

6. Use strong-backs.

7. Use jigs and fixtures to maintain proper fit-up and alignment during welding.

8. Make allowances for contraction when a joint is assembled.

9. Arrange the erection, fitting, and welding sequence so that parts will have freedom to move in one or more directions as long as possible.

10. Use subassemblies and complete the welding in each before final assembly and welding together.

11. If possible break the member into proper sections, so that the welding of each section is balanced about its own neutral axis.

12. Weld the more flexible sections together first, so that they can be easily straightened before final assembly.

Welded steel construction of ore bridge rail clamps reduced cost while increasing strength over previous cast steel design. Smooth operation of clamp demands good alignment, obtained in manufacture by use of jigs and proper welding sequence.

With modern welding positioners, high production techniques are applicable even on large press frames like these. Welded steel construction means better press performance at lower cost. Well-designed frames have high rigidity, permitting closer fits on slides and better control of both die life and stamping quality.

Beam Diagrams and Formulas

The following beam diagrams and formulas have been found useful in the design of steel weldments.

Proper signs, positive (+) and negative (–), are not necessarily indicated in the formulas. The following are suggested:

Shear diagram above reference line is (+)

Shear diagram below reference line is (–)

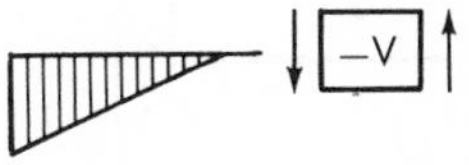

Reaction to left of (+) shear is upward (+)

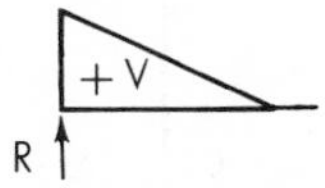

Reaction to left of (–) shear is downward (–)

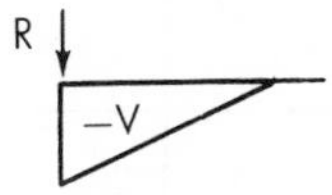

Reaction to right of (+) shear is downward (–)

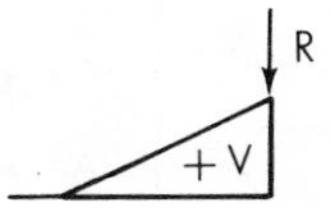

Reaction to right of (–) shear is upward (+)

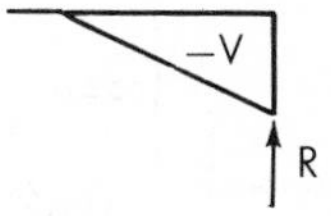

Moment above reference line is (+)
Compressive bending stresses on top fibers
also tends to open up a corner connection

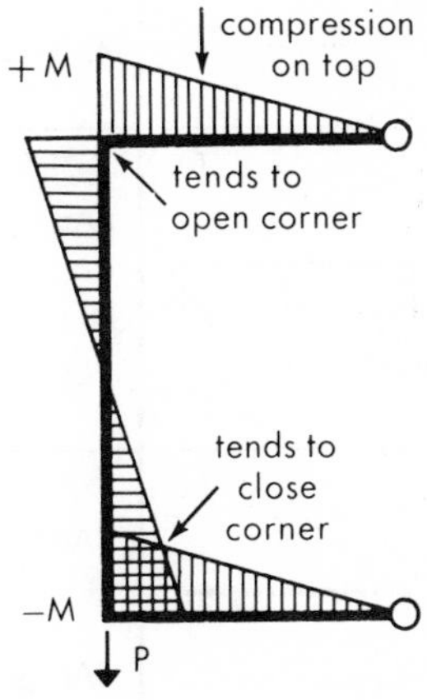

Moment diagram on same side as compressive stress

Moment below reference line is (–)
Compressive bending stresses on bottom fibers
also tends to close up a corner connection

Angle of slope, θ
    clockwise rotation (–), counter-clockwise rotation (+)

On the next page is a visual index to the various beam diagrams and formulas. As indicated, these are keyed by number to the type of beam and by capital letter to the type of load.

For some conditions, influence curves are included to illustrate the effect of an important variable. These are keyed to the basic beam diagram and are positioned as close as practical to the diagram.

1

VISUAL INDEX TO FORMULAS ON FOLLOWING PAGES
FOR VARIOUS BEAM-LOAD CONDITIONS

Type of LOAD / Type of BEAM	Concentrated force	Uniform load entire span	Uniform load partial span	Varying load	Couple
	(A)	(B)	(C)	(D)	(E)
(1) Cantilever — free / fixed	1Aa, 1Ab	1B	1C	1Da, 1Db	1E
(2) guided / fixed	2A	2B			
(3) Simply supported — supported / supported	3Aa, 3Ab, 3Ac, 3Ad	3B	3C	3Da, 3Db, 3Dc	3Ea, 3Eb, 3Ec
(4) fixed	4Aa, 4Ab, 4Ac	4Ba, 4Bb	4C	4D	4E
(5) supported / fixed	5Aa, 5Ab	5B	5C	5Da, 5Db	5E
(6) Single span with overhang	6Aa, 6Ab	6Ba, 6Bb	6Ca, 6Cb		
(7) Continuous two span	7Aa, 7Ab	7B		7D See adjacent to (3D)	For other multi-span load conditions, see discussion under (7)

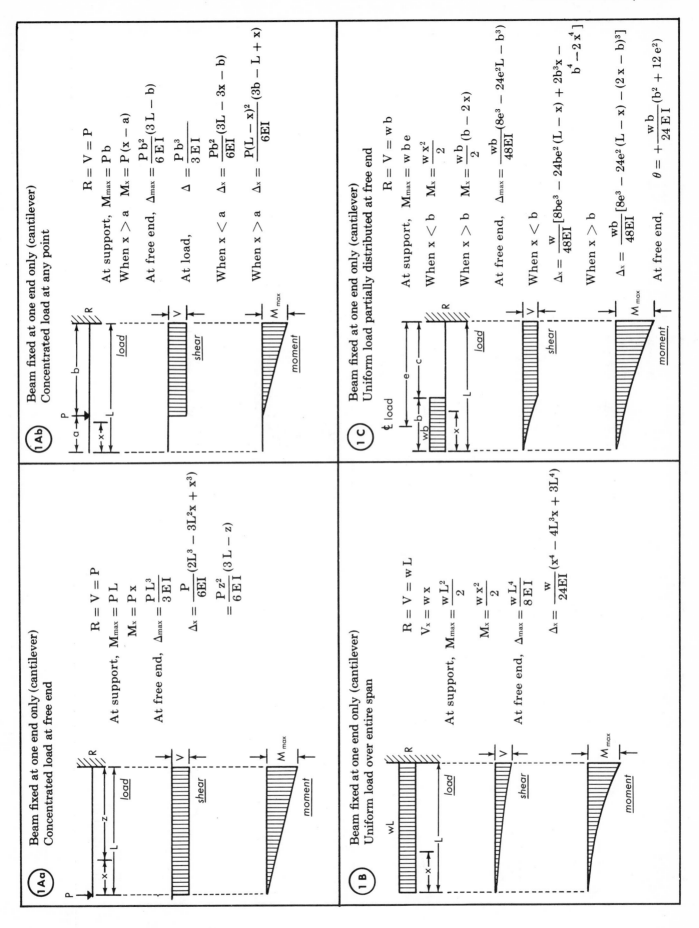

1Aa Beam fixed at one end only (cantilever)
Concentrated load at free end

$$R = V = P$$

At support, $M_{max} = PL$

$$M_x = Px$$

At free end, $\Delta_{max} = \dfrac{PL^3}{3EI}$

$$\Delta_x = \dfrac{P}{6EI}(2L^3 - 3L^2x + x^3)$$
$$= \dfrac{Pz^2}{6EI}(3L - z)$$

1Ab Beam fixed at one end only (cantilever)
Concentrated load at any point

$$R = V = P$$

At support, $M_{max} = Pb$

When $x > a$, $M_x = P(x - a)$

At free end, $\Delta_{max} = \dfrac{Pb^2}{6EI}(3L - b)$

At load, $\Delta = \dfrac{Pb^3}{3EI}$

When $x < a$, $\Delta_x = \dfrac{Pb^2}{6EI}(3L - 3x - b)$

When $x > a$, $\Delta_x = \dfrac{P(L - x)^2}{6EI}(3b - L + x)$

1B Beam fixed at one end only (cantilever)
Uniform load over entire span

$$R = V = wL$$
$$V_x = wx$$

At support, $M_{max} = \dfrac{wL^2}{2}$

$$M_x = \dfrac{wx^2}{2}$$

At free end, $\Delta_{max} = \dfrac{wL^4}{8EI}$

$$\Delta_x = \dfrac{w}{24EI}(x^4 - 4L^3x + 3L^4)$$

1C Beam fixed at one end only (cantilever)
Uniform load partially distributed at free end

$$R = V = wb$$

At support, $M_{max} = wbe$ $\qquad M_x = \dfrac{wx^2}{2}$

When $x > b$, $M_x = \dfrac{wb}{2}(b - 2x)$

At free end, $\Delta_{max} = \dfrac{wb}{48EI}(8e^3 - 24e^2L - b^3)$

When $x < b$,
$$\Delta_x = \dfrac{w}{48EI}[8be^3 - 24be^2(L - x) + 2b^3x - b^4 - 2x^4]$$

When $x > b$,
$$\Delta_x = \dfrac{wb}{48EI}[8e^3 - 24e^2(L - x) - (2x - b)^3]$$

At free end, $\theta = + \dfrac{wb}{24EI}(b^2 + 12e^2)$

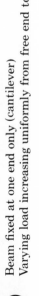
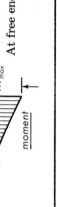

1Db Beam fixed at one end only (cantilever)
Varying load increasing uniformly from support to free end

$$R = V = W$$

$$V_x = \frac{2Wx}{L^2}\left(L - \frac{x}{2}\right)$$

At support, $\quad M_{max} = \frac{2WL}{3}$

$$M_x = \frac{Wx^2}{3L^2}(x - 3L)$$

At free end, $\quad \Delta_{max} = \frac{11WL^3}{60EI}$

$$\Delta_x = \frac{W}{60EIL^2}[L^4(15x - 11L) - x^4(5L - x)]$$

At free end, $\quad \theta = +\frac{WL^2}{4EI}$

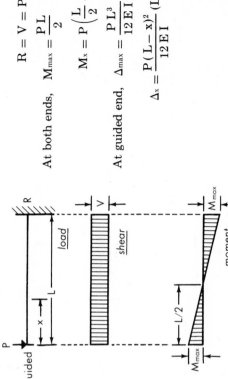
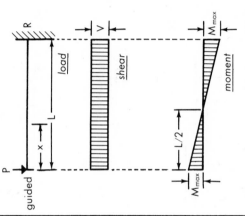

2A Beam fixed at one end and free but guided at the other end
Concentrated load at guided end

$$R = V = P$$

At both ends, $\quad M_{max} = \frac{PL}{2}$

$$M_x = P\left(\frac{L}{2} - x\right) \qquad \Delta_{max} = \frac{PL^3}{12EI}$$

At guided end, $\quad \Delta_x = \frac{P(L-x)^2}{12EI}(L + 2x)$

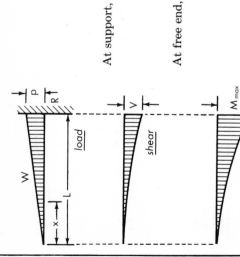

1Da Beam fixed at one end only (cantilever)
Varying load increasing uniformly from free end to support

$$W = \frac{pL}{2}$$

$$R = V = W$$

$$V_x = W\frac{x^2}{L^2}$$

At support, $\quad M_{max} = \frac{WL}{3}$

$$M_x = \frac{Wx^3}{3L^2}$$

At free end, $\quad \Delta_{max} = \frac{WL^3}{15EI}$

$$\Delta_x = \frac{W}{60EIL^2}(x^5 - 5L^4x + 4L^5)$$

At free end, $\quad \theta = +\frac{WL^2}{12EI}$

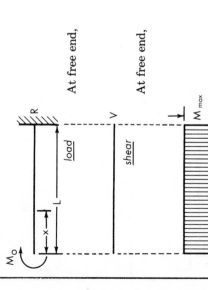
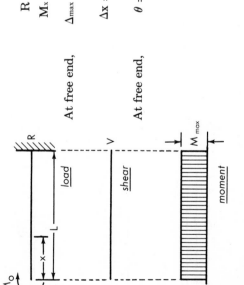

1E Beam fixed at one end only (cantilever)
Moment applied at free end

$$R = V = O$$

$$M_x = M_o$$

At free end, $\quad \Delta_{max} = \frac{M_oL^2}{2EI}$

$$\Delta_x = \frac{M_o}{2EI}(L - x)^2$$

At free end, $\quad \theta = -\frac{M_oL}{EI}$

(3Ab) Beam supported at both ends
Concentrated load at any point

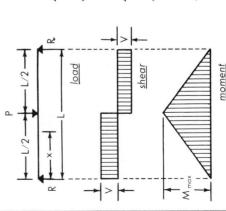

Max when a < b $R_1 = V_1 = \dfrac{Pb}{L}$

Max when a > b $R_2 = V_2 = \dfrac{Pa}{L}$

At load, $M_{max} = \dfrac{Pab}{L}$

When x < a $M_x = \dfrac{Pbx}{L}$

At x = $\sqrt{\dfrac{L^2 - b^2}{3}}$

when a > b $\Delta_{max} = \dfrac{Pb}{3EIL}\sqrt{\left(\dfrac{L^2 - b^2}{3}\right)^3}$

At load, $\Delta = \dfrac{Pa^2 b^2}{3EIL}$

When x < a $\Delta_x = \dfrac{Pbx}{6EIL}(L^2 - b^2 - x^2)$

When x < b $\Delta_L = \dfrac{Pa}{48EI}(3L^2 - 4a^2)$

At ends, $\theta_1 = -\dfrac{P}{6EI}\left(2aL + \dfrac{a^3}{L} - 3a^2\right)$

$\theta_2 = +\dfrac{P}{6EI}\left(aL - \dfrac{a^3}{L}\right)$

(2B) Beam fixed at one end and free but guided at the other end
Uniform load over entire span

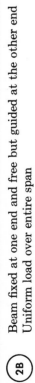
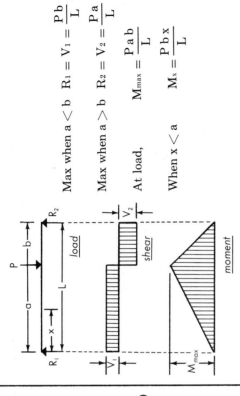

$R = V = wL$

$V_x = wx$

At support, $M_{max} = \dfrac{wL^2}{3}$

At guided end, $M_1 = \dfrac{wL^2}{6}$

$M_x = \dfrac{w}{6}(L^2 - 3x^2)$

At guided end, $\Delta_{max} = \dfrac{wL^4}{24EI}$

$\Delta_x = \dfrac{w(L^2 - x^2)^2}{24EI}$

(3Aa) Beam supported at both ends
Concentrated load at mid-span

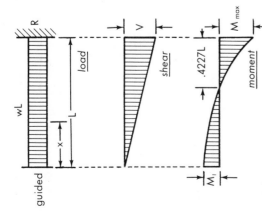

$R_1 = R_2 = V = P/2$

At load, $M_{max} = \dfrac{PL}{4}$

When x < L/2 $M_x = \dfrac{Px}{2}$

At load, $\Delta_{max} = \dfrac{PL^3}{48EI}$

When x < L/2 $\Delta_x = \dfrac{Px}{48EI}(3L^2 - 4x^2)$

At end, $\theta_1 = -\dfrac{PL^2}{16EI} = -\theta_2$

3c Beam supported at both ends
Uniform load partially distributed over span

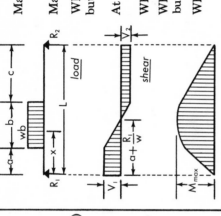

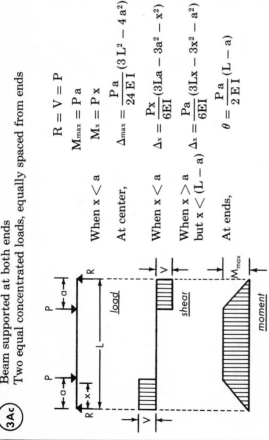

Max when a < c $R_1 = V_1 = \frac{wb}{2L}(2c + b)$

Max when a > c $R_2 = V_2 = \frac{wb}{2L}(2a + b)$

When x > a
but x < (a + b) $V_x = R_1 - w(x - a)$

At $x = a + \frac{R_1}{w}$ $M_{max} = R_1\left(a + \frac{R_1}{2w}\right)$

When x < a $M_x = R_1 x$

When x > a
but x < (a + b) $M_x = R_1 x - \frac{w}{2}(x - a)^2$

When x > (a + b) $M_x = R_2(L - x)$

When a = c
$$R = V = \frac{wb}{2}$$

$$V_x = w\left(a + \frac{b}{2} - x\right)$$

At center, $M_{max} = \frac{wb}{2}\left(a + \frac{b}{4}\right)$

When x < a $M_x = \frac{wbx}{2}$

When x > a
but x < (a + b) $M_x = \frac{wbx}{2} - \frac{w}{2}(x - a)^2$

At center, $\Delta_L = \frac{wb}{384EI}(-8L^3 + 4b^2L - b^3)$

3Ac Beam supported at both ends
Two equal concentrated loads, equally spaced from ends

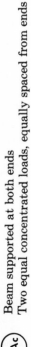

$$R = V = P$$

$$M_{max} = Pa$$

$$M_x = Px$$

When x < a

At center, $\Delta_{max} = \frac{Pa}{24EI}(3L^2 - 4a^2)$

When x < a $\Delta_x = \frac{Px}{6EI}(3La - 3a^2 - x^2)$

When x > a
but x < (L − a) $\Delta_x = \frac{Pa}{6EI}(3Lx - 3x^2 - a^2)$

At ends, $\theta = \frac{Pa}{2EI}(L - a)$

3Ad Beam supported at both ends
Two unequal concentrated loads, unequally spaced from ends

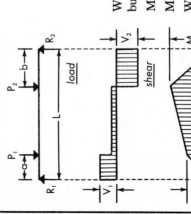

$R_1 = V_1 = \dfrac{P_1(L - a) + P_2 b}{L}$

$R_2 = V_2 = \dfrac{P_1 a + P_2(L - b)}{L}$ $V_x = R_1 - P_1$

Max when $R_1 < P_1$ $M_1 = R_1 a$

Max when $R_2 < P_2$ $M_2 = R_2 b$

When x < a $M_x = R_1 x$

When x > a
but x < (L − b) $M_x = R_1 x - P_1(x - a)$

Also see formulas on page 8

3B — Beam supported at both ends / Uniform load over entire span

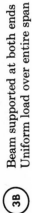

$$R = V = \frac{wL}{2}$$

$$V_x = w\left(\frac{L}{2} - x\right)$$

At center, $\quad M_{max} = \frac{wL^2}{8}$

$$M_x = \frac{wx}{2}(L - x)$$

At center, $\quad \Delta_{max} = \frac{5WL^4}{384EI}$

$$\Delta_x = \frac{wx}{24EI}(L^3 - 2Lx^2 + x^3)$$

At ends, $\quad \theta = \frac{wL^3}{24EI}$

3Da — Beam supported at both ends / Varying load, increasing uniformly to one end

$$W = \frac{PL}{2}$$

$$R_1 = V_1 = \frac{W}{3}$$

$$R_2 = V_{2\,(max)} = \tfrac{2}{3}W$$

$$V_x = \frac{W}{3} - \frac{Wx^2}{L^2}$$

At $x = L/\sqrt{3} = .5744\,L$

$$M_{max} = \frac{2WL}{9\sqrt{3}} = .1283\,WL$$

$$M_x = \frac{Wx}{3L^2}(L^2 - x^2)$$

At $x = L\sqrt{1 - \sqrt{8/15}} = .5193\,L$

$$\Delta_{max} = .01304\,\frac{WL^3}{EI}$$

$$\Delta_x = \frac{Wx}{180EIL^2}(3x^4 - 10L^2x^2 + 7L^4)$$

At center, $\quad \Delta_{\frac{L}{2}} = \frac{5WL^3}{384EI}$

At ends, $\quad \theta_1 = -\frac{7WL^2}{180EI}$

$$\theta_2 = +\frac{8WL^2}{180EI}$$

3Db — Beam supported at both ends / Varying load, increasing uniformly to center

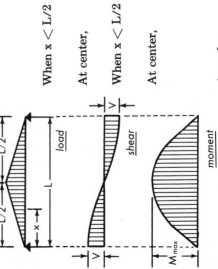

$$R_1 = R_2 = V = \frac{W}{2}$$

When $x < L/2$, $\quad V_x = \frac{W}{2L^2}(L^2 - 4x^2)$

At center, $\quad M_{max} = \frac{WL}{6}$

When $x < L/2$, $\quad M_x = Wx\left(\frac{1}{2} - \frac{2x^2}{3L^2}\right)$

At center, $\quad \Delta_{max} = \frac{WL^3}{60EI}$

$$\Delta_x = \frac{Wx}{480EIL^2}(5L^2 - 4x^2)^2$$

At ends, $\quad \theta = \frac{5WL^2}{96EI}$

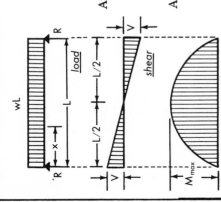

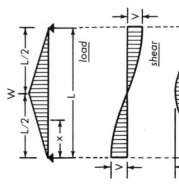

BEAM FORMULAS APPLIED TO SIDE OF TANK, BIN OR HOPPER
(p = pressure, psi; m = width of panel considered)

3Da

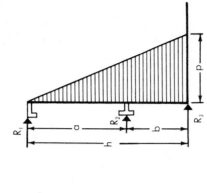

$$R_1 = \frac{p\,h\,m}{6} \qquad R_2 = \frac{p\,h\,m}{3} = V_{max}$$

$$M_{max} = \frac{p\,h^2\,m}{9\sqrt{3}} = .0642\,p\,h^2\,m$$

$$M_x = \frac{p\,x\,m}{6\,h}(h^2 - x^2)$$

$$\Delta_{4L} = \frac{5\,p\,h^4\,m}{768\,E\,I}$$

$$\Delta_x = \frac{p\,x\,m}{360\,E\,I\,h}(3\,x^4 - 10\,h^2\,x^2 + 7\,h^4)$$

$$\Delta_{max} = .00652\frac{p\,h^4\,m}{E\,I}$$
$$(\text{at } x = .5193\,h)$$

3Dc

$$M_{4L} = \frac{h^2\,m}{16}(p_1 + p_2) \quad *$$

$$\Delta_{4L} = \frac{5\,h^4\,m}{768\,E\,I}(p_1 + p_2) \quad *$$

$$V_{max} = \frac{m\,h}{6}(p_1 + 2\,p_2)$$

(* These values are within 98% of maximum.)

7D

Maximum bending moment is least when

a = .57 h
b = .43 h

$M_{max} = .0147\,p\,h^2\,m$ (negative moment at middle support, 2)

$R_1 = +.030\,p\,h\,m$
$R_2 = +.320\,p\,h\,m$
$R_3 = +.150\,p\,h\,m$

$V_{max} = +.188\,p\,h\,m$ (at middle support, 2)

Also see formulas on page 7

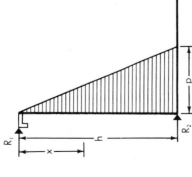

(7 D) Influence Lines

Effect of location of middle support (2) upon reactions (R) and moments (M)

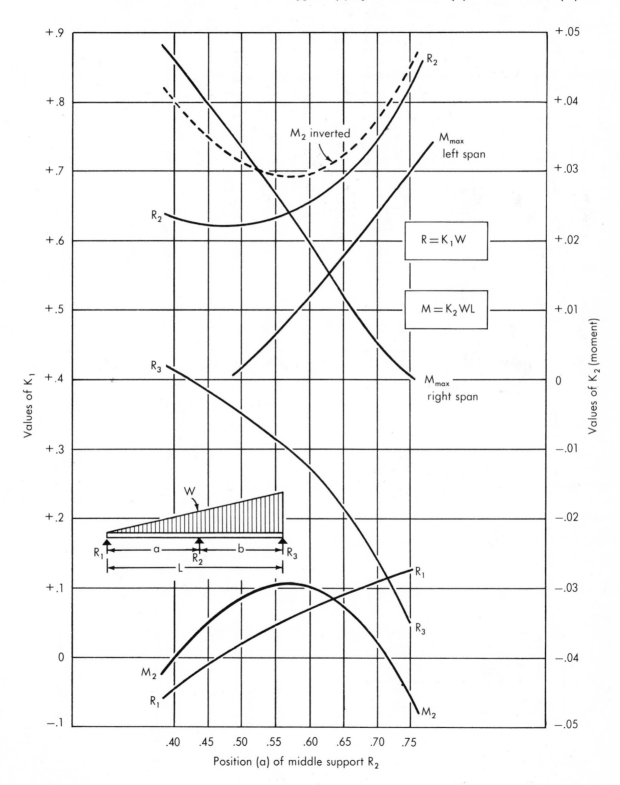

Position (a) of middle support R₂

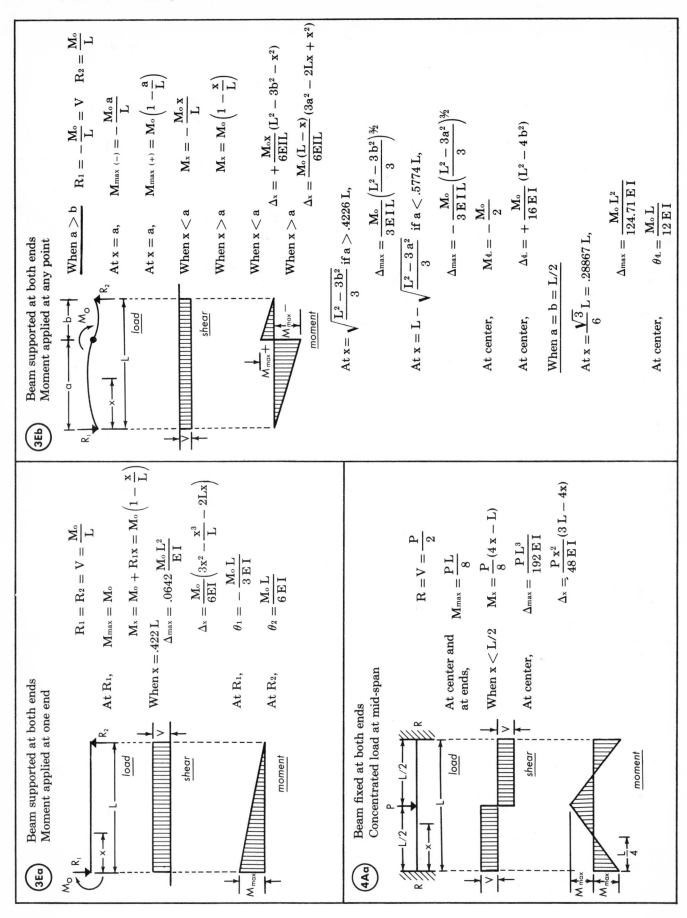

(3Eb) Beam supported at both ends — Moment applied at any point

$$R_2 = \frac{M_o}{L}$$

$$R_1 = -\frac{M_o}{L} = V$$

When $a > b$

At $x = a$, $\quad M_{max\,(-)} = -\frac{M_o\,a}{L}$

At $x = a$, $\quad M_{max\,(+)} = M_o\left(1 - \frac{a}{L}\right)$

When $x < a$ $\quad M_x = -\frac{M_o\,x}{L}$

When $x > a$ $\quad M_x = M_o\left(1 - \frac{x}{L}\right)$

When $x < a$ $\quad \Delta_x = +\frac{M_o x}{6EIL}(L^2 - 3b^2 - x^2)$

When $x > a$ $\quad \Delta_x = \frac{M_o(L-x)}{6EIL}(3a^2 - 2Lx + x^2)$

At $x = \sqrt{\dfrac{L^2 - 3b^2}{3}}$ if $a > .4226\,L$,

$$\Delta_{max} = \frac{M_o}{3EIL}\left(\frac{L^2 - 3b^2}{3}\right)^{3\!/\!2}$$

At $x = L - \sqrt{\dfrac{L^2 - 3a^2}{3}}$ if $a < .5774\,L$,

$$\Delta_{max} = -\frac{M_o}{3EIL}\left(\frac{L^2 - 3a^2}{3}\right)^{3\!/\!2}$$

At center, $\quad M_{\text{\tiny L}} = -\frac{M_o}{2}$

At center, $\quad \Delta_{\text{\tiny L}} = +\frac{M_o}{16EI}(L^2 - 4b^2)$

When $a = b = L/2$

At $x = \dfrac{\sqrt{3}}{6}L = .28867\,L$,

$$\Delta_{max} = \frac{M_o L^2}{124.71\,EI}$$

At center, $\quad \theta_{\text{\tiny L}} = \frac{M_o L}{12\,EI}$

(3Ea) Beam supported at both ends — Moment applied at one end

$$R_1 = R_2 = V = \frac{M_o}{L}$$

At R_1, $\quad M_{max} = M_o$

$$M_x = M_o + R_1 x = M_o\left(1 - \frac{x}{L}\right)$$

When $x = .422\,L$ $\quad \Delta_{max} = .0642\,\frac{M_o L^2}{EI}$

$$\Delta_x = \frac{M_o}{6EI}\left(3x^2 - \frac{x^3}{L} - 2Lx\right)$$

At R_1, $\quad \theta_1 = -\frac{M_o L}{3EI}$

At R_2, $\quad \theta_2 = \frac{M_o L}{6EI}$

(4Aa) Beam fixed at both ends — Concentrated load at mid-span

$$R = V = \frac{P}{2}$$

At center and at ends, $\quad M_{max} = \frac{PL}{8}$

When $x < L/2$ $\quad M_x = \frac{P}{8}(4x - L)$

At center, $\quad \Delta_{max} = \frac{PL^3}{192\,EI}$

$$\Delta_x = \frac{P x^2}{48\,EI}(3L - 4x)$$

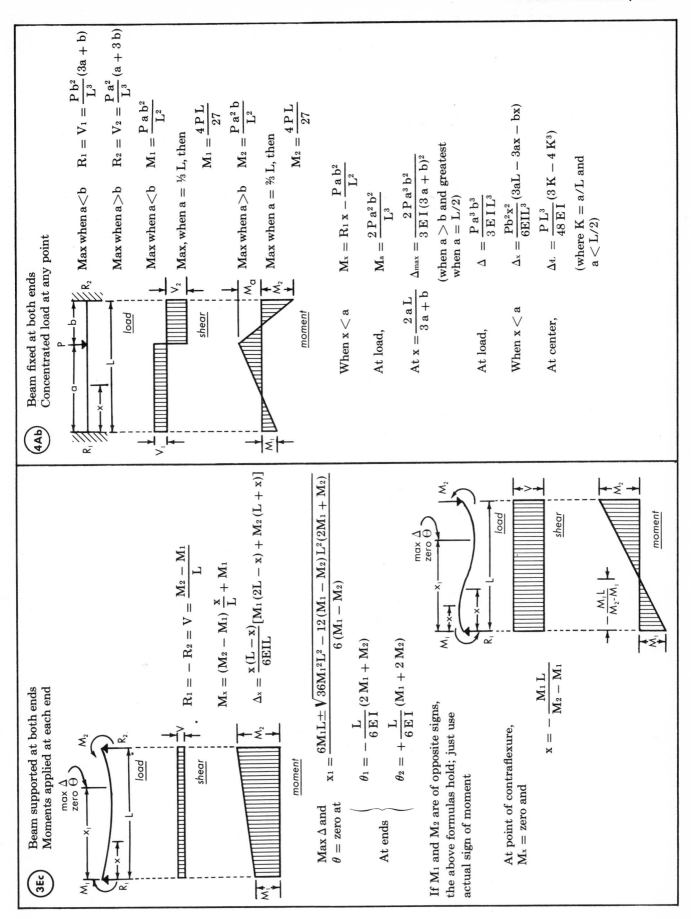

4Ab Beam fixed at both ends
Concentrated load at any point

$R_1 = V_1 = \dfrac{Pb^2}{L^3}(3a+b)$ Max when a<b

$R_2 = V_2 = \dfrac{Pa^2}{L^3}(a+3b)$ Max when a>b

$M_1 = \dfrac{Pab^2}{L^2}$ Max when a<b

Max, when a = ⅓ L, then $M_1 = \dfrac{4PL}{27}$

$M_2 = \dfrac{Pa^2b}{L^2}$ Max when a>b

Max when a = ⅔ L, then $M_2 = \dfrac{4PL}{27}$

When x < a, $M_x = R_1x - \dfrac{Pab^2}{L^2}$

At load, $M_a = \dfrac{2Pa^2b^2}{L^3}$

At x = $\dfrac{2aL}{3a+b}$, $\Delta_{max} = \dfrac{2Pa^3b^2}{3EIL(3a+b)^2}$

(when a > b and greatest when a = L/2)

At load, $\Delta = \dfrac{Pa^3b^3}{3EIL^3}$

When x < a, $\Delta_x = \dfrac{Pb^2x^2}{6EIL^3}(3aL - 3ax - bx)$

At center, $\Delta_{\mathfrak{c}} = \dfrac{PL^3}{48EI}(3K - 4K^3)$

(where K = a/L and a < L/2)

3Ec Beam supported at both ends
Moments applied at each end

$R_1 = -R_2 = V = \dfrac{M_2 - M_1}{L}$

$M_x = (M_2 - M_1)\dfrac{x}{L} + M_1$

$\Delta_x = \dfrac{x(L-x)}{6EIL}[M_1(2L-x) + M_2(L+x)]$

Max Δ and θ = zero at

$x_1 = \dfrac{6M_1L \pm \sqrt{36M_1^2L^2 - 12(M_1 - M_2)L^2(2M_1 + M_2)}}{6(M_1 - M_2)}$

At ends
$\theta_1 = -\dfrac{L}{6EI}(2M_1 + M_2)$

$\theta_2 = +\dfrac{L}{6EI}(M_1 + 2M_2)$

If M₁ and M₂ are of opposite signs,
the above formulas hold; just use
actual sign of moment

At point of contraflexure,
Mx = zero and

$x = -\dfrac{M_1L}{M_2 - M_1}$

(4Ab)   Influence Lines

Effect of position of force (F) upon moments M_a, M_1, M_2 and upon Δ_{max}

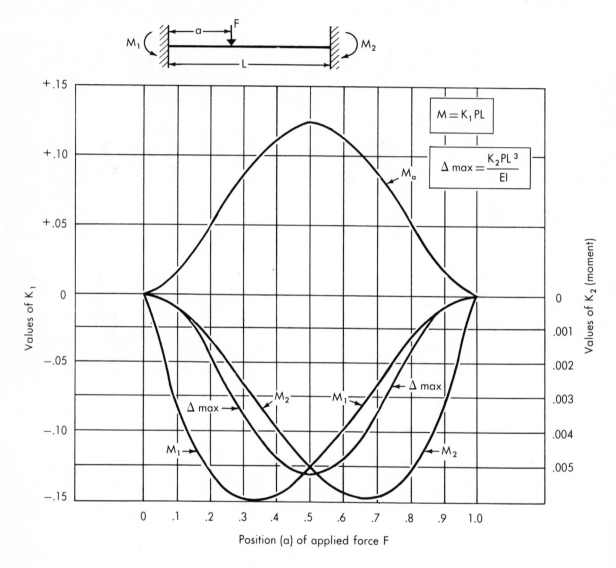

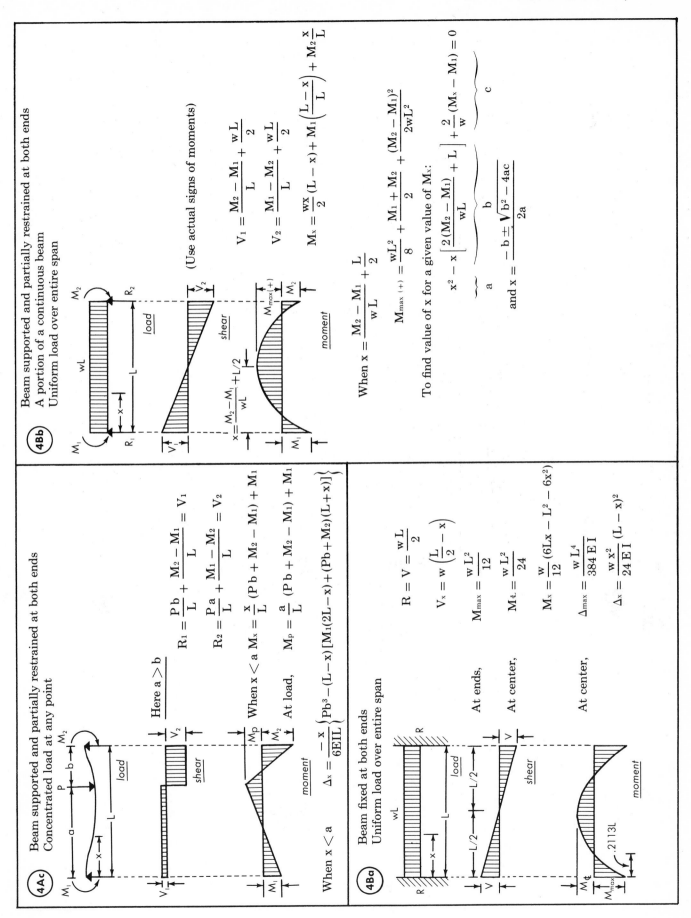

4Bb Beam supported and partially restrained at both ends
A portion of a continuous beam
Uniform load over entire span

(Use actual signs of moments)

$$V_1 = \frac{M_2 - M_1}{L} + \frac{wL}{2}$$

$$V_2 = \frac{M_1 - M_2}{L} + \frac{wL}{2}$$

$$M_x = \frac{wx}{2}(L-x) + M_1\left(\frac{L-x}{L}\right) + M_2\frac{x}{L}$$

When $x = \dfrac{M_2 - M_1}{wL} + \dfrac{L}{2}$

$$M_{max\,(+)} = \frac{wL^2}{8} + \frac{M_1 + M_2}{2} + \frac{(M_2 - M_1)^2}{2wL^2}$$

To find value of x for a given value of M_x:

$$x^2 - x\underbrace{\left[\frac{2(M_2-M_1)}{wL} + L\right]}_{b} + \underbrace{\frac{2}{w}(M_x - M_1)}_{c} = 0$$

$$\text{and } x = \frac{-b \pm \sqrt{b^2 - 4ac}}{2a}$$

4Ac Beam supported and partially restrained at both ends
Concentrated load at any point

Here a > b

$$R_1 = \frac{Pb}{L} + \frac{M_2 - M_1}{L} = V_1$$

$$R_2 = \frac{Pa}{L} + \frac{M_1 - M_2}{L} = V_2$$

When $x < a$ $M_x = \dfrac{x}{L}(Pb + M_2 - M_1) + M_1$

At load, $M_p = \dfrac{a}{L}(Pb + M_2 - M_1) + M_1$

When $x < a$ $\Delta_x = \dfrac{-x}{6EIL}\left\{Pb^3 - (L-x)[M_1(2L-x)+(L-x)(Pb+M_2)(L+x)]\right\}$

4Ba Beam fixed at both ends
Uniform load over entire span

$$R = V = \frac{wL}{2}$$

$$V_x = w\left(\frac{L}{2} - x\right)$$

At ends, $M_{max} = \dfrac{wL^2}{12}$

At center, $M_{\text{cl}} = \dfrac{wL^2}{24}$

$$M_x = \frac{w}{12}(6Lx - L^2 - 6x^2)$$

At center, $\Delta_{max} = \dfrac{wL^4}{384EI}$

$$\Delta_x = \frac{wx^2}{24EI}(L-x)^2$$

.2113L

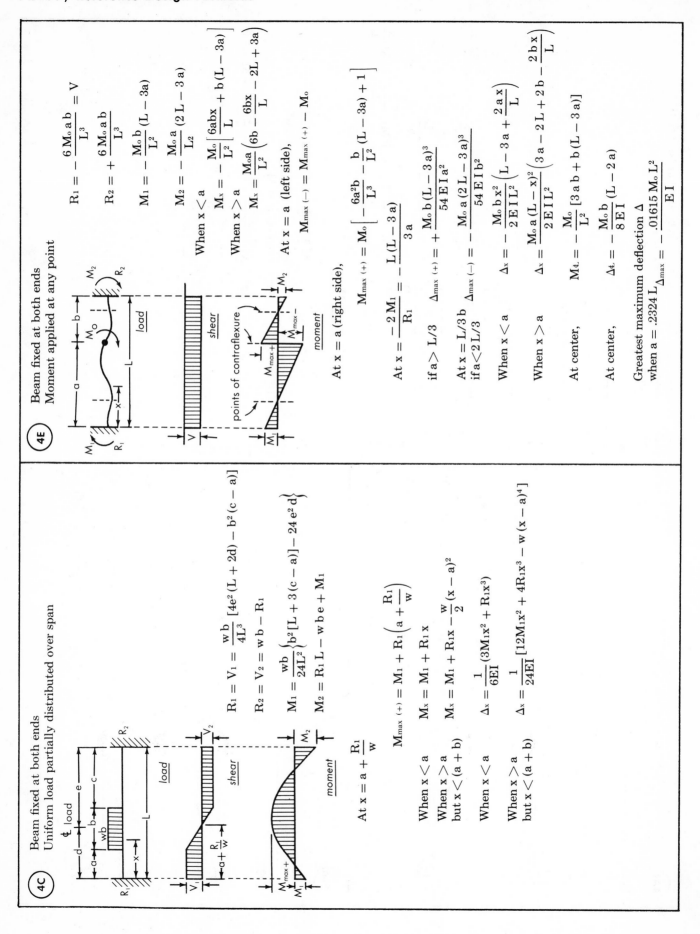

4E Beam fixed at both ends
Moment applied at any point

$$R_1 = -\frac{6 M_o a b}{L^3} = V$$

$$R_2 = +\frac{6 M_o a b}{L^3}$$

$$M_1 = -\frac{M_o b}{L^2}(L - 3a)$$

$$M_2 = -\frac{M_o a}{L^2}(2L - 3a)$$

When $x < a$

$$M_x = -\frac{M_o}{L^2}\left[\frac{6abx}{L} + b(L - 3a)\right]$$

When $x > a$

$$M_x = \frac{M_o a}{L^2}\left(6b - \frac{6bx}{L} - 2L + 3a\right)$$

At $x = a$ (left side),

$$M_{max\,(-)} = M_{max\,(+)} - M_o$$

At $x = a$ (right side),

$$M_{max\,(+)} = M_o\left[-\frac{6a^2b}{L^3} - \frac{b}{L^2}(L - 3a) + 1\right]$$

$$At\ x = \frac{-2 M_1}{R_1} = -\frac{L(L - 3a)}{3a}$$

if $a > L/3$ $\qquad \Delta_{max\,(+)} = +\frac{M_o b(L - 3a)^3}{54 E I a^2}$

At $x = L/3b$
if $a < 2L/3$ $\qquad \Delta_{max\,(-)} = -\frac{M_o a(2L - 3a)^3}{54 E I b^2}$

When $x < a$ $\qquad \Delta_x = -\frac{M_o b x^2}{2 E I L^2}\left(L - 3a + \frac{2ax}{L}\right)$

When $x > a$ $\qquad \Delta_x = \frac{M_o a(L - x)^2}{2 E I L^2}\left(3a - 2L + 2b - \frac{2bx}{L}\right)$

At center, $\qquad M_{¢} = -\frac{M_o}{L^2}[3ab + b(L - 3a)]$

At center, $\qquad \Delta_{¢} = -\frac{M_o b}{8 E I}(L - 2a)$

Greatest maximum deflection Δ
when $a = .2324 L$ $\Delta_{max} = -\frac{.01615\ M_o\ L^2}{E I}$

4C Beam fixed at both ends
Uniform load partially distributed over span

$$R_1 = V_1 = \frac{w b}{4 L^3}[4e^2(L + 2d) - b^2(c - a)]$$

$$R_2 = V_2 = w b - R_1$$

$$M_1 = \frac{w b}{24 L^2}\left\{b^2[L + 3(c - a)] - 24 e^2 d\right\}$$

$$M_2 = R_1 L - w b e + M_1$$

$$M_{max\,(+)} = M_1 + R_1\left(a + \frac{R_1}{w}\right)$$

$$M_x = M_1 + R_1 x$$

$$M_x = M_1 + R_1 x - \frac{w}{2}(x - a)^2$$

$$\Delta_x = \frac{1}{6EI}(3M_1 x^2 + R_1 x^3)$$

$$\Delta_x = \frac{1}{24EI}[12M_1 x^2 + 4R_1 x^3 - w(x - a)^4]$$

$$At\ x = a + \frac{R_1}{w}$$

When $x < a$

When $x > a$
but $x < (a + b)$

When $x < a$

When $x > a$
but $x < (a + b)$

4 E Influence Lines

Effect of position of moment (M_O) upon M_1, M_2, $M+$ and $M-$

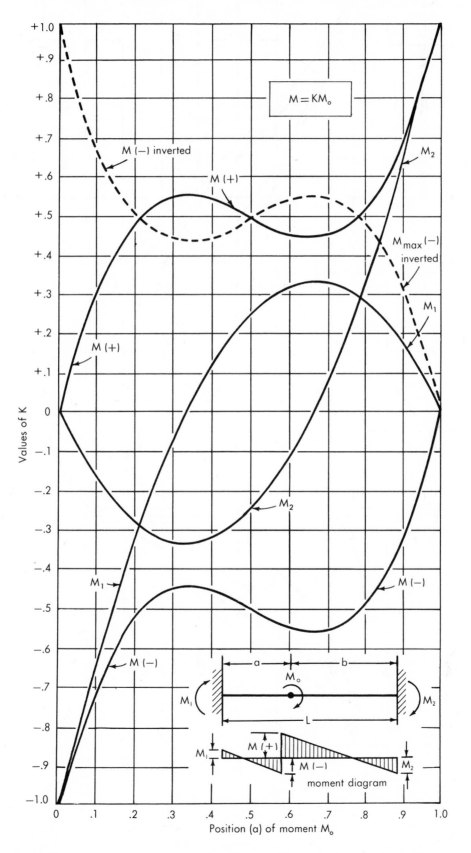

$$M = KM_o$$

Position (a) of moment M_o

Values of K

Influence Line for Maximum Deflection

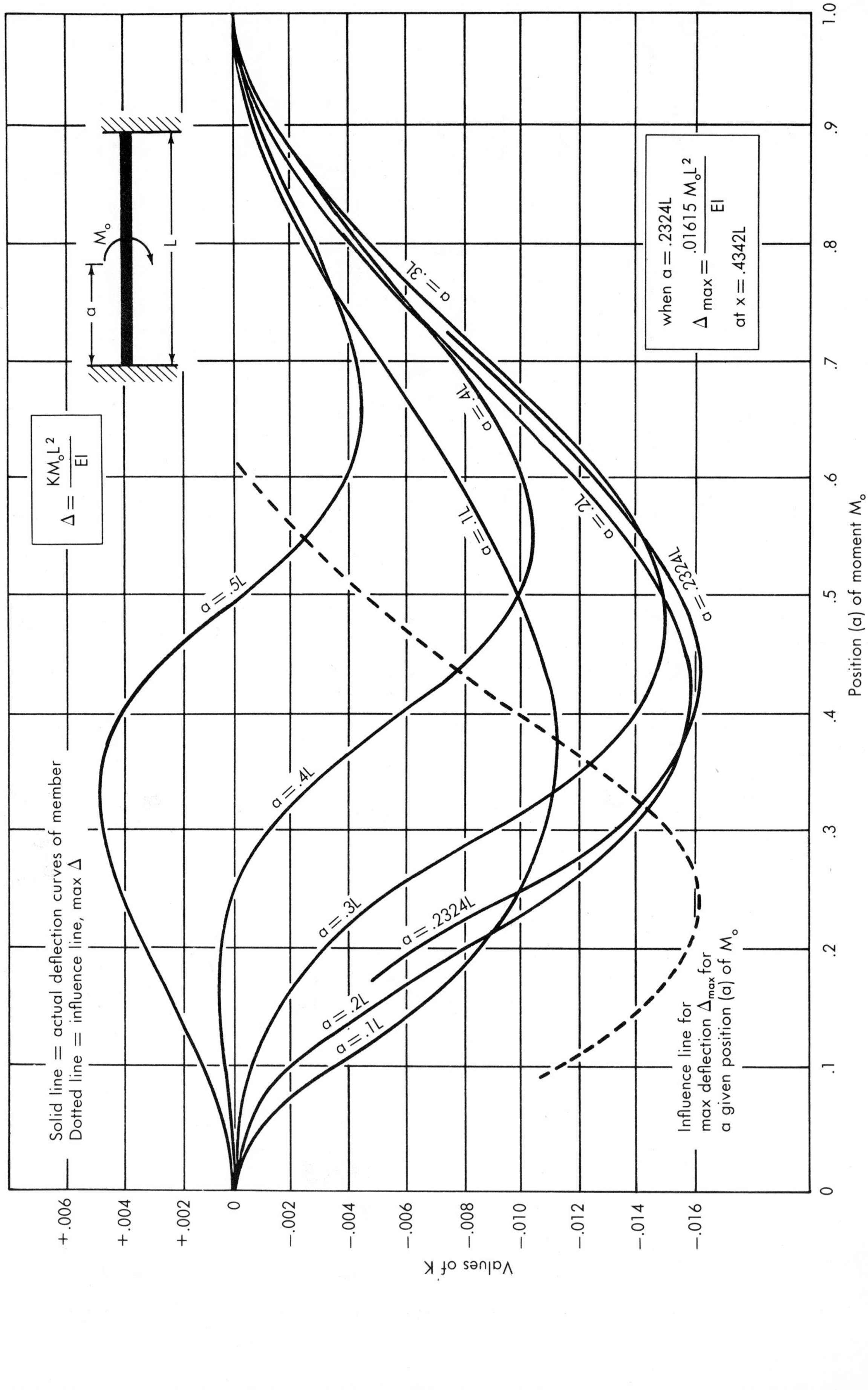

$$\Delta = \frac{KM_o L^2}{EI}$$

Solid line = actual deflection curves of member
Dotted line = influence line, max Δ

when $a = .2324L$
$$\Delta_{max} = \frac{.01615\, M_o L^2}{EI}$$
at $x = .4342L$

a = .5L

a = .4L

a = .3L

a = .2324L

a = .2L

a = .1L

a = .1L

a = .2L

a = .2324L

a = .3L

a = .4L

Influence line for max deflection Δ_{max} for a given position (a) of M_o

Position (a) of moment M_o

Values of K

+.006
+.004
+.002
0
−.002
−.004
−.006
−.008
−.010
−.012
−.014
−.016

0   .1   .2   .3   .4   .5   .6   .7   .8   .9   1.0

(4 E)

(5Ab) Beam fixed at one end and supported at the other end
Concentrated load at any point

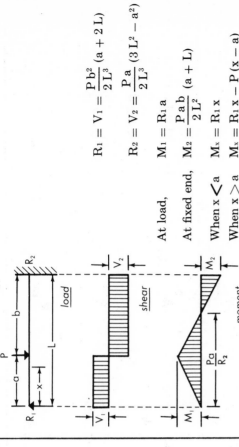

$$R_1 = V_1 = \frac{Pb^2}{2L^3}(a + 2L)$$

$$R_2 = V_2 = \frac{Pa}{2L^3}(3L^2 - a^2)$$

At load, $\quad M_1 = R_1 a$

At fixed end, $\quad M_2 = \frac{Pab}{2L^2}(a + L)$

When $x < a$ $\quad M_x = R_1 x$

When $x > a$ $\quad M_x = R_1 x - P(x - a)$

$$\Delta_{max} = \frac{Pa}{3EI}\frac{(L^2 - a^2)^3}{(3L^2 - a^2)^2} \quad \text{when} \quad a < .414\,L$$

At $x = L\sqrt{\dfrac{L^2 + a^2}{3L^2 - a^2}}$

$$\Delta_{max} = \frac{Pab^2}{6EI}\sqrt{\frac{a}{2L+a}}\,(3L+a) \quad \text{when} \quad a > .414\,L$$

At $x = L\sqrt{\dfrac{a}{2L+a}}$

At load, $\quad \Delta = \dfrac{Pa^2 b^3}{12EIL^3}(3L + a)$

When $x < a$ $\quad \Delta_x = \dfrac{Pb^2 x}{12EIL^3}(3aL^2 - 2Lx^2 - ax^2)$

When $x > a$ $\quad \Delta_x = \dfrac{Pa}{12EIL^3}(L - x)^2(3L^2 x - a^2 x - 2a^2 L)$

(5Aa) Beam fixed at one end and supported at the other end
Concentrated load at mid-span

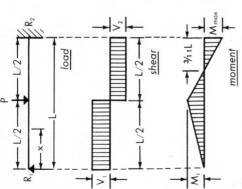

$$R_1 = V_1 = \frac{5P}{16}$$

$$R_2 = V_{2\,max} = \frac{11P}{16}$$

At fixed end, $\quad M_{max} = \dfrac{3PL}{16}$

At load, $\quad M_1 = \dfrac{5PL}{32}$

When $x < L/2$ $\quad M_x = \dfrac{5Px}{16}$

When $x > L/2$ $\quad M_x = P\left(\dfrac{L}{2} - \dfrac{11x}{16}\right)$

At $x = L\sqrt{.2} = .4472\,L,$

$$\Delta_{max} = \frac{PL^3}{48EI\sqrt{5}} = .009317\,\frac{PL^3}{EI}$$

At load, $\quad \Delta = \dfrac{7PL^3}{768\,EI}$

When $x < L/2$ $\quad \Delta_x = \dfrac{Px}{96\,EI}(3L^2 - 5x^2)$

When $x > L/2$ $\quad \Delta_x = \dfrac{P}{96EI}(x - L)^2(11x - 2L)$

5C — Beam fixed at one end and supported at the other end. Uniform load partially distributed over span

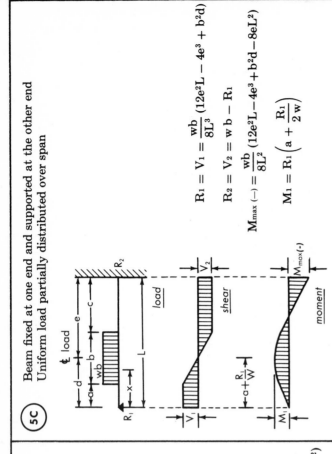

$$R_1 = V_1 = \frac{wb}{8L^3}(12e^2L - 4e^3 + b^2d)$$

$$R_2 = V_2 = wb - R_1$$

$$M_{max\,(-)} = \frac{wb}{8L^2}(12e^2L - 4e^3 + b^2d - 8eL^2)$$

$$M_1 = R_1\left(a + \frac{R_1}{2w}\right)$$

When $x < a$: $M_x = R_1 x$

When $x > a$ but $x < (a+b)$: $M_x = R_1 x - \frac{w}{2}(x-a)^2$

When $x > (a+b)$ but $x < L$: $M_x = R_1 x - wb(x-d)$

When $x < a$: $\Delta_x = \frac{x}{24EI}[4R_1(x^2 - 3L^2) + wb(b^2 + 12e^2)]$

When $x > a$ but $x < (a+b)$: $\Delta_x = \frac{1}{24EI}[4R_1x(x^2 - 3L^2) + wbx(b^2 + 12e^2) - w(x-a)^4]$

When $x > (a+b)$ but $x < L$: $\Delta_x = \frac{1}{6EI}[3M_{max}(L-x)^2 + R_2(L-x)^3]$

5B — Beam fixed at one end and supported at the other end. Uniform load over entire span

$$R_1 = V_1 = \frac{3wL}{8}$$

$$R_2 = V_2 = \frac{5wL}{8}$$

$$V_x = R_1 - wx$$

$$M_{max} = \frac{wL^2}{8}$$

At $x = 3/8\,L$, $\qquad M_1 = \frac{9}{128}wL^2$

$$M_x = R_1 x - \frac{wx^2}{2}$$

At $x = \frac{L}{16}(1 + \sqrt{33}) = .4215\,L$,

$$\Delta_{max} = \frac{wL^4}{185EI}$$

$$\Delta_x = \frac{wx}{48EI}(L^3 - 3Lx^2 + 2x^3)$$

$$\theta_1 = \frac{wL^3}{48EI}$$

5E — Beam fixed at one end and supported at the other end. Moment applied at the flexible end

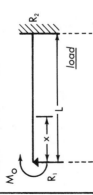

$$R_1 = R_2 = V = \frac{3M_o}{2L}$$

$$M_1 = M_o$$

$$M_2 = 1/2\,M_o$$

$$M_x = \frac{M_o}{2L}(2L - 3x)$$

At $x = L/3$, $\qquad \Delta_{max} = \frac{M_o L^2}{27EI}$

$$\Delta_x = \frac{M_o x}{4EIL}(L-x)^2$$

At supported end, $\quad \theta = -\frac{M_o L}{4EI}$

6Ab

Single span, simply supported beam, with overhang
Concentrated load at outer end

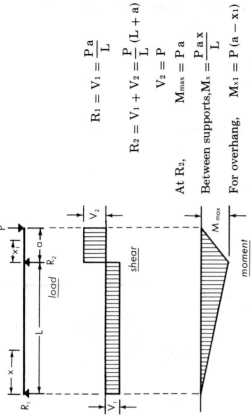

$$R_1 = V_1 = \frac{Pa}{L}$$

$$R_2 = V_1 + V_2 = \frac{P}{L} = \frac{P}{L}(L+a)$$

$$V_2 = P$$

At R_2, $\quad M_{max} = Pa$

Between supports, $M_x = \frac{Pax}{L}$

For overhang, $\quad M_{x1} = P(a - x_1)$

Between supports at $x = L/\sqrt{3}$,

$$\Delta_{max} = -\frac{PaL^2}{9\sqrt{3}EI}$$

For overhang $x_1 = a$, $\quad \Delta_{max} = \frac{Pa^2}{3EI}(L+a)$

Between supports, $\quad \Delta_x = -\frac{Pax}{6EIL}(L^2 - x^2)$

For overhang, $\quad \Delta_{x1} = \frac{Px_1}{6EI}(2aL + 3ax_1 - x_1^2)$

6Aa

Single span, simply supported beam, with overhang
Concentrated load at any point between supports

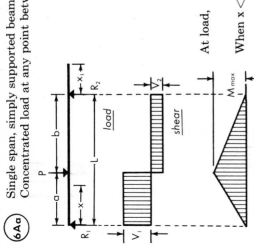

$$R_1 = V_1\left(\begin{array}{c}\max \\ \text{when} \\ a < b\end{array}\right) = \frac{Pb}{L}$$

$$R_2 = V_2\left(\begin{array}{c}\max \\ \text{when} \\ a > b\end{array}\right) = \frac{Pa}{L}$$

$$M_{max} = \frac{Pab}{L}$$

$$M_x = \frac{Pbx}{L}$$

At $x = \sqrt{\dfrac{a(a + 2b)}{3}}$

$$\Delta_{max} = \frac{Pab(a+2b)\sqrt{3a(a+2b)}}{27EIL} \quad \begin{array}{c}\text{when}\\ a > b\end{array}$$

At load, $\quad \Delta = \frac{Pa^2b^2}{3EIL}$

When $x < a$ $\quad \Delta_x = \frac{Pbx}{6EIL}(L^2 - b^2 - x^2)$

When $x > a$ $\quad \Delta_x = \frac{Pa(L-x)}{6EIL}(2Lx - x^2 - a^2)$

For overhang, $\quad \Delta_{x1} = -\frac{Pabx_1}{6EIL}(L+a)$

(6Ba) Single span, simply supported beam, with overhang
Uniform load over entire beam

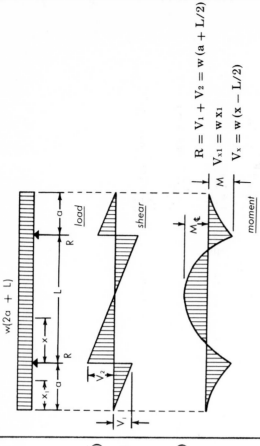

$$R_1 = V_1 = \frac{w}{2L}(L^2 - a^2)$$

$$R_2 = V_2 + V_3 = \frac{w}{2L}(L + a)^2$$

$$V_2 = wa$$

$$V_3 = \frac{w}{2L}(L^2 + a^2)$$

Between supports, $\quad V_x = R_1 - wx$

For overhang, $\quad V_{x1} = w(a - x_1)$

At $x = \frac{1}{2}\left(L - \frac{a^2}{L}\right)$

$$M_1 = \frac{w}{8L^2}(L^2 - a^2)^2$$

At R_2, $\quad M_2 = \frac{wa^2}{2}$

Between supports, $M_x = \frac{wx}{2L}(L^2 - a^2 - xL)$

For overhang, $\quad M_{x1} = \frac{w}{2}(a - x_1)^2$

Between supports, $\Delta_x = \frac{wx}{24EI}(L^4 - 2L^2x^2 + Lx^3 - 2a^2L^2 + 2a^2x^2)$

For overhang, $\Delta_{x1} = \frac{wx_1}{24EI}(4a^2L - L^3 + 6a^2x_1 - 4ax_1^2 + x_1^3)$

At free end, $\quad \Delta = \frac{wa}{24EI}(3a^3 + 4a^2L - L^3)$

When $a = .414\,L$, $M_1 = M_2 = .08579\,wL^2$

(6Bb) Single span beam, overhanging at both ends
Uniform load over entire beam

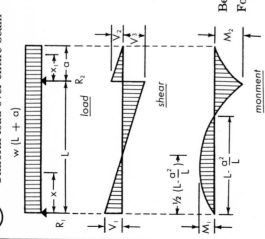

$$R = V_1 + V_2 = w(a + L/2)$$

$$V_{x1} = w\,x_1$$

$$V_x = w(x - L/2)$$

For overhang, $\quad M_{x1} = \frac{w\,x_1^2}{2}$

At support, $\quad M = \frac{w\,a^2}{2}$

Between supports, $M_x = \frac{w}{2}(Lx - x^2 - a^2)$

At center, $\quad M_{\mathbb{C}} = \frac{w}{8}(L^2 - 4a^2)$

At ends, $\quad \Delta = \frac{wa}{24EI}(L^3 - 6a^2L - 3a^3)$

At center, $\quad \Delta_{\mathbb{C}} = \frac{wL^2}{384EI}(5L^2 - 24a^2)$

When $a = .207 \times$ total length or $a = .354\,L$

$$M = M_{\mathbb{C}} = \frac{w\,L^2}{16}$$

6Cb Single span, simply supported beam, with overhang
Uniform load on overhang

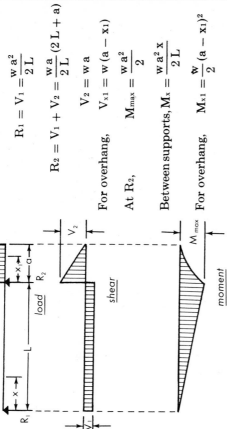

$$R_1 = V_1 = \frac{w\,a^2}{2\,L}$$

$$R_2 = V_1 + V_2 = \frac{w\,a}{2\,L}(2\,L + a)$$

$$V_2 = w\,a$$

For overhang, $\quad V_{x1} = w\,(a - x_1)$

At R_2, $\quad M_{max} = \dfrac{w\,a^2}{2}$

Between supports, $M_x = \dfrac{w\,a^2\,x}{2\,L}$

For overhang, $\quad M_{x1} = \dfrac{w}{2}\,(a - x_1)^2$

At $x = L/\sqrt{3}$, $\quad \Delta_{max} = -\dfrac{w\,a^2\,L^2}{18\sqrt{3}\,E\,I}$

At free end, $\quad \Delta_{max} = \dfrac{w\,a^3}{24\,E\,I}(4\,L + 3\,a)$

Between supports, $\Delta_x = -\dfrac{w\,a^2\,x}{12\,E\,I\,L}(L^2 - x^2)$

For overhang, $\quad \Delta_{x1} = \dfrac{w\,x_1}{24\,E\,I}(4a^2L + 6a^2x_1 - 4ax_1^2 + x_1^3)$

6Ca Single span, simple supported beam, with overhang
Uniform load over entire span

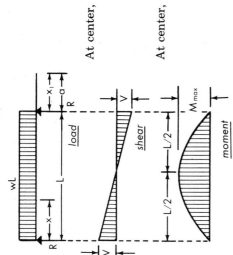

$$R = V = \frac{w\,L}{2}$$

$$V_x = w\left(\frac{L}{2} - x\right)$$

At center, $\quad M_{max} = \dfrac{w \cdot L^2}{8}$

$$M_x = \frac{w\,x}{2}(L - x)$$

At center, $\quad \Delta_{max} = \dfrac{5\,w\,L^4}{384\,E\,I}$

$$\Delta_x = \frac{w\,x}{24\,E\,I}(L^3 - 2Lx^2 + x^3)$$

$$\Delta_{x1} = \frac{w\,L^3\,x_1}{24\,E\,I}$$

⑦ THEORY OF THREE MOMENTS

Consider the following continuous beam:

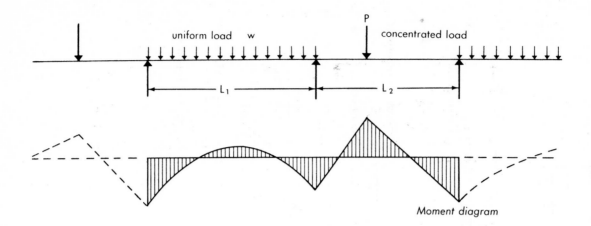

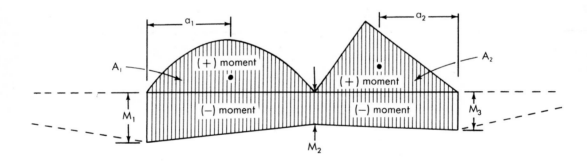

The above moment diagram may be considered as made up of two parts: the positive moment due to the applied loads, and the negative moment due to the restraining end moments over the supports.

For any two adjacent spans, the following relationship is true:

$$+ \frac{M_1 L_1}{6\,EI_1} + \frac{M_2}{3\,E}\left(\frac{L_1}{I_1} + \frac{L_2}{I_2}\right) + \frac{M_3 L_2}{6\,E I_2} + \frac{A_1 a_1}{E I_1 L_1} + \frac{A_2 a_2}{E I_2 L_2} = 0$$

where:

    M_1, M_2, and M_3 are the end moments at the 1st, 2nd, and 3rd supports.

    L_1 and L_2 are the lengths of the 1st and 2nd span.

    I_1 and I_2 are the moments of inertia of the 1st and 2nd span.

    A_1 and A_2 are the areas under the positive moment diagrams of the 1st and 2nd span.

    a_1 and a_2 are the distance of the centroids of the areas of the positive moment diagrams to the 1st and 3rd outer supports.

By writing this equation for each successive pair of spans, all of the moments may be found.

The moment diagram for a simply supported, uniformly loaded beam is a parabola; and a concentrated load produces a triangular moment diagram. The following shows the area and distance to the centroid of these areas.

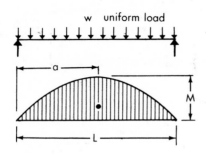

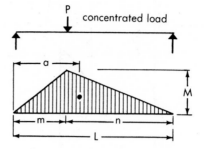

Area

$$A = 2/3\,M\,L$$

Distance to centroid

$$a = L/2$$

Area

$$A = 1/2\,M\,L$$

Distance to centroid

$$a = \frac{m + L}{3}$$

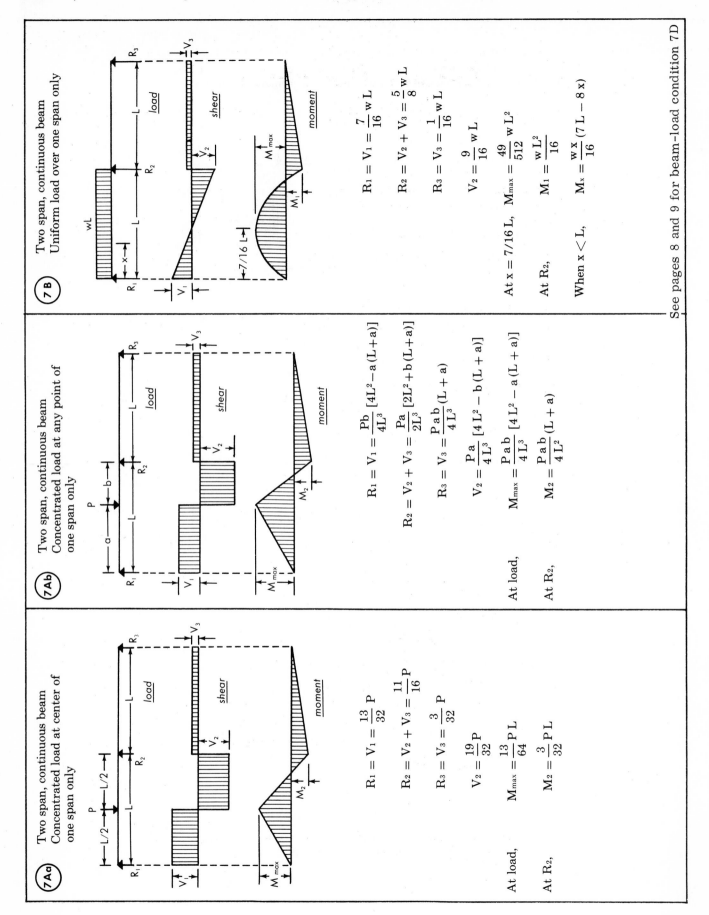

7Aa

Two span, continuous beam
Concentrated load at center of
one span only

load

shear

moment

$$R_1 = V_1 = \frac{13}{32}\,P$$

$$R_2 = V_2 + V_3 = \frac{11}{16}\,P$$

$$R_3 = V_3 = \frac{3}{32}\,P$$

$$V_2 = \frac{19}{32}\,P$$

At load, $M_{max} = \frac{13}{64}\,PL$

At R_2, $M_2 = \frac{3}{32}\,PL$

7Ab

Two span, continuous beam
Concentrated load at any point of
one span only

load

shear

moment

$$R_1 = V_1 = \frac{Pb}{4L^3}\,[4L^2 - a(L+a)]$$

$$R_2 = V_2 + V_3 = \frac{Pa}{2L^3}\,[2L^2 + b(L+a)]$$

$$R_3 = V_3 = \frac{Pab}{4L^3}\,(L+a)$$

$$V_2 = \frac{Pa}{4L^3}\,[4L^2 - b(L+a)]$$

At load, $M_{max} = \frac{Pab}{4L^3}\,[4L^2 - a(L+a)]$

At R_2, $M_2 = \frac{Pab}{4L^2}\,(L+a)$

7B

Two span, continuous beam
Uniform load over one span only

load

shear

moment

$$R_1 = V_1 = \frac{7}{16}\,wL$$

$$R_2 = V_2 + V_3 = \frac{5}{8}\,wL$$

$$R_3 = V_3 = \frac{1}{16}\,wL$$

$$V_2 = \frac{9}{16}\,wL$$

At $x = 7/16\,L$, $M_{max} = \frac{49}{512}\,wL^2$

At R_2, $M_1 = \frac{wL^2}{16}$

When $x < L$, $M_x = \frac{wx}{16}\,(7L - 8x)$

See pages 8 and 9 for beam-load condition 7D

Circular Flat Plates

The following table of formulas is for stress and deflection of circular flat steel plates.   (Poisson's ratio = .3)

σ_r = tensile stress in radial direction (psi)

σ_t = tensile stress in tangential direction (psi)

t = thickness of plate (inches)

r = outer radius of plate (inches)

r_1 = inner radius of plate (inches)

E = modulus of elasticity (for steel = 30,000,000 psi)

W = total load on plate (pounds)

p = uniform load on plate (psi)

M = couple or moment applied to central portion (inch-lbs)

log to the base (e) (Natural or Naperian logarithms):

$\log_e x = 2.3026 \log_{10} x$

A positive sign for the stress indicates tension on the top surface and compression on the lower surface.

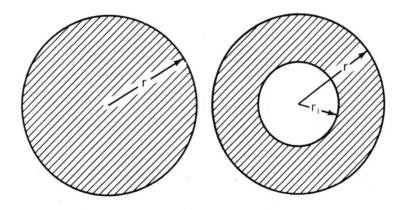

Adapted from Roark "Formulas for Stress and Strain", and Timoshenko "Theory of Plates and Shells".

(1) Outer edge fixed and supported
Uniform load over entire area

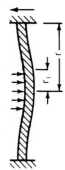

At center, $\sigma_r = \sigma_t = -\dfrac{39\,p}{80}\left(\dfrac{r}{t}\right)^2$

At edge, $\text{Max } \sigma_r = \dfrac{3\,p}{4}\left(\dfrac{r}{t}\right)^2$

At center, $\text{Max } \Delta = -\dfrac{273\,p\,r^4}{1600\,E\,t^3}$

---

(3) Outer edge supported
Uniform load over entire area

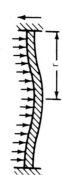

At center, $\text{Max } \sigma_r = \sigma_t = -\dfrac{99\,p}{80}\left(\dfrac{r}{t}\right)^2$

At center, $\text{Max } \Delta = -\dfrac{1113\,p\,r^4}{1600\,E\,t^3}$

At edge, $\theta = \dfrac{21\,p}{20\,E}\left(\dfrac{r}{t}\right)^3$

---

(2) Outer edge fixed and supported
Uniform load over concentric circular area of radius r_1

At center (max when $r_1 < .588\,r$),
$$\sigma_r = \sigma_t = -\frac{3\,p}{80}\left(\frac{r_1}{t}\right)^2\left[52\log\frac{r}{r_1} + 13\left(\frac{r_1}{r}\right)^2\right]$$

At edge (max when $r_1 > .588\,r$),
$$\sigma_r = \frac{3\,p}{4}\left(\frac{r_1}{t\,r}\right)^2(2\,r^2 - r_1^2)$$

At edge, $\sigma_t = \dfrac{9\,p}{40}\left(\dfrac{r_1}{t\,r}\right)^2(2\,r^2 - r_1^2)$

At center, $\text{Max } \Delta = -\dfrac{273\,p\,r_1^2}{1600\,E\,t^3}\left(4\,r^2 - 3\,r_1^2 - 4\,r_1^2\log\dfrac{r}{r_1}\right)$

<u>When r_1 is very small (concentrated load)</u>

At center, $\text{Max } \Delta = -\dfrac{273\,W\,r^2}{400\,\pi\,E\,t^3}$

For stress, Roark suggests using the following in which r_e is equal to either r_1 or the effective radius $\left(\sqrt{1.6\,r_1^2 + t^2} - .675\,t\right)$ whichever is largest:

At center, $\text{Max } \sigma_r = \sigma_t = -\dfrac{3\,W}{80\,\pi\,t^2}\left[52\log\dfrac{r}{r_e} + 13\left(\dfrac{r_e}{r}\right)^2\right]$

At edge, $\sigma_t = \dfrac{9\,W}{40\,\pi\,t^2\,r^2}(2\,r^2 - r_b^2)$

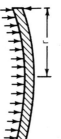
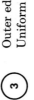

5 Outer edge supported
Uniform load on concentric circular ring of radius r₁

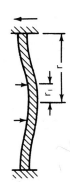

At $< r_1$,　Max $\sigma_r = \sigma_t = -\dfrac{3\,W}{40\,\pi\,t^2}\left[7 + 26 \log \dfrac{r}{r_1} - 7\left(\dfrac{r_1}{r}\right)^2\right]$

At center,　Max $\Delta = -\dfrac{273\,W}{5200\,\pi\,E\,t^3}\left[33\,(r^2 - r_1^2) - 26\,r_1^2 \log \dfrac{r}{r_1}\right]$

---

6 Outer edge fixed and supported
Uniform load on concentric circular ring of radius r₁

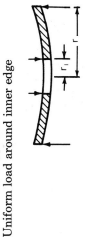

At $< r_1$ (max when $r_1 < .31\,r$),

$$\sigma_r = \sigma_t = -\dfrac{39\,W}{40\,\pi\,t^2}\left[2 \log \dfrac{r}{r_1} + \left(\dfrac{r_1}{r}\right)^2 - 1\right]$$

At edge (max when $r_1 > .31\,r$),

$$\sigma_r = \dfrac{3\,W}{2\,\pi\,t^3}\left[1 - \left(\dfrac{r_1}{r}\right)^2\right]$$

At edge,　$\sigma_t = \dfrac{9\,W}{20\,\pi\,t^2}\left[1 - \left(\dfrac{r_1}{r}\right)^2\right]$

At center,　Max $\Delta = -\dfrac{273\,W}{400\,\pi\,E\,t^3}\left(r^2 - r_1^2 - 2\,r_1^2 \log \dfrac{r}{r_1}\right)$

---

4 Outer edge supported
Uniform load over concentric circular area of radius r₁

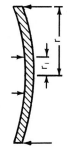

At center,　Max $\sigma_r = \sigma_t = \dfrac{3\,p}{80}\left(\dfrac{r_1}{t}\right)\left[40 + 52 \log \dfrac{r}{r_1} - 7\left(\dfrac{r_1}{r}\right)^2\right]$

At center,　Max $\Delta = -\dfrac{21\,p\,r_1^2}{1600\,E\,t^3}\left(132\,r^2 - 52\,r_1^2 \log \dfrac{r}{r_1} - 73\,r_1^2\right)$

<u>When r₁ is very small (concentrated load)</u>

At center,　Max $\Delta = -\dfrac{693\,W\,r^2}{400\,\pi\,E\,t^3}$

At edge,　$\theta = \dfrac{21\,W\,r}{10\,\pi\,E\,t^3}$

For stress, Roark suggests using the following in which
r_e is equal to either r₁ or the effective radius
$\left(\sqrt{1.6\,r_1^2 + t^2} - .675\,t\right)$ whichever is largest:

At center,　Max $\sigma_r = \sigma_t = \dfrac{3\,W}{80\,\pi\,t^2}\left[40 + 52 \log \dfrac{r}{r_e} - 7\left(\dfrac{r_e}{r}\right)^2\right]$

---

7 Outer edge supported
Uniform load around inner edge

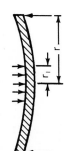

At inner edge,　Max $\sigma_r = -\dfrac{3\,W}{20\,\pi\,t^2}\left[\dfrac{26\,r^2}{(r^2 - r_1^2)} \log \dfrac{r}{r_1} + 7\right]$

At inner edge,　Max $\Delta = -\dfrac{273\,W}{36,400\,\pi\,E\,t^3}\left[231\,(r^2 - r_1^2) + \dfrac{676\,r^2\,r_1^2}{(r^2 - r_1^2)}\left(\log \dfrac{r}{r_1}\right)^2\right]$

8

Outer edge fixed and supported
Uniform load around inner edge

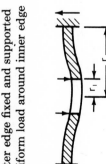

At outer edge (max when $r_1 > .416\,r$),

$$\sigma_r = \frac{3\,W}{2\,\pi\,t^2}\left[1 - \frac{20\,r_1^2 - 26\,r_1^2 \log \dfrac{r}{r_1}}{7\,r^2 + 13\,r_1^2}\right]$$

At inner edge (max when $r_1 < .416\,r$),

$$\sigma_t = \frac{9\,W}{20\,\pi\,t^2}\left[1 + \frac{70\,r^2 - 130\,r_1^2 - 182\,r^2 \log \dfrac{r}{r_1}}{21\,r^2 + 39\,r_1^2}\right]$$

At inner edge,

$$\text{Max } \Delta = -\frac{273\,W}{400\,\pi\,E\,t^3}\left[r^2 - r_1^2 + \frac{20\,r_1^2\,(r^2 - r_1^2) - 80\,r^2\,r_1^2 \log \dfrac{r}{r_1} + 52\,r^2\,r_1^2 \left(\log \dfrac{r}{r_1}\right)^2}{7\,r^2 + 13\,r_1^2}\right]$$

9

Outer edge supported; inner edge fixed
Uniform load around inner edge

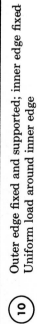

At inner edge,
$$\text{Max } \sigma_r = \frac{3\,W}{2\,\pi\,t^2}\left[\frac{7\,(r^2 - r_1^2) + 26\,r^2 \log \dfrac{r}{r_1}}{13\,r^2 + 7\,r_1^2}\right]$$

At inner edge,
$$\text{Max } \Delta = -\frac{273\,W}{400\,\pi\,E\,t^3}\left[\frac{33\,r^4 - 7\,r_1^4 - 26\,r^2\,r_1^2 - 80\,r^2\,r_1^2 \log \dfrac{r}{r_1} - 52\,r^2\,r_1^2 \left(\log \dfrac{r}{r_1}\right)^2}{13\,r^2 + 7\,r_1^2}\right]$$

10

Outer edge fixed and supported; inner edge fixed
Uniform load around inner edge

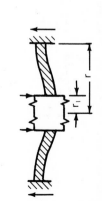

At inner edge,
$$\text{Max } \sigma_r = \frac{3\,W}{2\,\pi\,t^2}\left[1 - \frac{2\,r^2}{r^2 - r_1^2}\log \frac{r}{r_1}\right]$$

At outer edge,
$$\sigma_r = \frac{3\,W}{2\,\pi\,t^2}\left[1 - \frac{2\,r_1^2}{r^2 - r_1^2}\log \frac{r}{r_1}\right]$$

At inner edge,
$$\text{Max } \Delta = -\frac{273\,W}{400\,\pi\,E\,t^3}\left[r^2 - r_1^2 - \frac{4\,r^2\,r_1^2}{r^2 - r_1^2}\left(\log \frac{r}{r_1}\right)^2\right]$$

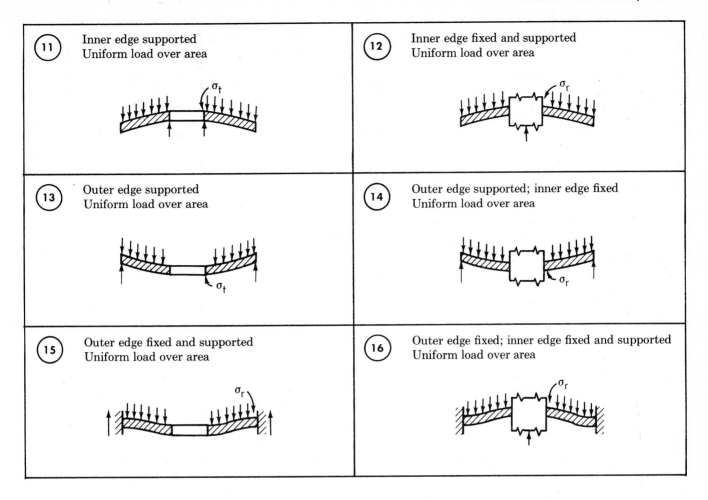

TABLE 1 – VALUES OF K FOR MAXIMUM STRESS AND DEFLECTION FORMULAS

$$\sigma_{max} = \frac{K_1 \, p \, r^2}{t^2} = \frac{K_1 \, W}{t^2}$$

$$\Delta_{max} = \frac{K_2 \, p \, r^4}{E \, t^3} = \frac{K_2 \, W \, r^2}{E \, t^3}$$

Type of disc	Type of load	$\frac{r}{r_1} = 1.25$		$\frac{r}{r_1} = 1.5$		$\frac{r}{r_1} = 2.0$		$\frac{r}{r_1} = 3.0$		$\frac{r}{r_1} = 4.0$		$\frac{r}{r_1} = 5.0$	
		K_1	K_2	K_1	K_2	K_1	K_2	K_1	K_2	K_1	K_2	K_1	K_2
5	W	.199	.136	.345	.226	.557	.338	.832	.437	1.02	.480	1.16	.501
7	W	1.10	.341	1.26	.519	1.48	.672	1.88	.734	2.17	.724	2.34	.704
8	W	.194	.00504	.320	.0242	.454	.0810	.673	.172	1.02	.217	1.305	.238
9	W	.227	.00510	.428	.0249	.753	.0877	1.205	.209	1.51	.293	1.745	.350
10	W	.115	.00129	.220	.0064	.405	.0237	.703	.062	.933	.092	1.13	.114
11	P	.660	.202	1.19	.491	2.04	.902	3.34	1.22	4.30	1.30	5.10	1.31
12	P	.135	.00231	.410	.0183	1.04	.0938	2.15	.293	2.99	.448	3.69	.564
13	P	.592	.184	.976	.414	1.44	.664	1.88	.824	2.08	.830	2.19	.813
14	P	.122	.00343	.336	.0313	.740	.1250	1.21	.291	1.45	.417	1.59	.492
15	P	.105	.00199	.259	.0139	.480	.0575	.657	.130	.710	.162	.730	.175
16	P	.090	.00077	.273	.0062	.710	.0329	1.54	.110	2.23	.179	2.80	.234

See related graphs on following pages

FIGURE 1 - K_1 CURVES FOR VARIOUS PLATE-LOAD CONDITIONS

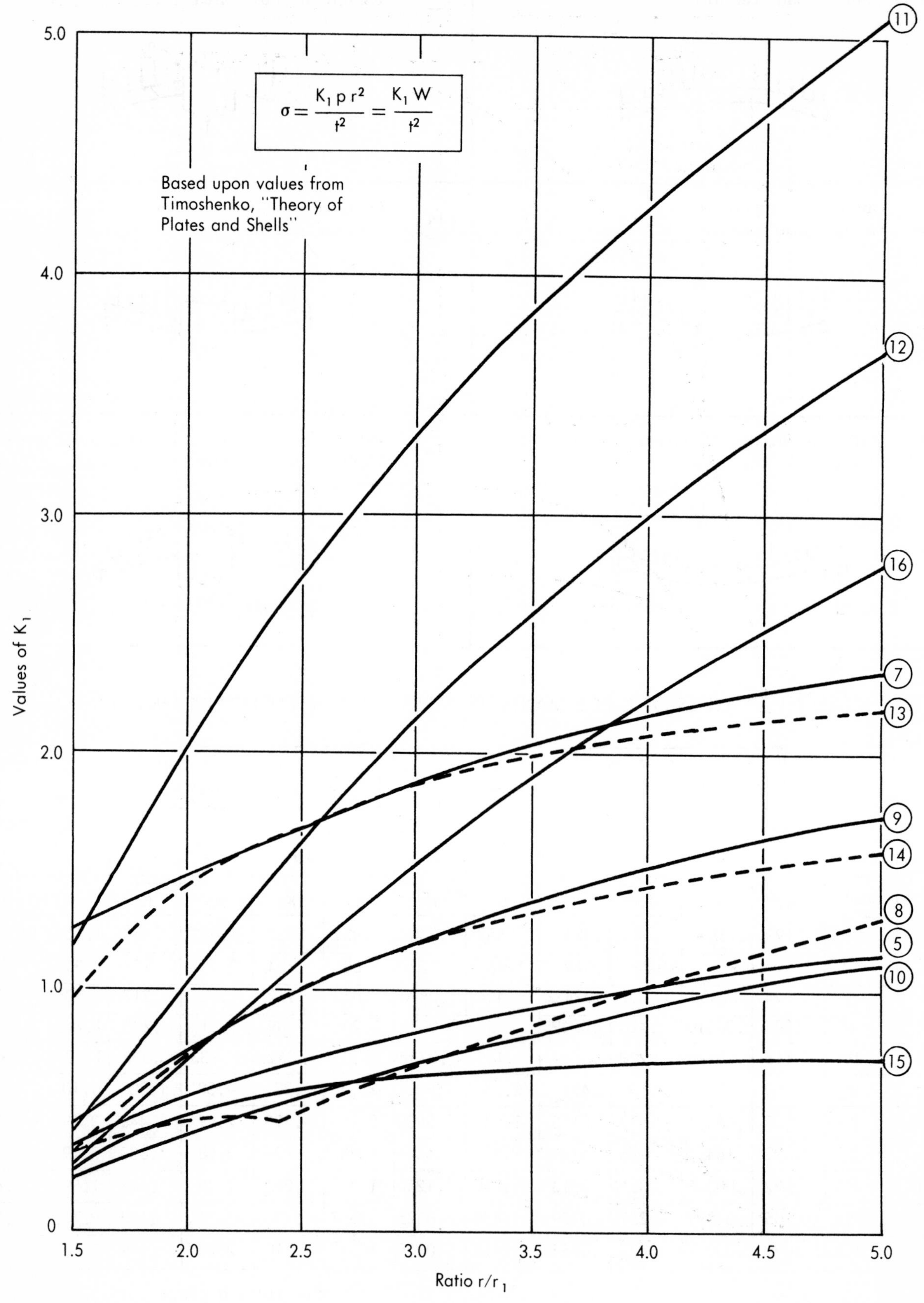
$\sigma = \frac{K_1 p r^2}{t^2} = \frac{K_1 W}{t^2}$
Based upon values from Timoshenko, "Theory of Plates and Shells"
Values of K_1
Ratio r/r_1
5.0
4.0
3.0
2.0
1.0
0
1.5
2.0
2.5
3.0
3.5
4.0
4.5
5.0
11
12
16
7
13
9
14
8
5
10
15

FIGURE 2 – K₂ CURVES FOR VARIOUS PLATE-LOAD CONDITIONS

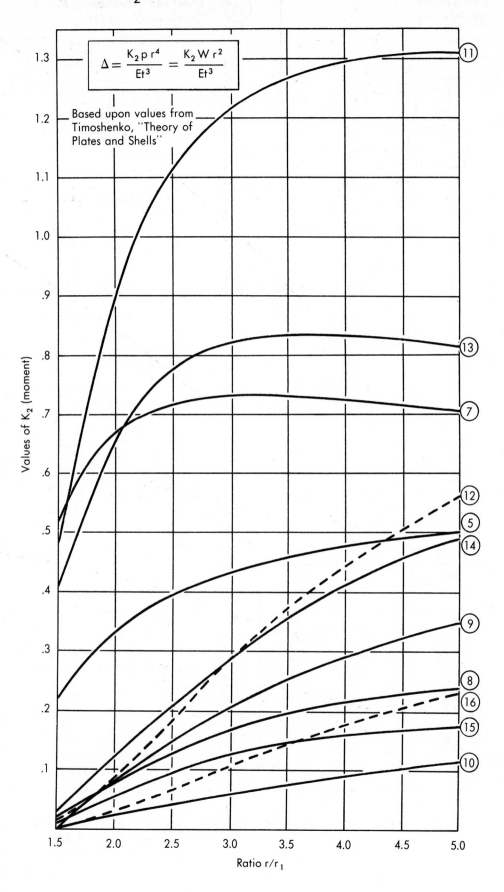

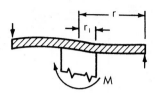

17 Outer edge supported
Couple applied at hub

At hub (r_1), $\quad$ Max $\sigma_r = \dfrac{69\,M}{40\,\pi\,r_1\,t^2}\ \log\dfrac{2\,(r-r_1)}{k\,r}$

$\qquad\qquad$ where $\quad k = \dfrac{.49\,r^2}{(.7\,r+r_1)^2}$

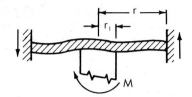

18 Outer edge fixed and supported
Couple applied at hub

At hub (r_1), $\quad$ Max $\sigma_r = \dfrac{3M}{40\,\pi\,r_1\,t^2}\left[1+1.3\ \log\dfrac{2\,(.45\,r-r_1)}{.45\,k\,r}\right]$

$\qquad\qquad$ where $\quad k = \dfrac{.1\,r^2}{(.28\,r+r_1)^2}$

TABLE 2 – VALUES FOR α AND β FOR SIMPLIFIED STRESS AND ROTATION FORMULAS

$$\text{Max } \sigma_r = \frac{\beta\,M}{r\,t^2}\ \text{(at hub)} \qquad\qquad \text{Max } \theta = \frac{\alpha\,M}{E\,t^3}\ \text{(at hub)}$$

		SUPPORTED EDGE 17			FIXED EDGE 18		
$\dfrac{r}{r_1}$	$\dfrac{r_1}{r}$	β Roark	β Timoshenko	α Timoshenko	β Roark	β Reissner	α Reissner
10.	.1	5.05	9.48	1.40	4.92	9.36	1.325
6.67	.15	3.70	6.26	1.06	3.60	6.09	.819
5.00	.20	2.75	4.62	.820	2.65	4.41	.597
4.00	.25	2.30	3.63	.643	2.20	3.37	.438
3.33	.30	2.00	2.95	.503	1.95	2.66	.321
2.86	.35		2.50	.391		2.13	.233
2.50	.40		2.06	.301		1.73	.167
2.22	.45		1.75	.228		1.41	.118
2.00	.50		1.49	.169		1.14	.081
1.82	.55		1.27	.121		.93	.0542
1.67	.60		1.07	.0844		.75	.035
1.54	.65		.89	.0560		.60	.0216
1.43	.70		.73	.0356		.47	.0125
1.33	.75		.59	.0199		.36	.0067
1.25	.80		.45	.0101		.26	.0032

Table from Roark "Formulas for Stress and Strain"

Torsional Members

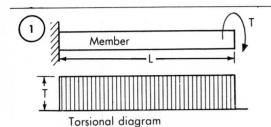

①

$$T = T$$

At support, $\quad \theta = \dfrac{T L}{E_s R}$

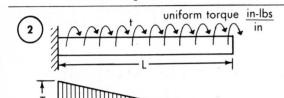

②

At support, $\quad T = t L$

$$\theta = \dfrac{t L^2}{2 E_s R}$$

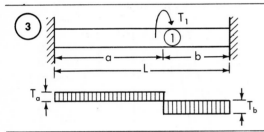

③

Section a: $\quad T_a = \dfrac{T_1 b}{L}$

Section b: $\quad T_b = \dfrac{T_1 a}{L}$ $\qquad \theta_1 = \dfrac{T_1 a b}{L E_s R}$

When $a = b = L/2$ $\qquad \theta_{\mathcal{L}} = \dfrac{T L}{4 E_s R}$

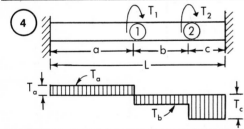

④

Section a: $\quad T_a = \dfrac{T_1 (b + c) + T_2 c}{L}$

Section b: $\quad T_b = \dfrac{T_2 c - T_1 a}{L}$

Section c: $\quad T_c = - \dfrac{T_1 a + T_2 (a + b)}{L}$

$\theta_1 = \dfrac{T_a a}{E_s R}$

$\theta_2 = \dfrac{T_c c}{E_s R}$

When $a = b = c = L/3$
$T_1 = T_2 = T/2$

and $\quad \theta_1 = \theta_2 = \dfrac{T L}{6 E_s R}$

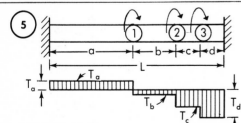

⑤

$T_a = \dfrac{T_1 (b + c + d) + T_2 (c + d) + T_3 d}{L}$

$T_b = \dfrac{- T_1 a + T_2 (c + d) + T_3 d}{L}$

$T_c = \dfrac{- T_1 a - T_2 (a + b) + T_3 d}{L}$

$T_d = \dfrac{- T_1 a - T_2 (a + b) - T_3 (a + b + c)}{L}$

$\theta_1 = \dfrac{T_a a}{E_s R}$

$\theta_2 = \dfrac{T_b b + T_a a}{E_s R}$

$\theta_3 = \dfrac{T_d d}{E_s R}$

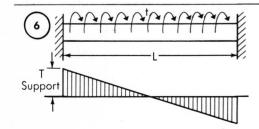

⑥

$$T_{support} = \dfrac{t L}{2}$$

$$\theta_{\mathcal{L}} = \dfrac{t L^2}{8 E_s R}$$

FIGURE 1 – BEAMS ON A HORIZONTAL CURVE, UNDER UNIFORM LOAD (w)

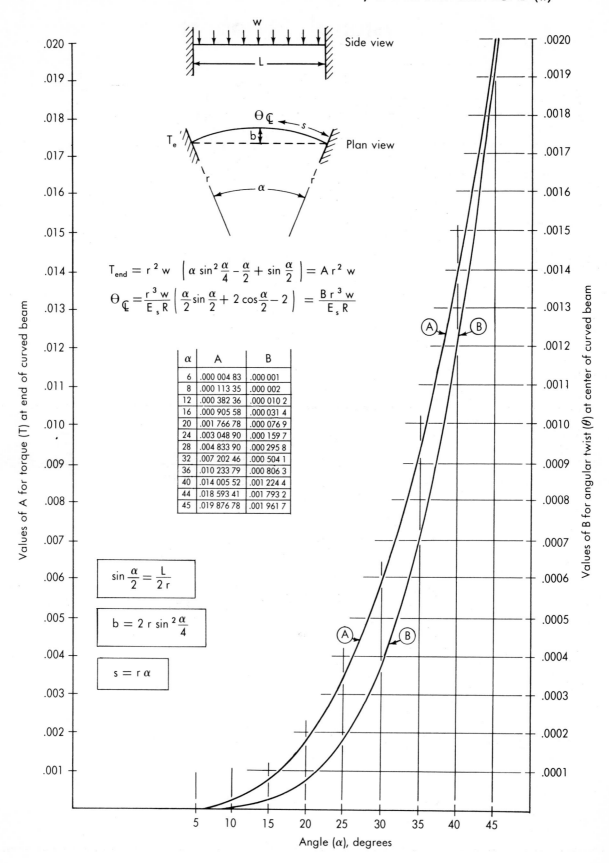

$$T_{end} = r^2 w \left[\alpha \sin^2 \frac{\alpha}{4} - \frac{\alpha}{2} + \sin \frac{\alpha}{2} \right] = A r^2 w$$

$$\Theta_{\mathbb{C}} = \frac{r^3 w}{E_s R} \left(\frac{\alpha}{2} \sin \frac{\alpha}{2} + 2 \cos \frac{\alpha}{2} - 2 \right) = \frac{B r^3 w}{E_s R}$$

α	A	B
6	.000 004 83	.000 001
8	.000 113 35	.000 002
12	.000 382 36	.000 010 2
16	.000 905 58	.000 031 4
20	.001 766 78	.000 076 9
24	.003 048 90	.000 159 7
28	.004 833 90	.000 295 8
32	.007 202 46	.000 504 1
36	.010 233 79	.000 806 3
40	.014 005 52	.001 224 4
44	.018 593 41	.001 793 2
45	.019 876 78	.001 961 7

$$\sin \frac{\alpha}{2} = \frac{L}{2 r}$$

$$b = 2 r \sin^2 \frac{\alpha}{4}$$

$$s = r \alpha$$

Values of A for torque (T) at end of curved beam

Values of B for angular twist (θ) at center of curved beam

Angle (α), degrees

Frame Diagrams and Formulas

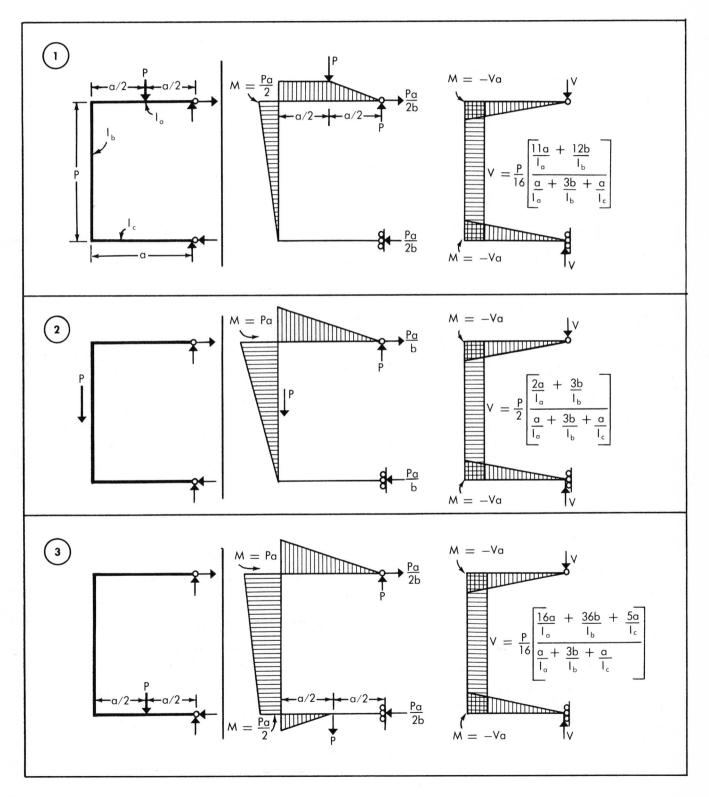

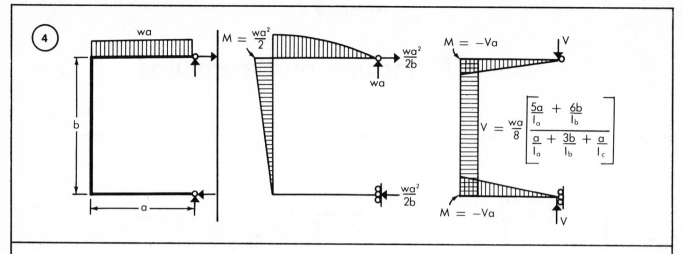

4

$$M = \frac{wa^2}{2}$$

$$\frac{wa^2}{2b}$$

$$wa$$

$$\frac{wa^2}{2b}$$

$$M = -Va$$

$$M = -Va$$

$$V = \frac{wa}{8} \left[\frac{\dfrac{5a}{I_a} + \dfrac{6b}{I_b}}{\dfrac{a}{I_a} + \dfrac{3b}{I_b} + \dfrac{a}{I_c}} \right]$$

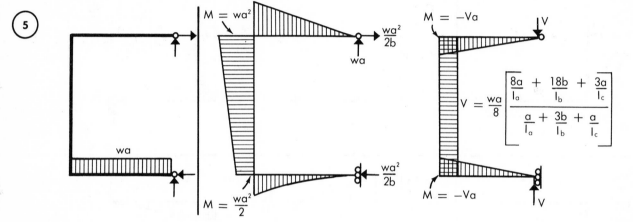

5

$$M = wa^2$$

$$\frac{wa^2}{2b}$$

$$wa$$

$$wa$$

$$\frac{wa^2}{2b}$$

$$M = \frac{wa^2}{2}$$

$$M = -Va$$

$$M = -Va$$

$$V = \frac{wa}{8} \left[\frac{\dfrac{8a}{I_a} + \dfrac{18b}{I_b} + \dfrac{3a}{I_c}}{\dfrac{a}{I_a} + \dfrac{3b}{I_b} + \dfrac{a}{I_c}} \right]$$

6

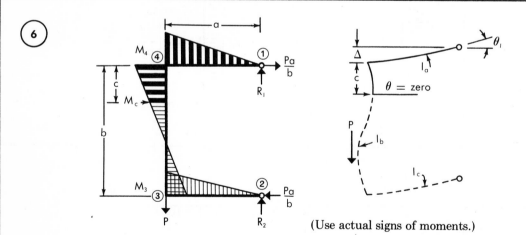

$$M_4 \quad ④ \qquad ① \quad \frac{Pa}{b}$$

$$R_1$$

$$M_c$$

$$M_3 \quad ③ \qquad ② \quad \frac{Pa}{b}$$

$$P \qquad R_2$$

$$\theta_1$$

$$I_a$$

$$\theta = \text{zero}$$

$$P \qquad I_b$$

$$I_c$$

(Use actual signs of moments.)

$$R_1 = P - V$$

$$R_2 = V$$

$$M_3 = -Va$$

$$M_4 = R_1 a = a(P - V)$$

$$c = \frac{3M_4 b - b\sqrt{9M_4{}^2 - 3(M_4 - M_3)(2M_4 + M_3)}}{3(M_4 - M_3)}$$

$$M_c = (M_3 - M_4)\frac{c}{b} + M_4$$

$$V = \frac{P}{2} \left[\frac{\dfrac{2a}{I_a} + \dfrac{3b}{I_b}}{\dfrac{a}{I_a} + \dfrac{3b}{I_b} + \dfrac{a}{I_c}} \right]$$

$$\Delta = \frac{a}{6E} \left[\frac{2aM_4}{I_a} + \frac{3c(M_c + M_4)}{I_b} \right]$$

$$\theta_1 = \frac{aM_4}{2EI_a} + \frac{c(M_c + M_4)}{2EI_b}$$

(7)

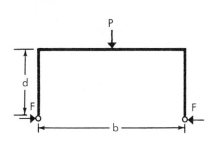

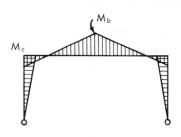

(Use proper signs for moments.)

At corners,
$$M_c = -\frac{Pb}{8}\left[\frac{\dfrac{3b}{I_b}}{\dfrac{3b}{I_b}+\dfrac{2d}{I_d}}\right]$$

At center,
$$M_b = M_c + \frac{Pb}{4}$$

$$F = \frac{M_c}{d}$$

(8)

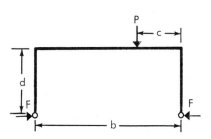

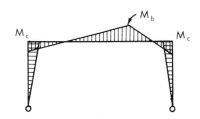

(Use proper signs for moments.)

At corners,
$$M_c = -\frac{Pc(b-c)}{2d}\left[\frac{\dfrac{3b}{I_b}}{\dfrac{3b}{I_b}+\dfrac{2d}{I_d}}\right]$$

$$M_b = M_c + \frac{Pc(b-c)}{b}$$

$$F = \frac{M_c}{d}$$

(9)

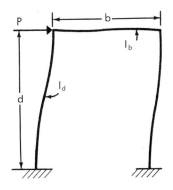

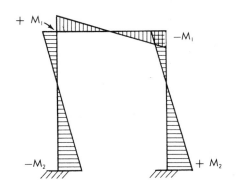

At upper corners,
$$M_1 = \frac{Pd}{2}\left[\frac{\dfrac{3d}{I_d}}{\dfrac{b}{I_b}+\dfrac{6d}{I_d}}\right]$$

At bottom,
$$M_2 = \frac{Pd}{2} - M_1$$

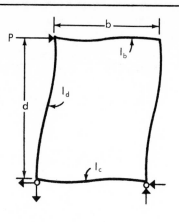

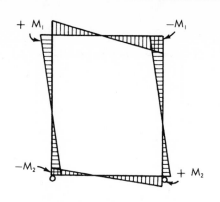

10

At top corners,

$$M_1 = + \frac{P\,d}{2}\,\frac{I_b\,(b\,I_d + 3\,d\,I_c)}{(b\,I_b\,I_d + b\,I_c\,I_d + 6\,d\,I_b\,I_c)}$$

At bottom corners,

$$M_2 = \frac{P\,d}{2} - M_1$$

11

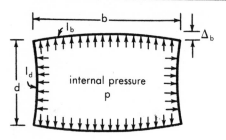

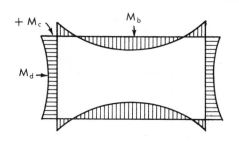

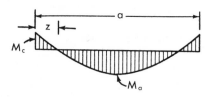

At corners, (always positive)

$$M_c = + \frac{p}{12}\left[\frac{\dfrac{b^3}{I_b} + \dfrac{d^3}{I_d}}{\dfrac{b}{I_b} + \dfrac{d}{I_d}}\right]$$

At center,

$$M_b = + M_c - \frac{p\,b^2}{8}$$

At center,

$$M_d = + M_c - \frac{p\,d^2}{8}$$

Deflection of frame:

$$\Delta = \frac{a^2}{48\,E\,I_a}\,(M_c + 5\,M_a)$$

Point of contraflexure:

$(M_z = \text{zero})$

$$z = \frac{a}{2}\left[1 \pm \frac{\sqrt{(M_c - M_a)^2 - M_c\,(M_c - M_a)}}{(M_c - M_a)}\right]$$

12

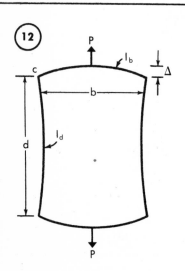

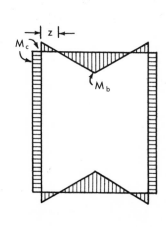

At corners,

$$M_c = + \frac{P\,b}{8}\left[\frac{\dfrac{b}{I_b}}{\dfrac{b}{I_b} + \dfrac{d}{I_d}}\right]$$

At center,

$$M_b = M_c - \frac{P\,b}{4}$$

Point of contraflexure:

$(M_z = \text{zero})$

$$z = \frac{2\,M_c}{P}$$

Deflection of frame:

(top half only)

$$\Delta = \frac{b^2}{24\,E\,I_b}\,(2\,M_b + M_c)$$

Thin Curved Bars

(1)

Deflection at b:

$$\Delta_v = \frac{3\,\pi\,P\,r^3}{2\,E\,I}$$

$$\Delta_h = \frac{2\,P\,r^3}{E\,I}$$

(2)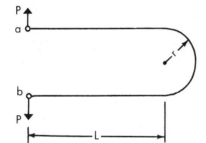

Vertical movement between a and b:

$$\Delta_v = \frac{2\,P}{E\,I}\left[\frac{L^3}{3} + r\left(\frac{\pi}{2}\,L^2 + \frac{\pi}{4}\,r^2 + 2\,L\,r\right)\right]$$

(3)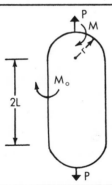

$$M_o = \frac{P\,r^2}{2}\left(\frac{\pi - 2}{2\,L + \pi\,r}\right)$$

$$M = M_o - \frac{p\,r}{2}\ \text{(max moment)}$$

(4)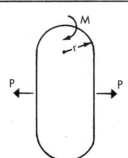

$$M = \frac{P}{2} \times \frac{r^2\,(\pi - 2) + 2\,r\,L + L^2}{\pi\,r + 2\,L}$$

See "Strength of Materials" Part II, Timoshenko, pp. 440-442

LIST ADDITIONAL DESIGN FORMULAS HERE FOR READY REFERENCE

Thin Circular Rings

UNDER CONCENTRATED FORCES

Forces (P) normal to the shell set up tangential tensile forces (T) and bending moments (M) in the ring of the shell.

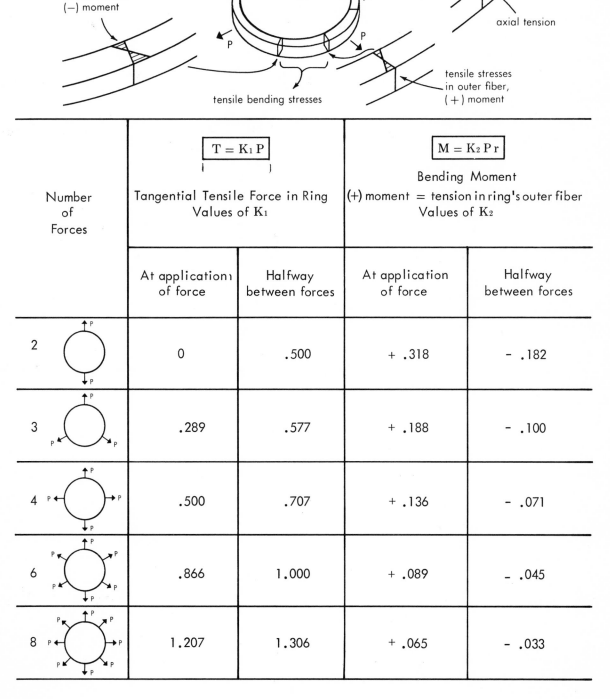

Number of Forces		$T = K_1 P$ Tangential Tensile Force in Ring Values of K_1		$M = K_2 P r$ Bending Moment (+) moment = tension in ring's outer fiber Values of K_2	
		At application of force	Halfway between forces	At application of force	Halfway between forces
2		0	.500	+ .318	− .182
3		.289	.577	+ .188	− .100
4		.500	.707	+ .136	− .071
6		.866	1.000	+ .089	− .045
8		1.207	1.306	+ .065	− .033

LIST ADDITIONAL DESIGN FORMULAS HERE FOR READY REFERENCE

Thin Rings

UNDER INTERNAL PRESSURE (p)

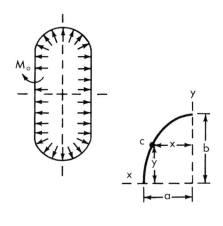

$$M_o = \frac{p\,a^2}{2} - \frac{p}{2\,s}(I_x + I_y)$$

where s, I_x and I_y come from this quadrant

s = length of quadrant of ring

$$I_x = \int_0^s y^2 \, ds$$

$$I_y = \int_0^s x^2 \, ds$$

If the above ring has this shape: $a = r$ $b = L + r$

then

$$M_o = \frac{p\,a^2}{2} - \frac{p}{2\,b + (\pi - 2)\,a}\left[\frac{(b-a)^3}{3} + \frac{\pi\,a^3}{2} + 3\,a^2\,(b-a) + \frac{\pi}{2}\,a\,(b-a)^2\right]$$

At any point c, $M_c = M_o - \dfrac{p\,a^2}{2} + \dfrac{p\,x^2}{2} + \dfrac{p\,y^2}{2}$

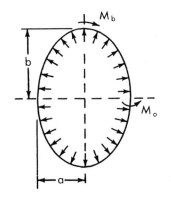

Thin Elliptical Rings

$$M_o = -\beta\,p\,a^2$$

$$M_b = \alpha\,p\,a^2$$

a/b	1.0	.9	.8	.7	.6	.5	.4	.3
β	0	.057	.133	.237	.391	.629	1.049	1.927
α	0	.060	.148	.283	.498	.870	1.576	3.128

Adapted from "Strength of Materials" Part II, Timoshenko, pp. 443-444

1

LIST ADDITIONAL DESIGN FORMULAS HERE FOR READY REFERENCE

Miscellaneous Tables

NAPERIAN (NATURAL) LOG TABLES

No.	Log	No.	Log	No.	Log	No.	Log	No.	Log	No.	Log
1.00	0.0000	1.50	0.4055	2.00	0.6931	2.50	0.9163	3.00	1.0986	3.50	1.2528
1.01	0.0099	1.51	0.4121	2.01	0.6981	2.51	0.9203	3.01	1.1019	3.51	1.2556
1.02	0.0198	1.52	0.4187	2.02	0.7031	2.52	0.9243	3.02	1.1053	3.52	1.2585
1.03	0.0296	1.53	0.4253	2.03	0.7080	2.53	0.9282	3.03	1.1086	3.53	1.2613
1.04	0.0392	1.54	0.4318	2.04	0.7129	2.54	0.9322	3.04	1.1119	3.54	1.2641
1.05	0.0488	1.55	0.4383	2.05	0.7178	2.55	0.9361	3.05	1.1151	3.55	1.2669
1.06	0.0583	1.56	0.4447	2.06	0.7227	2.56	0.9400	3.06	1.1184	3.56	1.2698
1.07	0.0677	1.57	0.4511	2.07	0.7275	2.57	0.9439	3.07	1.1216	3.57	1.2726
1.08	0.0770	1.58	0.4574	2.08	0.7324	2.58	0.9478	3.08	1.1249	3.58	1.2754
1.09	0.0862	1.59	0.4637	2.09	0.7372	2.59	0.9517	3.09	1.1282	3.59	1.2782
1.10	0.0953	1.60	0.4700	2.10	0.7419	2.60	0.9555	3.10	1.1314	3.60	1.2809
1.11	0.1044	1.61	0.4762	2.11	0.7467	2.61	0.9594	3.11	1.1346	3.61	1.2837
1.12	0.1133	1.62	0.4824	2.12	0.7514	2.62	0.9632	3.12	1.1378	3.62	1.2865
1.13	0.1222	1.63	0.4886	2.13	0.7561	2.63	0.9670	3.13	1.1410	3.63	1.2892
1.14	0.1310	1.64	0.4947	2.14	0.7608	2.64	0.9708	3.14	1.1442	3.64	1.2920
1.15	0.1398	1.65	0.5008	2.15	0.7655	2.65	0.9746	3.15	1.1474	3.65	1.2947
1.16	0.1484	1.66	0.5068	2.16	0.7701	2.66	0.9783	3.16	1.1506	3.66	1.2975
1.17	0.1570	1.67	0.5128	2.17	0.7747	2.67	0.9821	3.17	1.1537	3.67	1.3002
1.18	0.1655	1.68	0.5188	2.18	0.7793	2.68	0.9858	3.18	1.1569	3.68	1.3029
1.19	0.1740	1.69	0.5247	2.19	0.7839	2.69	0.9895	3.19	1.1600	3.69	1.3056
1.20	0.1823	1.70	0.5306	2.20	0.7885	2.70	0.9933	3.20	1.1632	3.70	1.3083
1.21	0.1906	1.71	0.5365	2.21	0.7930	2.71	0.9969	3.21	1.1663	3.71	1.3110
1.22	0.1988	1.72	0.5423	2.22	0.7975	2.72	1.0006	3.22	1.1694	3.72	1.3137
1.23	0.2070	1.73	0.5481	2.23	0.8020	2.73	1.0043	3.23	1.1725	3.73	1.3164
1.24	0.2151	1.74	0.5539	2.24	0.8065	2.74	1.0080	3.24	1.1756	3.74	1.3191
1.25	0.2231	1.75	0.5596	2.25	0.8109	2.75	1.0116	3.25	1.1787	3.75	1.3218
1.26	0.2311	1.76	0.5653	2.26	0.8154	2.76	1.0152	3.26	1.1817	3.76	1.3244
1.27	0.2390	1.77	0.5710	2.27	0.8198	2.77	1.0188	3.27	1.1848	3.77	1.3271
1.28	0.2469	1.78	0.5766	2.28	0.8242	2.78	1.0225	3.28	1.1878	3.78	1.3297
1.29	0.2546	1.79	0.5822	2.29	0.8286	2.79	1.0260	3.29	1.1909	3.79	1.3324
1.30	0.2624	1.80	0.5878	2.30	0.8329	2.80	1.0296	3.30	1.1939	3.80	1.3350
1.31	0.2700	1.81	0.5933	2.31	0.8372	2.81	1.0332	3.31	1.1969	3.81	1.3376
1.32	0.2776	1.82	0.5988	2.32	0.8416	2.82	1.0367	3.32	1.1999	3.82	1.3403
1.33	0.2852	1.83	0.6043	2.33	0.8458	2.83	1.0403	3.33	1.2030	3.83	1.3429
1.34	0.2927	1.84	0.6098	2.34	0.8502	2.84	1.0438	3.34	1.2060	3.84	1.3455
1.35	0.3001	1.85	0.6152	2.35	0.8544	2.85	1.0473	3.35	1.2090	3.85	1.3481
1.36	0.3075	1.86	0.6206	2.36	0.8587	2.86	1.0508	3.36	1.2119	3.86	1.3507
1.37	0.3148	1.87	0.6259	2.37	0.8629	2.87	1.0543	3.37	1.2149	3.87	1.3533
1.38	0.3221	1.88	0.6313	2.38	0.8671	2.88	1.0578	3.38	1.2179	3.88	1.3558
1.39	0.3293	1.89	0.6366	2.39	0.8713	2.89	1.0613	3.39	1.2208	3.89	1.3584
1.40	0.3365	1.90	0.6419	2.40	0.8755	2.90	1.0647	3.40	1.2238	3.90	1.3610
1.41	0.3436	1.91	0.6471	2.41	0.8796	2.91	1.0682	3.41	1.2267	3.91	1.3635
1.42	0.3507	1.92	0.6523	2.42	0.8838	2.92	1.0716	3.42	1.2296	3.92	1.3661
1.43	0.3577	1.93	0.6575	2.43	0.8879	2.93	1.0750	3.43	1.2326	3.93	1.3686
1.44	0.3646	1.94	0.6627	2.44	0.8920	2.94	1.0784	3.44	1.2355	3.94	1.3712
1.45	0.3716	1.95	0.6678	2.45	0.8961	2.95	1.0818	3.45	1.2384	3.95	1.3737
1.46	0.3784	1.96	0.6729	2.46	0.9002	2.96	1.0852	3.46	1.2413	3.96	1.3762
1.47	0.3853	1.97	0.6780	2.47	0.9042	2.97	1.0886	3.47	1.2442	3.97	1.3788
1.48	0.3920	1.98	0.6831	2.48	0.9083	2.98	1.0919	3.48	1.2470	3.98	1.3813
1.49	0.3988	1.99	0.6881	2.49	0.9123	2.99	1.0953	3.49	1.2499	3.99	1.3838

NAPERIAN (NATURAL) LOG TABLES

No.	Log	No.	Log	No.	Log	No.	Log	No.	Log	No.	Log
4.00	1.3863	4.50	1.5041	5.00	1.6094	5.50	1.7047	6.00	1.7918	6.50	1.8718
4.01	1.3888	4.51	1.5063	5.01	1.6114	5.51	1.7066	6.01	1.7934	6.51	1.8733
4.02	1.3913	4.52	1.5085	5.02	1.6134	5.52	1.7084	6.02	1.7951	6.52	1.8749
4.03	1.3938	4.53	1.5107	5.03	1.6154	5.53	1.7102	6.03	1.7967	6.53	1.8764
4.04	1.3962	4.54	1.5129	5.04	1.6174	5.54	1.7120	6.04	1.7984	6.54	1.8779
4.05	1.3987	4.55	1.5151	5.05	1.6194	5.55	1.7138	6.05	1.8001	6.55	1.8795
4.06	1.4012	4.56	1.5173	5.06	1.6214	5.56	1.7156	6.06	1.8017	6.56	1.8810
4.07	1.4036	4.57	1.5195	5.07	1.6233	5.57	1.7174	6.07	1.8034	6.57	1.8825
4.08	1.4061	4.58	1.5217	5.08	1.6253	5.58	1.7192	6.08	1.8050	6.58	1.8840
4.09	1.4085	4.59	1.5239	5.09	1.6273	5.59	1.7210	6.09	1.8066	6.59	1.8856
4.10	1.4110	4.60	1.5261	5.10	1.6292	5.60	1.7228	6.10	1.8083	6.60	1.8871
4.11	1.4134	4.61	1.5282	5.11	1.6312	5.61	1.7246	6.11	1.8099	6.61	1.8886
4.12	1.4159	4.62	1.5304	5.12	1.6332	5.62	1.7263	6.12	1.8116	6.62	1.8901
4.13	1.4183	4.63	1.5326	5.13	1.6351	5.63	1.7281	6.13	1.8132	6.63	1.8916
4.14	1.4207	4.64	1.5347	5.14	1.6371	5.64	1.7299	6.14	1.8148	6.64	1.8931
4.15	1.4231	4.65	1.5369	5.15	1.6390	5.65	1.7317	6.15	1.8165	6.65	1.8946
4.16	1.4255	4.66	1.5390	5.16	1.6409	5.66	1.7334	6.16	1.8181	6.66	1.8961
4.17	1.4279	4.67	1.5412	5.17	1.6429	5.67	1.7352	6.17	1.8197	6.67	1.8976
4.18	1.4303	4.68	1.5433	5.18	1.6448	5.68	1.7370	6.18	1.8213	6.68	1.8991
4.19	1.4327	4.69	1.5454	5.19	1.6467	5.69	1.7387	6.19	1.8229	6.69	1.9006
4.20	1.4351	4.70	1.5476	5.20	1.6487	5.70	1.7405	6.20	1.8245	6.70	1.9021
4.21	1.4375	4.71	1.5497	5.21	1.6506	5.71	1.7422	6.21	1.8262	6.71	1.9036
4.22	1.4398	4.72	1.5518	5.22	1.6525	5.72	1.7440	6.22	1.8278	6.72	1.9051
4.23	1.4422	4.73	1.5539	5.23	1.6544	5.73	1.7457	6.23	1.8294	6.73	1.9066
4.24	1.4446	4.74	1.5560	5.24	1.6563	5.74	1.7475	6.24	1.8310	6.74	1.9081
4.25	1.4469	4.75	1.5581	5.25	1.6582	5.75	1.7492	6.25	1.8326	6.75	1.9095
4.26	1.4493	4.76	1.5602	5.26	1.6601	5.76	1.7509	6.26	1.8342	6.76	1.9110
4.27	1.4516	4.77	1.5623	5.27	1.6620	5.77	1.7527	6.27	1.8358	6.77	1.9125
4.28	1.4540	4.78	1.5644	5.28	1.6639	5.78	1.7544	6.28	1.8374	6.78	1.9140
4.29	1.4563	4.79	1.5665	5.29	1.6658	5.79	1.7561	6.29	1.8390	6.79	1.9155
4.30	1.4586	4.80	1.5686	5.30	1.6677	5.80	1.7579	6.30	1.8405	6.80	1.9169
4.31	1.4609	4.81	1.5707	5.31	1.6696	5.81	1.7596	6.31	1.8421	6.81	1.9184
4.32	1.4633	4.82	1.5728	5.32	1.6715	5.82	1.7613	6.32	1.8437	6.82	1.9199
4.33	1.4656	4.83	1.5748	5.33	1.6734	5.83	1.7630	6.33	1.8453	6.83	1.9213
4.34	1.4679	4.84	1.5769	5.34	1.6752	5.84	1.7647	6.34	1.8469	6.84	1.9228
4.35	1.4702	4.85	1.5790	5.35	1.6771	5.85	1.7664	6.35	1.8485	6.85	1.9242
4.36	1.4725	4.86	1.5810	5.36	1.6790	5.86	1.7681	6.36	1.8500	6.86	1.9257
4.37	1.4748	4.87	1.5831	5.37	1.6808	5.87	1.7699	6.37	1.8516	6.87	1.9272
4.38	1.4770	4.88	1.5851	5.38	1.6827	5.88	1.7716	6.38	1.8532	6.88	1.9286
4.39	1.4793	4.89	1.5872	5.39	1.6845	5.89	1.7733	6.39	1.8547	6.89	1.9301
4.40	1.4816	4.90	1.5892	5.40	1.6864	5.90	1.7750	6.40	1.8563	6.90	1.9315
4.41	1.4839	4.91	1.5913	5.41	1.6882	5.91	1.7766	6.41	1.8579	6.91	1.9330
4.42	1.4861	4.92	1.5933	5.42	1.6901	5.92	1.7783	6.42	1.8594	6.92	1.9344
4.43	1.4884	4.93	1.5953	5.43	1.6919	5.93	1.7800	6.43	1.8610	6.93	1.9359
4.44	1.4907	4.94	1.5974	5.44	1.6938	5.94	1.7817	6.44	1.8625	6.94	1.9373
4.45	1.4929	4.95	1.5994	5.45	1.6956	5.95	1.7834	6.45	1.8641	6.95	1.9387
4.46	1.4951	4.96	1.6014	5.46	1.6974	5.96	1.7851	6.46	1.8656	6.96	1.9402
4.47	1.4974	4.97	1.6034	5.47	1.6993	5.97	1.7867	6.47	1.8672	6.97	1.9416
4.48	1.4996	4.98	1.6054	5.48	1.7011	5.98	1.7884	6.48	1.8687	6.98	1.9430
4.49	1.5019	4.99	1.6074	5.49	1.7029	5.99	1.7901	6.49	1.8703	6.99	1.9445

NAPERIAN (NATURAL) LOG TABLES

No.	Log	No.	Log	No.	Log	No.	Log	No.	Log	No.	Log
7.00	1.9459	7.50	2.0149	8.00	2.0794	8.50	2.1401	9.00	2.1972	9.50	2.2513
7.01	1.9473	7.51	2.0162	8.01	2.0807	8.51	2.1412	9.01	2.1983	9.51	2.2523
7.02	1.9488	7.52	2.0176	8.02	2.0819	8.52	2.1424	9.02	2.1994	9.52	2.2534
7.03	1.9502	7.53	2.0189	8.03	2.0832	8.53	2.1436	9.03	2.2006	9.53	2.2544
7.04	1.9516	7.54	2.0202	8.04	2.0844	8.54	2.1448	9.04	2.2017	9.54	2.2555
7.05	1.9530	7.55	2.0215	8.05	2.0857	8.55	2.1459	9.05	2.2028	9.55	2.2565
7.06	1.9544	7.56	2.0229	8.06	2.0869	8.56	2.1471	9.06	2.2039	9.56	2.2576
7.07	1.9559	7.57	2.0242	8.07	2.0882	8.57	2.1483	9.07	2.2050	9.57	2.2586
7.08	1.9573	7.58	2.0255	8.08	2.0894	8.58	2.1494	9.08	2.2061	9.58	2.2597
7.09	1.9587	7.59	2.0268	8.09	2.0906	8.59	2.1506	9.09	2.2072	9.59	2.2607
7.10	1.9601	7.60	2.0281	8.10	2.0919	8.60	2.1518	9.10	2.2083	9.60	2.2618
7.11	1.9615	7.61	2.0295	8.11	2.0931	8.61	2.1529	9.11	2.2094	9.61	2.2628
7.12	1.9629	7.62	2.0308	8.12	2.0943	8.62	2.1541	9.12	2.2105	9.62	2.2638
7.13	1.9643	7.63	2.0321	8.13	2.0956	8.63	2.1552	9.13	2.2116	9.63	2.2649
7.14	1.9657	7.64	2.0334	8.14	2.0968	8.64	2.1564	9.14	2.2127	9.64	2.2659
7.15	1.9671	7.65	2.0347	8.15	2.0980	8.65	2.1576	9.15	2.2138	9.65	2.2670
7.16	1.9685	7.66	2.0360	8.16	2.0992	8.66	2.1587	9.16	2.2148	9.66	2.2680
7.17	1.9699	7.67	2.0373	8.17	2.1005	8.67	2.1599	9.17	2.2159	9.67	2.2690
7.18	1.9713	7.68	2.0386	8.18	2.1017	8.68	2.1610	9.18	2.2170	9.68	2.2701
7.19	1.9727	7.69	2.0399	8.19	2.1029	8.69	2.1622	9.19	2.2181	9.69	2.2711
7.20	1.9741	7.70	2.0412	8.20	2.1041	8.70	2.1633	9.20	2.2192	9.70	2.2721
7.21	1.9755	7.71	2.0425	8.21	2.1054	8.71	2.1645	9.21	2.2203	9.71	2.2732
7.22	1.9769	7.72	2.0438	8.22	2.1066	8.72	2.1656	9.22	2.2214	9.72	2.2742
7.23	1.9782	7.73	2.0451	8.23	2.1078	8.73	2.1668	9.23	2.2225	9.73	2.2752
7.24	1.9796	7.74	2.0464	8.24	2.1090	8.74	2.1679	9.24	2.2235	9.74	2.2762
7.25	1.9810	7.75	2.0477	8.25	2.1102	8.75	2.1691	9.25	2.2246	9.75	2.2773
7.26	1.9824	7.76	2.0490	8.26	2.1114	8.76	2.1702	9.26	2.2257	9.76	2.2783
7.27	1.9838	7.77	2.0503	8.27	2.1126	8.77	2.1713	9.27	2.2268	9.77	2.2793
7.28	1.9851	7.78	2.0516	8.28	2.1138	8.78	2.1725	9.28	2.2279	9.78	2.2803
7.29	1.9865	7.79	2.0528	8.29	2.1150	8.79	2.1736	9.29	2.2289	9.79	2.2814
7.30	1.9879	7.80	2.0541	8.30	2.1163	8.80	2.1748	9.30	2.2300	9.80	2.2824
7.31	1.9892	7.81	2.0554	8.31	2.1175	8.81	2.1759	9.31	2.2311	9.81	2.2834
7.32	1.9906	7.82	2.0567	8.32	2.1187	8.82	2.1770	9.32	2.2322	9.82	2.2844
7.33	1.9920	7.83	2.0580	8.33	2.1199	8.83	2.1782	9.33	2.2332	9.83	2.2854
7.34	1.9933	7.84	2.0592	8.34	2.1211	8.84	2.1793	9.34	2.2343	9.84	2.2865
7.35	1.9947	7.85	2.0605	8.35	2.1223	8.85	2.1804	9.35	2.2354	9.85	2.2875
7.36	1.9961	7.86	2.0618	8.36	2.1235	8.86	2.1815	9.36	2.2364	9.86	2.2885
7.37	1.9974	7.87	2.0631	8.37	2.1247	8.87	2.1827	9.37	2.2375	9.87	2.2895
7.38	1.9988	7.88	2.0643	8.38	2.1258	8.88	2.1838	9.38	2.2386	9.88	2.2905
7.39	2.0001	7.89	2.0656	8.39	2.1270	8.89	2.1849	9.39	2.2396	9.89	2.2915
7.40	2.0015	7.90	2.0669	8.40	2.1282	8.90	2.1861	9.40	2.2407	9.90	2.2925
7.41	2.0028	7.91	2.0681	8.41	2.1294	8.91	2.1872	9.41	2.2418	9.91	2.2935
7.42	2.0041	7.92	2.0694	8.42	2.1306	8.92	2.1883	9.42	2.2428	9.92	2.2946
7.43	2.0055	7.93	2.0707	8.43	2.1318	8.93	2.1894	9.43	2.2439	9.93	2.2956
7.44	2.0069	7.94	2.0719	8.44	2.1330	8.94	2.1905	9.44	2.2450	9.94	2.2966
7.45	2.0082	7.95	2.0732	8.45	2.1342	8.95	2.1917	9.45	2.2460	9.95	2.2976
7.46	2.0096	7.96	2.0744	8.46	2.1353	8.96	2.1928	9.46	2.2471	9.96	2.2986
7.47	2.0109	7.97	2.0757	8.47	2.1365	8.97	2.1939	9.47	2.2481	9.97	2.2996
7.48	2.0122	7.98	2.0769	8.48	2.1377	8.98	2.1950	9.48	2.2492	9.98	2.3006
7.49	2.0136	7.99	2.0782	8.49	2.1389	8.99	2.1961	9.49	2.2502	9.99	2.3016
										10.00	2.3026

METRIC CONVERSION FACTORS

Km. × .621 = mi.
Km. ÷ 1.609 = mi.
m. × 39.37 = in.
m. × 3.281 = ft.
m. × 1.094 = yd.
cm. × .3937 = in.
cm. ÷ 2.54 = in.
mm. × .03937 = in.
mm. ÷ 25.4 = in.
sq. km. × 247.1 = A.
sq. m. × 10.764 = sq. ft.
sq. cm. × .155 = sq. in.
sq. cm. ÷ 6.451 = sq. in.
sq. mm. × .00155 = sq. in.
sq. mm. ÷ 645.1 = sq. in.
cu. m. × 35.315 = cu. ft.
cu. m. × 1.308 = cu. yd.
cu. m. ÷ 264.2 = gal. (U.S.)
cu. cm. ÷ 16.383 = cu. in.
1. × 61.022 = cu. in
1. ÷ .2642 = gal. (U.S.)
1. × 3.78 = gal. (U.S.)
1. ÷ 28.316 = cu. ft.

g. × 15.432 = gr.
g. × 981 = dynes.
g. ÷ 28.35 = oz. (avoir.)
grams per sq. cm. × 14.22 = lb. per sq. in.
Kg. × 2.205 = lb.
Kg. × 35. = 3 oz. (avoir.)
Kg. × 1,102.3 = tons (2000 lb.)
Kg. per sq. cm. × 14,233 = lb. per sq. in.
Kg.-m. × 7.233 = ft.-lb.
kilowatts (k. w.) × 1.34 = H. P.
watts ÷ 746 = H. P.
watts × .7373 = ft.-lb. per sec.
Joules × .7373 = ft.-lb.
Calorie (kilogram-degr. C.) × 3.968 = B. T. U.
Calorie (kilogram-degr. C.) ÷ .252 = B. T. U.
Joules × .24 = gram-calories
gram-calories × 4.19 = Joules
gravity (Paris) = 981 cm. per sec. per sec.
(Degrees Centigrade × 1.8) + 32° degrees F.

WEIGHTS AND AREAS OF CARBON STEEL BARS
Weight per Linear Foot and per Linear Inch, in Pounds

Size, Round or Square, In.	ROUND BARS Area, Sq. In.	ROUND BARS Weight, Per In.	ROUND BARS Weight, Per Ft.	SQUARE BARS Area, Sq. In.	SQUARE BARS Weight, Per In.	SQUARE BARS Weight, Per Ft.	OCTAGON BARS Weight, Per Ft.	OCTAGON BARS Weight, Per In.	HEXAGON BARS Weight, Per Ft.	HEXAGON BARS Weight, Per In.
	0.0031	0.00087	0.010	0.0039	0.001083	0.013	0.011	0.00091	--------	-----------
	0.0123	0.0035	0.042	0.0156	0.00441	0.053	0.044	0.00367	0.046	0.00383
	0.0276	0.00783	0.094	0.0352	0.00991	0.119	0.099	0.00825	0.10	0.00833
	0.0491	0.0139	0.167	0.0625	0.01766	0.212	0.176	0.0147	0.18	0.015
	0.0767	0.0217	0.261	0.0977	0.0278	0.333	0.276	0.023	0.29	0.0242
	0.1105	0.0312	0.375	0.1406	0.0398	0.478	0.397	0.033	0.41	0.0342
	0.1503	0.0425	0.511	0.1914	0.0543	0.651	0.540	0.045	0.56	0.0466
	0.1964	0.0555	0.667	0.25	0.0708	0.850	0.706	0.0588	0.74	0.0616
	0.2485	0.0704	0.845	0.3164	0.0897	1.076	0.893	0.0744	0.93	0.0775
	0.3068	0.0867	1.043	0.3906	0.1106	1.328	1.102	0.09183	1.15	0.0958
	0.3712	0.105	1.262	0.4727	0.134	1.608	1.325	0.1104	1.40	0.1166
	0.4418	0.125	1.502	0.5625	0.1594	1.913	1.588	0.1323	1.66	0.1383
	0.5185	0.1469	1.763	0.6602	0.187	2.245	1.863	0.1552	1.94	0.1617
	0.6013	0.1703	2.044	0.7656	0.217	2.603	2.161	0.1801	2.25	0.1875
	0.6903	0.1955	2.347	0.8789	0.249	2.989	2.481	0.2067	2.59	0.2158
1	0.7854	0.2225	2.670	1.000	0.283	3.400	2.822	0.2351	2.94	0.245
	0.8866	0.2511	3.014	1.1289	0.320	3.838	3.186	0.2655	3.32	0.2766
	0.9940	0.2815	3.379	1.2656	0.3585	4.303	3.572	0.2976	3.73	0.3108
	1.1075	0.3138	3.766	1.41	0.3996	4.795	3.980	0.3316	4.15	0.3458
	1.2272	0.3477	4.173	1.56	0.4427	5.312	4.409	0.3674	4.60	0.3833
	1.3530	0.3833	4.600	1.72	0.488	5.857	4.861	0.405	5.06	0.4216
	1.4849	0.4207	5.049	1.89	0.5357	6.428	5.335	0.4445	5.54	0.4616
	1.6230	0.4598	5.518	2.07	0.5855	7.026	5.832	0.486	6.06	0.505
	1.7671	0.5007	6.008	2.25	0.6375	7.650	6.350	0.529	6.63	0.5525
	1.9175	0.5433	6.520	2.44	0.6917	8.301	6.890	0.5741	7.17	0.5975
	2.0739	0.5875	7.051	2.64	0.748	8.978	7.452	0.621	7.78	0.6483
	2.2365	0.6336	7.604	2.85	0.8068	9.682	8.036	0.6696	8.37	0.6975
	2.4053	0.6815	8.178	3.06	0.8675	10.41	8.640	0.72	9.02	0.7514
	2.5802	0.731	8.773	3.29	0.9308	11.17	9.271	0.7725	9.67	0.8058
	2.7612	0.782	9.388	3.52	0.9958	11.95	9.919	0.8265	10.36	0.8633
	2.9483	0.835	10.02	3.75	1.063	12.76	10.59	0.899	11.05	0.92
2	3.1416	0.89	10.68	4.00	1.133	13.60	11.29	0.9408	11.78	0.9817
	3.3410	0.947	11.36	4.25	1.205	14.46	12.00	1.0	12.51	1.1042
	3.5466	1.005	12.06	4.52	1.279	15.35	12.74	1.062	13.30	1.108
	3.7583	1.065	12.78	4.79	1.355	16.27	13.50	1.125	14.08	1.173
	3.9761	1.126	13.52	5.06	1.435	17.22	14.29	1.1908	14.91	1.243
	4.200	1.19	14.28	5.35	1.515	18.19	15.10	1.2583	15.74	1.312
	4.4301	1.255	15.07	5.64	1.598	19.18	15.92	1.3266	16.62	1.383
	4.6664	1.32	15.86	5.94	1.683	20.20	16.77	1.3975	17.50	1.458
	4.9087	1.39	16.69	6.25	1.771	21.25	17.64	1.47	18.41	1.534
	5.1572	1.46	17.53	6.47	1.861	22.33	18.53	1.5441	19.35	1.612
	5.4119	1.533	18.40	6.89	1.952	23.43	19.45	1.62	20.30	1.691
	5.6727	1.607	19.29	7.22	2.046	24.56	20.38	1.698	21.28	1.773

WEIGHTS AND AREAS OF CARBON STEEL BARS

Weight per Linear Foot and per Linear Inch, in Pounds

Size, Round or Square, In.	ROUND BARS Area, Sq. In.	ROUND BARS Weight, Per In.	ROUND BARS Weight, Per Ft.	SQUARE BARS Area, Sq. In.	SQUARE BARS Weight, Per In.	SQUARE BARS Weight, Per Ft.	OCTAGON BARS Weight, Per Ft.	OCTAGON BARS Weight, Per In.	HEXAGON BARS Weight, Per Ft.	HEXAGON BARS Weight, Per In.
2¾	5.9396	1.683	20.20	7.56	2.083	25.00	20.75	1.729	22.28	1.857
2 13/16	6.2126	1.76	21.12	7.91	2.241	26.90	22.33	1.861	23.30	1.942
2⅞	6.4918	1.84	22.07	8.27	2.341	28.10	23.32	1.943	24.34	2.03
2 15/16	6.7771	1.916	23.04	8.63	2.445	29.34	24.35	2.029	25.40	2.117
3	7.0686	2.00	24.03	9.00	2.55	30.60	25.40	2.117	26.51	2.209
3 1/16	7.3662	2.087	25.04	9.3789	2.658	31.89	26.47	2.205	27.89	2.324
3⅛	7.6699	2.173	26.08	9.7656	2.766	33.20	27.56	2.296	28.77	2.397
3 3/16	7.9798	2.275	27.13	10.16	2.88	34.55	28.68	2.39	29.90	2.491
3¼	8.2958	2.35	28.20	10.56	2.993	35.92	29.81	2.484	31.10	2.591
3 5/16	8.6179	2.441	29.30	10.97	3.11	37.31	30.97	2.58	32.29	2.69
3⅜	8.9462	2.533	30.42	11.39	3.23	38.73	32.15	2.679	33.75	2.812
3 7/16	9.2806	2.63	31.56	11.82	3.348	40.18	33.35	2.78	34.75	2.895
3½	9.6211	2.726	32.71	12.95	3.47	41.65	34.57	2.88	36.08	3.00
3 9/16	9.9678	2.825	33.90	12.695	3.595	43.14	35.81	2.983	37.34	3.11
3⅝	10.321	2.92	35.09	13.14	3.723	44.68	37.08	3.09	38.70	3.225
3 11/16	10.680	3.026	36.31	13.60	3.853	46.24	38.38	3.20	40.00	3.333
3¾	11.045	3.13	37.56	14.06	3.993	47.82	39.69	3.31	41.43	3.452
3 13/16	11.416	3.234	38.81	14.54	4.118	49.42	41.02	3.42	42.75	3.562
3⅞	11.793	3.342	40.10	15.015	4.254	51.05	42.39	3.53	44.20	3.683
3 15/16	12.177	3.45	41.40	15.51	4.392	52.71	43.75	3.646	45.65	3.804
4	12.566	3.56	42.73	16.00	4.533	54.40	45.15	3.762	47.13	3.927
4 1/16	12.962	3.672	44.07	16.51	4.675	56.11	46.57	3.88		
4⅛	13.364	3.783	45.44	17.02	4.895	58.75	48.02	4.00		
4 3/16	13.772	3.9	46.83	17.54	4.968	59.62	49.48	4.123		
4¼	14.186	4.02	48.24	18.06	5.117	61.41	50.97	4.247	53.21	4.434
4 5/16	14.607	4.138	49.66	18.60	5.27	63.23	52.48	4.373		
4⅜	15.033	4.259	51.11	19.14	5.42	65.08	54.02	4.5		
4 7/16	15.466	4.381	52.58	19.70	5.58	66.95	55.57	4.63		
4½	15.904	4.505	54.07	20.25	5.737	68.85	57.15	4.762	59.64	4.97
4 9/16	16.349	4.632	55.59	20.82	5.898	70.78	58.75	4.895		
4⅝	16.800	4.76	57.12	21.39	6.06	72.73	60.37	5.03		
4 11/16	17.257	4.89	58.67	21.98	6.225	74.70	62.00	5.166		
4¾	17.721	5.02	60.25	22.56	6.392	76.71	63.67	5.305	66.46	5.538
4 13/16	18.190	5.153	61.84	23.164	6.562	78.74	65.35	5.446		
4⅞	18.665	5.288	63.46	23.77	6.734	80.81	67.07	5.59		
4 15/16	19.147	5.416	65.10	24.38	6.907	82.89	68.80	5.733		
5	19.635	5.563	66.76	25.00	7.083	85.00	70.55	5.879	73.54	6.128
5 1/16	20.129	5.703	68.44	25.63	7.262	87.14	72.33	6.028		
5⅛	20.629	5.845	70.14	26.27	7.441	89.30	74.12	6.176		
5 3/16	21.135	5.988	71.86	26.92	7.624	91.49	75.94	6.328		
5¼	21.648	6.133	73.60	27.56	7.81	93.72	77.79	6.483	81.18	6.765
5 5/16	22.166	6.28	75.37	28.23	7.997	95.96	79.65	6.637		
5⅜	22.691	6.43	77.15	28.89	8.185	98.23	81.53	6.794		

WEIGHTS AND AREAS OF CARBON STEEL BARS

Weight per Linear Foot and per Linear Inch, in Pounds

Size, Round or Square, In.	ROUND BARS Area, Sq. In.	ROUND BARS Weight, Per In.	ROUND BARS Weight, Per Ft.	SQUARE BARS Area, Sq. In.	SQUARE BARS Weight, Per In.	SQUARE BARS Weight, Per Ft.	OCTAGON BARS Weight, Per Ft.	OCTAGON BARS Weight, Per In.	HEXAGON BARS Weight, Per Ft.	HEXAGON BARS Weight, Per In.
5 7/16	23.221	6.579	78.95	29.57	8.375	100.5	83.42	6.951	89.09	7.424
5½	23.758	6.73	80.77	30.25	8.566	102.8	85.32	7.11		
5 9/16	24.301	6.885	82.62	30.95	8.77	105.2	87.31	7.275		
5⅝	24.850	7.04	84.49	31.64	8.97	107.6	89.31	7.442		
5 11/16	25.406	7.198	86.38	32.35	9.17	110.0	91.30	7.608	97.38	8.115
5¾	25.967	7.358	88.29	33.06	9.37	112.4	93.29	7.774		
5 13/16	26.535	7.518	90.22	33.79	9.58	114.9	95.37	7.947		
5⅞	27.109	7.68	92.17	34.52	9.783	117.4	97.44	8.12		
5 15/16	27.688	7.845	94.14	35.26	9.991	119.9	99.52	8.293	106.04	8.836
6	28.274	8.01	96.14	36.00	10.2	122.4	101.6	8.466		
6 1/16	28.50	8.178	98.14	36.76	10.416	125.0	103.8	8.65		
6⅛	29.465	8.35	100.2	37.52	10.633	127.6	105.9	8.825		
6 3/16	30.06	8.51	102.2	38.29	10.85	130.2	108.1	9.00		
6¼	30.680	8.69	104.3	39.06	11.07	132.8	110.2	9.183		
6 5/16	31.29	8.875	106.4	39.85	11.3	135.5	112.47	9.372		
6⅜	31.92	9.04	108.5	40.64	11.51	138.2	114.7	9.558		
6 7/16	32.55	9.225	110.7	41.45	11.74	140.9	116.9	9.742		
6½	33.18	9.4	112.8	42.25	11.97	143.6	119.2	9.933	124.42	10.368
6 9/16	33.80	9.575	114.9	43.07	12.2	146.5	121.6	10.133		
6⅝	34.49	9.766	117.2	43.89	12.43	149.2	123.8	10.316		
6 11/16	35.12	9.95	119.4	44.73	12.675	152.1	126.2	10.516		
6¾	35.78	10.14	121.7	45.56	12.99	154.9	128.6	10.716		
6 13/16	36.44	10.325	123.9	46.42	13.15	157.8	131.0	10.916		
6⅞	37.13	10.51	126.2	47.27	13.4	160.8	133.5	11.125		
6 15/16	13.79	10.708	128.5	48.14	13.633	163.6	135.8	11.316		
7	38.48	10.908	130.9	49.00	13.883	166.6	138.3	11.525	144.38	12.031
7 1/16	39.18	11.1	133.2	49.89	14.13	169.6	140.8	11.733		
7⅛	39.88	11.3	135.6	50.77	14.383	172.6	143.3	11.941		
7 3/16	40.59	11.5	137.9	51.67	14.633	175.6	145.7	12.141		
7¼	41.28	11.7	140.4	52.56	14.891	178.7	148.3	12.36		
7 5/16	42.00	11.9	142.8	53.48	15.15	181.8	150.8	12.57		
7⅜	42.73	12.108	145.3	54.39	15.408	184.9	153.5	12.79		
7 7/16	43.45	12.308	147.7	55.32	15.675	188.1	156.1	13.00		
7½	44.17	12.517	150.2	56.25	15.94	191.3	158.8	13.23		
7⅝	45.68	12.85	155.2	58.14	16.475	197.7	164.2	13.68		
7¾	47.19	13.358	160.3	60.06	17.016	204.2	169.5	14.125		
7⅞	48.73	13.8	165.6	62.33	17.566	210.8	175.0	14.58		
8	50.26	14.25	171.0	64.00	18.133	217.6	180.6	15.05	188.61	15.718
9	63.61	18.2	218.4	81.00	22.966	275.6	227.8	18.983	238.58	19.88
10	78.54	22.266	267.2	100.00	29.166	340.0	282.4	23.533	294.50	24.542
11	95.03	26.916	323.0	121.00	34.266	411.2	340.6	28.38	356.38	29.698
12	113.10	32.033	384.4	144.00	40.8	489.6	405.8	33.33	428.64	35.72

SAE STEEL NUMBERING SYSTEM

TYPE OF STEEL	NUMERALS (AND DIGITS)
Carbon Steels	1xxx
Plain Carbon	10xx
Free Cutting (Screw Stock)	11xx
Free Cutting, Manganese	X13xx
High-Manganese Steels	T13xx
Nickel Steels	2xxx
0.50% Nickel	20xx
1.50% Nickel	21xx
3.50% Nickel	23xx
5.00% Nickel	25xx
Nickel-Chromium Steels	3xxx
1.25% Nickel, 0.60% Chromium	31xx
1.75% Nickel, 1.00% Chromium	32xx
3.50% Nickel, 1.50% Chromium	33xx
3.00% Nickel, 0.80% Chromium	34xx
Corrosion and Heat Resisting Steels	30xxx
Molybdenum Steels	4xxx
Chromium	41xx
Chromium-Nickel	43xx
Nickel	46xx and 48xx
Chromium Steels	5xxx
Low-Chromium	51xx
Medium-Chromium	52xxx
Corrosion and Heat Resisting	51xxx
Chromium-Vanadium Steels	6xxx
Tungsten Steels	7xxx and 7xxxx
Silicon-Manganese Steels	9xxx

WELDING PROCESSES CHART

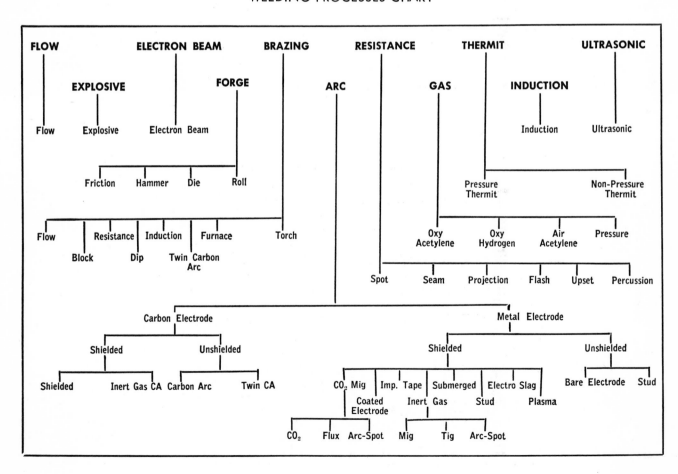